Studies in
GENETICS

Studies in
GENETICS

The Selected Papers
of H. J. Muller

INDIANA UNIVERSITY PRESS

BLOOMINGTON   1962

FOREWORD

STUDENTS who, like myself, have not had the fortune to study with Muller will find this collection a special benefice. Contemporary science shouts the triumphs of specialized concentration and technical finesse; fewer of its pioneers can also claim the breadth of intellect that is displayed in these pages. It is not easy to find an original thought in biological theory that has not, in some way, been anticipated here—whether the topic be the ultramicroscopic gene, the fate of mankind on earth, or the cosmic origins of life.

To advert to my own field, bacterial genetics is not often pointedly connected with Muller's research. But I happily recall how he clarified "bacterial transformation" with an incredibly unconventional interpretation that is now the basic idea in this field . . . "there were, in effect, still viable bacterial 'chromosomes' or parts of chromosomes floating free in the medium used. These might, in my opinion, have penetrated the capsuleless bacteria and in part at least taken root there, perhaps after having undergone a kind of crossing-over with the chromosomes of the host. In view of the transfer of only a part of the genetic material at a time, at least in the viruses, a method appears to be provided whereby the gene constitution of these forms can be analysed, much as in the cross-breeding tests on higher organisms. However, unlike what has so far been possible in higher organisms, viable chromosome threads could also be obtained from these lower forms for *in vitro* observation, chemical analysis, and determination of the genetic effects of treatment" ("The Gene," Proc. Roy. Soc. London, B134: 1-37 [1947]).

Thoughtful reader—you will find a world of rediscovery here.

Joshua Lederberg (1961)

H. J. MULLER AS A TEACHER

ON THOSE of us who have had the extraordinary fortune of being his students, H. J. Muller has made a profound impression. His kindness, understanding, tolerance, and continuous encouragement in respect of his juniors is matched only by his pugnacious intolerance of imposition, incompetence, and pomposity in those in power. The contrast of these two qualities, and the episodes—often amusing—arising from them, are a most endearing feature of life near him. Nor is this contrast confined to activity in academic circles: H. J. Muller can always be found fighting Goliath and championing the underdog whenever the opportunity arises. His outlook on the prospects of mankind—dismissed as utopian by obscurantists—is the result of a powerful mind combined with kindness and a deep sense of justice.

If working near Muller is an unforgettable experience, the intellectual excitement of learning from him is even more so.

The two most striking characteristics of Muller as a teacher are undoubtedly his dexterity in the design of experiments and his imagination. Every student has had repeatedly the enjoyment of seeing Muller work out in a few instants the details of complicated series of *Drosophila* crosses required to test a question just arisen in discussion. Even more enjoyable is the experience of Muller rushing into the student's lab, with his characteristic brisk pace and a twinkle in his eye, expounding a technical solution which he has just found.

But the greatest and most lasting influence on his students comes from Muller's enormous imagination, the imagination which found its highest expression in the concept of the gene as the basis of life. It is this imagination which has given to his contributions such a general biological value, in spite of the fact that his experimental work has been almost exclusively with a single species of organisms.

Muller's conversations with his students are something the equal of which few of us have met again. Of this experience, and of his kindness and encouragement, all of us carry a vivid and grateful memory through life.

G. Pontecorvo (1961)

ACKNOWLEDGMENTS

THE PAPERS in this volume were first published in the following books and scientific journals. (Further facts of publication are given in footnotes accompanying the papers.)

*Acta Genetica et Statistica Medica**
American Journal of Human Genetics
The American Naturalist
Anatomical Record
Birth Control Review
The Collecting Net
Comptes Rendus de l'Académie de l'URRS
Drosophila Information Service
Eugenics, Genetics and the Family (*Proceedings of the Second International Congress of Eugenics*)
Evolution after Darwin (Sol Tax, ed.)
Genetica
Genetics
The Harvey Lectures, Series XLIII, 1947-1948*
Journal of Cellular and Comparative Physiology
The Journal of Experimental Zoology
Journal of Genetics
Journal of Heredity
Nature
The New Systematics (J. S. Huxley, ed.)*
Proceedings of the Eighth International Congress of Genetics
Proceedings of the Fifteenth International Physiological Congress
Proceedings of the Fourth International Radiologen Kongress
Proceedings of the International Conference of Radiobiology (Stockholm, 1956)
Proceedings of the International Congress of Plant Sciences
Proceedings of the Medico-Genetical Institute
Proceedings of the National Academy of Sciences
Proceedings of the Royal Society (B)
Proceedings of the Sixth International Congress of Genetics
Proceedings of the Society for Experimental Biology and Medicine
Proceedings of the Zoological Society
*Progress in Nuclear Energy Series VI, Vol. 2—Biological Sciences**

Records of the Genetics Society of America
Science
The Scientific Monthly
Year Book of the American Philosophical Society
Zeitschrift für induktive Abstammungs-und vererbungslehre

* Publishers wishing to be named in the Acknowledgments are listed here with the publications cited:

Acta Genetica et Statistica Medica (Basel and New York: S. Karger, 1956)
Evolution after Darwin (Chicago: University of Chicago Press, 1959)
The Harvey Lectures (Springfield, Ill.: Charles C. Thomas, 1950)
The New Systematics (Oxford: The Clarendon Press, 1940)
Progress in Nuclear Energy Series VI (London: Pergamon Press, 1959)

CONTENTS

Contents • xi

PART SEVEN: Heterochromatin

*The text figures in this volume are numbered as they were in
the publications from which the writings of Professor Muller were
selected.*

1 The Chromosome Basis of Heredity and Linkage

See also in this volume:

"The Genetic Basis of Truncate Wing—an Inconstant and Modifiable Character in Drosophila," pp. 97-102

"Genetic Variability, Twin Hybrids and Constant Hybrids, in a Case of Balanced Lethal Factors," pp. 69-94

A separately published paper having a bearing on the subject of "The Chromosome Basis of Heredity and Linkage" is listed in the bibliography, pp. 593-612, entry 172.

EXPLANATORY NOTE NO. 1

The idea of a publication for my seventieth birthday was originated by my former students Elof Carlson and Irwin I. Oster. To them and others of my students and colleagues, past and present, belongs the credit (or should I say the onus?) for sponsoring this publication. They soon adopted the policy of publishing, not a jubilee volume composed by others, but a collection of my own writings on genetics and related subjects, to be selected by me and to comprise some 600 pages. The plans for this publication had already reached an advanced stage before they were finally divulged to me in November, 1960, a month before the anniversary, in order to have me make the selection. I must, however, bear the responsibility for having accepted these plans, and I wish to express my gratitude to my friends for having conceived them and brought them to fruition, and to Indiana University for having supported them.

In choosing the works to be given a place here, I have thought it appropriate to follow my sponsors' suggestion that a larger proportion of my earlier writings be included than of my later ones, since the former are less known and less available to present readers. I have also given preference, other things being equal, to the writings in which there was earlier mention of given principles, rather than to papers that consisted mainly of restatements. These procedures have, however, entailed the omission of much or all of such inclusive articles as "Bearings of the Drosophila Work on Systematics" (1940), "The Gene" (1947), "The Darwinian and Modern Conceptions of Evolution" (1949), chapters 7 and 8 of *Radiation Biology* (1954), and "Evolution and Genetics" (1960), in which the primary aim was to integrate already existing knowledge. Limitations of space have also necessitated the omission of the major portion of longer treatments that included a considerable bulk of new data, such as "The Mechanism of Crossing Over" (1916), "The Measurement of Gene Mutation Rate" (1928), and "An Analysis of the Process of Structural Change" (1940); in the case of those papers of this kind that were used at all, only their summaries and a fraction of their discussional material have been selected for reprinting. This exclusion of most of the methodological treatments, data, appraisals of data, and lists of references has left the meat without the skeleton which supported it, and so has tended to give the whole an appearance of fabrication or "speculation" which can only be corrected by consulting the originals or by comparing the conclusions reached with our knowledge of today.

To many of the newest generation of geneticists, who may with justified pride call themselves biophysicists or biochemists instead, it may seem that a reprinting like the present one is a step

3

backward, and in a sense it is. An occasional step backward within the road that led forward is needed, however, for consolidation of our gains, for better utilization of our acquisitions, for improved perspective and orientation, for avoiding the repetition of mistakes, and to bring one an awareness of methods of thinking and investigating that may be re-adapted. Moreover, there is a justifiable human gratification in the extension of one's short-term personality so as to allow one's closer identification with the larger being of man in general, the scientist and explorer, in his long-range progress. Thus, such retrospection will give ground for feelings of greater achievement.

It is true that in genetic biology there have been some enormous sudden breakthroughs, such as those achieved by Schleiden and Schwann, Darwin and Wallace, Mendel, Weismann and Roux, and Watson and Crick. However, retrospection of the type here under discussion will also tend to show how minute were *most* of the steps that the participants thought of at the time as highly discontinuous, yet what a distance was spanned by the summation of such steps. In this way the retrospection will tend to give hope for the future even to him who cannot see his own progress. Finally, let me say to my physicochemical friends who have recently arrived so far, that fifty years from now they may wish their own intellectual grandchildren to know a little about the struggles that *they* went through in setting up their by then so outmoded-seeming "classical" doctrines or dogmas.

We do not wish to imply by the above remarks any agreement on our part with the adolescent notion that genetic work utilizing the older methods and materials is no longer worthwhile. There are enormous areas of great importance still to be explored that cannot at present be inquired into as well in any other way, and that promise rewarding results. Included here are work on mechanisms of segregation, crossing over, mutation, position effect, gene expression, selection, and speciation, and analyses of differentiations within chromosomes and within "loci." Increasingly, moreover, the physicochemical techniques and findings worked out in microorganisms and in the cell cultures of higher forms will be of aid when taken in combination with the opportunities afforded by the older-style methods and biological materials. Thus we must keep the fire of genetic research burning for a long time yet under the pot of such organisms as Drosophila. For a recent review of current methodologies in Drosophila mutation work the reader may be referred to an article on the subject, by Muller and Oster, now in press in the book *Methodology in Genetics* (edited by W. J. Burdette; San Francisco, Holden-Day, Inc.).

Apologies are extended to the reader for the inclusion (despite such drastic cutting) of much repetition that had been inextricably interwoven into the presentation of newer results or thoughts. It had been necessary in the first place in order to preserve continuity and to allow new readers to see where they were going. Apologies are due even more for the opposite practice: that of cutting down so many themes to the bare summaries or abstracts which left them seeming to hang in a vacuum. We will, however, be well satisfied if the attempt to follow these condensations throws the reader into a similar orbit!

The grouping of the papers here adopted is into subdivisions that classify them according to the problem chiefly treated by them. Papers that deal in a major way with problems in more than one of the subdivisions are cross-referred to in the listings at the heads of those relevant subdivisions under which their text has not been included. In each subdivision the order followed is chronological, according to date of publication. Although this arrangement is less rational and less informative than one which attempts a maximum systematization of the concepts involved, it may be better suited for tracing things down.

The reader should bear in mind at every turn that these papers represent the inquiries and thoughts of many men, as represented in only one of their number. This is only one kind of thread, and by no means the most important or informative one, by which the succession of scientific findings in any field may be strung together. Yet this kind of presentation does have a justification of its own, for it helps to clarify some relations that would not otherwise be so readily evident.

For their very considerable expenditure of initiative, time and effort in making this presentation possible, as by getting the articles and excerpts together, retyped, and repeatedly proofread, and in many other ways implementing this publication in the face of serious difficulties, the author expresses his deep appreciation to his co-workers Dr. Irwin I. Oster and Dr. Stanley Zimmering. He also thanks the members of the sponsoring committee for instituting the project and, among these, Dr. Tracy M. Sonneborn especially for his active part in the negotiations for publishing. In addition, he wishes to acknowledge his great indebtedness to his secretary, Mrs. Sue Lena Hickam, for her efforts "beyond the call of duty" in the work of typing the material.

The sponsoring committee, which came together (without the author's knowledge) in August, 1960, in Stillwater, Oklahoma, at the time of the AIBS meeting there, also made arrangements then for a septuagenary celebration for the author, which was held in December, 1960, in New York, at the time of the AAAS meeting there. Among the features of this celebration were an announcement that the Indiana University Press had undertaken to publish the book and the displayal of a mock-up of it presented by them. The members of the committee most actively participating in this celebration were Edgar Altenburg, Elof Carlson, James F. Crow, Seymour Fogel,

H. Bentley Glass, Clarence P. Oliver, Irwin I. Oster, and Stanley Zimmering. Others of the committee whose participation should be acknowledged with warm thanks are Seymour Abrahamson, Irwin H. Herskowitz, Edward Novitski, and Katherine Brehme Warren. The author also wishes to thank his many other friends not on the committee, who took part in the expressions of good will connected with this occasion.

H. J. Muller, Bloomington, Ind.

July 23, 1961

PRINCIPLES OF HEREDITY

[Explanatory Note No. 2: The following passages, which have not been published hitherto, were written by Muller early in 1912 as parts of a book (to be given the above title) that was then in preparation by Altenburg and Muller. Muller at that time was Fellow in Physiology at the Cornell Medical College in New York City, and Altenburg was Graduate Assistant in the Department of Botany at Columbia University. Work on this book was discontinued some six months after it had been begun, when Morgan, who never knew of it, made the proposal to Sturtevant, Bridges, Muller, and Altenburg (who declined) that they all collaborate in writing a joint book on genetics. The latter was first published in 1915, under the title *The Mechanism of Mendelian Heredity*. The passages reproduced below are unchanged from the manuscript of the earlier work except for the omissions noted, the deletion (with smoothing over of the breaks) of a little repetition, the insertion of sub-headings and of the words in brackets, and the infrequent revision of punctuation or grammar. Most of that portion of Chapter II which is here omitted was prepared by Altenburg and Muller jointly and was published, with revisions and deletions, as the treatment of genetics in the 1914 edition of W. C. Curtis' *The Nature and Development of Plants*.]

CHAPTER I. THE CELL AND ITS CHROMATIN

The most complicated machinery ever manufactured cannot compare in the intricacy of its working with the processes which must take place whenever a tiny egg gradually transforms itself into a man. What is the essential structure of this material which operates to build a living creature, what is the manner of its action, how did it originate in the remote past, and how is the constitution of this basic substance itself determined? How does it happen that the creature which is formed resembles in all its complex organization the parent which produced the egg, yet differs in so many details? The intrinsic interest of these questions is matched by their extrinsic importance, for their solution would help us to predict the characteristics of offspring yet unborn and would ultimately enable us to modify the nature of future generations. It is an encouraging fact that some actual progress has already been made in solving these problems and that the principles already discovered have proved of great value to the student of evolution, to the breeder of plants and animals, and to the eugenist.

1. *The Cellular Basis of Organisms*

For a proper understanding of the discoveries in the science of heredity (or genetics) it is essential for the reader to have a clear knowledge of the fundamental facts concerning reproduction and the development of the egg into the adult. Every creature is composed of minute elementary units called "cells"; the substance of these cells, which carries on the reactions constituting life, is termed "protoplasm." Some very small organisms consist of but a single cell, but a man is an aggregation of many millions of cells. Different groups of the cells in a man are especially modified in different ways so that those in one group perform, together, certain of the tasks necessary for the maintenance of the organism more efficiently than could be done were each cell to help equally in all the different lines of activity. Thus, the nerve cells are specially modified physicochemically and are drawn out long and narrow so as to serve like a system of telegraph wires throughout the organism; the cells of the gut are specially constructed, placed and grouped, so as to absorb food, etc. So it is often said that, from the cellular standpoint, a man or other higher organism resembles a civilized community in which specialization of labor exists. And, as in the case of men in a community, the different cells, although greatly specialized, are fundamentally very much alike, as we shall see later.

In any species which survives, the functions of the animals or plants composing it must be nicely adapted for self-preservation and for reproducing their kind. The ordinary cells of the body (or "soma"), most of which function for the preservation of that individual body and only indirectly for reproduction, are called body or "somatic" cells. Those which are allotted the task of directly producing the next generation are called the germ cells. A ripe or "mature" germ cell is called a "gamete." As a rule these gametes are of two kinds, eggs and sperm, and in the case of man and many other species these two kinds of gametes are borne in different organisms, so that there exist in these species two kinds of individuals—the females, which produce only eggs, and the males, which produce only sperm.

Mating brings about the union of sperm cells with egg cells. Only one sperm unites with (fertilizes) any given egg. The combined cell or fertilized egg so formed develops into a large mass of cells arranged in a highly complex and definite manner; in other words, the mass of cells so formed constitutes a new individual resembling the parents. This formation of many cells from one is brought about by a spontaneous division of the original fertilized egg into two cells, the division again of each of these into two, so that four in all are now formed, and the continual repetition of this process of cell-division until the number of cells characteristic of the adult is produced. All cells have at some time been derived from previous cells by cell-division. Accompanying the process of cell-division, which would tend to make the cells extremely small though numerous, is the process of growth, and also the process of differentiation—i.e. the gradual changing of the character of different groups of cells until they become specialized for their particular functions. Among these groups is the group of cells which are destined to become gametes, and which will therefore repeat the above cycle of reproduction and development. This sequence of events may be represented in diagrammatic form.

The reader is now in a position to see that the problem of how the structure of a creature is determined and brought into being may be roughly divided into two general problems: firstly, how does the fertilized egg develop into the adult offspring, how do its characteristics determine the characteristics of the individual into which it becomes transformed; and secondly, what are these characteristics, this fundamental machinery, in the egg, and how are they themselves determined? The first problem may be termed that of development—embryology; surprisingly little progress has as yet been made here in the discovery of scientific principles. The second is the problem of genetics proper, or heredity, and it is this topic which will occupy most of the following pages.

2. The Operations Within Cells

As the fertilized egg from which the individual develops is a cell, and is descended from other cells, it will be interesting first to examine a little more in detail our knowledge of cell structure and activity. Chemically considered, the greater part of the bulk of every cell consists of a very complex substance called protein (white of egg is the classical example of protein), together with carbohydrates (starch, sugar, etc.) and fat-like substances, all dissolved or else mixed with water. These substances are continually being used up and so changed into waste material, in the activity of the cell, and so, if a cell is to maintain itself, it must constantly secure new material to take the place of what was lost. But the cells of no two species are just alike in the materials they contain (e.g. they never possess just the same kind of protein) and therefore the nutriment which a cell obtains for its maintenance or growth must be changed over into material of the kind and disposition characteristic of that particular cell. Thus we see that there is a continual construction — "anabolism" — and destruction — "catabolism" — of material going on within the cell, which, like a whirlpool, is gradually but constantly changing the substance of which it is composed. This entire series of chemical reactions is termed "metabolism."

Most of the chemical reactions in cells are accomplished with the aid of substances called enzymes, present in minute amounts. The enzymes are of unknown chemical composition, though believed by some to be proteins. The enzymes are of many different kinds, and to each is allotted, as it were, the task of facilitating a particular cellular reaction. For example, some help to digest raw material; others build up the digested material into cell substances, still others help to conserve fuel. Almost every chemical reaction of a cell has some enzyme assigned for facilitating it. In all these reactions the enzymes themselves are not used up except to a very minute degree. A similar effect of hastening chemical reactions without change to themselves is known for many simple inorganic substances, called "catalysts" (e.g. colloidal solutions of the heavy metals), but in the case of these inorganic catalysts the substance facilitates practically any chemical reaction, i.e. it is not specific like the enzymes, each of which facilitates only a particular reaction.

It seems fairly well established that the effect of an enzyme is merely to hasten its particular reaction. However, without the enzymes the cell could not exist, for the [given] reaction would be almost imperceptibly slow and the various reactions would not be properly timed with reference to each other and to processes going on in the external world so as to result in a living, adapted organism. Thus the enzymes may in a sense be considered each as the cause of its own particular reaction.

The activities of a cell, other than the building up of new material for its maintenance or growth, are principally such as will directly or indirectly aid either the maintenance or growth of that cell, or of other cells of the body or of the same species. These activities are of the most varied sort, e.g. cell-division, the changes in shape and structure of cells such as take place during development, active movement such as occurs in muscle cells during contraction, secretion or the passing out from the cell of certain substances manufactured within it from other substances which may or may not have been very different from the end product, absorption or else active swallowing of food material, the changing over of this food into more convenient form, the conduction of "impulses" such as occurs in nerve, etc., etc. The chemical and physical basis of none of these activities is at all properly understood, although in many particular cases we can tell, without understanding how, that the activity was largely conditioned by, for example, certain enzymes or proteins present, and by certain other structures in the cell, such as membranes or fibrils, whose presence was in turn due to previous activities, conditioned likewise.

All the differences between various kinds and species of cells are thus due to differences in the nature of the activities, the physical and chemical reactions, which occur or have occurred in them. It is moreover thought by some that practically all these differences in reactions may in turn ultimately be due to differences in the nature of the enzymes present in the cells. This point is interesting in connection with our central problem, which was to discover what is the fundamental machinery which determines the characteristics of the egg-cell (or any other cell), and which thus determines what characteristics will be possessed by the individual into which the egg develops.

3. *Chromatin as the Determiner of the Cell's Properties*

In our search for this mechanism let us now leave the field of chemistry as such and inquire whether or not there can be seen in the cell some actual bodies or structures which might be regarded as containing these enzymes or else as containing material still more fundamental, which in some way determines the character of the enzymes or whatever substances or structures exist that are responsible for the particular activities and characteristics of a given cell. Apparently just such a structure has been found. It is called "chromatin," and consists of long thread-like bodies which occur in the nucleus of every cell, and which at cell division become more compact and easily visible so as to form rod-like bodies known as chromosomes.

As we shall see, there is strong reason for believing (1) that different parts or "loci" of the chromatin differ from one another and from corresponding parts in other species or varieties in regard to the composition or structure of the substance they contain, each minute portion or "locus" thus having its own individuality; (2) that they are able to grow, by their activity in some way transforming other substances, which they add to themselves, into material specifically like themselves, while, conversely, in their absence substance like themselves cannot be formed. The retention by the loci of their own particular character or individuality, throughout the growth and the various activities of the cell, means (3) that the substances in them are influenced little, if at all, by the processes and the special peculiarities of the cell around them, but (4) that these various substances [of the chromatin], each in its own way, influence profoundly the structure and activities of the cell.

Of course, it is not the chromatin alone which determines a cell's nature, for all sorts of external and internal influences other than the chromatin also react upon it; moreover, under different conditions of the cell, different ones of the above chromosomal substances are active or inactive. It is believed by many, however, (5) that of the various agents, the differences between which ordinarily cause cells to differ from one another, the chromosomes almost alone (and in plant cells, probably also the "plastids") have all the above four properties, that is, are strictly hereditary, in that they themselves act specifically to perpetuate themselves as such from generation to generation.

On the other hand, the other important constituents which may cause differences between cells (e.g. the droplets of fat) have no such property and so play no specific part in their own transmission from one generation to another. Thus, if we should change the exact chemical composition of the fat in an egg, the organism which develops from it might show certain abnormalities, but it would not keep on producing more fat of this unusual kind, consequently its eggs would not inherit this peculiarity. It might be conceded, however, that in certain special cases differences in cell constituents other than the chromosomes might be self-perpetuating and so would be inherited. For example, the complete absence of fat might be imagined to render impossible, in some obscure way, the production of more fat (yet without death of the organism ensuing).

A few cases are known [even] in inorganic chemistry where the same substance which is one of the end products of a reaction happens also to act as a catalyzer for (i.e. hastens) that reaction; thus the catalyst causes more substance of its own kind to be formed and the reaction is called autocatalytic. An understanding of such comparatively simple reactions helps us very little in understanding the autocatalytic [capability] of chromatin, however, for [this] is of a very special kind. It is special both because the reaction to produce any particular sort of chromatin must be very special and also because (as we shall see) the chromatin may undergo various changes, whereby the catalytic power of that chromatin undergoes corresponding changes of such a nature that the reaction now catalyzed results in chromatin of the new kind.

This process is so remarkable that it is hard to believe it could have come to exist in any but a few sporadic coincidences. There is no evidence that any cell substance or organ besides the chromatin have this peculiarity as a general property, in the sense that the substance could be changed in various ways and still retain the power to perpetuate itself in the form in which it happened at the time to be. It is undoubtedly the possession of this general property which enabled the chromatin to retain the differentiations it happened to acquire and so to serve as the substance of heredity.

[At the same time,] it may be that many other protoplasmic structures, etc., have the property of self-perpetuation [in a narrower sense], but either do not change (differentiate) or if they do are destroyed or return to a primitive condition with each generation. For example, the centrosome and the contractile vacuole perpetuate [propagate] themselves. But there is no evidence that their modifications are perpetuated also. Moreover, many body cells seem to retain their peculiar properties even during growth *in vitro*. But even in this case the chromatin is set aside as practically the only substance for heredity from one generation to the next, as recent work indicates.

Bearing these considerations in mind, then, we may say that the chromosomes have been supposed to contain at least most of the strictly *hereditary* substances that cause the differences between cells and therefore between individuals developed from cells. In other words, the chromosomes are thought to contain the factors of heredity. Most differences between organisms, moreover, are ultimately traceable mainly to differences in the factors of heredity, not in the other factors concerned. What then is the evidence for the preceding five points?

4. Evidence of the Unique Role Played by Chromatin

Chemistry has not yet helped us much here. Chromatin, or "nuclein," seems to consist, for the most part at least, of protein and nucleic acid. Nucleic acid in turn consists of phosphoric acid, sugar (pentose), and certain nitrogen-containing substances called purin bases, in chemical combination. Morphological observation has helped us more. The chromatin in a cell is usually practically invisible unless the cell has been subjected to a process of staining. Basic stains will combine with the acid present in the chromatin and so render it visible. If the chromatin of a cell which is "resting" (i.e. not dividing) is thus stained it will be observed to be in the form, apparently, of an irregular network which lies enclosed within a sac-like membrane. The membrane with its contents is called the "nucleus" of the cell.

Some recent observations, especially by Miss Bonnevie and by Vejdovsky, and also, as we shall see, our theoretical expectations, would lead us to believe that the apparent network probably consists of a number of very long delicate threads which are separate but coiled and folded and which therefore happen to cross each other in various ways. At any rate, prior to cell division the fibres of the apparent network gradually become more distinct, thicker, and shorter, so that at this stage it is quite evident that they consist of discrete threads. The threads now continue to shorten and thicken until they become rod shaped or even ball shaped. The separate threads or rods are called chromosomes. The work of Bonnevie and Vejdovsky indicates that what really happens in this process is that each very long delicate thread of the so-called "network" gradually coils up into a very fine, closely wound spiral. Their work is not yet accepted by all. But it fits in so well with the ideas derived from indirect evidence that critics will later be driven to this view. As the diameter of turns of the spiral and their closeness to one another gradually increase, the thread appears to shorten, darken, and thicken into a rod, although it is merely being wound up, as it were. The term chromosome is often used merely to designate such a rod, into which a thread was transformed at cell-division, but it may also refer to a thread at any other stage.

In the rod stage the chromosomes are often distinct enough to be counted accurately. When such counts were made it was found that all the cells in the same individual have the same number of chromosomes; in fact, the number is usually the same in cells of all individuals of the same sex and species. Moreover, not only are the chromosomes in the different cells alike in number, but they can also be seen to correspond in their sizes and shapes. The few exceptions (to be noted later) are of a sort which tend to strengthen the same principles as are supported by the above observations.

Let us now examine the behavior of the chromosomes in cell-division. While the threads are shortening into rods they may be seen to split lengthwise into two parallel threads. (According to some observers this split may occur long before cell-division and even as early as the latter part of the preceding division.) These threads later become parallel rods. Then a curious mechanism is brought into play which causes these two rods to be separated and transmitted into opposite daughter cells. By these means each of the two daughter cells gets an exact half of every previously existing chromosome, and in fact gets half of every portion of every chromosome. The individuality of the chromosomes therefore seems to be maintained through cell division, each portion of the chromatin in the mother cell giving rise directly to a daughter portion in each daughter cell. Cell-division is called "mitosis" from the Greek "miton," meaning thread.

[There follows a consideration of the processes in mitosis and of their possible mechanisms.]

Whatever may be the mechanism of mitosis, the most important facts of mitosis for the student of heredity are that the chromatin parts preserve their individuality and that, because of the chromosomes' lengthwise splitting when finely spun out, followed by separation of the daughter chromosomes, each daughter cell contains a half of every portion of every mother chromosome, to the minutest detail. Therefore, as Roux long ago pointed out, mitosis consists in an elaborate process that secures the transmission of a share of every individual part of the chromatin to both daughter cells. As he observed, it would seem very remarkable if this process had become evolved unless there were some function subserved by it, i.e. unless it was of advantage for the cells to obtain a share of every individual part of the chromatin rather than to obtain simply a certain amount of chromatin in cell-division. But, as Roux further noted, this amounts to saying that the different parts along the length of the chromatin threads differ qualitatively from each other and have special roles to perform in the work of the cell. For if the parts were alike it would not matter which parts a daughter cell received and so it would be of no advantage for it to get a half of each part rather than the whole of half the parts.

Roux therefore maintained that the chromatin is linearly differentiated, i.e., contains along its threads substances of different kinds arranged in line, these substances having their own special functions to fulfill. Although there were, even at that time, other indications that the nucleus or, more specifically, the chromatin, was of profound importance to the cell, this brilliant piece of reasoning formed the first argument of any value for the differentiation of the various parts of the chromatin from each other in composition and function, each part having its own individuality. As we shall see later, this conception has since received confirmation.

It will be seen that the above conclusions might be true and that nevertheless the chromatin would not contain the "substance of heredity," did not it and its parts *retain* their individuality throughout the history of the cell and from generation to generation. It is evident that the chromatin preserves its continuity through cell-division, but it is harder to determine by observation whether or not the chromatin and its parts maintain their continuity and individuality throughout the long so-called "resting period" usually intervening between one cell-division and the next, when the chromatin appears to form an indistinct network. The indirect evidence on this point—derived from a consideration of results of breeding experiments in connection with cytology—is quite decisive and will be considered in the next chapter. It is interesting, however, to see what evidence has been obtained more directly by observation.

The evidence obtained from observation of the chromosomes of course cannot concern itself with the maintenance of individuality by the smallest portions of the chromatin, for these are not visibly distinguishable from one another at any time. (The claim has been made very recently by two observers that they have succeeded in distinguishing certain small granules in the chromatin from the rest and have been able to follow them from generation to generation, but most "chromomeres" are coagulation products and inconstant.) This evidence must then confine itself to a study of the continuity of the chromosomes as wholes. As before stated, Bonnevie, Vejdovsky and others claim that in a number of cases they have by careful technique and study been able to distinguish the separate chromosome threads throughout the resting period. Stout and others have maintained that they could distinguish "prochromosomes" during this stage.

The most obvious fact which might be used as evidence for chromosome continuity is that whenever accurate counts of chromosomes can be made it is found that the different cells in the same individual (in fact, in the same sex and species) have the same number and types of chromosomes. This means that the chromosomes which form from the "resting" nucleus before a given cell-division are in number and kind like those which at the end of the previous cell-division apparently disintegrated in forming the "resting" nucleus. What conclusion, then, is more natural than that the chromosomes did not really disintegrate but merely became less distinctly visible as separate threads because of changes in their form and staining properties and, at the approach of the next cell-division, simply returned to their previous condition?

On the other hand, so far as this latter evidence alone is concerned, an opposite position might readily be maintained, for the chromosomes might be regarded as completely losing their individuality after cell-division and then being formed anew from the "resting" nucleus before the next cell-division by a sort of crystallizing process. Since the cells of the same individual are to some extent chemically similar it might well happen that they would always form a similar set of chromosomes in this process of secretion or pseudo-crystallization.

Cases have however been discovered, especially by Boveri, which cannot be so explained. Various accidental irregularities in the distribution of the chromosomes to the daughter cells occur, though rarely, without apparent cause. It occasionally happens that one or more of the chromosomes lag behind in moving toward the poles, and rarely they lag so much that they do not become enclosed in the new nucleus which is formed. The nucleus of one or both daughter cells accordingly comes to lack one or more chromosomes. The chromosome left outside the nucleus usually degenerates. In other cases the two halves of a chromosome may both be carried to one pole, so that one daughter nucleus lacks a chromosome, the other contains an extra one. Extreme irregularity in chromosome distribution may occur when, by any chance, more than two centromeres are present at cell-division. For then a so-called polyaster is formed instead of the usual amphiaster. Since the chromosomes split into only two parts whereas they must here be distributed to more than two poles it is obvious that each pole cannot receive its full quota of chromosomes. Accordingly, hardly any of the cells produced in such a case contain the number and assortment of chromosomes characteristic of the species. In all such cases the cells descended from one with an abnormal number of chromosomes agree in showing the same abnormalities in number and types of chromosomes. That is, the chromosomes must in each case have come out of the "resting" nucleus just as they went into it.

Similar observations have been made which show that the chromosomes even tend to have the same position and form at the time of division in sister cells. We cannot imagine that the obviously accidental positions the chromosomes happened to take at the end of one cell-division would correspond to their positions before the succeeding division if they crystallized anew—i.e. if they had not preserved their continuity in the interim. Moreover, if they did not maintain their own individuality we should not expect that in a case where by some unusual circumstances certain chromosomes were added to or subtracted from the original normal aggregate, this identical abnormality in chromosome composition would be apparent at the next and all succeeding divisions.

CHAPTER II. MENDELIAN INHERITANCE AND ITS BASIS

[The first part of this chapter, which was written jointly by Altenburg and Muller, presents, with examples, the principles of segregation (using first the backcross of the nondominant red-white difference in four-o'clocks), of independent segregation, and of linkage (including sex linkage), crossing over, and mapping, all in terms of the behavior of the chromosomes. The second part, by Muller, which is reproduced below, considers multifactorial determination and mutation.]

Throughout the above discussion we have been speaking, for simplicity's sake, as though the "red" factor were the sole cause of the red color in the eyes of fruit flies, the "tall" factor the sole cause of tallness in sweet peas, etc. It should, however, be recognized that in these cases the factors under discussion are merely the *deciding* causes: all other causes necessary for the production of these characteristics were present in all the individuals, and thus the determination of whether or not the character was to be produced in a given individual depended merely upon whether the particular factor under discussion was present or whether instead its allelomorph was present.

A great many factors together are really necessary to cause the production of a given character, some being absolutely necessary, some having slight effect upon it. The character is merely the end product of a series of reactions in which many genes and also environmental agencies take part, but we may, as above, name any particular factor after the character if all other factors are constantly present, and this factor, being present only in some individuals, thus decides, as it were, by its presence, whether or not the character shall be produced. In other cases it is found that individuals which are crossed differ in regard to two or more of the pairs of chromosomes which affect the particular character studied.

Not only is it true that each character is caused by many factors but a single factor often influences the production of more than one character, so that in no sense can we think of each character as having one factor corresponding to it. If, then, two individuals differ in regard to characters the heredity of which has not previously been investigated, it is impossible to tell in regard to how many factors they differ, unless we cross the individuals and by breeding the hybrid thus determine how many pairs of factors contain different allelomorphs (i.e. how many can be seen to segregate from one another in the hybrid).

The question now arises as to how differences between allelomorphs arise in the first instance. They arise by a sudden change or mutation in the factor, of unknown origin; those individuals which contain the factor in its changed form thus contain an allelomorph which may be demonstrated to segregate, in a hybrid, from the original factor. By the gradual accumulation of such changes, races are supposed to become different from one another, finally so different as to become different species, and it has been supposed that in this way the descendants of the original primitive ancestors of all organisms gradually became more and more different until we have the diverse forms of plant and animal life to be seen around us today. Of course, only those types became established in which the changed factors gave the organisms containing them some advantage over those around them, a principle known as natural selection.

These changes in factors are, however, for the most part extremely rare, although the factors differ somewhat in that slight amount of variation which they do possess. A very few factors, indeed, change frequently. But in these cases (called ever-mutating or ever-sporting) the degree and nature of the change is fixed and when the change is once accomplished there is no tendency for [frequent] further change.

Nothing is known of the causes of mutation, and mutations have not been artificially induced except [possibly] in a few cases which are still under dispute. Differences between organisms due merely to the effects of different environments are, then, not inherited. Even if an unusual environment might in some way cause a mutation there is no reason to believe that the mutated factor contained in the gametes would give rise to a character in the offspring at all similar to that produced in the parent by direct effect of the environment. In other words, "acquired characters are not inherited."

The principles of heredity outlined in this chapter have already been of use to the student of evolution in interpreting the method by which the differentiation of species from one another must have come about, and to the practical breeder who wished to arrive at certain desired types by the recombination, into one race, of certain of the characters already present in different existing races, or just arisen by mutation. Needless to say, further knowledge of, for example, the chemical and physical nature of genes and the means of controlling their mutations (subjects concerning which we are at presently entirely in the dark) would be of almost unlimited value in both of these lines of work.

A GENE FOR THE FOURTH CHROMOSOME
OF DROSOPHILA*

Hermann J. Muller

From the Zoölogical Department of Columbia University

Drosophila ampelophila contains two pairs of long 'autosomes' (chromosomes other than sex-chromosomes) and one pair of minute 'autosomes'; there are, in addition, a pair of long sex-chromosomes alike in the female ('X's) but unlike in the male ('X' and 'Y').[1] Correspondingly, breeding tests of the numerous mutants of Drosophila have revealed a great group of genes (containing over thirty members) which are sex-linked in such a way that they are distributed, in the reduction division, to exactly the same cells as is the X-chromosome, and two other great groups (with about twenty members each) which are not sex-linked and so have been considered to follow in their distribution two of the pairs of autosomes (presumably the long ones). The genes in these three groups are therefore said to lie in Chromosomes I, II and III, respectively. The members of any group of genes are linked with one another; in the female the linkage is partial and is of the linear type to be expected on the basis of the chiasmatype theory of Janssens and Morgan; in the male the linkage is complete (no crossing-over). All the members of one group assort independently of the members of either of the other groups, in both sexes, as would be expected on the generally accepted postulate of the random assortment of non-homologous chromosomes in the reduction division.

It will be seen that the above grouping of genes leaves one pair of autosomes (presumably the small ones) and the Y-chromosome without any genes to correspond. As regards the Y, it seems at first sight surprising that no mutations have been found involving genes which follow it in their distribution (i.e., genes which are always transmitted from father to son), for it is of about the same length as the X, in which over thirty genes are known. This fact would force us to one of three conclusions: (1) Either the genes connected with the Y-chromosome for some reason do not mutate; or (2) these mutations are all recessive to dominant normal allelomorphs present in X (in spite of the fact that mutations in X are not dominated, conversely, by allelomorphs in Y); or (3), as Mr. C. W. Metz first suggested, genes are degenerate or entirely absent in the Y-chromosome. The first conclusion is a priori unlikely; the third may now be supported by a number of considerations, which it will

*The Journal of Experimental Zoology, Vol. 17, No. 3, October, 1914.

be of interest to discuss briefly in this connection, before proceeding to our acount of the fourth chromosome.

In the first place, the Y-chromosome is known to vary greatly in size and number in closely related species of animals. Secondly, as Mr. C. B. Bridges has recently shown, a female occasionally, owing to an abnormal reduction division ('non-disjunction'), receives a Y-chromosome in addition to the two X's, yet such a female is indistinguishable from the ordinary form, which contains no Y. The Y-chromosome therefore either contains no genes or else only genes which are allelomorphic to those in X, but never dominant to them. This is proved also by the fact that mosaic flies sometimes develop, of which a part of the body is female but another part is male, owing to the accidental loss of one of the X-chromosomes in an embryonic cell-division. These male parts must have an X, but no Y, and yet they are indistinguishable from corresponding parts on real males which contain a Y. Furthermore, Mr. C. B. Bridges has obtained (again by 'non-disjunction') males which must have two Y's, yet these also show no peculiarities. It is therefore certain that Y either contains no genes at all which have an effect upon the individual or it contains genes allelomorphic to those in X. It can be proved, however, that if it contains allelomorphs to the genes in X, these are not normal allelomorphs (i.e., the same kind as those present in the X of the wild fly) for they are recessive to mutant genes in X to which the normal genes in X are dominant, i.e., a male always manifests all the genes, mutant or normal, recessive or dominant, that are present in its single X-chromosome. In other words, if there be genes in Y allelomorphic to those in X, they are abnormal allelomorphs of those in X, and are always recessive to all genes in X. It is difficult to conceive why genes in Y should be recessive, on the one hand, to normal genes in X, in those cases where the mutant genes in X are dominant to the normal, and, on the other hand, to mutant genes in X, in those more frequent cases where the normal genes in X are dominant to the mutant, unless the genes in Y are mere 'absences' or nearly so.[2]

There is an *a priori* explanation for this lack of genes, or lack of dominant genes, in the Y-chromosome, an explanation in the development of which Dr. A. H. Sturtevant has coöperated with me. Owing to the fact that crossing-over never occurs in the male Drosophila, any mutation which originally occurred in Y remained in that chromosome and was never exchanged for a normal gene from X. Furthermore, these mutations in Y which were recessive would not have been subject to the action of natural selection for, since the normal gene in the X-chromosome will dominate over them, individuals containing them will not be abnormal. In the course of time, therefore, recessive changes in the Y-chromosome will tend to accumulate. If, now, we assume that mutations sometimes consist in losses[3] of genes, a degeneration of the Y-chromosome (so far as its *genes* are concerned) would result. This is because most losses of genes, if they occurred, would be recessive (i.e., one 'dose' of a factor usually has the same effect as two), as indicated by the fact that the one-X part of a mosaic is like the XX part in respect to all characters affected by X except the sex characters (provided the two X's of the XX part are alike). Now, if, as seems likely, recessive losses are more apt to occur than recessive additions of genes (since one 'dose' usually has the same effect as two) the Y-chromosome will gradually become functionless. On *a priori* grounds, we should expect such a fate, in any species, for the sex-chromosomes peculiar to the heterozygous sex, if crossing-over never occurs between it and its homologue.[4]

These considerations will also explain the size difference which often exists between X and Y, the apparent unimportance of supernumerary Y-chromosomes in development, when these occur, and other irregularities of the Y-chromosome. Hitherto it has been a mystery why the difference merely in the sex factor or factors contained in the sex chromosomes should often be correlated with such a large difference between the two chromosomes, whereas differences in respect to other factors did not involve any visible size differences in the chromosomes concerned, which presumably contain hundreds of genes.

There is, therefore, all things considered, no cause for surprise in the fact that no mutations have occurred involving a group of genes transmitted only from father to son, and thus following in their distribution the Y-chromosome. The chief gap, if it may be so termed, then remaining in the parallelism between the configuration of the chromosomes and the distribution of genes in Drosophila has been due to the fact that no genes were found in a fourth independent group (a third independent non-sex-linked group) to correspond with the fact that there are three pairs of autosomes. Supposing, however, that mutations are equally likely to occur at any locus in the chromatin, it could be explained as a result of pure chance that no mutations had as yet happened to lie in the restricted space of the small autosome. It was expected, nevertheless, that mutations in a fourth group would eventually be found, and such a mutation has now in fact arisen.

The new character is a recessive wing and leg abnormality, the wings being held out from the body but bent backwards near the base, and the metatarsal joint of the legs being frequently greatly shortened and thickened. The wing is also apt to be curved, with the dorsal surface convex, and shortened. The character varies somewhat, but there is very rarely any difficulty in distinguishing it from the normal form, unless the flies have been raised in very dry bottles. Drought therefore hinders the manifestation of this character, as it may also, and to a greater degree, in some way hinder the development of the character 'abnormal abdomen,' a case reported by Morgan.

I found the mutation 'bent wing' in a race with bifid wings and vermilion barred eyes, all three of these characters being in Chromosome I (sex-linked). A cross of bifid vermilion barred bent male by a pink-eyed female (pink is in Chromosome III) gave in F_1 all the males normal, and the females also normal except in respect to barred, which is dominant; in the next generation, F_2, all combinations of the factors concerned appeared. If bent had been in Chromosome III, no crossing-over would have occurred between bent and pink in the F_1 *male*, consequently, no pink bent spermatozoa could have been formed, and thus (since pink and bent are both recessive) no pink bent F_2 individuals could have been produced. Since these were produced, bent did not lie in the *third* chromosome. Similarly, if bent had been in the first (X) chromosome or in the Y, no crossing-over between it and the sex-factor would have taken place in the P_1 or F_1 male, and consequently no bent females could have been produced in F_2. As bent females were produced, bent did not lie in the *first* (X) chromosome, or in the Y.

A bent barred eyed F_2 male was then crossed to a female containing three mutant genes in the *second* chromosome, namely, the genes for black body color, purple eyes, and curved wings. Here, too, some flies were obtained in F_2 which showed the characters of both grandparents at once (i.e., were both bent, and black, purple, and curved, and sometimes also barred). This proved that bent did not lie in Chromosome II. The details of the count are shown in table 1.

TABLE 1

Not bent

WILD TYPE	BLACK PURPLE CURVED	BLACK	PURPLE CURVED	CURVED	BLACK PURPLE
84	30	1	3	6	5

Bent

| 43 | 9 | 1 | 1 | | |

The number of barred and non-barred, also of males and females, in each class of moderately large size, were approximately equal. The linkage manifested between black, purple, and curved corresponds as closely with expectation based on the previous linkage results of Bridges, as could be demanded for the small numbers involved. The determination of curved was at times uncertain, owing to the tendency of bent to curve too, and the determination of purple in eyes which were barred was also sometimes uncertain. But as far as the results go, they show that bent is independent of black, purple, curved, barred, and sex.

As no counts had been made in the cross with pink, and few were obtained in the cross with black purple curved, it was still conceivable that although bent was not absolutely linked, in the male, with the members of one of the three previously known groups, as has always been found to be the case with other genes, still it might perhaps be partially linked, in either or both sexes. New crosses were therefore made with the object of securing accurate counts. Some bent males descended from F_2 of the cross with pink were mated to black pink females. These males were found to be heterozygous for pink, as half of the F_1 flies were pink (although none were black or bent). The red-eyed F_1 flies were mated together, to show the distribution of bent with respect to all three previously known chromosomes. The pinks were also mated together. The latter cross should show the distribution of bent with respect to Chromosomes I and II only, as all the flies were homozygous for pink, the mutant gene in Chromosome III.

The composition of the pink flies used as parents, with the paternal and maternal genes which they contained, was as follows:

F_1 male   Paternal genes   —   Gray Pink Bent

              Maternal genes sex Black Pink Straight

F_1 female Paternal genes sex Gray   Pink Bent

              Maternal genes sex Black Pink Straight

The count of offspring of this cross of pink flies resulted as shown in table 2.

TABLE 2

All individuals pink

		WILD TYPE	BLACK	BENT	BLACK BENT
F_2 numbers observed	females..	83	30	24	8
	males....	77	24	31	9
	Total....	160	54	55	17
Total numbers expected on independence		162	54	54	18

Numbers of females expected = numbers of males expected.

The results conform with the theoretical expectation on the assumption of independent segregation between black, sex and bent.

The composition of the parents in the cross of red flies was as follows:

F_1 male*   Gray Red Bent

　　　sex Black Pink Straight

F_1 female sex Gray Red Bent

　　　sex Black Pink Straight

The offspring were as seen in table 3.

TABLE 3

		WILD TYPE	BLACK	PINK	BENT	BLACK PINK	BLACK BENT	PINK BENT	BLACK PINK BENT
F_2 numbers observed	females..	87	40	36	17	5	6	12	3
	males....	98	27	39	29	17	10	10	3
	Total....	185	67	75	46	22	16	22	6
Total numbers expected on independence		185	62	62	62	20.6	20.6	20.6	6.9

Numbers of females expected = numbers of males expected.

A considerable differential viability came into play in these bottles, as is proved by the fact that certain 'contrary' or opposite classes which were necessarily produced in equal numbers at fertilization (no matter whether linkage was involved or not), gave rather different counts of adult flies (e.g., 206 females; 233 males; 97 pink straight, 62 red bent; which were the worst discrepancies). On allowing for these differences obviously due to viability, we find that there are no discrepancies due to linkage of bent with black or pink, for the average between black straights and gray bents (pink plus red), is to the black bents as 3:1, and the average between pink straights and red bents (gray plus black) is to the pink bents as 3:1, as expected on independence. These results therefore confirm those previously obtained in regard to the independence of black (Chromosome II) and bent; they show in addition, however, that bent is independent of pink (Chromosome III).

The distribution of bent with regard to black and pink was next determined separately for each sex, by means of back-crosses. A normal male was mated to black pink bent females. The F_1 males, which were heterozygous for all three factors, as well as for sex, were then mated to triply recessive black pink bent females. If the factors were independent, all classes in the next generation should be equal in number. The actual result was as shown in table 4.

*The paternally derived allelomorphs are on the upper line, the maternal on the lower.

TABLE 4

CLASSES	WILD TYPE	BLACK	BENT	BLACK BENT	PINK	BLACK PINK	PINK BENT	BLACK PINK BENT
females....................	29	28	23	30	16	14	15	9
males.....................	25	22	22	17	14	18	16	15
Total....................	54	50	45	47	30	32	31	24

Here practically the only irregularity not due to chance is obviously caused by a deficiency (low viability) of pink flies of all classes, and by a lower viability of males than of females. The independent assortment of bent with respect to the other factors, and of the other factors with respect to each other, is best brought out (especially in a case involving differential viability) by a tabulation of the per cent of cases in which any two pairs of factors, considered by themselves, underwent recombination in the formation of the germ cells of the heterozygous parent. Thus, in the case of sex and bent, the factors for sex and for bent in the heterozygous male parent were both derived from the mother, the Y-chromosome and the normal allelomorph of bent ('straight') both coming from the father. Yet in the segregation division by which the sperm were formed, a recombination occurred as frequently as a persistence of the old combination, so that as many eggs were fertilized by sperm bearing the sex factor and straight, or the Y-chromosome and bent, as were fertilized by sperm with sex and bent or Y and straight. As a result, straight females and bent males formed 50 per cent of the total number, as we should expect on the basis that the factors were in non-homologous chromosomes which were assorted independently. The other per cents of recombination were as follows:

	per cent
Sex-black	50.0
sex-pink......................................	55.0
black-pink	50.5
black-bent	50.5
pink-bent	49.0

In a reciprocal cross some of the triply heterozygous F_1 females were back-crossed to triply recessive males. Here, too, we should expect all classes equal, barring differential viability, on the basis of independent assortment, and approximately 50 per cent of recombination between any two factors. The result was similar to that obtained in the back-cross of the males (table 5).

The per cents of recombination were as follows:

	per cent
Black-pink	54.0
black-bent	45.5
pink-bent	52.0

TABLE 5

CLASSES	WILD TYPE	BLACK	BENT	BLACK BENT	PINK	BLACK PINK	PINK BENT	BLACK PINK BENT
females......................	23	14	16	22	19	11	15	10
males.......................	22	23	17	22	15	12	9	8
Total....................	45	37	33	44	34	23	24	18

Here we cannot obtain the per cents of recombinations between sex and the other factors, since the parent which was heterozygous for the other factors was not the one which was heterozygous for sex.

Conclusions

The foregoing experiments prove that the gene for bent wings segregates independently of the sex-linked group of genes and of the two hitherto known non-sex-linked groups; accordingly, the genes of Drosophila now fall into four divisions, one sex-linked, corresponding to the X-chromosome, and three non-sex-linked, corresponding to the three pairs of autosomes. Thus the chief gap yet remaining in the series of genetic phenomena that form a parallel to the known cytological facts in Drosophila ampelophilia has now been filled. It may therefore be predicted that no genes undergoing independent assortment of those at present known can hereafter be discovered in individuals of Drosophila ampelophila that show the chromosome configuration normal to the species, and it also seems probable that when other mutations are discovered in the fourth group, the genes in which they occur will be found to be linked strongly to the gene for bent wings, since the fourth chromosome is probably the small one, and so any genes in it must lie near together. The close parallel existing between the number and relative *sizes* of the groups of genes and of the chromosomes leaves little doubt that it must be the pair of small chromosomes with which the factor for bent wings is connected, and that mutations occur more frequently in larger groups of genes, which are connected with larger chromosomes, than in smaller groups; mutation therefore would happen pretty much at random, in that it would usually take place about as often in one group as in another of equal size.[5] This, too, makes it probable that the mutations in the larger chromosomes have occurred at various points scattered throughout their whole length, and are not confined, *as a group*, to a particular region or regions. The exceptional case of no mutations having been observed in the Y-chromosome, as we have seen, does not really form an argument against this view, which other facts support. That more mutations have been found in the X-chromosome than in either of the two long autosomes, which are nevertheless about the same size as X, is also to be expected, because a larger proportion of the mutations occurring in X would be noticed, since the male flies manifest all genes present in their single X, whereas in the case of other chromosomes, any mutant gene that is recessive to normal cannot manifest itself unless it be present in duplex. Granting, then, the correspondence between size and number of chromosomes and of groups of genes, it is difficult to see why larger groups of genes should follow the distribution of the larger chromosomes unless we conceive the connection between the genes and the chromosomes to be that the genes are material particles actually lying in and forming a part of the chromosomes with which they go. In any case, we must admit that the occurrence of a mutation in a fourth independent group of genes in Drosophila forms a further argument, if any more still be needed, in favor of the chromosome theory of heredity.

Notes

[1]Two lines of recent cytological investigation, the one followed by Mr. C. W. Metz, the other by Mr. C. B. Bridges, have given evidence (not yet fully published) which goes far towards refuting the view suggested by Stevens that the so-called 'X' chromosome of Drosophila actually consists of a short autosome with the real X-chromosome joined to it and that the 'Y' chromosome represents this short autosome without any 'X' attached.

[2]This might be otherwise explained on the very improbable hypothesis that all of the mutations which occurred in X were in a restricted part (the end?) of the chromosome, and that the Y lacked only this part of the chromosome and so appeared to contain genes recessive to all those in X which underwent mutation, although it actually contained normal genes in the other part of the chromosome, which never mutated. This is not quite equivalent, although nearly so, to the idea that X is attached to an autosome (see footnote 1).

[3]By losses of genes are meant not necessarily their total bodily disappearance (losses of loci from the chromatin) but also any changes in them whereby they are rendered permanently inactive and incapable, under any circumstances, of exerting an influence on the organism.

[4]Conversely, where this chromosome appears degenerate or different genetically from its homologue (in addition to the difference in the sex factors) we should expect to find no crossing-over between the two sex-chromosomes in the heterozygous sex, i.e., complete, not partial, sex-linkage. This argument applies to all known cases of sex-linkage, for in all these cases a recessive mutant factor will manifest itself in the heterozygous sex, proving that the sex-chromosome peculiar to the heterozygous sex is different from the other sex-chromosomes in that it contains no dominant normal allelomorph of the mutant factor.

[5]This should not be taken to mean that any particular gene mutates as often as any other; it is definitely known that, both in Drosophila and in other forms (corn, *Marabilis*, etc.), some genes are more likely to mutate than others.

THE MECHANISM OF CROSSING-OVER*
II

Hermann J. Muller

Rice Institute

The Manner of Occurrence of Crossing-over

A. Interference

As soon as it seemed probable that the factors were linked in line, and that crossing-over was the actual method of interchange, it became of interest (so the writer believed) to analyze the exact mode of incidence of the interchange. The questions suggested themselves, for example, what was the total frequency of crossing-over, did any factors separate more often than they remained together, how often did crossing-over occur at two points simultaneously, and was there any tendency, in such cases, for the two points of crossing-over to be a definite distance apart, or in definite positions, etc. For answers to these questions might throw light on the mechanism of crossing-over, what cytological phenomena it was connected with, and what stage in synapsis it occurred at.

With these points in view the author calculated the linkage relations that would result on several possible schemes of interchange. The simplest possibility was that the chromosomes always twisted in loops of fixed length, though not of fixed position, and always underwent breakage, with recombination of homologous strands (*i. e.*, "crossed-over" in the technical sense), at each place that the strands crossed one another. In such a case there would always be a definite distance between one point of crossing-over and another; moreover, all factors which were separated by a distance great enough for double crossing-over to occur between them, *i. e.*, by the length of at least one loop, must always have either double or single (or multiple) crossing-over between them. Sturtevant's data, however, showed that this was not true, and accordingly it had to be concluded that the length of the loop was variable, or that "crossing-over" did not always occur where the strands crossed.

Another possibility was that crossings-over were quite independent of one another, having an entirely random or chance distribution in the chromosome, with reference to each other. This would mean that when crossing-over occurred at one point, another crossing-over would be just as likely to occur coincidently at any other given point—whether this be very near or far away—as when no crossing-over took place at the first point. But this latter scheme would not be that expected on the method of crossing-over proposed by

The American Naturalist, Vol. L. No. 592, 1916; section IV, parts A-B (with figure 6); and summary, included.

Janssens and followed by Morgan, for in the stages when Janssens supposed crossing-over to occur the chromosomes are rather loosely twisted, so that loops of very small length do not occur as often as longer ones (thus, very near one point of crossing-over the strands seldom cross back again). I therefore determined the mathematical relations which would exist between crossing-over frequencies, if crossings-over had a chance distribution with reference to one another, in order to compare these figures with those obtained by experiment. On the assumption that separation between A and B has no influence on separation between B and C, if crossing-over occurs between A and B in 10 per cent of cases and between B and C in 20 per cent of cases, then, among those ten cases in a hundred where crossing-over between A and B occurs, 20 per cent (*i. e.*, two cases) would be cross-overs between B and C as well; in other words, the per cent of double cross-overs would be equal to the product of per cents AB and BC (formula 1). The easiest way to determine the correctness of the assumption in any given case, therefore, is to compare the observed per cent of double cross-overs with per cent AB × per cent BC.

Another relation besides was found to hold between the theoretical linkage values, dependent upon the relation in formula 1. For it is easily seen that the number of *separations* between A and C must always be equal to the sum of the number of crossings-over between A and B, and between B and C, minus all those crossings-over contained in the cases where coincidence occurred, and in which A and C, therefore, failed to separate,—*i. e.*, minus twice the number of *cases* of double crossing-over. Hence, if formula 1 is correct, then it must also be true that per cent AC = per cent AB + per cent BC - 2 (per cent AB × per cent BC) (formula 2). This formula was originally expressed not only in the above terms, where the "per cent of separations" (*i. e.*, ratio of separations to the total number of cases) is used as the index of separation frequency, but also in terms of the so-called "gametic ratio"—the ratio of cases of non-separation to those of separation—for this was the way of indicating degree of linkage then used by all investigators of the subject. The latter index gives much more complicated formulas, however, so the writer pointed out at the same time that per cent of separations would afford a much more useful measure of linkage.

Later, Trow also worked out and published the same formula (no. 2)—in terms of the "gametic ratio"—and it is generally known as "Trow's special hypothesis." But on the reduplication hypothesis held by Trow, and by the other English geneticists who do not accept the chromosome explanation, the formula would be supposed to result, not from the fact that crossing-over between A and B was independent of that between B and C, but from the fact that "reduplications" AB and BC were independent, not being disturbed by any "primary reduplication" AC. Adherents of the reduplication hypothesis have been much concerned as to whether or not their results confirmed the assumptions made in Trow's formula, and have in one or two instances calculated that they did. Let us examine for a moment the requisites for proving such a conclusion. As above shown, the whole matter turns on the frequency of coincidence of separations AB and BC (*i. e.*, on the frequency of "double crossing-over") and the question can be settled by determining directly the amount of this coincidence. If the per cent of double cross-overs = per cent AB × per cent BC (formula 1), then the assumption that separation frequencies AB and BC are independent is correct. As offspring from a back-cross all show what factors they received from the hybrid parent, a back-cross involving the three factors A, B, and C at the same time will answer the question at once, for all the cases of coincident separation (double cross-overs) that occur can be counted. But where the hybrids, instead of being back-crossed, are inbred—a practice followed by adherents of the reduplication hypothesis—then it is impossible to tell which F_2 individuals come from gametes of the classes which we may term double·cross-overs, unless one of these classes is the triple recessive, and then the only double cross-overs which can be known as such are those very rare individuals that happen to result from the union of two double cross-over gametes. The British workers have, therefore, not been able to find the proportion of double cross-overs directly, to compare this with formula 1, but have tried to determine the frequency of coincidence indirectly, by using the method followed in formula 2. That is, they determined the relations existing between frequencies AC, AB, and BC, as calculated from their F_2 counts, for, as above shown, the greater the frequency of double crossing-over, the more will AC be cut down in proportion to AB and BC. And it seemed evident that, if the relation of AC to AB and BC was just that given by Trow's formula ("2"), then coincidence of separations must have the frequency demanded on the assumption that separations (or "reduplications") AB and BC occur independently of one another. As a matter of fact, however, this method offers no answer to the question, unless almost impossibly large F_2 counts are obtained, for otherwise *the independent random fluctuations of these three values in this kind of count are so great that any deviation in AC due to excess or deficiency of double crossing-over would be quite lost to sight.*

The question was, however, immediately and definitively answered in *Drosophila*, before Trow's paper appeared, by examination of Sturtevant's extensive back-crosses, especially of those involving three pairs of factors at once. As the results did not conform to the formula, it was not published, but as Trow has since raised this question publicly and the adherents of the reduplication hypothesis are still discussing it, it may not be out of place to have given an analysis of it here, and to recall the fact that it had already been tried and rejected. Besides, as will appear below, a discussion of the relations which would exist if crossings-over were independent of one another is a necessary preliminary for a treatment of the relations which do exist between linkage values.

The results showed that double crossing-over does not, as a rule, occur as frequently as would be expected if, as the above formulae assumed, it were purely a matter of chance whether or not two cross-overs happen coincidently. In a sense, then, the occurrence of one crossing-over interferes with the coincident occurrence of another crossing-over in the same pair of chromosomes, and I have accordingly termed this phenomenon *"interference."* The amount of interference is determined by comparing the actual per cent of double cross-overs with the per cent expected if crossings-over were independent, *i. e.*, if they had a purely chance distribution with reference to each other. Now, the per cent which would occur on the latter expectation has already been given by formula 1 as per cent AB × per cent BC. If, then, the observed per cent of double cross-overs were divided by per cent AB × per cent BC, we would obtain a fraction showing what proportion of the coincidences which would have happened on pure chance really took place. This ratio of observed double cross-overs to the chance expectation appears to me to furnish the most useful measure of interference. The ratio is itself best expressed in per cent, and it may be called the relative coincidence, or simply "coincidence." If the "coincidence" is low, this means that there has been much interference, for most of the double cross-overs expected on chance were prevented from appearing; conversely, if coincidence is high, the interference must have been very weak. Some illustrations may make the meaning of this index clearer. If, for example, coincidence is 0 per cent no double crossing-over is occurring; the interference between one crossing-over and another is then complete. If coincidence is 45 per cent, this figure does not mean that 45 per cent of the individuals are double cross-overs, but that 45 per cent of the number of double cross-overs which would be expected as a result of pure chance (whatever that number may have been) actually appeared, 55 per cent having been "interfered with," or somehow prevented from occurring. If coincidence is 100 per cent, there has been no interference, for the same number of double cross-overs appeared as expected on the ground that the two crossings-over did not interfere with each other's occurrence. 110 per cent would mean that if one crossing-over occurred, the other was 10 per cent *more* likely to occur than in cases of random distributions of crossings-over. This would be "negative interference," for as coincidence increases interference decreases.

On Janssens' theory that crossing-over takes place in the strepsinema stage, when the chromosomes are twisted in loose loops, crossing-over would very seldom take place at two points very near together, for this would require a tight twisting of the chromosomes. Accordingly, on this theory interference was to be expected; furthermore it would be expected that interference was very great between crossings-over that were in neighboring regions; but between crossings-over further apart there should be little or no interference. The results were according to this expectation; they indicated strongly that the interference was very great for crossings-over short distances apart, but progressively diminished as the distances considered became greater. The conclusion drawn was that crossing-over took place as postulated on Janssens' theory, when the strands were loosely twisted in strepsinema, although the twisting and crossing-over did not take place in the stereotyped manner suggested as a first possibility, in the earlier part of this section. For there was evidence that the distances between the two points of crossing-over in double cross-overs were variable; but this again corresponded with the fact that the chromosomes of *Batracoseps* and other forms, as seen under the microscope, did not always twist in loops of the same length.•Furthermore, if it be supposed that in most maturing eggs of the fly the homologous chromosomes twist tightly enough to cross at least once or twice, as is certainly the case in *Batracoseps* and many other forms, it must be concluded that at not every point of crossing does actual "crossing-over" (recombination of strands) take place, for it was found that nearly half of the factor-groups emerged without having undergone any crossing-over at all. And this, in turn, corresponded with the observations of Janssens and others, which showed that at some at least of the points of crossing of homologous chromosomes, the latter merely untwisted again without having undergone the "chiasmatype" process. Here, then, was a theory of crossing-over that seemed complete, so far as connecting the genetic facts with the cytological observations was concerned.

B. Possible Mechanisms of Crossing-Over

There is one very unsatisfying point, however, in this original scheme of crossing-over. That is, it postulates that crossing-over occurs at a comparatively late stage in synapsis, when the strands have become very much shorter and thicker than the long delicate threads which first came into contact with their homologues (see Fig. 6). Now, in crossing-over the chromosomes must come into contact, and break, at *precisely* homologous points, otherwise factors would be lost or gained by them when crossing-over occurs. But presumably the factors are set very close together in the line, judging by the fact that mutations in new "loci" (positions in the chromosomes) are still as numerous as ever, and that, if the whole chromosome is packed with factors as close together as, judging by their linkage relations, they seem to be at certain places in it, it must contain at the very least 200 factors. It is difficult to conceive how this cleavage of ultramicroscopic nicety can take place properly at a stage when the chromosomes are so coarse and short. The observations of Vejdovsky and others, taken in connection with the genetic results from *Drosophila*, render it practically certain that the factors are really disposed in an extremely fine, long thread or "chromonema," which, during the metaphase and anaphase of mitosis, is coiled up very closely in more or less spiral fashion (probably within a viscous sheath of some sort), to form the thick dense chromosomes, but which, in the resting period and during the early stages of synapsis, becomes, to some extent at least, uncoiled and drawn out again. In this state, then, the chromosomes first pair, as shown in Fig. 6. Thus precisely homologous parts of the

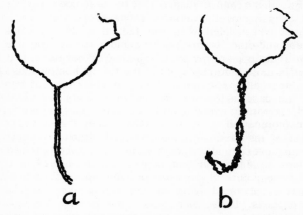

a   *b*

Fig. 6. Chromosomes during an early stage of synapsis (amphitene). In some preparations the apposed threads seem parallel, as in *a*; in others they seem twisted about each other, as in *b*.

frail threads may become apposed to each other, so that this stage, which is called the "amphitene" stage, would seem to be the one best "adapted" for the occurrence of crossing-over. Later, when each chromosome becomes, presumably, a thick spiral, there would seem to be much greater mechanical difficulties in the way of exact apposition and breakage of parts.

On any possible theory of crossing-over, however, the known facts concerning interference should be capable of interpretation. If crossing-over occurred during the "amphitene" stage, or not long after, would there be any possible explanation of the fact that one point of crossing-over is generally far removed from another? The explanation might be found simply in the fact that each of the "leptotene" chromosomes—*i. e.*, the finely drawn out chromosomes which are just about to undergo synapsis—pursued a general course that had few close turns in it. (For possibly it maintains the same general direction as it had when it was short and thick; the reader will recall that Boveri found that chromosomes preserve their approximate shape and position from one cell division to the next.) When, therefore, the leptotene chromosomes are being brought together by the synaptic attraction which homologous loci then bear for each other, the threads are usually crossed only at a few points, and these are generally far apart. If these initial points of crossing—which, it will be observed, have been determined by the original positions of the threads, and not by any twisting—are the points of crossing-over, interference would be accounted for, and would, in effect, be of the same general nature as on the mechanism of crossing-over postulated by Janssens.

On this second scheme of crossing-over, it might at first seem hard to see why recombination—*i. e.*, "crossing-over"—should occur where the threads cross, but it should be remembered that the two threads, while coming together, often lie in about the same plane both above and below the point of crossing. If they keep to this original plane as they draw together, they will come to have the same plane of apposition just above and just below the crossing point,—although the sides of the filaments that face each other will be just the opposite in the two places; consequently, the threads at the crossing point must undergo a very sharp twist, and if, as we must suppose, they are somewhat viscous, this may result in their breakage and recombination, or, perhaps, first in their fusion, and, later, when the pieces of the same chromosome above and below the point of crossing are wrenched apart in opposite directions by mutual repulsion of the strands or by pulling of spindle fibres, in breakage of parts originally together. (So perhaps fusion might occur during the amphitene and breakage in the strepsinema stage; this would be a combination of schemes 1 and 2 which would account both for the exact apposition of parts and for the phenomena observed by Janssens.) Be this as it may, at any rate, the negative argument may be given that it is just as hard to account for recombination at a later stage in synapsis as at this stage, even overlooking the objection of the the the thickness of the threads.

There is a serious objection to the scheme just given, however, in that, as the threads come together, they seem, in many preparations, not to keep their original plane of apposition, but to twist tightly about each other, like the strands of a rope, throughout their entire length (see Fig. 6). It is possible that the twisting of one thread about the other is merely apparent, however, and that the threads lie parallel but are simply coiling up in a spiral, in the process of forming the shorter, thicker prophase chromosomes; for, unless the spiral were very delicately preserved by the fixing agent, there would be apparent knots in it as though there were a twisting of two strands about each other. Moreover, there is evidence indicating that this tight twisting occurs only in certain species of animals. But let us assume for the moment that this very tight twisting really takes place during the amphitene stage in flies, and that crossing-over takes place at this period (this we may call scheme of crossing-over number three). Would there then be any way of explaining why one crossing-over should interfere with another near by, in view of the fact that the loops are of such small dimensions? In seeking an answer to this question, it will be helpful to bear in mind that crossing-over can be divided into just three essential processes—a bending of the chromosomes across each other, a breaking of the threads, and then a fusion of adjoining pieces (or, perhaps, the fusion of the homologous chromosomes comes first, and then the breaking of the original chromosomes at that point). It follows from this that interference must in any case be due to one of the following three general causes: (1) Either the chromosomes are not likely to bend across each other twice at points near together (*i. e.*, the loop tends to be long), or (2) breakage at one point for some reason interferes with another breakage near by (even though the threads are crossed at both of these points), or (3) fusion of chromosomes at one point in some way interferes with fusion of threads which are crossed in a neighboring region. That fusion at one point could interfere with fusion at another point can scarcely be imagined. And if crossing-over occurs according to scheme number three, the "loop explanation" must also be thrown out. Consequently, if crossing-over occurs at a stage of tight twisting the breakage of the threads at one point must somehow be considered to prevent another break near by. In explanation of this, breakage might be thought of as resulting from the tightness of the twisting, for then a breakage of the threads at one point would relieve the tension of the filaments for some distance along the line and so tend to prevent another breakage from occurring near by. (Later, when threads reunited at the point of breakage, pieces from homologous chromosomes would be as apt, or more apt, to lie end to end, and therefore to join, than pieces of the same chromosome. As a partial explanation of why the fragments should join again at all, it might be supposed that only the chromonemas break, the fused sheath which envelops the pair still holding the pieces together.)

It is fully realized that the above discussion is highly speculative. It is intended, however, not as a presentation of conclusions, but as a tentative suggestion of possibilities, in order to obtain some system of ideas that may furnish a temporary basis for a real attack—experimental and observational—upon the subject.

Summary

1. Recent results complete the parallelism between factor groups and chromosomes in *Drosophila*. This strengthens the evidence that

separation of linked factors is due to an *interchange between chromosomes*.

2. The chief gaps in the information regarding the total frequency of interchange in the different groups have been filled, and it is found that the usual total frequencies of separation correspond to the lengths of the chromosomes. This constitutes specific evidence that *crossing-over is the method of interchange* between the chromosomes, and that the frequency of crossing-over between factors is determined by their distance apart in the chromosome.

3. Other evidence for these conclusions, found by Sturtevant in the linear manner of linkage of factors in groups I and II, is shown to hold in the case of group III also.

4. It seems uncertain whether crossing-over occurs in the strepsinema stage, as concluded by Janssens, or earlier in synapsis. The cytological evidence at present at hand would seem insufficient to settle this point. Various alternative mechanisms of crossing-over, together with possible tests for them, are suggested.

5. In order to study the nature of crossing-over by means of "interference," stocks were made up that differed in regard to many factors. Females heterozygous for twenty-two pairs of factors were thus obtained, and a special method was devised for testing their output. Other special methods for obtaining multiple stocks, and for eliminating discrepancies due to differential viability, have also been presented.

6. The results have been arranged in the form of a curve showing the amount of interference for various distances. The results thus far obtained confirm those obtained by less exact methods, and also give evidence that interference decreases gradually with distance from a point of crossing-over; this, taken together with certain evidence from non-disjunction, lends some probability to the view that crossing-over occurs at an early stage in synapsis.

7. A case of crossing-over in an embryonic cell of a male is reported.

8. Incidentally, the experiments have afforded an extensive test of Castle's assumption of contamination of factors by their allelomorphs. Outcrossing in each generation for seventy-five generations has failed noticeably to change any of the factors.

The author is deeply indebted to Professor Morgan, and wishes also to convey his appreciation of the active cooperation so often rendered him by E. R. Altenburg and A. H. Sturtevant, who, moreover, on several occasions helped to tide the stocks over critical periods during which it was not possible for the author to carry on the work. Thanks are also due to C. B. Bridges, for supplying several multiple stocks as well as for the use of a number of mutants which he had already located but an account of which he has not yet published.

ARE THE FACTORS OF HEREDITY ARRANGED IN A LINE?*

Dr. H. J. Muller
Columbia University

In the February (1919) number of the *Proceedings of the National Academy of Sciences*, Professor Castle states that he has "shown that the arrangement of the genes in the sex-chromosome of *Drosophila ampelophila* is probably not linear, and a method has been developed for constructing a model of the experimentally determined linkage relationships."[1] This declaration is so widely at variance with the conclusions jointly agreed upon by all *Drosophila* workers, that the arguments or assumptions which it involves would seem to call for careful examination. It may be stated at the outset that the principle upon which Professor Castle constructs his models appears exceedingly direct and simple—it is merely to make a figure such that the distances between all the points represented on it are exactly proportional to the frequencies of separation actually found between the respective factors in the most reliable experiments. If this is done, Castle contends, the models will be three-dimensional instead of linear in shape.

1. The first argument which Castle gives against the view that the groups of genes (which he admits, at least for purposes of argument, to be in the chromosomes) are linear, is that "it is doubtful . . . whether an elaborate organic molecule ever has a simple string-like form." This argument is therefore based upon the unique assumption that the whole chromosome (or that part of it containing the genes) consists of one huge molecule. Later, he speaks still more explicitly of this "chromosome molecule" and says, "the duplex linkage systems of a germ cell at the reduction division must be . . . twin organic molecules," so that "a purely mechanical theory [of crossing over] seems inadequate to account for interchange of equivalent parts between them." The argument may therefore be paraphrased as follows: since (1) the whole group of genes is but a single organic molecule, and since (2) an organic molecule can not be linear, then it must follow that (3) the group of genes is not linear, and that the theory of crossing over is therefore erroneous. Although the premises of this argument are both entirely gratuitous, it must be admitted that there is no flaw in the reasoning, once the premises are admitted.

2. The second argument brought forward against the linear arrangement of genes is that, in the linear maps, the distances between widely separated loci are not strictly proportional to the per cents of crossing over actually found, being relatively too large, in

The American Naturalist, Vol. LIV, No. 631, March-April, 1920.

comparison with the per cents of crossing over. This he terms a "discrepancy" in the map, which has required the "subsidiary hypothesis" of double crossing over, in order to harmonize it with the theory of linear linkage. The answer to this is that it has never been claimed, in the theory of linear linkage, that the per cents of crossing over are actually proportional to the map distances: what has been stated is that the per cents of crossing over are *calculable* from the map distances—or, to put the matter in more mathematical terms, that the per cents of crossing over are a *function* of the distances of points from each other along a straight line. As will be shown presently, this circumstance alone is sufficient to show that the factors must be bound together in a linéar series; the precise nature of the function (involving coincidence, etc.) will then determine for us precisely the mode of incidence of the crossing over— *i. e.*, granted the linear series, it is then possible to calculate from the data the exact frequency of single crossing over, double crossing over of the various possible types, and multiple crossing over. Double crossing over thus becomes, not a "subsidiary hypothesis," but a phenomenon directly demonstrated.

It may, however, be noted in passing that, even if there had been no experimental evidence at all in regard to the nature of the linkage it could not have been conceded that Castle's alternative postulate—that no double crossing over can ever occur at all—would have been any more plausible *a priori* than that of the *Drosophila* workers which admits the existence of double crossing over. For, once the occurrence of single breaks in a chromosome is admitted —a point agreed upon by both sides—it is just as arbitrary to deny the possibility of double breaks as to assert their existence. Although Castle nowhere does explicitly admit that he has adopted this alternative "subsidiary hypothesis"—the denial of the possibility of double crossing over—yet an inspection of the theory of linkage which he himself has proposed shows that in this it has been tacitly assumed throughout, being necessary for the purposes of the solid models. Were double crossing over once admitted to occur, it could no longer be claimed that the distances between the factors in the three-dimensional models are exactly proportional to their per cents of separation—a condition which it is the sole aim of the existence of the models to fulfill.

We may now return to examine more carefully the main argument upon which linear arrangement and its corollaries (double crossing over, coincidence, etc.) is based. The fact previously stated that the linkage relations between the genes are such that they are all calculable from the positions of points in a linear series may also be expressed as follows: given any three linked factors, A, B and C, if any two of the linkages between them are known—say, the linkage AB and BC—then the third linkage—AC—is determined (the most convenient practical method for calculating it is to make use of the "curve of coincidence" of the particular chromosome). That is, two of the linkage values may be taken as "independent variables" and the third is then "dependent" on them—in this sense we may say that B is linked directly to A and to C, but that A is only linked to C through the linkage of each of these factors with B. Since this is true of any combination of three-linked factors (ABC, BCD, CDE, ACD, etc.) it can be shown that the factors are all linked together in chain arrangement, any one factor being linked directly to only two others (those which we may regard as being on either side of it), its linkage with the rest being entirely dependent on these intermediary linkages.[2] This remains true as a discovered mathematical fact of the linkage relationships, shown first in experiments of Sturtevant's designed to investigate the problem, and this is what the writer has designated as "the law of linear linkage." Whether or not we regard the factors as lying in an actual material thread, it must on the basis of these findings be admitted that the forces holding them linked together—be they physical, "dynamic" or transcendental—are of such a nature that each factor is directly bound, in segregation, with only two others—in bipolar fashion—so that the whole group, dynamically considered, is a chain. This does not necessarily mean that the spatial relations of the factors accord with these dynamic relations, for it is conceivable *a priori* that factor A might be far off from B, in another part of the cell, or that both might be diffused throughout the cell, and that they might nevertheless attract each other, during the segregation division, by some sort of chemical or physical influence. In the discussion that follows, no implication as to the actual physical arrangement of the genes is intended when the terms "linear series," "distance," etc., are used; these will refer only to the relations existing between the points in the linear map, which may be regarded merely as a mathematical mode of representation of the data themselves. It will be shown, however, at the conclusion of this article, that when the various conditions which have to be fulfilled at segregation are taken into consideration, any other explanation for these peculiarly linear linkage findings than an arrangement of the genes in a spatial, physical line proves to be hazardously fanciful.

In the case of the larger distances, in order to discover what function of the distance the per cent of separation represents, it would be necessary to conduct extremely delicate determinations, involving very extensive data in experiments dealing with many points simultaneously. Nevertheless enough has been done to show that even for the larger distances the per cents of separation do depend on the distance in the linear map—being less than the distance by an amount which varies in a fairly regular manner according to the distance itself; hence it is known that the higher per cents of separation certainly involve some function of the linear distance.

In the case of the smaller distances, on the other hand, the function has been rather accurately ascertained; it is very close to the simplest one possible, that is, there is an almost exact proportionality here between the map distances and the per cents of separations. Just as distance AB plus distance BC on a line are equal to distance AC, so the corresponding small frequency of separation between A and B, plus the small frequency between B and C, are found to be almost exactly equal to the frequency of separation between A and C; for this reason if the factors A, B and C are represented as points in a straight linear map, the distances between any two of them will represent the corresponding separation frequencies in an almost proportionate manner. A new example of this principle is shown in Table I; it has been confirmed in innumerable other crosses, with many different factors. Moreover, it is found that the smaller the distance involved, the more exact is the proportionality that obtains, the less being the relative discrepancy between the frequency AC as found by experiment, and the value AC obtained, as on the map, by the summation of values AB and BC. The relationship which exists between the small separation values is hence just the sort which Castle himself would demand, for a proof of linear linkage. But whereas Castle would require this relationship to hold for all values, small or large, it may be shown that its existence in the case of the small alone is all that would be necessary for a complete proof of the doctrine of linear linkage, even if the large values were no sort of function of the linear series. For, if we proceed according to Castle's own method, and construct a map to represent the relations of the small values just described, showing each of the frequencies by a proportionate distance on the map, we necessarily obtain a map each section of which is practically a straight line. In the case, for example, of the data for v, g, and f, shown in Table I, if we represent the separation frequencies by proportionate distances in space, we must place point v at 10.7 units from g, and g at 11.3 units from f; if these two conditions are both to hold, then the only possible way of bringing f to its distance at 21.8 units from v is to put the three points in a nearly straight line,

TABLE I

BACK CROSS OF FEMALES HETEROZYGOUS FOR v, g AND f. (PERFORMED BY BRIDGES; REPORTED BY WEINSTEIN)

I. Non-separations	II. Separations of v from g and f	III. Separations of f from v and g	IV. Separations of g from v and f	V. Total Flies
2651	360	380	3	3394

Resultant Per Cent of Separations Between v and g	Resultant Per Cent of Separations Between g and f	Resultant Per Cent of Separations Between v and f
$\dfrac{(\text{II} + \text{IV})}{\text{V}}$	$\dfrac{(\text{III} + \text{IV})}{\text{V}}$	$\dfrac{(\text{II} + \text{III})}{\text{V}}$
10.7	11.3	21.8

Fig. 1. Direct representation of the linkages in Table I. (*vg*, *gf*, and *vf* are each represented by a line of length proportionate to the respective frequency of separation.) The dotted curve shows the "average angular deviation" of the factors from a straight line.

as shown in Fig. 1. Other results indicate that the line would be exactly straight if still smaller distances were studied. Enough data have been obtained in the case of chromosome I of *Drosophila* to determine in this way the "shape" of each part of the linkage group, and each part, by itself, is thus found to follow the rules for linear distances in an extraordinarily rigorous manner. That is, given the factors ABCDE, etc.,—or to take an actual case, y, w, A, bi, cl,— it is found that the linkages of y, w, and A are proportional to their distances in a straight line, so are the linkages of w, A, and bi, for A, bi, and cl, etc. But, since every part of the group is thus linear, it must then be true that the entire group is linear. A line all of the parts of which are straight is a straight line. Any differences then observed between the size of the larger distances and the per cents of crossing over, even if they were so irregular that they could not be thought of as a function of the linear system itself, would then have to be regarded as due to peculiarities in the incidence of the crossing over, superimposed upon a system of genes which was really linear in formation,—modifications due to specific correlations between crossings over in different regions. But since, as has been stated, the differences between the larger per cents of crossing over and the linear distances are not unregulated, but do give clear evidence of being themselves a function of the map distances, these larger per cents of separation as well as the smaller ones can be used in proof of the linear system of linkage. The systematic differences between the frequencies and the map are hence due to double and other multiple crossovers, which vary in frequency in accordance with the distance involved.

It is true that a certain amount of the differences actually found between the larger frequencies and their corresponding distances on a straight linear map might be thought of as due to the cumulation of minor discrepancies which existed between the small frequencies and distances but each one of which was by itself too small to be detected in the data for the smaller distances, being within the limits of experimental error. As the small discrepancies in such a case would, to be always cumulative, all have to have a bias in the same direction, this would amount to saying that the line along which the points were really disposed had a slow, even curve, too slight to be detected except when large distances were considered. The straight line would then be sufficiently accurate as a proportionate representation of all the small values but not of the large ones. If the validity of the evenly curved figure were accepted, it would in no way disagree with the finding of a linear arrangement of the genes, but would merely substitute a curved line for a straight one. In a really non-linear figure, such as shown in Fig. 2, the relations be-

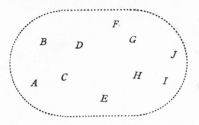

Fig. 2. Example of the sort of relations which would hold between factors arranged non-linearly (although in a plane figure). It is evident from this figure that more remote factors, such as *AE* and *J*, are likely to be arranged more nearly in a straight line than factors nearer together, such as *AB* and *C*.

tween the smaller distances would be (if anything) less of a linear type than the relations between the larger distances,—factors further apart in a thick rod, for example, would have to be more in line than those near together. The fact that the opposite relation holds in the actual data shows conclusively that the factors are in some sort of a line. There is an *a priori* objection, however, to accepting a curved line as an explanation of the linkage relations, in that it is very difficult to imagine a plausible set of conditions in the chromosome which would hold the factors rigidly in this curved line but which would at the same time determine the number of separations between the factors according to their direct (straight) distances from each other, instead of according to their distances along this line. But, quite aside from *a priori* reasons, there is an experimental result absolutely fatal to the curved line "explanation"; this consists in the finding of those classes which are termed by the *Drosophila* workers "triple crossovers." In the case of these classes the separations are of such a type as to require the assumption of a break in the curved line at three points simultaneously. As it is obvious that a break in only one plane could not cut the curve at more than two points, the triple crossovers therefore would have to be due to a break in more than one plane. The occurrence of breaks in more than one plane, however, disturbs the assumed relation of simple proportionality between separation frequencies and map distances, which was the basic postulate upon which the curved line was constructed. If the distances are after all once admitted to be not exactly proportional to the separation frequencies, then there remains no reason to assume, just because the larger separation frequencies are out of exact proportion to the distances on a straight linear map, that this is because the line is curved, and the factors thus nearer together. If still more evidence against the curved line idea be desired, it may be added that when the curve is constructed so as to be in good agreement (statistically) with the relations found between the smaller frequencies, it is then not sufficiently arched to permit the representation of the larger frequencies by proportionate distances (see section 4). A detailed compilation which I have made of all the data has shown that experimental error will not well account for the differences thus obtained between the two sets of results. The curved line being abandoned, it becomes, therefore, necessary to revert to "double crossing over," in explanation of the deviation of the large frequencies from the straight map values.[3]

3. If we examine further into Castle's argument, however, we find that he objects, not only because the larger separation frequencies are not proportional to the distances in linear maps, but also because he believes that the smaller frequencies are not proportional; in fact, according to his solid models, none of the kinds of frequencies, small or large, could even be a function of the distances in a linear map. In his solid, or rather, three-dimensional, models, which purport to have the factors so spaced that all distances between them are exactly proportional to the corresponding linkages, the factors are scattered about at all angles to each other, in such a way that their distances could never be represented as a function of distances in a single line. The cause of this discrepancy between Castle's figures and the relationships observed by the *Drosophila* workers lies in the nature of the data which Castle uses, or rather, in his manner of using the data. For Castle constructs his maps, or models, on all the data obtainable, indiscriminately, and regardless of the fact that most of the data for the linkage values involved have been secured in as many different experiments. On the contrary, it is necessary, in order to determine exactly the relationships existing between interdependent linkage values, that all the data be obtained from the same experiment. This is because the precise value obtained for any given linkage is not only subject to the ordinary error of random sampling but may vary significantly in different experiments, in response to different environmental conditions, the age of parents, genetic factors, and the amount of discrepancy due to differential viability. Piling up enormous counts does not eliminate these sources of variation. Any slight aberration thus produced in the absolute value of one of the linkages (say AC) will then alter so materially its relative value, as compared with the other linkages (AB and BC), obtained in two different experiments, that the different values no longer fit into the linear system; they will not be expressible as any sort of function of the system. That is why Castle found that the *Drosophila* workers' own data gave the per cent of crossing over between y (yellow) and w (white) as

1.1, between w and bi (bifid) as 5.3, and between y and bi as 5.5, a relationship quite at odds with their claims concerning linear linkage for short distances. Castle could have pointed out numerous similar "discrepancies," by similarly choosing to compare exactly (within, say, one unit of distance), the results of different experiments. In fact, had we been allowed to select the experiments for him, we could have chosen values such as the following: Sb (frequency between star and black) 39.3; bp (frequency between black and purple) 5.9; Sp 0.4. If Castle will follow his usual procedure here, and represent these frequencies by proportionate distances in a model, he will disprove not only linear linkage but both Euclidean and non-Euclidean geometry and plain arithmetic. The trouble in the case just cited arises in the fact that the first two values are those obtained under ordinary circumstances whereas the third is a value obtained in the presence of the factor CIIL which decreases enormously the amount of crossing over. Clearly it will be unfair to expect a single map to represent all three values simultaneously. Nevertheless, similar although less exaggerated, disturbing influences may be, and frequently are, at work causing discrepancies between the results of "ordinary" experiments, so that it should be evident that the latter are not ordinarily fit to be subjected to the delicate comparison which is necessary for the purpose of determining the nature of the linkage system.

To some critics, it might at first sight appear inconsistent for the *Drosophila* workers to use the above argument against Castle's system, in view of the fact that these workers themselves also combine the results of different experiments in constructing their chromosome maps. The answer to this is that the variations in linkage between ordinary experiments are usually so small absolutely, that, if all the data for independent linkage values, like AB, BC, CD, etc.— are joined together and represented in one linear map, the latter will be accurate enough for the usual purpose of computing approximately the per cents of separation: the factors will appear in their correct order, and with approximately the correct distances between them. If, however, a study of the nature of the system of linkage is to be made, much more precise knowledge than this is required, for it is necessary to know exactly the relative strengths of interdependent linkages—like AB, BC and AC—as compared with one another. In such a case the small absolute deviations occurring in the different experiments become large relative deviations of the linkages as compared with each other—this is particularly true the smaller the absolute per cents of separation are—and so a totally erroneous impression of the nature of the linkage system may be produced. The nature of the linkage system—whether it is linear and, if so, what function of a line is involved—can only be studied to the best advantage in experiments involving several factors at the same time, but if our judgments regarding it have already been arrived at, or verified, in this way, it is then quite legitimate to use

TABLE II

SEPARATION FREQUENCIES BETWEEN EVERY TWO OF THE SIX SEX-LINKED
FACTORS y, bi, cl, v, s, B, AS SHOWN IN A COUNT OF 712 FLIES FROM
A CROSS IN WHICH TWELVE SEX-LINKED FACTORS WERE
FOLLOWED SIMULTANEOUSLY. (MULLER)

Directness of the Linkage, According to the Linear Map	Factors Considered	Number of Separations	Per Cent of Separations	Sum of Numbers of Separations of Each from an Intermediate Factor	Sum of Per Cents of Separations of Each from an Intermediate Factor
"Primary" (for the experiment)	y and bi	39	5.5		
	bi and cl	53	7.4		
	cl and v	112	15.7		
	v and s	57	8.0		
	s and B	95	13.3		
Dependent on two "primaries"	y and cl	92	12.9	y bi + bi cl = 92	12.9
	bi and v	165	23.1	bi cl + cl v = 165	23.1
	cl and s	167	23.4	cl v + v s = 169	23.7
	v and B	152	21.3	v s + s B = 152	21.3
Dependent on three "primaries"	y and v	198	27.8	y cl + cl v = 204	28.6
	bi and s	216	30.3	bi v + v s = 222	31.2
	cl and B	240	33.7	cl v + v B = 264	37.0
Dependent on four "primaries"	y and s	247	34.7	y cl + cl s = 259	36.4
	bi and B	275	38.6	bi v + v B = 317	44.5
Dependent on five "primaries"	y and B	296	41.6	y v + v B = 350	49.2

this knowledge for other factors, and to join the results of different experiments involving them into one linear map.

In the experiments previously cited, the nature of the linkage in various sections of the chromosome has been studied by following the inheritance of three factors in that region simultaneously. By a series of extensive counts of this sort the nature of the linkage in each individual section of the first chromosome has been studied, and found to be linear. The data in Table II are derived from an experiment which involves less extensive numbers than these, but illustrates to better advantage the linear behavior of all parts of the chromosome at once. These data are taken from Muller's cross of flies heterozygous for twelve mutant sex-linked factors. The results for six of these factors—those scattered most evenly along the chromosome—are shown in the table, which gives the number and per cent of separation between every one of these factors and each of the other five. It will be seen that it happened that in this particular experiment, for all per cents of separation below 23, the per cent of separation between any two factors was exactly equal to the sum of the per cents of separation of each from a third factor lying between them, whereas for factors less closely linked, the larger per cent was less than the sum of the other two by an amount varying closely with the size of the large frequency itself. The data obtained in this same experiment for the three factors y, w and bi are given separately in Table III, in order that they may be compared to better advantage with the non-linear relation for these factors which Castle claims, as a result of his combination into one map of the results of separate experiments. Whereas Castle obtained a triangular figure to represent the three frequencies (y w 1.1, w bi 5.3, and y bi 5.5) it is seen that in this experiment, where all three were followed at the same time, an exactly linear relationship was obtained (y w 1.7, w bi 3.8, y bi 5.5). An experiment of Sturtevant's involving just these three factors is shown in the same table (III); here too the relations are entirely linear. In like manner the values obtained in the 12-factor experiment for the loci of y w and A are given in Table IV (y w 1.7, w A 1.4, y A 3.1) to be compared with the "triangular" values (y w 1.1, w A 1.7, y A 2.0) claimed by Castle. The numbers in these experiments are quite sufficient to have revealed clearly any such triangular relationships as shown in the data chosen and figured by Castle.

4. Although it has been shown that the linkage relations existing among the factors in any one experiment are functions of a linear series it might still be questioned whether there might not, after all, be some advantage in using Castle's system of graphic representation—whereby each separation frequency is supposed to be shown by an exactly proportionate distance on the figure, no matter how many dimensions may be required for this purpose. It will now be shown, however, that such a system of representation is impossible, quite aside from the fact that the models shown in Castle's papers are based upon data which can not legitimately be combined together. That is, no matter whether the data used are all derived from one experiment, or whether the results of different experiments are combined according to Castle's method, they could not be represented either in a three-dimensional or in any other geometrical figure in such a way that all the distances would be proportional to the separation frequencies.

This may be illustrated by the data reported in Table II. It has been seen that the per cent of separations between y and cl is exactly equal to the per cent of separations between y and bi plus that between bi and cl. If then we represent these frequencies by actual distances, we must make the distance between points y and cl exactly equal to the distance between y and bi plus that between bi and cl. The only possible way to do this, on any kind of geometry— one-dimensional, three-dimensional or n-dimensional—is to put these three points in one straight line. In a similar manner we must place bi cl v in a straight line, and also v s B. Cl v and s are in al-

TABLE III

SEPARATION FREQUENCIES OF y, w AND bi

A. Data from the same experiment as that which furnished Table II.
(Muller)

I. Non-separations	II. Separations of y from w and bi	III. Separations of bi from y and w	IV. Separations of w from y and bi	V. Total Flies
673	12	27	0	712
Resultant Per Cent of Separations Between y and w $\dfrac{(II + IV)}{V}$		Resultant Per Cent of Separations Between w and bi $\dfrac{(III + IV)}{V}$	Resultant Per Cent of Separations Between y and bi $\dfrac{(II + III)}{V}$	
1.7		3.8	5.5	

B. Data from a cross involving just these three factors. *(Sturtevant)*

I. Non-separations	II. Separations of y from w and bi	III. Separations of bi from y and w	IV. Separations of w from y and bi	V. Total Flies
487	3	16	0	506
Resultant Per Cent of Separations Between y and w $\dfrac{(II + IV)}{V}$		Resultant Per Cent of Separations Between w and bi $\dfrac{(III + IV)}{V}$	Resultant Per Cent of Separations Between y and bi $\dfrac{(II + III)}{V}$	
0.6		3.2	3.8	

TABLE IV

SEPARATION FREQUENCIES OF y, w AND A.

(From the same experiment as that which furnished Tables II and IIIA.
Muller)

I. Non-separations	II. Separations of y from w and A	III. Separations of A from y and w	IV. Separations of w from y and A	V. Total Flies
690	12	10	0	712
Resultant Per Cent. of Separations Between y and w $\dfrac{(II + IV)}{V}$		Resultant Per Cent. of Separations Between w and A $\dfrac{(III + IV)}{V}$	Resultant Per Cent. of Separations Between y and A $\dfrac{(II + III)}{V}$	
1.7		1.4	3.1	

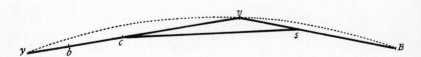

Fig. 3. Direct representation of the strongest and second strongest linkages in Table II. *(y bi, bi cl, cl v, v s, s B,* and *y cl, Bi v, cb s, v B,* are each represented by a line of length proportionate to the respective frequency of separation.) The dotted curve shows the "average angular deviation" of the line of factors, according to this system.

most a straight line, but there would have to be a slight bend at v, owing to the fact that cl s is very slightly shorter than cl v plus v s (on account of just one double crossover having occurred between them); this is correlated with the fact that cl s is a longer distance than the others considered. The figure so constructed, on the basis of Castle's own methods, is shown in Fig. 3; it is quite evident that this is the only figure which will represent directly (proportionately) the frequencies above considered. If, however, we now measure the distance on this figure between the extreme points, y and B, we find that it turns out to be 49.3, or very nearly the sum of the intermediate distances (50.0), whereas the frequency of separation found between y and B in the actual experiment is 41.6. Similarly, the "model" shows too high a frequency for the other longer distances involved. (The long distances y s and bi B are 36.2 and 43.9 respectively on the model, but only 34.6 and 38.6 in the data; the moderately long distances y v, bi s, and cl B are 28.6, 30.8, and 36.6, respectively, on the model, but 27.8, 30.3, and 33.7 in the data.) It would, on the other hand, have been possible to bring y and B close enough together in the diagram, and at the same time have adjacent factors the correct distance apart, by giving the line a curve, or bending it, as shown in Fig. 4. But if this is done it is

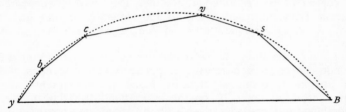

Fig. 4. Direct representation of the strongest and weakest linkages in Table II. (y bi, bi cb, cb v, v s, s B, and y B are each represented by a line of length proportionate to the respective frequency of separation.) The dotted curve shows the "average angular deviation" of the line of factors, according to this system.

found that the distances of intermediate length (y cl, bi v, cl s, and v B) are not properly represented, all of them being relatively too short on the diagram. It would be unsafe to attribute these discrepancies, so uniform in direction, to the "errors of random sampling." The present experiment is cited, however, purely as an illustration, to show what kind of discrepancies are meant. Discrepancies of exactly the same character and direction appear when the diagrams obtained by this method from experiments involving three points close together are compared with those from other experiments having three points far apart; that is, the former figures are repeatedly found to be nearer in form to a straight line than the latter; in such three-point experiments, moreover, highly extensive counts have been made, involving altogether (in the published experiments on the first chromosome), approximately a hundred thousand flies, and thousands of double cross overs.

5. The relation which has just been described, whereby the larger frequencies of separation are relatively smaller than could be directly represented in a curve constructed on the basis of the small frequencies, is due, according to the phraseology of the *Drosophila* workers, to the fact that the relative frequency of double crossing over ("coincidence") is so much larger for large frequencies than for small ones. Castle realizes to a certain extent the difficulty which this circumstance entails for his models, and he endeavors to meet it by means of the "subsidiary hypothesis" that the breaks in his models are more frequent in certain directions than in others. This assumption would, in some measure, explain away in a formal manner certain of the discrepancies (although cases of "triple crossing over" still remain an insurmountable obstacle), but the adopting of any such hypothesis really amounts to cutting away the ground from under the main theory of "proportionate representation," for the hypothesis involves an abandonment of the claim that the model represents each frequency by a proportionate distance between the nodes. For it is evident that if, in a given region, breaks in one direction are more frequent than in another, then points in this region which are an equal distance apart will be separated with different frequency according to the direction of the line joining them. A given distance then no longer represents a given frequency.

6. It has been shown in the above two sections that a single figure will not represent accurately, by proportionate distances, the various linkage frequencies actually found in experiments involving many factors at once. If, on the other hand, it had been attempted to combine into one map the absolute frequencies obtained in a series of different experiments with two factors at a time, as Castle claims to do, the number and extent of discrepancies irreconcilable with any possible geometrical figure would have been much greater still. For, since the absolute frequencies found in different experiments necessarily have all sorts of irregular relationships to each other, it follows that it would be even less possible to show in one solid model separation frequencies which were obtained in this way. One such irreconcilable value has already been recognized by Castle—namely, the frequency y B. He is forced to represent this frequency by a curved wire in his model, because it is longer (being 47) than the longest distance possible (41) between these two points in any figure founded on a proportionate representation of the other frequencies. Of course, if distance on the model is to have any meaning, it cannot arbitrarily be represented along a straight line in some instances, and along lines having various degrees of curvature in other instances. In this one case, then, Castle is compelled to assume that the wrong value has been obtained, owing to experimental error, even though in all other cases he has assumed that it is quite legitimate to combine the results of different experiments.

It would have been strange if, in making a model of this sort representing the separation frequencies of so many combinations of factors, Castle had not encountered more of these refractory cases. He does not mention any more, but it is noticeable that several other curved lines appear in his model. Moreover there is a conspicuous absence in the model of the factor lethal 2. It would have been inconvenient to represent the observed linkage results for this factor by proportionate lines in the model, for, according to the results, lethal 2 would have to be placed at 9.6 from w and 17.7 from v, thus making the distance between w and v not greater than 27.3, whereas the established distance between w and v themselves is as much as 30.5; similarly, although only 9.6 from w, lethal 2 must be placed only 15.5 from m, although w and m are known to be at least 33.2 units from each other. Either the wv and wm lines would have to be considerably curved, therefore, or the lines between lethal 2 and the other factors would have to be *stretched* in some way—perhaps dotted lines would meet the difficulty!

Although any scheme of representing linkage results by exactly proportionate distances encounters the contradictions discussed above, it is noticeable that nearly all the most extreme departures from a plane curved figure (that figure which *comes nearest* to representing, by strictly *proportionate* distances, the ratios resulting from that type of linear linkage which actually exists) occur in the case of factors whose linkage ratios are distorted by differential viability or difficult classification. This is why the factors A, fr, sh, cl, bi, and the lethals stand out from the fairly regular curved line which Castle's models would otherwise conform to. The first two of the above factors are uncertain of classification, the others mentioned affect viability markedly. In the case of nearly all the remaining factors of the model, even though the results were taken from different experiments, it was nevertheless found, when the data were plotted, that they agreed pretty well with the expectations based on linear linkage. Moreover, the better the experimental conditions are in regard to viability, certainty of classification, and size of counts,—the more closely are these synthesized results of individual experiments found to coincide with the linear findings of experiments involving three or more points simultaneously. (It is for this reason that Sturtevant was first able to hit upon the general fact of linear linkage, on the basis of numerous careful experiments involving only two factors at a time.)

7. Owing to the inherent inconsistencies of the methods that were used to construct the solid models, it is to be expected that any predictions regarding separation frequencies which are deduced from them would be extremely unsafe. Castle states, however, that if any newly discovered gene has been located in the model, by obtaining its frequencies of separation from any three of the other genes contained therein, then the relation of the new gene "to all the others could be predicted by direct measurement from the model." In the case of two of the four predictions which Castle has made in this

way, some evidence concerning the distance between the loci involved is already in existence.

One of the frequencies of separation in question is that between the loci of the recessive mutant factors glazed eye and rugose eye, in *Drosophila virilis*. Castle predicts, on the basis of his model, that the per cent of crossing over between them should be found to be 4 or 5, or "probably a little greater." The work of Metz, and unpublished work of Weinstein, have shown, however, that hybrid females which carry both mutant factors exhibit the somatic character sterility possessed by the more extreme mutant type. When this dominance of an ordinarily recessive character in F_1 is taken together with the close similarity between the unusual effects produced by the two mutant factors (both produce a similar, peculiar effect on the eye, which is sex-limited, being more marked in the males), and with the fact that there is also a third mutant member of the series, with similar peculiar effects and similar linkage relations, it becomes highly probable that these factors are all allelomorphs. In that case they occupy "identical loci," and the frequency of separation between them must be 0. A direct determination of the per cent of crossing over between them is obviously impossible to obtain, on account of the sterility of the females carrying both factors.

Another prediction based on the solid models dealt with the frequency of separation between the factors hairy and magenta, of *Drosophila virilis*. It had been found by Metz that the per cent of crossovers between hairy and forked was 3.1 and between forked and magenta 3.7; this would make the per cent for hairy-magenta 6.8 (or 0.6), if the factors were in a straight line. In the solid model, however, the arrangement of these factors, based on separate determinations of their frequencies of crossing over with distant loci,—is shown as triangular; and on the basis of this model Castle predicts that the frequency hairy-magenta will be found to be 4 or 5. The frequency has recently been determined by Weinstein, who has kindly consented to allow its use in this connection. He finds it to be 6.6.

It should be pointed out that Castle has endeavored to protect himself, in these predictions, by saying that they only hold, provided the relations given "have been determined with sufficient accuracy"!

8. One of Castle's specific objections to the linear maps, on which he lays much stress, is that on them the distances between the extreme factors is much more than 50 units, whereas factors which are linked must have a separation frequency of less than 50 per cent. It is only necessary to point out here that since, as we have seen, the linear maps, unlike the models, do not imply a proportionate relationship between the distances and the separation frequencies, these distances of over 50 do not connote separation frequencies of over 50 per cent. On account of the progressive reduction in separation frequency, due to double crossing over, that

occurs with increasing distance, even distances of 100 or 110 in the second chromosome do not connote separation frequencies as high as 50 per cent. On the other hand, it should also be remarked that separation frequencies of over 50 per cent would not be impossible *a priori*, as Castle maintains; consequently any system of representing linkage which permitted or showed such values would not be *ipso facto* inconsistent. The mere fact that all factors hitherto worked with in a single chromosome have less than 50 per cent of separation, and that those in different chromosomes have just 50 per cent, does not mean that factors can never be found which are so far apart, and which lie in such a rigid chromosome (little double crossing over) that they separate more often than they remain together at segregation. Whether this phenomenon should then be called linkage is but a question of words; the chromosomes themselves would have no regard for the 50.0 per cent mark, or for the idiosyncrasies of our terminology.

The proof of the law of linear linkage, including all the main aspects of it which have been given above, has been stated on several previous occasions. It seems unfortunate that the argument has had to be repeated each time that a new "theory of crossing over" has arisen, for the discussion and data given in the original papers supply all the material necessary for a decision of the matter, at least so far as the germ plasm of *Drosophila* is concerned.

Before closing, it may be desirable to supplement these arguments for a mathematically linear mode of linkage, by a statement of the considerations which indicate that this mathematically linear linkage can have its basis only in a linear physical connection between the genes.

If the genes are not spatially arranged, or physically connected, in the same linear sequence as that in which they have been found to attract each other in linkage, then the forces of linkage attraction must be such as to "act at a distance." But, although acting at a distance, these linkage forces must nevertheless be extraordinarily specific—binding each gene directly to just two specific associate genes. Hence the forces could not be of an electrical nature, for, since there are only two kinds of electricity, electric forces could not be specific enough. Similarly, the attractions could not be magnetic, nor could they be due to any kind of diffuse "physical" forces, such as those that emanate from centers of surface tension change or from centers of vibrational disturbances. Those who deny linear arrangement, while admitting the mathematically linear linkage results would therefore be driven to assume that the linkage attraction depended on the specific chemical nature of the genes, which, by virtue of their chemical composition, exerted a specific attraction at a distance, as the substances of adsorption compounds are sometimes supposed to do. But such a theory, as a method of accounting for linkage, becomes stretched to the breaking point when it is remembered that each gene must be assumed to have such an attraction for just two of the others, never more nor less, and that when this attraction is broken it is always exchanged for that of the allelomorph. Moreover, it would be exceedingly hard to reconcile this theory with the finding that changes in the nature of the genes—mutations—alter in nowise the sequence of their linkage attractions, and very rarely change even the strength of the linkages. And when we come to analyze the linkage relations in detail, and encounter the phenomenon of interference, we find relations that are entirely at variance with all our preconceptions concerning chemical attractions or chemical activity in general,—results that would force us to assume (1) that a breakage of the attraction between two genes leads to an increased attraction between the other genes and (2) that the amount of this increased attraction ("interference") depends solely on the directness of the connection ("distance") between these other genes and the one whose attraction was broken, being not at all influenced by the chemical nature of the broken attraction, or by the chemical nature of the other attractions themselves. The facts of "interference" or "coincidence" are thus diametrically opposed to a chemical view of linkage, although they, like all the other facts of linkage, are quite in accord with ideas of a spatial, physical linear arrangement, their interpretation on the latter basis being natural and obvious.

The idea that the genes are bound together in line, in order of their linkage, by material, solid connections thus remains as the only interpretation which fits the genetic findings. In view of the additional fact that the chromosomes—themselves known to be specifically linked to the factor groups—can, at certain stages of their history, be seen to have the linear structure required, it would indeed be rash to adopt a different theory, without most cogent evidence of a startlingly new character.

Notes

[1]Sturtevant, Bridges and Morgan also have published a defense of the view of linear linkage, in the *Proceedings* of the National Academy of Sciences (5, 1919, pp. 168-173) and Professor Castle has just replied to them in the same journal (5, 1919, pp. 501-506). It is believed that the present paper, although written and accepted for publication in the *Naturalist*, previously to Castle's later article, meets all the points therein brought forward.

[2]*I. e.*, all the linkages ($n/2$ $(n-1)$ in number) between the n factors in a group, can be shown to be dependent on (functions of) only $n-1$ "primary" or "independent" linkages. To obtain the most perfect expression of this dependency it is necessary to chose as the $n-1$ independent values the two strongest linkages involving each of the n factors (what we should call linkages AB, BC, CD, DE, etc., as contrasted with AC, AD, AE, BD, etc.). On this system, the other linkages all become definitely determined, the secondary linkages being in each case a function involving the sum of certain of the primary linkages. If, however, the primary linkages are not chosen

according to the above rule, so as to constitute a "chain formation," no formula can definitely express the relationships of the linkages, for the secondary linkages will then in some cases depend upon the sum, in other cases upon the difference between the linkages taken as primary.

[3]The fact that the *geometrical* line which represents the linkages of the factors should be taken as straight does not imply that the supposed *physical* line in which the factors lie is straight. So long as the factors lie in any kind of physical line at all, then, if their linkages are determined, in some way, by their distances as measured *along* this line, these linkages should be representable on the basis of a straight geometrical map, inasmuch as all distances taken *along* a curved line must have the same interrelationships as distances in a straight line. Hence the curving of the chromosome filament is a matter entirely aside from the issue here involved, since the separation frequencies of the factors in the supposed filament are not conceived of as dependent upon their direct distances from each other but rather upon their distances along this filament. Thus the filament may, for these purposes, be treated as if it were straight.

INDUCED CROSSING-OVER VARIATION IN THE X-CHROMOSOME OF DROSOPHILA*

It has been shown by the author that, although doses of X-rays up to fifty-four Holzknecht units cause an increase in the frequency of crossing over in the central regions of both of the long, centrally attached, V-shaped autosomes of Drosophila, they produce no or only a very slight effect (decrease?) in the distal regions. These results paralleled the already known effects of temperature found by Plough and of age found by Bridges in one or more of the autosomes. In studying the cause of this peculiar regional differentiation, it would seem that results obtained with the X-chromosome might throw light on the problem, since the latter has the spindle fiber attached at the end (the "right-hand" end, as has now been proved by L. V. Morgan and by Anderson), but is not bent there. Thus it might be expected, if the point of attachment somehow determined the susceptibility to crossing-over variation, that most of the X-chromosome would respond to the above agents as do the distal regions of the long autosomes; the attached end of the X might or might not respond like their central regions, depending upon whether the bend in the autosomes, or other peculiarities due to a central attachment, are essential for the effect. It was indeed found by Plough and by Bridges that temperature and age fail to affect the greater part of the X, though they did not study the terminal regions. Mavor, however, found that X-rays did affect the X (again the terminal portions were not studied), causing a marked decrease in crossing-over frequency. This result, in comparison with the author's results with X-rays on the autosomes, seems to put the X in

The American Naturalist, Vol. LX, March-April, 1926.

a class by itself, making it not comparable to the other chromosomes. If so, results from it would not be so pertinent to a solution of the problem concerning the autosomes.

In view of the above considerations, the author has attempted a partial repetition of the X-ray experiments on the X, and their extension to other regions of the X. The preliminary data are given here, as they tend to reconcile the results on the X with those on the autosomes, and it may be a considerable time before larger numbers can be obtained. The preliminary experiment involved the short extreme "left-hand" region, from scute to the apricot (white eye allelomorph) locus, the long section from apricot to bar, and a short "right-hand" section from bar to "beadex" (wing). Unfortunately the most extreme right region (beadex to bobbed) was not studied; this would have involved more complicated stock as bobbed males appear normal, and since at that time the left end was thought more probably to be the attached end, it was judged that bar-beadex might serve to represent the right region. The cross was as follows: females containing the mutant genes for scute and apricot in one X and those for white, bar and beadex in the other were backcrossed to scute apricot males. Only the sons could be classified with certainty for all four loci, but the females (not counted in all bottles) were reliable for scute and bar at least. Seven mothers served as controls, twelve mothers (sisters of these) were treated for fifteen minutes with X-rays from a current of fifty thousand volts and four milliamperes, at a distance of sixteen centimeters from the target (54 H). The flies counted were derived from eggs laid from the fourth to the tenth day after raying. The results in brief were:

	Males + females			Males only							
	Scute-bar crossovers		Total counted	Scute-apricot crossovers		Apricot-bar crossovers		Bar-beadex crossovers		Total counted
	Number	%		Number	%	Number	%	Number	%	
X-rayed	410	44.5	922	15	2.3	299	46.5	14	2.2	644
Controls	414	46.7	883	16	3.5	212	45.8	5	1.1	462

It will be seen that, although the numbers here are as yet comparatively small, the results differ significantly from Mavor's over a similar period and with a similar dose, for there could have been no such considerable decrease in crossing over in the central region as he found—unless, indeed, there was a decrease in the white-miniature region (studied by him) and a "compensatory" increase in the miniature-bar region. Although apricot-bar and scute-bar are long distances, so that the percentage of "crossovers" (really, of recombinations) does not include all cases of crossing over in this region, nevertheless in previous work we have never found double crossing over in this region of the X frequent enough to obscure any considerable decrease of the total crossing over such as Mavor found. Very large counts are necessary to obtain reliable estimates of coincidence; the values for X-rayed and control lots obtained in the present experiments, so far as they go, show no significant differences from the values normally obtained or from each other.

It is not intended here to question the accuracy of Mavor's extensive results, but merely to show that under certain conditions, with given stocks and crosses, effects of X-rays may be obtained over the greater part of the X-chromosome which sensibly agree with those found by the present author in those parts of the autosomes not near the spindle fiber. Possibly too, then, further work with the autosomes might reveal in those regions under some circumstances a significant decrease in crossing over caused by X-rays, similar to what Mavor found in the X. This will require investigation, with the employment of larger doses of rays; there was, however, a suggestion of such effects in the results already reported for the autosomes.

As for the effects on other parts of the X than those previously investigated in this connection, it is interesting to note that the extreme left end—furthest from the attachment—did show an apparent decrease. On the other hand, the results, if taken at their face value, certainly suggest strongly an actual increase in crossing-over frequency in the right-hand region. This would be interesting, if borne out by larger numbers, in view of the location of the spindle fiber nearby, and the increases observed in the neighborhood of the spindle fiber in the long autosomes.

From the foregoing it is seen to be quite possible, or even likely, that the X-chromosome does not react to X-rays in a manner greatly different from the autosomes, *when regions are compared which correspond in their relation to the point of fiber attachment.* If this is true, it would mean that the bend in the autosomes is not a causal agent in the effects, since the X is not thus bent. Beyond this, however, it would seem at the present time premature to speculate regarding the mechanism by which the spindle fiber might operate, in thus making the chromatin especially susceptible to variation in crossing over as a result of X-rays, and, presumably, of heat, age and other non-genetic factors.

H. J. MULLER

University of Texas

REGIONAL DIFFERENCES IN CROSSING OVER AS A FUNCTION OF THE CHROMOSOME STRUCTURE*

Carlos A. Offermann and H. J. Muller
University of Texas, Austin, Texas

Differences in the degree of crowding of mutant genes in different regions of the linkage maps first led to the conclusion (Muller) that crossing over differs greatly in its frequency in different parts of the chromosomes. Presently, regional differences were found in the effects of heat, X-rays, age, and crossing over in other loci (coincidence studies), on crossover frequency (Plough, Mavor, Bridges, Muller, Stern). Recent studies of the cytological size of chromosome fragments as compared with their size on linkage maps have confirmed the conception of regional differentiation in "normal" crossover frequency (Painter, Muller, Dobzhansky). The question arises, to what are the regional peculiarities of crossing over due? Are they inherent in the regions themselves, or are they caused, as certain of the above results suggested, by the positions of the regions with reference to distinctive features of chromosome structure, such as spindle fibres, termini, nodal length, or specific genes? This question has now been attacked by studies of crossover frequency in cases where the position of a region with reference to one or more such features has been considerably changed by inversion, translocation, or deletion, produced by irradiation.

In this study it is necessary to use individuals homozygous for the rearrangement to avoid complications caused by non-matching of partners. Relatively few homozygous rearrangements are viable and fertile. At the same time the individual must be heterozygous for genes used as locus-markers. It is often very difficult to get mutant genes into rearranged chromosomes by means of crossing over between the latter and normally arranged chromosomes, because of the non-matching of the partners. Hence, many of the mutant genes needed in the rearranged chromosomes, especially those in the most critical positions, near the points of breakage and reattachment, had to be produced there intentionally by extensive irradiation work before the crossover frequency experiments proper could be carried out. The accompanying diagram will show the position of the breaks studied, with reference to markers used in various of the experiments herein reported.

The effect of a free end was studied in translocation X-IV4. Crossing over in "XR" (the right segment of the X), which was

*Proceedings of the Sixth International Congress of Genetics, 1933, 2: 143-45.

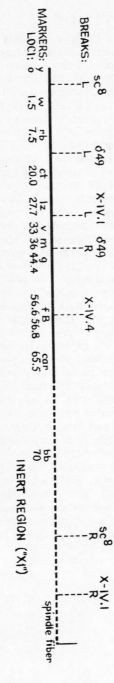

Diagram of X Chromosome, Showing Positions of Breaks Dealt With. Spacings shown are proportional to those in actual chromosome (see Painter and Muller, page 147). Numerical values given to loci are those of linkage map (crossover frequencies).

57

broken off close to B, was reduced to 70 per cent of its normal value, in the B-car region (data of Stone). The effect of an end bearing a fibre-attachment locus is much greater. Thus, in the case of the same translocation, XL (the left segment of X) has chromosome IV, with its fibre locus, attached near f. Crossing over in the neighboring m-f region is much reduced, but crossing over further to the left is little affected. Again, in translocation X-IV1, crossing over in XM, the middle segment of X, which is deleted from the remainder and attached to chromosome IV near v, is reduced to about 15 per cent of normal in region v-g, adjoining the fibre-locus, to 25 per cent in region g-f, and to about 30 per cent in the more distant f-car region. The XL and XR segments are joined to each other in this case, making another chromosome having a portion of the inert region, with the fibre locus, attached near by. In this shortened chromosome crossing over becomes 4 per cent of normal in the ct-lz region, adjoining the fibre-locus, about 40 per cent in the ec-ct region next to this, and remains normal in region y-ec, farthest from the fibre-locus. The graduation of effect is evident.

In the scute-8 containing inversion, Serebrovsky found that the inverted XM segment includes the major portion of the chromosome. We find that here the w-ct region, which has by the inversion been brought nearer the fibre-locus, has 65 per cent of normal crossing over; the m-f region in the middle is little affected, and the region normally on the right, but now further removed from the fibre-locus, has crossing over increased. On the other hand, the transposed part of the inert region still seems to have little or no crossing over in it. Hence this peculiarity of the inert region is independent of the fibre-locus, as was previously thought probable on other grounds (see Muller and Painter).

In several rearrangements temperature effects have been determined (compare Graubard's work on rearrangements that did not normally affect crossover frequency).

In the "delta 49" inversion a comparatively short region, far from spindle fibre, terminus, and inert region, was inverted. Detailed studies here showed no change in values for the inverted c_{mn}-lz-m-f_w region, nor for the y-rb and g-f regions on either side, nor for the inclusive y-f crossover frequency. Hence, rearrangement by itself was not the cause of the changes above noted.

2 Genotype-Phenotype Relations

THE BEARING OF THE SELECTION
EXPERIMENTS OF CASTLE AND PHILLIPS
ON THE VARIABILITY OF GENES*

Castle and Phillips have recently reviewed the results of six years' work in which they selected for and against "hoodedness" in rats.[1] In "hooded" or "piebald" rats only part of the coat is pigmented; the area of dark (versus white) coat varies greatly in different animals, but tends, in those of medium grade, to cover the head, shoulders and middle of the back, like a hood. Starting with a strain which was probably hybrid, although of unknown ancestry, and selecting during thirteen generations for a larger extent of colored coat ("plus" selection), they succeeded in obtaining animals with a greater and greater area of pigmentation. The average, the mode, and the extremes were raised. Conversely, selection for less pigmentation ("minus" selection) was accompanied by a gradual but decided and continual diminution in the dark area. "Return" selection also succeeded; that is, plus selection was effective even in a line which was already lighter than the average on account of a previous minus selection, and, *vice versa*, minus selection caused a lightening of a strain that had been made exceptionally dark by a prior plus selection.

Certain crosses proved that more than one factor affecting hoodedness is involved in the difference between the different races. Therefore the production of animals of desired grade by selection may perhaps be explained as a mere sorting out, into different lines of descent, of different combinations of the various factors for hoodedness originally present in the heterozygous ancestors. It is the opinion of Castle and Phillips, however, that this explanation will not suffice to account fully for the continued efficacy of selection in their experiments, and they believe it probable that a factor or factors for hoodedness are undergoing variation of a fluctuating nature.

A conclusion so radical and so opposed to previous work should not be accepted, however, as long as it remains at all reasonably possible to use instead an explanation in harmony with the results of Johannsen and other investigators. Johannsen dealt with a character—dimensions of seed—which must beyond any doubt have been partially dependent upon a very great many factors, yet he found that selection had no effect whatever after he had separated the dif-

*The American Naturalist, Vol. XLVIII, September, 1914.

ferent genotypes from one another. Thus he proved the constancy of a great many genes "at one blow"—namely, of all the genes appreciably concerned in seed size. Of course, if there had been a chance for cross-fertilization in his experiments, he, like Castle, would have obtained a result from selection, but this would have been due to recombination, not variation, of genes. All our evidence points to the conclusion that the vast majority of genes are extremely constant, although they differ somewhat in that very slight amount of variation which they do show. For example, in *Drosophila*, although in the case of most genes not more than one mutation has been found, yet in one case (possibly in two or three cases) a locus has mutated three times, each time in a different way, thus giving rise to a system of multiple allelomorphs containing four members. This gene evidently is more subject to mutation than the others, yet this formation of a series of multiple allelomorphs can not even remotely be compared to fluctuating variability, for the three mutations were all large steps (much smaller could easily have been detected), and they were found only during the examination of some millions of individuals in the rest of which the locus was not observed to mutate at all. Some few genes are known, however, which really do change frequently *(e. g.*, that for "variegated" corn), but these cases are extremely rare; moreover, here the degree and nature of the change are fixed, and also, after the change has once occurred the instability of the gene is lost. Thus, in no known case do the variations of a gene among, let us say, several thousand immediate descendants of the individual possessing it, form a probability curve, as neo-Darwinians might perhaps suppose, nor even are any cases known where genes can undergo frequent changes that may vary at all in kind or amount or occur successively.

Let us then inquire into the probability and adequacy of that explanation of Castle and Phillips' results which does not require the assumption that a gene or genes involved change comparatively frequently and successively, but which assumes a sorting out of numerous factors. It is now pretty generally accepted by Mendelians that the germ plasm of any of the higher organisms contains a large number of genes, which play various rôles in the numberless processes and reactions of development whereby the egg is transformed into the adult individual. The exact nature and intensity of any one characteristic of this adult organism *(e. g.*, hoodedness in rats) is dependent upon the nature of each of the various reactions which were involved in producing this character, and thus dependent upon all the genes (and environmental factors also) involved in any of those reactions. Now, in an ordinary Mendelian cross, all the individuals are usually homozygous and alike in respect to all but one of the pairs of genes that noticeably affect the character concerned. In such a case, then (so far as differences in environmental influences do not obscure the outcome), one obtains the simple Mendelian results derived from the segregation, at reduction, and recombination, at fertilization, of but this one pair of allelomorphs.

The strain of hooded rats, however, was probably a hybrid between two races of rather remote relationship. When two such races are crossed, the individuals often differ in more than one pair of those factors that affect the character studied, especially if the character is such as to be influenced by a relatively large number of genes. It can not be questioned that some characters are thus determined or influenced by a much larger number of developmental reactions than are others, and such characters will therefore vary more in inheritance, since if a difference exists between two individuals in respect to any given gene, these characters are more likely to be affected than others. Gross size, for example, is a character dependent in this way upon an exceptionally large number of genes, for any gene which influences the size of any organ must affect to some extent the total size. In some other cases in which characters are found to be influenced by relatively many genes, the reason for this is not so evident, *e. g.*, in the case of the red flower-color of flax, or the truncated condition of the wing in some races of *Drosophila.* Here the production of the character may be conceived to be dependent upon some reaction that can be easily modified by various means.[2] For our present purpose we must assume that the character "hoodedness" belongs in this class and that the ancestral hooded rats used by Castle and Phillips were the descendants of a cross involving many genes for that character.

The results of such a cross are of course complicated, for the different pairs of allelomorphs generally can undergo recombination at the reduction division of the hybrid, so that in F_2 or subsequent generations as many different genetic types of individuals are formed as there are possible different combinations of those factors wherein the ancestors differed. Not all these genetic types, of course, will fall into different phenotypes, yet generally there will be a large number of overlapping phenotypes among the progeny.

The larger the number of factors in which the two ancestral lines differed, the larger will be the number of different possible combinations of these factors, and accordingly the smaller will be the chance of any individual having one of those particular combinations necessary to a relatively high or a relatively low intensity of the character. In other words, the larger the number of factors (for one character) for which a population is heterogeneous, the more numerous are the possible different grades of intensity of this character among the different individuals, but the fewer will be the individuals which approach the more extreme grades theoretically possible in such a population.[3] Suppose, for example, that two parents differ in five pairs of factors for hoodedness, which are partially dominant[4] to their allelomorphs and summative in their action. Then in F_2 not one individual in a thousand will have the most extreme dark or light grade of hoodedness possible. However, by selecting the more extreme individuals, and mating them together, a still more extreme grade of hoodedness may be obtained in F_3 (both as to average and limiting values), and the same process may be continued for a good many generations. The number of generations during which effective selection is possible depends on the number of factors concerned, the rigor of selection, and the amount of inbreeding of brother to sister.

In regard to the latter point, since brother and sister are much more apt to be alike in their genetic constitution than are other individuals, offspring from such a mating are more apt to be homozygous and alike, or, we may say, such offspring will tend to be homozygous and alike in a larger number of factors; then, mating two individuals homozygous for these factors together, there will be much less variation and so less opportunity to continue selection among their progeny. In the case of Castle and Phillips' experiments, however, no such attempt at inbreeding was reported. Here, then, the individuals mated together would be more apt to differ genetically, even though they looked alike (thus, one might be AA bb, the other aA bB), and their descendants would therefore present a larger number of different combinations of factors for the selector. Often a greater effect may be eventually produced in this manner than by inbreeding, for a larger number of combinations of factors are thus produced, some of which may be of more extreme type. The effect would usually be slower, however, since such matings tend to keep the strain heterozygous and are often steps backwards. Cross-breeding, then, will help to explain the relatively slow but long-continued and eventually large effect of selection in Castle and Phillips' experiments, although such a result could also be obtained without cross-breeding if the factors were numerous enough.

The "return selections" also are easily explicable on the multiple factor view. Due to the original difference in so many factors, and the fact that cross-breeding diminishes the tendency to homozygosis which selection favors, the rats were presumably heterozygous even after generations of selection. They would not be as heterozygous as before, of course, and, correspondingly, Castle and Phillips did find less variation in the rats after selection. Yet there would still be a good chance for recombination, and an alteration in the race could therefore be produced by further selection or by return selection. As we have seen, this is especially true if certain factors are completely dominant, although dominance is by no means a necessary condition.

As a very simple illustration, let us suppose that the "plus" factors A and B dominate over the "minus" factors "a" and "b," respectively, and each increase the pigmented area to about the same extent. To begin with, two moderately hooded individuals, Aa bb and aa Bb, were mated together. They produced 1aa bb—light-hooded,

1aa Bb and 1Aa bb—both moderate, and 1Aa Bb—dark. We first select for dark; mating the dark rats together, 9 darks, 6 moderates,
and 1 light, would be produced (F_2). The average color of the offspring has thus been increased by selection (the limiting color, too,
if dominance is incomplete). It can be still further increased in
subsequent generations. On the other hand, the color can be made
lighter again by a "return selection," for if, instead of mating the
F_2 or F_3 darks together, we mate the moderates or mate darks with
moderates, many of the matings will give offspring lighter, on the
average, than in the preceding generation; e. g., Aa Bb by Aa bb
gives 3 dark, 4 moderate, 1 light, as compared with the previous
9 dark, 6 moderate, 1 light. In subsequent generations, the average
could be brought still lower.

Let us now see whether there is any experimental evidence in
support of the multiple factor explanation of Castle and Phillips'
results, aside from the fact that it is adequate and is the only one
consistent with other work. One point of evidence we have noted—
the variability of the rats continued to decrease as a result of selection in either direction. This we should of course expect on the
multiple factor view, for selection gradually tends toward homogeneity in a population, even though it may require a long time to
produce complete homogeneity. The second and strongest evidence
is from crosses.

The crosses show that one of the factors concerned in differentiating hooded rats from wild rats, which are pigmented all over, or
from "Irish" rats, which are almost completely pigmented, is
"hypostatic." In other words, a rat having the normal allelomorphs
of this factor will always be self-colored, or nearly so; one having
the other allelomorphs will always be distinctly hooded, although the
amount of the hoodedness varies. "Self," as it happens, is dominant,
in this case, over hooded. Thus, on crossing a hooded to a wild or
Irish rat, all the F_1 are self (or nearly so); in F_2 there are three
selfs to one hooded, but the hoodeds vary in intensity. The question
then is, does this variation (so far as it is not due to "environmental" differences) depend upon what other "epistatic" or "modifying"
factors for hoodedness may or may not be present, or is there evidence that it depends instead, or in addition, upon a variability of
one or more of the factors for hoodedness? As will be shown below,
it can be proved that different combinations of modifying factors do
occur in the different hooded individuals: this being true, there can
be no ground for making the unusual postulate that in this case or in
the selection experiments a factor or factors concerned undergo
variation.

The proof is that when light hooded rats from the minus strain
are crossed to wild or Irish rats the hooded rats in F_2 vary much
more than did the original strain of hooded rats and average much
darker. Obviously, the P_1 hooded rats differed from the wild or

Irish in a number of modifiers as well as in the hypostatic factor; moreover, as we should have expected, this difference consisted chiefly in the fact that the wild or Irish rats contained "plus" allelomorphs in place of some of the "minus" modifiers present in the P_1 strain that had undergone minus selection. Thus the F_2 hooded rats, containing various combinations of these modifying factors wherein the two strains differed, varied much more than did the parental strain of hooded rats, and were on the average much darker.

In order to escape this conclusion that modifying factors were involved, Castle and Phillips at first postulated that the reason that the F_2 hooded were darker than the original "minus" strain was because the factor for hooded had in many cases become contaminated by its allelomorph (the factor for self) in the F_1 rats. This is violating one of the most fundamental principles of genetics—the non-mixing of factors—in order to support a violation of another fundamental principle—the constancy of factors. The refutation of their supposition came unexpectedly soon. It would be expected, on the view of multiple factors, that the wild or Irish rats (containing the allelomorph for self in place of the hypostatic factor for hooded) would not possess as many "minus" modifiers as the hooded strain which had been specially selected to contain as many of these as possible; neither would these "self" rats contain as many "plus" modifiers as the hooded strain which had undergone plus selection (and which so contained nearly all of the plus modifiers originally present in *either* the self or the hooded ancestors). Thus it was to be expected that, just as a cross of self with the minus race gave F_2 hooded rats darker than the original minus strain, so a cross of wild or Irish rats with hoodeds resulting from the plus selection would give F_2 hooded rats *lighter* than those of the plus strain. This result was actually obtained. It was fatal to the idea that the difference between the P_1 strain of hooded rats and the F_2 hoodeds was due to contamination of the allelomorph for hooded with that for self, since such contamination should have resulted in F_2 hooded rats *darker* than those of P_1, not lighter. For wild and Irish rats are both much more extensively pigmented than hoodeds even of the plus strain.

The change in hoodedness from P_1 to F_2 was therefore due to recombinations of the modifying factors wherein the two strains differed. That many such modifiers were concerned is indicated by the evenly distributed variability of the F_2 hoodeds and the fact that very few were as extreme as the hooded grandparents. The same fact is brought out in a cross of the minus with the plus race; here no clear-cut ratios were obtainable, the classification into different genotypes being rendered impossible by the multiplicity of factors (no one of which was hypostatic as in the other crosses). Of course, this knowledge of so many factors being concerned in the crosses helps our interpretation of the selection results decidedly, for the more numerous are the factors concerned, the longer would it be possible to continue an effective selection on the progeny of the hybrids, and the original hooded rats of the selection experiments were admittedly in all likelihood descended from just such hybrids. The exact number and effect of the different factors can not be determined from Castle and Phillips' data, since to do this very special crosses must be made and individual pedigrees kept. Selection experiments can be of little value so long as there are factors for which the individuals may be heterozygous, unless these factors can be accurately followed in inheritance.

Of course, it is quite possible that in the course of these long-continued experiments mutations affecting the hoodedness occasionally happened to arise, especially since it seems likely that this character is dependent upon an unusually large number of genes, for then, as a matter of mere chance, any mutation which occurred would be more likely to affect it than it would be to affect most characters. It is interesting to note that one such mutation, of a very marked and unquestionable character, was in fact observed. The mutant factor proved to be a strong "plus" modifier, which was almost completely dominant, and itself showed no contamination or variation, so far as could be determined. It arose, as it happened, in the plus strain. A part of the effectiveness of selection may therefore have been due to the occurrence and sorting out of such occasional mutations, but there is no way of telling how many of these took place, or *any* need for assuming them at all in explaining the result. These rare mutations, however, would form a very different phenomenon from such fluctuating or frequent and progressive variation of a gene or genes concerned as Castle postulates. Although the academic possibility of variation of the latter type can not be denied, there is no experimental evidence which can be used to support it, and there is good evidence against it in many individual cases.

It is difficult to believe that this suggestion of Castle and Phillips was not made in a spirit of mysticism, when we consider also their suggestion that the genes may undergo contamination, and especially when we consider the following passage, with which their paper concludes:

It seems to us quite improbable that the plus mutation could have arisen in the minus selection series. We believe that the repeated selection which was practised had something to do with inducing this change in the plus direction. If one can increase at will the "modifiers" which make the pigmentation more extensive, it does not seem strange that after a time a readjustment should occur within the cell which should incorporate modifiers in that part of the cell which is responsible for the unit-character behavior of the hooded pattern. This would amount to a quantitative change in the unit-character for hooded pigmentation.

To thus suppose that independent genes *fuse* or induce changes in one another, merely because they happen to produce similar *end effects* upon the organism, and in spite of the fact that they usually lie in different chromosomes and are apt to differ from each other as much as do other genes, is utterly teleological.

A paper by A. L. and A. C. Hagedoorn criticizing Castle's work and conclusions, appeared at the same time as the paper of Castle and Phillips.[5] The Hagedoorns champion the multiple factor hypothesis as an explanation of Castle's results, and also cite certain rather inconclusive experiments of their own to support this point of view. They err, however, in supposing that the factors concerned must be incompletely dominant; as we have seen, this is not a necessary assumption, if we admit that in the case of some modifiers the "minus" allelomorph dominates, in others the "plus." They also err in denying the possibility, on the multiple factor view, of successful "return selection," if inbreeding be strictly followed. In fact they offer this as a test of their point of view. As we have seen, "return selection" would be possible in some cases, even if the animals were inbred; and in Castle and Phillips' experiments, where inbreeding was not followed, "return selection" was certainly very effective.

Finally, papers have recently appeared by MacDowell,[6] in which he gives evidence that certain other cases of inheritance *(e. g.*, head size in rabbits), formerly considered by Castle to support the idea of genic variation and contamination, are probably best interpreted on the view of multiple factors instead. His evidence consists in the fact that the characters concerned are somewhat more variable in the offspring of back-crosses than in F_1, as we should expect on the basis of recombination of multiple factors, but which he believes could not plausibly be explained otherwise.

Notes

[1]Castle and Phillips, "Piebald Rats and Selection, An experimental test of the effectiveness of selection and of the theory of gametic purity in Mendelian crosses." Published by the Carnegie Institute of Washington. See also Castle's "Pure Lines and Selection" in *American Breeders' Magazine*, 1914.

[2]It is conceivable that differences in respect to numerous genes have sometimes arisen even in the case of characters not naturally very easily influenced by diverse means, merely because one of the two races had been subjected to a very long and drastic selection, so that any of those rare mutations which affected that character in the desired direction had in this race been preserved. Selection in such a case, however, would have to involve many millions of individuals.

[3]One extreme, *e. g.*, the "plus," will be rather frequent, however, if all the "plus" factors dominate completely. But in the case of the hooded rats we must assume either that dominance is generally incomplete or that in the case of some factors the "minus" allelomorph dominates in the case of others the "plus," since F_1 rats from a cross of the plus by the minus strain are on the average intermediate in type between these two extremes.

[4]It is of course by no means necessary to assume incomplete dominance of the factors. If dominance is complete (in some cases the "minus" factor may dominate, in others the "plus"), the rigor of selection will be diminished, since heterozygous forms can not be distinguished from homozygous. Therefore, although a somewhat greater number of individuals will be found having the limiting values, it will take longer to bring the average up to the limit.

[5]A. L. & A. C. Hagedoorn, "Studies on Variation and Selection," *Zeit. f. ind. Abst. u. Vereb.*, 1914.

[6]E. C. MacDowell, "Multiple Factors in Mendelian Inheritance," *Jour. Exp. Zool.*, 1914, and Carnegie Inst. of Wash., 1914.

GENETIC VARIABILITY, TWIN HYBRIDS AND CONSTANT HYBRIDS, IN A CASE OF BALANCED LETHAL FACTORS*

Hermann J. Muller

The Rice Institute, Houston, Texas

[Received January 14, 1918]

Consideration of Related Phenomena, and General Discussion

The Lethal Effect of Dominant Mutants

The possibility has doubtless suggested itself to the reader that this whole mechanism of beaded inheritance may be merely a highly exceptional case, of no general interest. It is at first hard to believe that it could have any significance, or parallel in other cases. From this point of view it becomes of interest to know how widespread is the occurrence of factors similar in their properties to B_d'. An examination of other dominant mutant factors of Drosophila might be of value here, for it should disclose whether or not it is a mere coincidence that B_d', a dominant mutant factor, should, like the factor for yellow in mice, be lethal in its effect when homozygous.

Two dominant mutants which have for a long time been known in Drosophila are the sex-linked factors for abnormal abdomen and for bar eye. Unlike B_d', however, neither of these factors has been very difficult to obtain in pure stock, and the homozygotes are known to be viable and fertile. It should be noted that these factors are far from completely dominant to their allelomorphs; in fact, the heterozygote in each case is about midway in character between the two types of homozygotes. Data for ascertaining the viability of the

Genetics, September, 1918, 3:422-99; fourth section, parts 1-3, 5, 6, 8-10, and summary included.

homozygote existed in the case of only one other dominant mutant—the factor called notch—which also lies in chromosome I. This factor, which affects the wings somewhat in the same fashion as B_d', had first been found by Dexter (1914) (and called "perfect notch"), and the same factor afterwards arose again by mutation both in stocks of Bridges and of the writer. In the case of this factor the results are more encouraging for our present investigation, as Dexter's work has proved notch to be a lethal and Bridges and the author have each confirmed this finding for the notch which arose in their experiments.

To obtain further data upon the question under consideration, the writer tested the other dominant mutant factors of Drosophila. The first one studied was D' (dichaete). Heterozygous flies were made up of composition $\frac{s_e\ D'}{}$ [1], and these were bred *inter se*. As D' is only about ten units from sepia most of the homozygous sepia offspring would also be homozygous for D', and the count should be about as follows: non-crossovers: $\frac{s_e\ D'}{s_e\ D'}$ (appearing $s_e\ D'$) 22.5 percent, $\frac{s_e\ D'}{}$ (appearing D') 45 percent, — (appearing normal) 22.5 percent; crossovers: $\frac{s_e\ D'}{D'}$ (appearing D') 2.5 percent, $\frac{s_e\ D'}{s_e}$ (appearing $s_e\ D'$) 2.5 percent, $\frac{}{D'}$ (appearing D') 2.5 percent, $\frac{}{s_e}$ (appearing normal) 2.5 percent. Adding together the phenotypic classes we have $s_e\ D'$ 25 percent; D' 50 percent; normal 25 percent. The actual count consisted of $s_e\ D'$ 5, D' 59, normal 32. Thus there is a great deficiency of $s_e\ D'$ and a slight deficiency in the number of D'. Reference to the tabulation of expected classes will show that nine-tenths of the $s_e\ D'$ class is composed of homozygous D' and one-twentieth of the D' class also. If we subtract these homozygous D' flies from the expected ratios, we obtain $s_e\ D'$ 2.5, D' 47.5, normal 25. These are almost exactly the ratios that were actually obtained, and it is therefore evident that homozygous D' flies cannot live, i.e., that D' like B_d' is lethal when homozygous. That the D' when heterozygous does not lower the viability is indicated by a count obtained from a cross of heterozygous D' by homozygous normal. If the viability of heterozygous D' is as good as normal, half the offspring which hatch should be D' (heterozygous), and the rest normal. The count was D' 73, normal 65.

The dominant factors for star eye and for streaked thorax, which lie near together in chromosome II, were next tested by mating flies containing them to each other and then crossing together the F_1 flies which showed both characters and were therefore of composition $\frac{S'}{S_k'}$. The expectation, if there were no crossovers, would be $1\ \frac{S'}{S'} : 2\ \frac{S'}{S_k'} : 1\ \frac{S_k'}{S_k'}$. There would, however, be a small amount of crossing over, as judged by the fact that star and streak do not show quite the same linkage values with other factors; hence, in addition to the above classes, there would be a few $\dfrac{S'}{\ }$, $\dfrac{S_k{}'}{\ }$, $\dfrac{S'}{S'\,S_k{}'}$, and $\dfrac{S_k{}'}{S'\,S_k{}'}$. The count was: star 16, star streak 116, streak 61. The deficiency of stars shows that homozygous star flies die before hatching; the few stars that did appear were expected on account of the production, by crossing over, of a few $\dfrac{S'}{\ }$, and also because some of the $\dfrac{S'}{S_k{}'}$ were undoubtedly listed in this class, since heterozygous streak often fails to show the streak character. Here, then, is still another dominant which has a lethal effect when homozygous. Streak, however, turns out to be viable, although the homozygous streak flies have very poor fertility.

It will be recalled that the third-chromosome dominant factor for deformed eye, reported upon in the first section, presents an intermediate condition in regard to the present question; it was found often to be extremely inviable when homozygous, so that in many cases all homozygous $D_f{}'$ fail to appear, but in some cases a few, and in still others nearly all of the expected homozygous $D_f{}'$ do appear. These are invariably much smaller and weaker-looking than normals or heterozygous $D_f{}'$, however, and have besides an abnormality of the wings not exhibited by the latter, for the wings of these homozygous flies are usually crumpled together and are always very weak and flimsy in texture. The reproductive system too is affected, for offspring cannot be obtained from a mating of $\dfrac{D_f{}'}{D_f{}'}$ by $\dfrac{D_f{}'}{D_f{}'}$. This was found to depend upon a total sterility of the males (the females laid only a few eggs, but these were viable, when fertilized by normal sperm).

The case of truncate flies, which was investigated by Altenburg and the writer (see Morgan, Sturtevant, Muller and Bridges 1915), presents many similarities to the case of beaded, but it is being dealt with in another paper. Suffice it here to say that the more elaborate tests which were necessary in this case proved that T' (truncate), also, prevents a fly homozygous for itself from living, although in heterozygous condition it has little noticeable effect except upon the wings, being in this latter respect a dominant factor. The lethal effect in the homozygote is complete.

The intensifiers of beaded and truncate might perhaps be classed as dominants too, since they can exert a noticeable effect when heterozygous. But in this case not only is the effect of the heterozygous factor incomplete, but, as before noted, it fails to appear at all unless the chief factor is present. These intensifiers are not lethal, yet, like $D_f{}'$ and $S_k{}'$, they cause a marked reduction of fertility when homozygous.

Omitting these "weak" intensifiers from consideration, and also one or two very recently discovered factors which have not yet been sufficiently investigated, we may now list the dominant mutant factors of Drosophila as follows, with regard to their lethal effect when in homozygous condition: viable, S_k', A_b', B_r'; partially lethal, D_f'; completely lethal, N', S', T', D', B_d'. (The lethals, it should be noted, are scattered quite at random among the three chromosomes.)

This enumeration proves indisputably that there is a very strong tendency for dominant mutant factors to be lethal, in Drosophila at least, and so B_d' is in this respect rather an instance of the rule than an exception. This fact may seem somewhat surprising, but there are two series of considerations which would furnish ground for expecting such a result.

In the first place, it is likely that lethals are really among the commonest forms of mutants, but they would be discovered much more readily if they were dominant in regard to some visible character than if they were completely recessive, and this would cause the proportion of lethals among the dominant mutant factors to appear to be excessively high, when compared with the proportion among the recessives. Most present-day animals are the result of a long process of evolution, in which at least thousands of mutations must have taken place. Each new mutant in turn must have derived its survival value from the effect which it produced upon the "reaction system" that had been brought into being by the many previously formed factors in cooperation; thus a complicated machine was gradually built up whose effective working was dependent upon the interlocking action of very numerous different elementary parts or factors, and many of *the characters and factors which, when new, were originally merely an asset finally became necessary* because other necessary characters and factors had subsequently become changed so as to be dependent on the former. It must result, in consequence, that a dropping out of, or even a slight change in any one of these parts is very likely to disturb fatally the whole machinery; for this reason we should expect very many, if not most, mutations to result in lethal factors, and of the rest, the majority should be "semi-lethal" or at least disadvantageous in the struggle for life, and likely to set wrong any delicately balanced system, such as the reproductive system.[2]

Although this conclusion had suggested itself to the writer in 1912 it would manifestly have been very difficult to obtain experimental evidence for it, not only because of the great rarity with which mutations of any sort occur, but more especially because the detection of a lethal mutation, after it has occurred, requires special breeding tests of the particular flies containing the lethal factor. To detect a recessive lethal factor it is necessary not only to mate together two individuals both of which happen to be heterozygous for it, but also to determine what proportion of the offspring that receive a "visible" factor linked with this unsuspected lethal come to maturity. For this purpose it is usually necessary to have both the parents carry, in the same chromosome with the lethal, another recessive, non-lethal factor in heterozygous condition; the deviation from the expected ratio of 3 : 1 will then indicate the presence of a lethal. Hence, it is only in exceptional cases that a recessive lethal will be noticed.

Lethals that are linked with sex, however, will be discovered much more readily than the others, since the progeny of a female containing one of them will exhibit a 2 : 1 instead of 1 : 1 sex ratio (the Y chromosome in the male here takes the place of the lethal-bearing chromosome which the father must carry, since it is not dominant to any mutants in X). All flies the sex ratio of whose progeny has been determined will therefore exhibit their sex-linked lethals. This should result in the discovery of many more recessive lethals in chromosome I (the sex chromosome) than in any of the other chromosomes, although still it does not make the finding of recessive lethals in I nearly as easy as the finding of other recessive factors there, for mere inspection of a male will reveal any non-lethal sex-linked mutant that it carries. Even with this great handicap, about 17 mutant lethal factors have within the last few years been discovered in chromosome I of Drosophila; about 70 other factors, altogether, are known in this chromosome. When we allow for the much greater difficulty of finding lethals than other factors here[3] it becomes evident that *probably the majority, if not the vast majority, of mutants are lethals.* (Of course we do not take into account, in this statement, the unknown number of very "small" mutations, which have so slight an effect that they escape detection. Perhaps these are more numerous than the lethals.)

Experimental evidence for the above conclusion can at present be adduced only in the case of chromosome I, for, as we have seen, the lethals occurring in autosomes can be discovered even much less readily than the sex-linked ones. There is, however, no reasonable ground for believing that lethals arise less frequently in autosomes than in the sex chromosome, and so $l_{III\,1}$ is probably merely the first representative found of a large number of similar mutations that are continually occurring,—a number which, if our methods of detection were impartial, would exceed that of non-lethal mutations.

The conclusion that lethals have a much poorer chance of discovery than non-lethals applies, however, only to strictly recessive factors. In the case of dominants, if a factor is dominant only in regard to a visible, non-lethal effect, the probability of its being found will not be decreased by its being lethal when homozygous, for it can be discovered by inspection when in heterozygous condition, regardless of whether or not it can live when homozygous. This fact will tend to result in the finding, among the dominant mutant factors, of much more nearly the true proportion of lethals than among the recessive mutants. Even here, nevertheless, not the full proportion of lethals will be observed, since we have excluded from consideration in the above account all factors that are dominant in regard to the lethal effect itself (and not merely for a visible character); as such factors would kill even heterozygous individuals they have no means at all of perpetuating themselves and becoming known by any ordinary methods. We cannot tell how much to allow for factors of this sort. But in view of the unimpeded chance of detection of any dominants which are lethal only when homozygous, and of the great frequency with which lethals occur anyhow, it should not be surprising that such a large proportion of lethals have been found among the dominant mutants of Drosophila, as compared with such a small proportion among the autosomal recessive mutants.

It is also possible that not only would relatively more of the lethals occurring among dominant mutant factors be found, but that the excess of lethals observed among dominants is partly due to a greater chance of lethals actually occurring among dominant than among recessive mutant factors. The reasons for such a supposition are as follows:

The mutant factors which have been called dominants in Drosophila are not dominants in the same strict sense of the word as most of the normal factors are, in those cases where the normal allelomorphs are called dominant. For in the case of a mutant it has been called dominant if only it produces a conspicuous effect when heterozygous, regardless of whether in homozygous condition its effect is still more marked. Thus, bar is called a dominant, but heterozygous bar differs almost as much from homozygous bar as from normal, and so the mutant factor bar scarcely has any more right to be called the dominant in this case than has its normal allelomorph. The same is true of all the other so-called dominant mutants in which the homozygote can be examined; namely, abnormal, streak, deformed and the truncate and beaded intensifiers. This is in line with and adds significance to the fact that so many more recessives than even partial dominants have been found among the mutant factors of Drosophila. The great majority of the mutants, then, are recessive, while the few that are called dominant are very incompletely so.

We may generalize these two findings together in the single statement that, in Drosophila, there is a very strong tendency for the normal allelomorph to exert a more powerful influence than the mutant upon the character of the heterozygote; thus the latter inclines to resemble the normal much more closely than the homozygous mutant type. Cases of multiple allelomorphs have shown that two different mutant allelomorphs, on the other hand, tend to exert about equal effects upon the heterozygote, producing in the latter characters of intermediate grade. These facts are very striking, and undoubtedly of great significance; they might suggest, for example, that mutant factors are usually less active, and that possibly the mutations may often consist in a loss of some portion of the factor structure, but in our present ignorance of factor chemistry the real meaning of the facts must remain hidden. We are at present concerned, however, not with their cause but with their results.

In consequence of this more marked effect which all known mutant factors of Drosophila produce when in homozygous than heterozygous condition, it is to be expected that those customarily called dominants will, inasmuch as they produce appreciable effects even when heterozygous, cause especially pronounced abnormalities when homozygous. Homozygous dominants, therefore, would tend to produce more marked effects than homozygous recessives. Now since, for reasons already explained, the abnormalities produced by mutant factors are generally of an injurious nature, it follows that these dominants should be especially injurious when homozygous. A larger proportion of lethals might thus actually occur among these so-called dominant mutant factors than among the recessives.

To sum up, then, the observed excess of lethals among dominant mutant factors may be due both to the greater chance of lethals being detected among the dominants than among the recessives, and also to their actually occurring in greater relative numbers in the case of this class of mutants. It should thus be evident that, from an *a priori* standpoint as well as on the basis of experimental facts, the lethal effect of the dominant mutant B_d' can in no sense be considered an atypical finding.

The Balancing Lethal

The chief peculiarities of the beaded case depend upon the co-incidence of a factor (B_d') of the lethal-dominant type just discussed, with another lethal (in this case purely recessive) in the homologous chromosome. Now, the occurrence of a recessive lethal likewise cannot be considered, in the light of the preceding discussion, an unusual circumstance, as such lethals must be arising not infrequently. Why did just this lethal, so precisely adapted to produce the unusual results of the present case, happen to occur in just this stock, however, whereas lethals are not ordinarily found to be existing at all in usual stocks? There is an especial reason why a lethal should be found in this particular case, and why it should occur near the locus at which l_{III1} actually lies.

Granting that lethals are really arising by mutation not very infrequently, they would nevertheless tend, one by one, to be eliminated from stocks by natural selection (provided there is an appreciable amount of inbreeding). In the case of the beaded stock this invisible process of mutation and elimination would have occurred too, until a lethal arose in the chromosome homologous to that containing B_d', in some locus near-by; this factor, unlike the others, would tend to be selected by the very conditions of the experiment, which was aimed at getting stock producing as low a proportion of normals as possible. Once selected and established, moreover, the lethal would persist indefinitely in the stock by the process of "enforced heterozygosis" previously described. For if the two parents in a certain bottle both had happened to receive this factor (say from a mutant grandparent), this particular bottle would produce an unusually small percentage of normal flies, and since this would be a result desired, the offspring in this bottle would then be selected to continue the beaded race, rather than the offspring in other bottles. All of these offspring would, in such a case, contain the factor in question again, and so the pure race would at one jump be established, and both lethal factors, once selected, would persist indefinitely in the self-perpetuating stock.

Selection for stock pure in respect to one lethal thus automatically tends to result in the establishment of a *balancing* lethal, if I may call it so, in the homologous chromosome. When this happens, a state of enforced heterozygosis is set up which may be regarded as a kind of constant hybridism. Whereas any ordinary heterozygous population, when inbred, will separate more and more into the respective homozygous strains, one of this type must remain always and necessarily heterozygous for the two lethals it contains, except in so far as the "balancing" of the lethals is imperfect, i.e., so far as crossing over between them occurs. It remains heterozygous also for any other factors lying in the same chromosome with either one of the lethals, so long as they too do not cross over from it.

Effects of Balanced Lethals on Crosses

Since in such a race all individuals, though heterozygous, are alike in genetic composition, the stock would seem to be pure, until tests were made upon it by crossing it to other races. Then its heterozygosis would be made manifest by the appearance of "twin hybrids," provided only that the chromosome containing one of the lethals differed from the other in being dominant in regard to some visible character for which the foreign race was recessive. Thus, in the case of beaded, the chromosome containing B_d' differs from that containing $l_{\text{III}\,1}$ in being dominant for the visible character beaded wings, and so, when the stock is crossed to non-beaded races, twin hybrids—beadeds and non-beadeds—are produced. On being inbred, the F_1 beadeds of course would not breed true, since the B_d' in them is no longer "balanced" by another lethal; the non-beadeds, however, would appear to breed true, if the foreign stock had not differed from the beaded in any visible characters except those carried in the B_d'-bearing chromosome. The non-beaded F_1 would consequently be "constant hybrids," using the term here in a different sense from that employed in applying it to the beaded stock itself. By introducing other "visible" mutant factors into one of the third chromosomes of the beaded stock, these effects can be duplicated for other characters besides beaded itself.

Thus the factors s_s k e^s (and in one lot also r_o) were introduced, by appropriate crosses, into the chromosome with B_d', making the composition of the stock $\dfrac{s_s \; k \; e^s \; B_d'}{C' \; l_{\text{III} \; 1}}$; this stock perpetuated itself in heterozygous condition just like the original $\dfrac{B_d'}{C' \; l_{\text{III} \; 1}}$ stock. Since all three (or four) introduced factors were recessive and heterozygous there was nothing to indicate their presence in the stock, and all the flies were normal in appearance except for the beading in the wings, which was rather weak and uncertain of appearance owing to loss of the intensifiers in making the crosses. A sample of 103 flies taken from this stock gave the following count: much beaded 1, moderately beaded 49, slightly beaded 49, normal 14, flies showing any of the characters of $s_s \; k \; e^s$ or r_o 0. When this stock was crossed to the homozygous recessive stock $s_s \; k \; e^s \; r_o$, twin hybrids of very different appearance were produced, as expected. Half of the F_1 flies (all those that had received B_d') showed all of the characters of $s_s \; k \; e^s \; r_o$, and most of them showed B_d' in addition; the other half, which were all non-beaded, looked perfectly normal. The hybrid flies of the first type, when crossed to each other, were constant, i.e., bred true, for all four recessive characters, although they showed segregation for B_d'. They were therefore "constant hybrids" with respect to the former characters, if we use this term in its customary empirical sense. The normal-appearing class, on the other hand, split up, giving approximately 2 normal to 1 $s_s \; k \; e^s \; r_o$ in F_2. Similar results were obtained with a stock having only e^s in the chromosome with the B_d'.

In the stocks like $\dfrac{s_s \; k \; e^s \; r_o \; B_d'}{C' \; l_{\text{III} \; 1}}$ which contain s_s in the chromosome with B_d', a very small percent of crossing over is possible between s_s and the factors to the right of it (about 2 crossovers in 1000 gametes), although practically no crossing over occurs between any of the other loci. By such crossing over $s_s \; C' \; l_{\text{III} \; 1}$ and $k \; e^s \; r_o \; B_d'$ chromosomes are produced (say 1 of each kind in 1000). If the $s_s \; C' \; l_{\text{III} \; 1}$ chromosome meets in fertilization one of the $s_s \; k \; e^s \; r_o \; B_d'$ type, as it has an even chance of doing, a fly homozygous for s_s , and showing the spineless character, is produced. Thus one individual in 1000 that hatch is spineless; the rest appear normal in all characters but beaded. Here, then, is a stock apparently breeding true, except for the fact that it throws spineless about once in a thousand times. In ignorance of the condition of balanced lethals existing in this stock, and of the not quite complete linkage of s_s with one of these lethals, the appearance of this character in such small but constant proportions would ordinarily be attributed to mutation.

Similar results were obtained in the case of the factors s_e and p , except that, as these lie further to the left of C' than does s_s, there was more crossing over, and so a higher percent of "mutations"; in fact, sepia appeared in such numbers that it would rather have been ascribed to the action of multiple factors, by a casual observer.

This semblance of mutation with s_e and p was also obtained in the case of a stock of composition $\dfrac{s_e \ p \ s_s \ k \ e^s \ r_o \ B_d'}{s_d \ C'}$, which differs from those above discussed in that there is no lethal in the C'-bearing chromosome (though the flies homozygous for s_d, spread wings, are not as viable as the others). Flies of this type, mated together, should therefore give counts like those of the balanced lethal stock, with the addition of (nearly) 1 homozygous spread individual for every 2 of the others that hatch. The sample count gave 50 spread and 136 not spread; the latter consisted of 5 well beaded, 35 moderately beaded, 50 slightly beaded, and 49 normal-winged; these were all red-eyed with the exception of 1 pink and 15 sepia-eyed crossovers, in which the respective eye-color mutants had escaped from their bondage to the lethal B_d', and so emerged into visibility as though they had just arisen by mutation directly.

The Reason for the Origin of Enforced Heterozygosis

It has been shown how the state of enforced heterozygosis must have arisen in the case of beaded-winged Drosophila; similar considerations explain the origin of this phenomenon in other artificially bred organisms and also "in nature." The one and necessary condition for its production is the appearance in the species of some beneficial factor which is unable to exist in homozygous stock. By "beneficial" is meant in this connection the property of having survival value under the kind of natural or artificial selection which obtains at the time.

The inability to exist in pure stock may be due to a secondary lethal or sterilizing effect exerted on homozygotes or gametes either by the factor itself or by another factor closely linked with it. Given this sort of factor, there will be a tendency for such stock to be selected as contains the highest possible proportion of it, provided only that the advantage of having the factor is always enough to more than counterbalance the disadvantage of so many individuals being rendered sterile or inviable. In this way it happens that, when a balancing lethal (or even sterilizing factor) arises, as it has a very good chance of doing at some time or other if our conclusions regarding the frequency of lethal mutations are correct, the stock containing the balancing lethal in addition to the original "beneficial" factor will be selected rather than that containing the original factor alone. For such stock would maintain a constant output of individuals containing the beneficial factor; in fact all viable or fertile individuals would possess it. The competing energies of this stock, as a group, would thus not be sapped by the continual presence within it of a large number of undesirable individuals that forced a vitiating intra-group competition. The disadvantage of smaller total numbers might easily be compensated for by the fact that it was the "less desirables" which were weeded out.

It is easy to imagine that some time long ago in the history of the Oenothera group some dominant factor arose that was of such advantage when in heterozygous condition that it made headway in spite of a lethal effect on homozygotes; the establishment of a balancing lethal was then but a matter of time. In the case of beaded, the "beneficial" factor was of course beaded itself, since the experimenter consciously selected beaded-winged flies to breed from. Artificial selection was no doubt responsible for the case of stocks also, for double flowers are always considered desirable by the fancier. Moreover, there could have been no natural advantage in the flowers' having the factor for double, because it is recessive and so every time it produces its visible doubling effect, it also produces sterility. For a *natural* selection of a beneficial factor which cannot persist in pure stock, the factor must be *dominant* in respect to its beneficial effect (except where sterile workers are of advantage to a community). The case of stocks, then, differs from the others in that the desirable factor is here completely recessive, and it is actually the sterile homozygous individuals which must have been selected for, not heterozygotes in which the factor produced its beneficial without its harmful effect. This being the case, such races of singles would be selected as yielded the highest proportion of the sterile doubles; thus eventually the cultivated singles would be found to contain a balancing lethal.

It should also be pointed out that very long continued breeding from heterozygotes exclusively would in itself tend to result in the establishment of a balancing lethal, even without the special selection, in the way above described, of those strains which produced the smallest proportion of homozygotes among their viable and fertile offspring. For even though a balancing lethal were not specifically selected for, it would become established sooner or later unless it were specifically selected against, since when any lethal happened to arise in the appropriate position, there would be nothing to prevent its continuance in the race. Hence eventually all individuals would come to contain some balancing lethal.

This argument applies, moreover, not only to a second or "balancing" lethal factor, but also to the appearance of a lethal in the first place. That is to say, if for some reason heterozygotes are always selected as parents, then, even if there are no lethal factors present to begin with, one or more recessive lethals linked with the factor which is being kept heterozygous will eventually come to exist with it in the same chromosome, for there will be no selection against such lethals; meanwhile, in the opposite chromosome the balancing lethal will tend to arise. So, for example, it is likely that if the practice of breeding heterozygous pink Mirabilis were kept up for a very long time, even without purposive selection of those families which gave the highest proportion of pink offspring, the race would eventually come to "breed true" to the pink color.

The establishment of lethal factors in cases like the above would simply depend upon the fact that the individuals used as parents would in such cases always have to be heterozygous for any lethal factors that might arise. Lethal mutants that were innocuous in heterozygous condition might then not be selected against, and so they would become established some time or other. Now the same process would also take place not only when heterozygotes are specifically chosen as parents in each generation, but also when organisms are continually out-bred to unrelated lines, for here, although they are not necessarily kept heterozygous in regard to some factor present at the beginning, nevertheless, any mutant factor that might arise would be kept in heterozygous condition and, if recessive, it could not be selected against. For this reason it is to be expected that lethal factors and all sorts of "undesirable" recessive factors would gradually "creep into" the chromosomes of species which constantly out-crossed, so that if ever inbreeding were practiced upon them various abnormal types would appear and a state of balanced lethal factors in respect to one or more of the pairs of chromosomes would emerge. It might also very well happen that in such a contingency a lethal might "find itself" balanced by a non-lethal but disadvantageous recessive factor, such as one for sterility. Such a stock, if it persisted at all, would tend to change over into the condition of balanced lethals, for it would fulfill the condition of containing in one chromosome a dominant "beneficial" factor (the normal allelomorph of the disadvantageous one) which nevertheless could not exist in pure stock (here owing to its linkage with a lethal).

All the above outlined circumstances, that tend to lead to the production of balanced lethals can in fact be regarded as cases fulfilling the condition first mentioned as the only one necessary for producing such a result. For, in cases where heterozygotes only are bred from, this must be because each chromosome contains a factor or factors, that produce some effect in heterozygous condition which leads to their selection as parents (i.e., some "beneficial" effect), but which nevertheless for some reason cannot exist in pure stock (otherwise the homozygotes too would be chosen as parents). And, in cases where out-crossing is always practiced, each chromosome of course contains "beneficial" normal factors potentially dominant to any recessive lethal mutant that may arise, yet, on account of the out-crossing, not one of these chromosomes can be obtained in stock pure for its particular self (that is, in stock having the homologous chromosomes so closely related genealogically that in cases where a mutation has occurred, both of them are likely to contain the same mutant factor). So we see that the two modes of production of balanced lethals just considered are merely special cases of the general type first enunciated.

Effect of the Continued Heterozygosis on the Chromosomes and on the Evolution of the Race

The causes leading up to the state of balanced lethals having been examined, it now remains to consider what conditions the heterozygosis thus enforced would itself induce. The way for a treatment of this matter has already been paved by the consideration of the effects of out-crossing and of continually selecting heterozygotes as parents. In the balanced stocks, just as under the latter circumstances, any recessive mutant factors appearing in the chromosome regions involved cannot be selected against, for they would produce tangible effects only on homozygotes, which never appear (or at least never function as parents). Recessive mutants of all kinds would therefore gradually accumulate in the affected chromosomes, so that finally, even if it were possible to get rid of either of the original members of the pair of balanced lethal factors, it would still be impossible to obtain homozygotes, on account of the new lethals which had arisen near the old ones. In other words, the condition of balanced lethals itself gives rise to more balanced lethals, linked with the previous ones. If there were no crossing over, lethals anywhere within the affected chromosomes could persist, for no portion of them would ever become homozygous and subject to selection with respect to recessive factors. In chromosomes where crossing over occurred, only regions near the lethals could become homozygous infrequently enough for selection with respect to recessives in these loci to be negligible; lethals would come to exist here, however, and these secondarily formed lethals would then constitute new foci, protecting the existence of still other lethals in the regions next adjoining: thus the "degenerative" process would gradually spread throughout the chromosome. Besides the lethals, other abnormal factors also might arise, and these two would be protected by the balanced lethal mechanism from being weeded out; nevertheless they might occasionally become homozygous, by some rare crossing over from their enfettering lethal, and then they might be hailed as new mutations.

Knowing the frequency of mutations, it would be possible to calculate just how quickly these degenerative changes would take place. Thus, if recessive lethals in a particular chromosome arise with such frequency that (on the average) one out of 500 gametes of each normal individual contain one such mutant factor, then, after 500 generations of enforced heterozygosis in regard to this type of chromosome, each individual would (on the average) contain one lethal in each of its chromosomes of this type, for the lethal should have been present as a mutant in one of the 500 ancestral gametes that transmitted one of these chromosomes, and, once having arisen, the lethal would of course have persisted.[4] On the same supposition of lethal frequency, after 1000 generations (about 40 years in Drosophila), each of the chromosomes which has been kept heterozygous would tend to have two lethals in addition to what it may have had at the beginning. In this calculation it is assumed that the whole chromosome has been involved in the enforced heterozygosis; if part of it was beyond the influence of the latter, owing to crossing over, correspondingly fewer lethals would have become established —i.e., only those of the above which happened to lie in the restricted region that was under the "protective" influence of the enforced heterozygosis.

There is now evidence in Drosophila (Bridges 1917) that besides the "point-mutations," in single loci, changes occasionally occur that involve a whole region of the chromosome, perhaps destroying, or, more probably, "inactivating" all the contained factors in some way; for it is found that the latter no longer give any evidence of their existence, inasmuch as any recessive mutant allelomorphs that may be introduced into the opposite chromosome will not be dominated over by factors in such a region of the once normal chromosome. (Such a region, moreover, even if relatively short, is always found to be lethal when homozygous, corroborating our conclusion that not many changes, or losses, can occur among factors without undoing some mechanism that is necessary for life.) Now, these recessive regional mutations, or "deficiencies," like the point-mutations, could of course persist in the chromosomes protected by heterozygosis from the action of natural selection, and although these changes must be very rare,[5] they might make up for their infrequency by the quantity of change produced by them when they did come. By this sort of change too, then, the chromosomes originally containing one pair of balanced lethals may gradually degenerate.

It should be noted, however, that degenerative alterations of any kind (whether deficiencies or ordinary mutations) could not become established in one member of the pair of chromosomes, if they involved loci allelomorphic to any that had already become changed in the opposite member of the chromosome pair, for individuals so affected would die. Thus not more than half of the loci of each chromosome could, on the average, become changed. These loci would, of course, be scattered anywhere along the chromosome.

Since there would be no process of selection either for or against any of these mutants, corresponding chromosomes in different individuals might, in the course of time, come to have very different compositions. The accidental decline and spread of certain lines would however, tend to keep the number of different sorts of chromosomes from becoming very large, except in extremely populous groups, for although this process of "extinction of families" is slow, that of mutation is slow also.

Since the synapsis of homologous chromosomes must depend in some way on a specific attraction of (certain?) like loci (allelomorphs) for each other, the synaptic attraction of the members of the balanced pair would tend to diminish as they diverged more and more from one another through their unlike mutative processes.[6] This might lead to diminution in crossing over, which would be an advantage so far as productivity was concerned, for crossover chromosomes, containing lethals of both members, would cause death unless they met in fertilization with crossovers of just the opposite type. The weakening of the synaptic attraction might also lead to visible peculiarities of behavior in the maturation period, such as failure of homologous chromosomes to become finely spun out during maturation, and their late or imperfect (end-to-end?) conjugation. Non-disjunction too would then occur more often, for when chromosomes do not conjugate, it is a matter of chance whether or not they enter the same cell at the segregation divisions.

"Degeneration" of the general sort above described is not a process quite peculiar to pairs of chromosomes containing balanced lethals, but it must take place in every chromosome that is for any reason kept in company with homologous chromosomes of remote genealogical relationship to it, for the latter chromosomes, not having mutations in the same loci as the former, would by their dominant normal factors prevent the recessive mutants in the former chromosome from manifesting themselves, and so from being eliminated by selection. Thus, in hybrid Andalusian fowl or yellow mice, if the animals were for centuries bred from heterozygotes, and also in any of the chromosomes of species which propagate by continual out-crossing (as corn tends to do), lethals would tend to arise, as we have already seen, and this whole degenerative process would in fact gradually take place.

The best examples of this sort of change are to be found in the Y chromosome of species of the Drosophila (XY) type of sex determination, and in the W chromosome of species of the Abraxas (WZ) type, for these chromosomes (or at least the region of them opposite the sex factor, in cases where crossing over was possible), have been continuously in company with remotely related homologues ever since the respective types of sex determination have been established. Moreover, the "degenerative" changes in these cases could be much more extensive than in cases of balanced lethals, because the Y and W chromosomes were more completely protected by their homologues from the action of selection. This is because their homologues (X and Z respectively) themselves remained quite normal, owing to the fact that they were subjected to selection when in the homozygous sex (XX or ZZ). Recessive changes could consequently be established in any locus of Y and W, whereas in cases of balanced lethals, where both homologues might become involved, only half of either chromosome might, on the average, degenerate. This consideration would apply to any case where the back cross was continually performed, for one chromosome would be kept normal while the other would be completely protected from selection, so far as recessive mutations were concerned. It is probably needless to point out that the W and especially the Y chromosome (which is perhaps of more ancient origin), do show the expected evidences of this degeneration and differentiation from their homologues, both genetically and cytologically. The evidences are now as follows: (1) Recessiveness of W and Y in respect to any mutant factors arising in the homologue, even though these mutants are usually themselves recessive to the original normal allelomorph; (2) similar non-dominance over normal factors in the homologue, as shown in cases where the normals are themselves recessive to mutants; (3) failure of occurrence, or relative infrequency, of dominant mutations in W and Y (recessives would not be detected); (4) visible differences in size and shape between them and their homologues; (5) great variations in their own size and shape even in closely related species; (6) weak synaptic attraction between them and their homologues, as indicated by the tendency for the sex chromosomes in the heterozygous sex to remain condensed during the growth period, while the autosomes are spinning out for intimate conjugation, (7) and as shown by their frequently delayed synapsis, (8) and by the lack of crossing over between them and their homologues when they conjugate, even in the sex where other chromosomes are undergoing crossing over (shown in Bridges' [1916] non-disjunctional females of type XXY), (9) and by the tendency, in these XXY individuals, for X and X to conjugate more often than X and Y. All of these pecularities were to have been expected in the light of the previous considerations. The fate of the Y chromosome, then, illustrates what will eventually happen to the chromosomes in cases of balanced lethals, although in the latter cases each member of the pair can change only half as much.

Non-disjunction leads to the production of individuals with three, and eventually four, members of the chromosome pair originally involved. When this happened to chromosomes containing balanced lethals (as it probably would at some time), the members, A and a, of the originally balanced pair, would now tend to become two pairs, AA and aa, like pairing with like, provided the differentiation between A and a had become marked. Each of the members of these two pairs, now having identical mates, would (if this tendency was completely realized) behave like normal chromosomes, and every gamete would receive one of each pair, namely A and a. Every gamete and zygote would consequently contain all the dominant normal factors necessary for life; the lethal effect would thus be nullified and productivity would again rise to 100 percent.[7] If, however, the two pairs were not well differentiated and occasionally conjugated in a criss-cross fashion (Aa and aA), intermediate values for productivity would result. These individuals of higher productivity would obviously be selected in the struggle for existence (unless the alteration which had occurred in the proportions of the chromatin materials had disturbed the mechanism of development, as it does in *Oenothera lata*). Thus the race containing balanced lethals might eventually return to a condition of normal genetic behavior, through the occurrence of non-disjunction, which would itself have been favored by the weakening of synaptic attraction between the degenerating chromosomes.

A similar situation would develop if, instead of non-disjunction merely of the balanced chromosomes, the whole nucleus became tetraploid. Here similarly the balanced pair would tend to form two independent pairs, the lethal effect would then disappear, and productivity would rise, provided the tetraploid condition was not harmful in other ways. Other things being equal, however, a tetraploid condition of all the chromosomes would not be as advantageous as the tetraploid condition of only the balanced pair (produced by non-disjunction), for evolution is hindered in tetraploid individuals by the fact that recessive mutants can manifest themselves here only in the rare coincidence that more than two of the mutant allelomorphs enter the same zygote.

Another important consequence of enforced heterozygosis, besides its allowing the degeneration of chromosomes, is that it hinders the establishment of progressive changes in them. That is to say, not only are (recessive) mutant factors which ordinarily would be disadvantageous not selected against, but the much rarer beneficial ones that would, if homozygous, produce advantageous effects, cannot be selected for, since none of them has an opportunity to manifest itself except in case of the (initially) very remarkable accident that the same mutation has occurred independently in both members of the chromosome pair. The evolution of the race is therefore hindered almost exactly in proportion to the fraction which the affected chromosomes form of the whole bulk of chromatin—e.g., if they form one-fifth of the mass, selection has only four-fifths of the ordinary amount of genetic material to work upon, at least so far as recessive changes are concerned, and so evolution will (other things being equal) proceed at about four-fifths of the speed which it otherwise would have. For this reason, as well as on account of the disadvantage of their lowered productivity, species containing balanced lethals would in the long run have a poorer chance of survival than ordinary species. Nevertheless, in the long course of evolution by which any present-day form has been produced, this condition may have arisen more than once, especially since, as will now be explained, the retardation of evolution would not be absolutely permanent.

Although progressive change might for a long time be hindered in the way described, yet, after an extensive degeneration has taken place in either member of a pair of balanced chromosomes, many recessive changes in the other member will be able to "show," just as recessive mutants in the X chromosome can now manifest themselves in the XY male, owing to the "degenerate" condition of the Y. (In producing changes extensive enough to show these effects, point mutations would be vastly less effective than deficiencies.) Thus, after a long time, selection and progress can start in again, rendered possible, paradoxically enough, by the degeneration which preceded it. After this degeneration, in fact, recessive mutants will be able to manifest themselves, and will be selected, even more readily than under ordinary circumstances, for they do not need to be received from both parents in order to become evident, any more than sex-linked mutants do in the male Drosophila. A doubling in number of the balanced chromosomes through non-disjunction or "tetraploidy" would now make of them two ordinary pairs, the factors in one of which do not interfere with, or dominate over, the factors in the other. If the doubling had come before the differentiation, the same stage would nevertheless be reached in the end.[8]

Although the series of events described are entirely theoretical, they are the quite inevitable consequence of the random mutations and mitotic accidents that are continually though very infrequently occurring. Whether the course of processes outlined could actually come to pass therefore depends upon how long a race with balanced lethals would be able to maintain itself in competition with its less handicapped neighbors, and upon the actual frequency with which point-mutations, deficiencies, and mitotic abnormalities happen.

The Variability of the Character Beaded

Practically all the peculiarities of inheritance in the beaded case have been shown to have their origin in just two circumstances: (1) that the mutant B_d' is a dominant, and (2) that the reaction by which the character is produced is readily modifiable. The first circumstance has been shown to be causally connected with the lethal effect of B_d' itself, and this lethal effect in turn explained the establishment of a balancing lethal. The second circumstance must be responsible for the fact that the character is so variable somatically, and also for the fact that so many (5 or more) known genetic factors act as modifiers of it.[9] The question may now be asked, is there any connection between these two circumstances themselves.

There seems no *a priori* reason why dominant mutants should be more modifiable than recessives, although all the dominants so far found in Drosophila, without exception, are especially noteworthy for the relatively high variability of the characters they produce, as compared with the average of characters due to recessive mutants. Possibly the fact that the dominants are usually judged when in heterozygous condition has something to do with this result, although, again, there appears to be no theoretical reason why heterozygotes should be more variable than homozygotes. But whether or not individuals heterozygous for dominant mutant factors really are more variable than homozygous recessive mutants, as the facts certainly seem to show, there is a cogent reason for believing that mutant characters are more apt to be variable than normals are. The reason is that it is usually disadvantageous for an individual to have its characters depend on reactions that are easily modified, because then the normal, optimum, type would not so often be produced; fac‡ tors will therefore have been perpetuated, by natural selection, which are especially undeviating in their effects. (Of course, in special cases, normal characters may be modified by ordinary agencies, but then they are only modified "adaptively," and under particular conditions; this is in fact physiology). Thus normal factors produce reactions that are less changeable than those of the average factor, or conversely, the characters produced by mutants would be, on the whole, more modifiable. The modifiability of the beaded character is thus correlated with the fact that it is a mutant.

All this character variation has of course nothing to do with *factor* variability, and, so far as this question is concerned, it should now be evident that the known peculiarities of beaded inheritance are entirely explained by the findings above reported. *The argument for factor variability in this case therefore falls*, and in similar cases the burden of proof must hence be on the proponents of that hypothesis, until the genetic facts are thoroughly analyzed. But, besides these experimental findings, some considerations have been raised in the preceding discussion that lead to certain theoretical objections to factor variability. These and other general arguments bearing on the problem here at issue will now be examined.

General Considerations Concerning Factor Variability

If the conception of the organism sketched in the section dealing with the frequency of lethal mutations is correct, alterations in factors are very apt to have harmful, if not fatal, results on the individual. It is probable, moreover, that at least thousands of factors coöperate to make the individual. In view of these two circumstances, it is certainly venturesome to assume that the genetic factors are all continually varying from generation to generation. The individual formed of these factors would, to put it bluntly, have a very hard time holding together. Among thousands of fluctuating factors it would, on any such assumption, seem likely that a few at least in every individual would have varied so much as to be lethal or semi-lethal. In other words, as soon as it is postulated that the larger visible variations are merely the extremes of a fluctuation curve, and that innumerable factors in the individual are each producing curves of similar sort, it becomes difficult to see how an appreciable proportion of these visible, non-lethal changes can be taking place, without every individual also receiving many lethal, or at least very disadvantageous, variations at the same time. Under such circumstances, natural selection would be scarcely sufficient even for the work of conserving the factors as they are, and maintaining the race at its normal standard, let alone for the task of race improvement, or the alteration of particular characters in desirable directions, in addition to all this. On the other hand, if factor changes are rare and definite, these difficulties are not encountered.

Of course if the individual factor fluctuations were made indefinitely small, the total variation could be held within harmless bounds, but in that case it is very doubtful whether any one factor would vary enough for the changes in it to be appreciable, and it is difficult to see how, under such circumstances, natural selection could obtain a grip. Besides, it cannot be taken for granted that the variations may be indefinitely minute, for the factor itself is so tiny that changes in the number of its molecules, or in its radicles, might well produce quite discrete effects.

Factor changes, however, probably do not consist in mere variations in the number of molecules at all; they are probably qualitative, rather than quantitative in this sense, and so they should not be expected to follow a "normal curve." One reason against regarding factor changes as quantitative is that in Federley's (1913) crosses of butterflies, where zygotes are formed in which some of the chromosomes are half the size of others, due to an extra division of the former, the size differences are evened up again during development. The factors must necessarily have been halved when the chromosomes were; presumably they also recovered their form or size when the chromosome did, but if there is any doubt about this point it could be easily tested genetically. Another reason for believing that there is a definite size which each gene tends to approach as its equilibrium amount [10] is that, if this were not so, the sizes of corresponding genes in different cells would, by the accumulation of chance differences, surely come to vary enormously from each other after the long series of multiplications occurring during development (and generation after generation). For the genes, after all this time, to present just "tractable" differences from each other, of the order of magnitude postulated by the believers in fluctuation, would require a delimitation of variation adjusted with the utmost nicety, considering how many times the genes must reproduce themselves in all the cell generations from gamete to gamete. In doubling themselves in any one cell generation, then, their amount of growth would have to be regulated with infinite exactitude, and their course of variation would need to be steered along a knife edge.

The hypothesis of a continual fluctuation of factors, though regarded by many as such a natural assumption, really fails to account for the fact of continuous character variability which it was invented to explain. For if the factors are varying slightly all the time, they should vary in the embryo as well as in the adult, and in early gonia as well as late, but a variation in a factor at that early stage would give a bias to the size or nature of that factor in all descendant cells in the direction of this original variation. Thus the offspring of an individual should often have their factors varying about a mean different from the value of that factor in the parent, and the curve of offspring should not be a normal curve at all, but polymodal, with more individuals grouped about some of the modes, representing variations that occurred in earlier gonia, than about others, which would have been caused by variations in later cells that did not have so many descendants. Within the groups about each mode, moreover, there would be subsidiary centres of aggregation. This would seem true especially when we remember that the cells do not grow and divide synchronously but develop in more or less discontinuous groups.

To escape this dilemma it would seem to be necessary for the proponents of fluctuation to postulate that variation is confined to the maturation period of the germ cells, or at least to their later stages. But to do this is to dig the ground from under the very foundations of the hypothesis, for its chief claim to recognition lay in the inherent plausibility of the idea that factors, like so many other things, must be subject to continual slight variation, and could not be kept constant. To now admit that the factors may nevertheless be practically constant through most of the life cycle is to admit the existence of the whole mechanism necessary for factor constancy. To suppose that, in addition to this fixity, there is a variability at just about the time of maturation thus becomes a very special and unnecessary assumption; one not to be tolerated without the most cogent experimental proof.

In addition, then, to the experimental findings showing that there is another explanation for the cases used as arguments for factor fluctuation, we must bear in mind that the *a priori* basis for this hypothesis is very uncertain also. Now, when the definitely ascertained mutations are examined, still further evidence against this assumption appears, for *in factors in which large changes are found, small changes are not.more frequent;* at any rate, there is evidence against the existence of a probability curve of variations, one with the minuter plus and minus changes more and more numerous. Perhaps the best example of what is meant here may be seen in the case of the mutations in the locus *W* of Drosophila, a case which has at times been cited in support of the variability contention. Seven distinct allelomorphs (all affecting eye color) are already known at that locus, yet all six mutants are (in intensity of the color they produce) minus variants from the normal red, and furthermore, they show no tendency at all to group themselves in its vicinity. Instead of finding most of the allelomorphs very nearly like red in the character they produce, with the wider deviations most exceptional, there is only one factor ("blood") in the long interval between red and cherry, although cherry is, in intensity of color, about half way between red and white, the most extreme variant. The other four mutants are more extreme deviants than cherry. This is not because less extreme variants than cherry would be likely to escape observation, for hardly any of the mutations affecting eye color in other loci of Drosophila are even as extreme as blood, and very much smaller deviants than cherry or blood would be detected unfailingly. It is therefore quite gratuitous to assume here that there are a very large number of small variations; certainly the number does not increase as we approach the parent type within the limits of observation, but, in fact, decreases conspicuously.

Of course, it would be scholastic to deny that some mutant genes may ocasionally occur that are genetically unstable in some way or other. Emerson's (1911, 1914) variegated corn in fact proves this possibility, but it is noteworthy that even in this case there is no evidence of continuous fluctuation and a normal curve. Although such instability may be expected as an occasional abnormality, it is to the advantage of the organism that most genes shall be very stable, and present-day races are doubtless the products of a long process of selection in that respect as well as in regard to the constancy of the reactions whereby the factors produce the characters. In view of all the experimental data, and theoretical considerations, practically absolute factor fixedness seems the established rule, with the exception of occasional definite mutations that in any one locus must usually be exceedingly rare, and geneticists may well pause before ascribing any unusual results to a fluctuating variability of a single factor. The positive evidence against such a process still remains unchallenged by relevant facts or plausible hypotheses.

Contamination of Factors

It should be noted that, although $B_d{}'$ has been kept continually heterozygous, in company with its normal allelomorph, for years, without then being subjected to artificial selection, nevertheless it shows no evidence of having been contaminated by that association, or weakened in any way.

Summary

1. $B_d{}'$, the factor for beaded wings in Drosophila, is, like the factor for yellow in mice, a lethal which kills all individuals homozygous for it. Like yellow it is recessive for the lethal effect and behaves as dominant in regard to a visible character, but in the present case the dominance is rather irregular. $B_d{}'$ is located at about 2 units to the right of the locus of rough eyes; thus it lies at the extreme right-hand end of the known factors in the third chromosome.

2. In the so-called pure stock of beaded, although of course none of the individuals can be homozygous for $B_d{}'$, nevertheless all

show the character beaded. This is because they contain, in the third chromosome homologous to the one carrying B_d', another lethal factor, $l_{\text{III }1}$, which prevents individuals homozygous for itself from appearing. This factor, unlike B_d', produces no visible effect when in heterozygous condition. Its locus is situated about twelve units to the left of that of B_d'. Since here it lies in the same chromosome with the normal allelomorph of B_d' no flies of this stock that are homozygous for normal wings can live, except when $l_{\text{III }1}$ crosses over from the factor for normal wings.

3. There is, however, another mutant factor besides $l_{\text{III }1}$ in the chromosome containing the normal allelomorph of B_d'. This is the factor C', which produces no visible effect, but which, when heterozygous, practically prevents crossing over in the region of the chromosome near to it. C' is located somewhat to the left of $l_{\text{III }1}$, and effectually prevents the latter from becoming separated from the factor for normal wings, except in very rare cases. As neither the homogyzous normals nor the homozygous beadeds can live, the condition is created of a heterozygous stock which nevertheless breeds true to its own type.

It is proposed to designate a condition of this sort, in which heterozygosis is enforced by two opposed lethal factors, each of which in some way prevents the appearance of an opposite type of homozygote, as one of "balanced lethal factors."

4. l_{Bd}', the factor in chromosome II which intensifies the beaded character, is not a lethal, and it is probably not an allelomorph of v_g (the factor for vestigial wings). It is partially dominant.

The composition of all flies in the "pure" beaded stock may now be represented $\dfrac{l_{Bd}'}{l_{Bd}'} \dfrac{c'}{C'} \dfrac{L_{\text{III }1}}{l_{\text{III }1}} \dfrac{B_d'}{b_d'}$.

5. Investigation of the other dominant mutant factors of Drosophila showed that it is a phenomenon of general occurrence for dominant mutants to be lethal. There are nine dominant mutants known, excluding beaded and truncate intensifiers. The viability of the homozygote was known in the case of three (all sex-linked); the remaining six have been tested. The total enumeration shows that three of the nine factors are non-lethal, one is semi-lethal, and five are lethal. It is probable that lethals are more often found among the dominant mutants than among the recessives mainly because lethals have a better chance of being detected in the case of dominants, but perhaps also the dominants may on the whole exert more effect than recessives when they are homozygous, and therefore more harmful effect.

6. The lethal effect of B_d' not only explains why it was at first impossible to obtain pure stock of beaded, but also why stock that did breed true was finally secured; for if lethals are fairly frequent in occurrence (as there is good reason to believe) the selection of stock containing as high a proportion as possible of one lethal auto-

matically tends to the establishment of a race containing another lethal in the opposite chromosome. In general the condition of balanced lethals should tend to arise whenever a "beneficial" lethal factor (one that is selected for) already exists.

7. Although $l_{\text{III } 1}$ is the first lethal recessive factor found in autosomes of Drosophila, the evidence from sex-linked lethals, lethal dominants, and theoretical considerations, makes it probable that such factors form a large proportion of the factors arising by mutation. Hence they should be found to have arisen in any chromosome region that has been protected for a long time from the action of natural selection. The chromosomes involved in a case of balanced lethals are so protected by each other, and the Y chromosome is so protected by the X; chromosomes of stocks continually outcrossed or kept heterozygous are also removed from selection. In all these cases, then, lethal factors, and undesirable mutant factors of other sorts, would gradually accumulate in the affected chromosomes. Besides this, evolution of the species would be hindered in these cases by the fact that recessive mutant factors of a beneficial nature could not be selected for. It has been shown in the text, however, that if the race containing balanced lethals persisted very long, the degenerative processes themselves might cause it finally to revert to a condition of normal genetic behavior, in which each of the originally balanced chromosomes would be represented by an independent pair.

8. In out-crosses of the balanced lethal stock of beaded with other races *twin hybrids* and *constant hybrids* are produced, according to the Mendelian expectations for these cases. By the introduction of other factors into the affected chromosomes these results were made more striking. Balanced lethal stocks were obtained containing in heterozygous condition recessive factors that never came to light except on crossing, or as a result of a rare crossing over from one of the lethals. In the latter case *mutation* was simulated. The parallel results that have been obtained with Oenothera indicate clearly that this, too, constitutes a complicated case of balanced lethals. In double-flowered stocks there is a very similar situation.

9. Unusual and apparently non-Mendelian results of various other sorts can be, and have been, made to order with beaded flies. For example, it was possible to cause the total disappearance, on crossing, of a dominant character present in one of the parents, and its complete absence from all subsequent generations. Unfortunately for the geneticist who is still "open-minded" about the strict genotype interpretation of heredity, the Mendelian machinery at work here is quite transparent, owing to previous analysis. But of course one may always have recourse to taking the end results purely at their face value, as it is sometimes urged that, after all, we are concerned with facts, and that factors are merely concepts.

10. The apparently conclusive and unusually elaborate evidence of factor variability which the case at first presented has resolved itself, upon factorial analysis, into a quite different set of phenomena. This makes it imperative not to accept similar evidence in other cases until as complete genetic analyses have been made.

Theoretical objections to factor variability have also been presented.

Notes

[1] A blank above or below the line of course indicates that all the factors in the chromosome not represented are normal.

[2] Consequently, too, the larger the character change caused by a mutation, the greater would be the likelihood of the mutation being disadvantageous or lethal.

[3] Sex-linked lethals may be discovered only in females which are bred and among whose progeny a sex count is taken; "visible" sex-linked mutant factors, on the other hand, may be discovered in males by inspection. Since for each female that is bred there are produced on the average at least 50 males that are inspected this will seem to make the chance of finding a visible mutant in the X chromosome 50 times greater than that of finding a lethal there; as the female, however, has two X chromosomes, both of which are tested in this process, and each male only one, the chances of finding a visible mutant in X are really about 25 times as great as those of finding a lethal. To find the true proportion of visible to lethal mutations that have *occurred* here we must therefore multiply the number of lethals found by 25. This calculation applied to the above figures makes the occurrence of lethals about *six times* as frequent as that of "visible" mutations.

[4] It might be urged that the lethal could mutate back to normal or to some non-lethal factor. But even if this tendency were as strong, on the average, as the tendency for the original normal factors to mutate to lethals, a condition of equilibrium would not be established, wherein mutations in either direction were equally frequent, until half of the normal factors had been transformed into lethals. Until that time, then, lethals would gradually accumulate, and in the early stages of the "degeneration," reverse mutations would be so infrequent as to be negligible. It should be noted moreover that if the same tendency which made lethals revert also caused other factors to revert to an ancestral form, the occurrence of lethals would really be favored, for a normal factor on returning to an ancestral form would usually not be well adapted to the life complex of the existing race, and so would tend to be lethal.

[5] 15,000 F_1 flies were examined by the writer, in a cross of $s_e\, s_s\, k\, e^s\, r_o$ (all in chromosome III) by $p_r\, c_v\, s_p$ (in II) but not one case of deficiency was found among them. Yet these crosses were so arranged that all deficiencies involving any one of the eight rather widely separated loci would be detected.

[6] The reasoning in detail is as follows: Chromosomes and regions of chromosomes having a certain genetic composition usually conjugate in a certain distinctive way (i.e., with each other only), regardless of what their derivation or previous history may have been. Now since the genetic composition of these chromosomes or regions has been, *ipso facto*, the only persistent feature which caused them to retain their individuality, it follows that it must be their own genetic composition which determines these

distinctive features of their synapsis—i.e., how and with what they shall conjugate. That is to say, the genetic factors situated in each particular chromosome-segment cause a specific attraction between it and another chromosome-segment containing like factors. This means that the factors themselves or local products of them, attract each other, like for like. Of course there is no experimental evidence to prove that these genetic factors for synapsis are the same as the factors for the visible characters, but certainly there must be such "synapsis factors" present in every region of the chromonema, as shown by the exactness of the apposition which occurs. Moreover, these factors must, like the factors for visible characters, be subject to mutation, else they could never have become differentiated. This being true, the factors determing synapsis which are present in a balanced pair of chromosomes must gradually diverge more and more from one another in character, and so the synaptic attraction between the chromosomes of that pair will be weakened.

[7] Exception must be made of the special case in which the lethals are gamete lethals and dominant to their normal allelomorphs. In such a case, as all gametes would now receive the lethal, every gamete of the sex affected by that lethal would be killed.

[8] It is interesting to note that in tetraploid forms there would be a tendency for a series of changes to occur in the ordinary chromosomes similar to those occurring in balanced pairs. Groups of four would tend to differentiate into separate pairs, which would "protect" each other from selection; originally similar pairs would thus tend to undergo unlike degenerative changes, until they no longer protected one another, when degeneration would gradually cease, and selection of progressive mutants would at the same time gradually set in again.

[9] The occurrence of C' in the chromosome with $l_{III\,1}$ does, however, seem to be an exceptional coincidence, not referable to either of the two circumstances named.

[10] Although it is likely that the size of any particular gene is determined by a certain equilibrium point towards which its growth reactions tend, nevertheless we cannot, as in simple cases of mass action, consider all the genotypic material of a certain kind present in the cell as a whole, and say that this will tend to approach a certain amount, for the *total* amount is also dependent on the number of "units" of this gene that are present in the cell. Thus, if two units, or "doses," are present, there will be a different amount of genotypic material produced in the cell than if there is only one, as indicated by the different results produced by the sex factor, according to its dosage, and by the factors in a certain chromosome of Oenothera which in three doses cause the *lata* form and in two the *Lamarckiana*. Observations on the relative sizes of homologous chromosomes when they may be present in cells in varying numbers proves that the same principle holds here (thus each of the two sex chromosomes in a female is just as large, relatively, as the single one in an XO male), but of course one cannot surely argue from the size of the visible chromosome structure to that of the factors contained in it. We may therefore conclude that the growth of each individual gene and chromosome is carried on until a certain equilibrium point is attained, but that this equilibrium amount for any one gene or portion of a chromosome is more or less independent of how much material of this same sort is already present elsewhere in the cell. These principles appear to hold for the *visible structure* of chromosomes in Federley's crosses of butterflies, where different numbers of chromosomes may be present, some of which may have been reduced in size by a double division during maturation, but where all chromosomes nevertheless eventually attain the normal size.

THE GENETIC BASIS OF TRUNCATE WING—AN INCONSTANT AND MODIFIABLE CHARACTER IN DROSOPHILA*

Edgar Altenburg
The Rice Institute, Houston, Texas
and
Hermann J. Muller
Columbia University, New York City

The Initial Selection Experiments and Crosses

One of the first mutants which Morgan found in Drosophila was a fly with truncated wings. It appeared in 1910, in a stock having beaded wings, and the inheritance of truncate, like that of beaded, seemed from the first to be irreconcilable with Mendelian principles, or indeed with any theory of fixed and segregating factors.

The truncate and the beaded cases thus stood as a constant challenge to those workers who hoped for a completely rational explanation of inheritance in Drosophila. Beaded has been dealt with in another paper; the truncate case will be considered here.[1]

* * * * *

Applications of the Methods

It is believed by the authors that the general method of attack developed in the truncate case,—whereby, by the use of "identifying" genes, a refractory character may be taken apart, put together, or held in a desired combination—will become of more widespread applicability as the linkage groups of the organisms commonly used for genetic study become better known. Since a large part of the work on truncate was carried out nearly seven years ago this general method has already had a chance to be tried out rather extensively in Drosophila work, and it has been used with success by students of this organism in a considerable number of problems, some of which have been reported in the literature.

In the case of other organisms, however, it will be necessary to know and have the use of identifying factors in the various linkage groups concerned, before the present method can be used at all. Moreover, certain modifications are necessary in the case of organisms that have crossing over in both sexes, and also in case the

Genetics, January, 1920, 5: 1–59; pp. 1, 2 (part), 51–59 included.

character to be studied is recessive. In either of these circumstances, it will be desirable to have two identifying factors in each chromosome involved, one on each side of the factor under investigation,—in order to make sure that the factor has not crossed over from its identifier.

Remote as the possibilities of such work may seem to be in the case of such animals as mammals, it is nevertheless difficult to conceive how the genetic bases of the more elusive and complicated characters in them can be determined adequately by any other means. Even in the case of man, an attempt in such a direction would be justified, for here the most important characters,—such as the psychological ones,—are perhaps more plastic, obscure, and complicated in genetic basis, than any others in the entire animal kingdom, and it would seem next to impossible ever to give any real Mendelian analysis of most of them without studying them by the method of linked identifying factors. In place of controlled crosses, and large families, however, reliance would here have to be placed on finding, by means of wide examination of data, a sufficient number of crosses of similar type, and then seeking in them the requisite identifying factors.

It would accordingly be desirable, in the case of man, to make an extensive and thorough-going search for as many factors as possible that could be used in this way, as identifiers. They should, preferably, involve character differences that are (1) *of common occurrence*, that are (2) *identifiable with certainty*, and that are (3) *heritable in a simple Mendelian fashion.* It seems reasonable to suppose that in a species so heterozygous there must really be innumerable such factors present, if only an examination of the inheritance of *small, definite physical traits*[2] were made on a large scale. As the study of such factors should naturally be accompanied by an examination of their inheritance with relation to each other, a knowledge of their grouping would at the same time gradually become available. All this would of course require very detailed and intensive work (rather, perhaps, than a superficial study of numerous individuals), and as yet little work has been done that is of this character. For, hitherto, the study of factors which are inconspicuous, or unimportant in actual life, has been largely avoided, in order to make an immediate and direct attack on the more important, more difficult characters. Now, as any two parents of a human family would probably differ nearly always in a very large number of factors, it would not be at all surprising if it were found that there were usually differences in one or more identifying factors in the case of any given one of the twenty-four (±) pairs of chromosomes. Thus, if a far-reaching investigation of definite physical traits were carried out first, then, when investigation of the more difficult characters was later undertaken, the requisite identifying factors, suitably arranged in the appropriate chromosomes, would probably be found, in many crosses, ready provided for the study of the more complicated and important trait.

The implication is not intended that no results of importance in human genetics can be attained by simpler methods; it would of course be desirable to carry on such studies at the same time as the more rigorous ones, but the inconclusiveness of the pedigrees of most important human characters, when studied directly, and their resemblance to the early pedigrees in the truncate case, indicates that nothing like an adequate understanding of the intricacies of inheritance in man can be reached without some such far-reaching and difficult plan as that just outlined. Meanwhile, too, partial knowledge of "identifiers" would be of partial help, in the larger problems.

However the situation may be for human genetics, it does seem clear that in the more tractable organisms, such as the domesticated and laboratory races of animals and plants, character analysis by means of linkage studies with identifying factors will come into more general use, both for the investigation of general problems and for the dissection of particular characters.

Resumé
The general hereditary behavior of truncate

1. Truncate is a variable character, appearing in all grades between short-truncate and normal wing. Some normals are almost always thrown, even by the "best" truncates, and it was found impossible, through four years of selection, to secure a permanent stock that threw no normals, although the proportion of the normals was reduced to about 10 per cent, and the average grade of the truncates which did appear was increased markedly at the same time.

2. This variation is not only somatic, but also genetic, for in the selected truncate race the high-grade truncates that appear throw relatively more and "better" truncates than do the intermediates, and the latter in turn greatly surpass the normals in this respect. It is thus possible, in the final stock, to modify the average grade and percentage of truncates back and forth by selection, within the limits above stated.

3. When truncate is crossed to the wild-type fly it behaves as an incomplete recessive, the great majority of F_1 being normal, but a small percentage of flies that show some truncation usually appearing also. The ratios in F_2 vary greatly with individual pairs of F_1 flies, ranging from nearly four normals to one with truncation through various values down to over 100 normals to one truncate, while some of the F_2 families contain no truncates at all. The percentage of truncates in F_2 is higher if the P_1 truncate was a female, but in either case the truncates in F_2 consist of both males and females in comparable numbers. The extracted F_2 truncates throw

about two normals to one truncate but can often be improved by selection until they reach the limit shown by the selected stock.

4. It was found that on crossing to flies with black body-color (recessive), truncate behaves as a dominant, and manifests itself in some degree in nearly all of the F_1 flies that carry it. Two heterozygous factors, ordinarily recessive, may thus reenforce each other so that one becomes a dominant. Similar results were obtained in crosses with bar-eyed flies, and with star-eyed flies, but bar and star are both dominants themselves.

The dissociation of the truncate genotype

1. Truncate was crossed to stock having black body-color (chromosome II) and pink eye-color (chromosome III). In this cross, truncate could be used as a dominant (since black is present), and F_1 truncate males were back-crossed, separately, to black pink. In this way flies having all possible combinations of the chromosomes present in the truncate stock were obtained, and could be recognized, according to their sex, body color, and eye color, these latter being used as "identifying factors" for the chromosomes containing them. By then studying the amount of truncation in the flies having the different combinations, the effect of each of the chromosomes of the truncate stock, on the truncate character, could be determined. The following results were arrived at:

(a) There is a chief factor for truncate (T_2'), lying in the second chromosome; flies having only T_2', in heterozygous condition, and no other mutant factor for truncate, may occasionally have truncated wings. T_2' is partially dominant.

(b) The third chromosome of truncate stock also contains a mutant factor or factors for truncate, which may be designated as T_3'. This acts as an intensifier of T_2', and when it is heterozygous at least it produces no visible effect on the wing unless T_2' is present.

(c) These crosses, when made in both reciprocal forms, showed that there is a similar intensifier, T_1', in the first (X) chromosome, which intensifies truncate to about the same extent as does T_3'. When both intensifiers T_1' and T_3' are present they have a summative action. T_1' like T_3', produces no visible effect unless T_2' is present. T_1' is partially dominant, under the conditions of these experiments (with black present).

2. Crosses of truncate flies lacking T_1', obtained in these experiments, showed that the truncate character is also influenced by sex ("sex-limited"), in that it manifests itself more readily in females than in males.

3. Flies from these experiments, that were known to contain T_1' and T_3', but lacked T_2', were crossed with each other. As no wing modifications were produced, it was evident that both T_1' and T_3' together, in the absence of T_2', cannot cause truncation, or any visible effect on the wing, even when opportunity is given for them to become homozygous.

4. It was found possible to resynthesize truncate, according to calculation, from the flies of the non-truncate or imperfectly truncated classes of the dissociation experiment. Flies were chosen for mating together which were scheduled, by their identifying factors, each to contain factors for truncate that were missing in the other. High-grade truncate then appeared in the offspring in the classes expected to contain it. This result furnished a confirmation of the conclusions from the dissociation experiment, and showed that the flies of the non-truncate classes had received the factors for truncate which they were supposed to have, and transmitted them regularly to their descendants.

5. In the crosses just mentioned, T_3' was sometimes introduced through the mother, sometimes through the father. The slightly lower grade of truncation, when T_3' is derived from the mother, indicates that T_3' is multiple in composition, consisting of two or more factors that may cross over from one another in the female.

6. Similar tests with T_2' indicated that this includes only one factor (at any rate one dominant factor).

7. It was found in later crosses that this "chief factor," T_2', is located in the "left-hand" end of the second chromosome, about 12 units to the right of star.

8. Experiments involving, in addition to black and pink, a fourth-chromosome factor, bent, showed that the truncate stock does not contain an intensifier in chromosome IV. In these latter experiments the distribution of the entire germ plasm was under observation.

Tests of the constancy of the factors for truncate

1. Individual tests were made of brother and sister flies from the F_2 count of the "dissociation experiment," which could be seen, by their identifying factors, to have received from their father a given chromosome combination,— $T_1'T_2'T_3'$ in the case of the sisters, $T_2'T_3'$ in the case of the brothers. The tests showed that the differences in truncation between the flies having a given combination were not genetic; that is, the flies which receive the same chromosome combinations from their parents contain identical factors for truncate. It must be concluded from this that the factors for truncate follow exactly the distribution of the chromosomes, and that they do not undergo fluctuating variation.

2. A "pure-line" experiment was then undertaken, by repeated back-crossing of males of the above sort $\left(\dfrac{T_2' \cdot B}{b} \dfrac{T_3' \cdot P}{p}\right)$ to black pink females. In each generation, in such a cross, males with the same truncate combination as their father are again produced, and may be recognized by their identifying characters (gray body and red eye-color). These are then mated, as before, to black pink females from stock, and so the process may be repeated indefinitely. The danger

of recombination is here excluded as effectually as in the case ot self-fertilizing or asexually reproducing organisms, and so the purpose of a pure-line experiment is fulfilled. Two lines of flies were carried on in this way,—a "high" or plus-selected line, for twelve generations, and a "low" or minus line, for thirteen generations. The selection was absolutely ineffective; this corroborates the conclusion derived from tests of brothers and sisters, and shows that the factors for truncate are constant, and entirely contained in the (three large) chromosomes. It proves at the same time that the factors for truncate are not contaminated by their allelomorphs in the heterozygote.

The continual genetic variation occurring in the truncate stock must therefore be due to recombinations of factors for which the stock is perpetually heterozygous.

The cause of the inconstancy of the selected stock

1. To determine the reason for this perpetual heterozygosis of the stock, tests were undertaken to discover whether T_2' could exist homozygously. As it was next to impossible to determine this by direct tests, T_2' was placed in a chromosome with b (black), and flies with this combination were crossed to others having T_2' bound to B (gray). 72 offspring which had received at least one T_2' were then tested, by back-crossing to black, to discover whether they contained both the T_2' with black and the T_2' with gray. None of them, however, had more than one of the T_2' factors, and the ratios showed that T_2' acts as a lethal when homozygous.

Thus T_2' resembles the majority of dominant mutant factors of Drosophila in being lethal when homozygous, and pure stock of it cannot be obtained.

2. It follows that crosses of truncates should yield 1 non-viable: 2 potential truncates: 1 normal. As in the selected stock much fewer than one third of the flies that hatched were normal, tests were made to see whether any of the normals that should have occurred had been caused to appear truncate by reason of some other, recessive, "chief factor" for truncate. It was found, however, that no such factor existed; consequently the deficiency of normals was due, not to their appearing truncate, but to their actual absence,—this means that they were prevented from hatching by a lethal factor, which must have lain in the chromosome homologous to that bearing T_2'. Occasional crossovers between T_2' and the lethal would give rise to a few normals, however.

It is thus evident that there is in truncate stock a condition of "balanced lethal factors," similar to that existing in beaded Drosophila, Matthiola, and Oenothera.

3. Reciprocal out-crosses of truncate stock showed that T_1' was present, homozygous, in viable, fertile flies of the selected stock.

4. Crosses of flies from the dissociation experiment were ar-

ranged in such a way that T_3' was given opportunity to become homozygous, while T_1' and T_2' remained heterozygous. Many of the flies thus synthesized were as high-grade truncate as the best in-bred stock, and much higher than the truncates from out-crosses. This proved that T_3', when homozygous, is not lethal, but that its effect on truncation is much stronger than when heterozygous. Fe-males of this composition are so infertile, however, that it would be next to impossible to maintain stock pure for T_3'. This explains the occurrence of low-grade truncates, and normals carrying truncate, in the selected stock.

The origin of the truncate complex

1. Truncate is one of the most frequent characters to appear sporadically, by apparent mutation, in various stocks of Drosophila. In most of these cases, however, intensifiers of truncate are absent, and so the possibility is not excluded that truncate was present pre-viously in the stocks, and merely failed to manifest itself before. In accordance with these circumstances it is usually found that the truncate fails to reappear in the descendants of such flies, except in a minute percentage of individuals.

When, however, truncate appears in stocks containing bar, or other factors which themselves intensify truncate, it may be con-cluded that truncate has here arisen as a real mutation. Several such truncates have been tested, and found to be inherited, and evi-dence was obtained that their mutant factor for truncate was identi-cal with T_2', the chief factor of ordinary truncate stock. None of the intensifiers of the ordinary stock were present, however.

2. The hereditary behavior of the original truncate shows that one of the factors for truncate had been present, undetected, in the parental long-winged stock, and that the appearance of truncate was due to the origin, by mutation, of a second factor. Thus the first truncate-winged fly contained T_2' and an intensifier. The other mu-tant factors of the truncate stock appeared later, and they were per-petuated through the process of selection, because they influenced the truncation in the direction desired.

It is of significance for evolution, as well as for genetics, that particular races may thus have pre-existing in them factors which by themselves are invisible, but which favor the manifestation of a certain character.

3. The occurrence of more modifiers for truncate than for most characters is explained not only by the fact that the modifiers were specially picked out by selection in the case of truncate, but also by the marked instability of the developmental reaction whereby the truncate character is produced. This instability, or susceptibility of modification, is disclosed by (1) the somatic variability of the char-acter, when the genotype is kept constant, and (2) by the number of mutant factors for other characters which act upon truncate in ad-

dition. On account of this modifiability it should happen that relatively many of the mutant genes which arise would be able to affect truncate, and it should therefore be easier to find either intensifiers or "inhibitors" for truncate than for most characters. The reason for the readier discovery of modifiers would hence be, not that the process of mutation is influenced in some way by truncate, but, on the contrary, that truncate is especially susceptible of being influenced by mutation.

The existence, in certain races, of factors like T_2', which make a certain character (here, the wing shape) more highly modifiable, may be of particular importance in evolution.

General applications

1. The results described in the first section of this resumé would undoubtedly have been regarded by certain writers as positive proof of the ineradicable fluctuability, miscibility, or, as it were, fluidity, of a unit character. The case was, in fact, more extreme than those upon which they rely as evidence for their doctrine. And yet it has been found that the inheritance of this character is entirely confined to the recognized chromosome system, and depends on definite chromosomal factors which are neither miscible nor inconstant.

Although mutations affecting this character may occur with somewhat greater frequency than those for many other characters, the mutations are not nearly of the order of frequency which would be necessary in order for them, by themselves, to give rise directly to a true genetic fluctuability. Practically all the genetic variability and modifiability of the stock is, on the contrary, due to the occurrence of recombinations among those mutant factors which have, on rare occasions, previously arisen, and variation due to a real new mutation, although possible, is highly exceptional. Even in such cases, moreover, the mutations do not all consist in variations of some one particular factor, but they may affect any one of many factors that are concerned with the character.

The use of cases resembling the truncate case, in order to support the doctrine of fluctuating variability of single unit-factors, is therefore entirely unjustifiable, in the absence of analyses comparable with those made in this case.

2. It is believed that the general methods developed in this case will become increasingly useful with the growth of knowledge of the linkage groups in organisms. It has been shown how, by the use of "identifying factors," any given genotype may be cut up for study, put together again in various ways, or held in a particular combination for the maintenance of stock or for observations on factor constancy. At the same time the distribution among the offspring, of the entire (chromosomal) germ plasm of a parent may be completely exposed to view.

The suggestion is made that such methods may also be necessary before much progress can be made in the study of the more important characters in human genetics.

Notes

[1]A preliminary account of the truncate case was given by the authors in the book of Morgan, Sturtevant, Muller, and Bridges (1915, pp. 191-194). Most of the crosses there reported were made in 1913.
[2]Or chemical, such as the blood agglutinins.

THE NON-FUNCTIONING OF THE GENES IN SPERMATOZOA*

(Abstract)

H. J. Muller and F. Settles
University of Texas

Comparison of sex ratios of over 4000 Drosophilae derived from fresh sperm with those of 1500 derived from sperm that had been retained over one week in the body of the female at 26°C. showed no significant difference. A few flies were obtained from sperm that had been retained in the female over three months at 10°C.; these also showed a normal sex ratio. These results (obtained in the winter of 1924-1925) prove that the genes distinctive of the X-chromosome do not function, while in the spermatozoa, to maintain the life and activity of the latter. It was also proved, by specially designed crosses (in a total count of over 4500 flies), that absence of an entire section of the second chromosome ('Translocation I') did not reduce the viability and activity of spermatozoa so constituted, as compared with normal spermatozoa, since neither increased age of sperm nor treatment with x-rays, nor both conditions together, caused a decrease in the number of flies from deficient as compared with normal spermatozoa. The conclusion follows that the genes in spermatozoa (unlike those in pollen) are in a dormant condition, the cytoplasm of the spermatozoa functioning like a watch running down and utilizing only material produced during the operation of the prematuration diploid nucleus. Selective action by either natural or artificial agencies, discriminating between spermatozoa of a given individual on the basis of their genetic composition, would hence be impossible, except in cases where there is an associated morphological difference between the spermatozoa.

Anatomical Record, 1925, 31:347.

EFFECT OF DOSAGE CHANGES OF SEX-LINKED GENES, AND THE COMPENSATORY EFFECT OF OTHER GENE DIFFERENCES BETWEEN MALE AND FEMALE*

by H. J. Muller, B. B. League and C. A. Offermann
University of Texas

As it has hitherto been uncertain whether "deficiencies" represent multiple mutations or actual losses, and as the loss hypothesis meets with some difficulty where males differ from "exaggerated" females, other means were employed to determine effect of dosage changes upon gene expression. Flies having normal genes and others having given mutant genes—e.g., scute-1, eosin, apricot, Bar, etc.—were X-rayed, and X-chromosome fragments containing these genes were thereby produced. The fragments were then used to provide additional doses of the genes contained, the work being checked by studies of the effect of hyperploidy for somewhat smaller fragments, not containing the loci in question, and by studies of effect of known losses of the loci (hypoploidy). In cases of all the mutant genes mentioned, and some others, increased dosage caused noticeably increased phaenotypic effect. Adding more of the recessive mutant genes mentioned caused change towards, or even beyond, normality; these genes therefore produce an effect similar to that of the normal allelomorph, but a lesser effect—"hypomorphic." However, Bar and certain other dominants—Hairy-wing, Blond— were found to produce "neomorphic" effects—i.e., different from the normal allelomorph.

The results show sexual dimorphism of eosin to be due solely to its dosage difference in male and female; it is not "sex-limited." Conversely, the comparative lack of sexual dimorphism of apricot and other genes studied is due to a *compensatory* influence of the dosage difference between the sexes in respect to other genes in the X-chromosome. The facts are of particular interest from an evolutionary standpoint.

*Anatomical Record, Vol. 51, December, 1931.

FURTHER STUDIES ON THE NATURE
AND CAUSES OF GENE MUTATIONS*

H. J. Muller
University of Texas, Austin,. Texas

On the Character of Mutations

Methods of Attacking the Problem of Whether Mutations Are Merely Quantitative Changes

Probably some geneticists would welcome the problematical connection between induced gene mutations and rearrangements, and between the latter and chromosome contacts, as evidence for the view that gene mutations, or at any rate those produced by irradiation, are merely due to losses or transfers—the latter in some cases perhaps involving additions—of chromosome material of a type previously present. They would take it as evidence for a presence-and-absence, or at any rate for a quantitative, interpretation of mutational changes. Perhaps they might now extend the interpretation to parts of genes, or sub-genes, in order to account for cases like the scute or truncate series, but, so far as any given kind of gene material was concerned, they would see in the mutation process only a mechanical loss or diminution of the gene, by subtraction of material from the chromosome, or—as they would have to say in the case of some reverse mutations, for example—an increase of the gene, such as might be caused by its overgrowth or by the attachment to the chromosome of homologous material from a sister or homologous chromatid. Further plausibility is lent such a view by the fact that many allelomorphic series do give the phaenotypic appearance of being quantitative in their basis.

Fortunately X-rays provide us with a new tool which helps to shed light on these questions concerning the character of the mutations produced by them and by other influences. That is, we can induce gene rearrangements and so get fragments of chromosomes containing normal or mutant genes at given loci. We can then add or subtract such fragments, creating hyperploidy or hypoploidy, and can thus determine what the effects of changing the quantity of a given gene material really are. These known effects of purely quantitative changes may then be compared with the effects that were produced by the mutations themselves.

It has sometimes been assumed that one can judge the phaenotypic effect of different quantities of a gene simply by comparison of the appearances of heterozygotes and of homozygotes of the two

*Proceedings of the Sixth International Congress of Genetics, 1932, 1: 213–55; pp. 231 (part)–52 included.

opposite types, or, as a greater refinement, by comparison of the different grades of heterozygotes in polyploids. However, the situation in these cases is hopelessly complicated by the fact that in the comparison of such types we deal not merely with a difference in the dosage of one allelomorph, but always with a simultaneous and opposite difference in the dosage of the other allelomorph, since we must always reckon with a *substitution* of one allelomorph for the other, when chromosome fragments are not added or subtracted. We cannot legitimately assume in advance of the evidence that either the one or the other allelomorph is a mere absence, and so we cannot tell to what extent the observed effects may be due to the changed dosage of the one, to what extent to that of the other allelomorph, or to an interaction process. For example, in a comparison of the homozygous eosin-eyed Drosophila, the intermediate colored eosin-white compound, and the homozygous white, it need not be assumed, *a priori*, that the eosin gene has the effect of producing color, and produces more in double dose. It might be assumed instead (or in addition) that the white gene inhibited color, and inhibited more strongly in double dose. It might even be conceived that both allelomorphs inhibited the pigmentation which genes in other loci tended to produce, but that white was a more effective inhibitor than eosin.

Stern (1929) used actual dosage differences of a given allelomorph in his determination that each additional dose of mutants of the bobbed series adds to bristle length, up to a certain limit. In his work, instead of a small chromosome fragment, the practically inert Y chromosome served to furnish the extra doses. Mohr and Bridges, in their studies on deficiencies, realized that they might be dealing with real dosage differences, but at that time other interpretations, such as a peculiar sort of chain mutation, were not excluded. In an attempt to answer this question, however, I have examined cases in which there were known to be actual losses of the same region as was involved in the above cases of deficiencies, and find the effects to be the same.

Thus, for comparison with the Notch-8 deficiency of Mohr (1919, 1923), in which a piece near the left end of the X chromosome, extending from the left of white (1.7) nearly to echinus (5.5), is "deficient," we have certain cases of Patterson's (1932c) produced by X-raying. In these, a relatively large piece was removed from the left end of the X chromosome, though at the same time the very left end, which he has found (1932b) to be necessary for the life of the fly, was provided in advance, in the form of a fragment (called duplication X1 or "theta") attached to the right end. These known losses of the w-e_c region result in Notch wings, and allow recessives of the w, f_a and e_c loci, present in the homologous chromosome, to manifest themselves just as they would in a compound having them in one chromosome and the most extreme possible allelomorph of that sort in the other. I find females having apricot in one X chromosome and either white, Mohr's Notch-8 deficiency, or one of these known losses in the other, all to be indistinguishable from one another in shade. Again, to parallel Bridges' forked deficiency (1917), I have obtained, by X-raying special stocks, known losses in the region of forked, which allow forked in the other chromosome to show to an exaggerated degree. And Offermann and I, studying Burkart's (1931, 1932) Blond translocation, have been able to show that flies can be obtained from it which lack the right end of the second chromosome (this having been transferred to the X); in such flies the recessive speck, if present in the other second chromosome, manifests itself, and there is a plexus-like venation, as in Bridges' "Plexate deficiency."

There is now some evidence from Drosophila, but more especially from maize (McClintock 1931), that the two breaks in cases of double breakage within a chromosome may be at any distance apart, not being limited in their proximity by any principle of interference as rigorous as that which applies to crossings over. In view of this, and the above parallelisms, there can now be no reasonable doubt that the original proved "deficiencies" were small deletions, that is, actual removals of small regions, and so the studies involving them may now take their place definitely with the dosage studies. Later, I shall again refer to the results from this source. In the meantime, before the status of these deficiencies was established, I undertook, with the assistance of Miss League, purposely to produce fragments containing known genes, and to use these for studying the effects of dosage changes.

Hypomorphic Mutations

The first locus which we undertook to study was that of white-eye. We chose first flies containing the moderately pigmented mutant allelomorph of white called eosin, in which the color is considerably lighter than the normal red, and is distinctly sexually dimorphic, being much lighter in the male than in the female. By irradiation we produced a deleted X chromosome containing this gene. It was then found that the addition of this fragment to a male or female which was otherwise an ordinary eosin caused the eye color to become darker, more nearly like the normal red. This shows that the actual effect of the eosin gene is not to inhibit color, as might have been thought by comparison of it with red, but to produce color, since the addition of more of it results in more color,—*only it does not produce as much color as the normal "red" allelomorph does.* In the male, the addition of the fragment raises the dosage to two, and results in a color like that of the ordinary eosin female, which of course has two doses, while adding the fragment to the female, and so raising the dosage to three, results in a still darker color. This shows that the sexual dimorphism of eosin is due to the difference in dosage normally existing between the two sexes, and not to a difference in the action of the gene in male and female.[1] That the above observed results were not to be explained as effects of the excess dosage of other genes than eosin in the extra fragment was shown by producing a slightly smaller deleted X chromosome, not containing the locus of eosin, and repeating the same tests with it. It was found to have no effect upon the eye color.

The allelomorph of eosin known as apricot, which has a similar coloration except that male and female are alike, was then tried in the same way as eosin. It was thought that it might not show a phaenotypic effect of dosage changes, since the female with two doses looks like the male with one dose, but it responded similarly to eosin, additional doses darkening the color. Two doses of apricot in the male, therefore, give a considerably darker color than two doses in the female. Evidently it is the difference in dosage of other genes in the X chromosome of male and female which, interacting with the effect of apricot, causes the color, for a given dosage of apricot, to be darker in male than in female, in fact, just enough darker so that one dose in the male gives about the same phaenotype as two doses in the female. The same is presumably true of most of the other members of the white series of allelomorphs, which, except for eosin and ivory, look nearly the same in the two sexes.[2] The important thing for us now, however, is that apricot, like eosin, is a mutant gene which produces an effect similar to that of the normal allelomorph, but a lesser effect. That is, it works in the same direction (towards the same *superficial* end result) as the normal allelomorph, but not so strongly. It is, *in this sense,* like a lesser-normal. I therefore call it a "hypomorphic" mutant.

The above results agree perfectly with the findings of Mohr that if either apricot or eosin is in one X chromosome of a female, and the other X has Notch-8 deficiency, which includes a deficiency for this locus, the color is lighter than in the homozygous female. As mentioned above, the same result was obtained when this part of one X was known to have been removed by X-rays. Thus, one dose of this gene produces an effect less like normal than two, and two doses less than three.

Similar tests involving known additions or losses of fragments, or both, were then applied to genes in a number of other loci. A deleted fragment containing the gene scute-1 was first produced and was used to study the effect of increased dosages of scute-1, a gene which is said to "remove" certain bristles. (See, for example, Sturtevant in these *Proceedings.*) As with apricot, eosin, and bobbed, so here, the addition of an extra dose of scute in male or female made the individual more nearly normal, in this case almost completely normal, while the presence of two extra doses tended to result in slightly more of certain bristles than are present in the normal. Scute-1 is therefore a hypomorph. It does not "remove" bristles, except by comparison with normal. It produces them, though not as efficaciously.

In line with this conclusion derived from hyperploids, Agol (1932) found, by the use of a chromosome (from scute-19) from which we knew the extreme left end, containing the scute locus, had been removed, that a female with just one dose of scute-1 has fewer bristles than one with two. The test of the effect of underdoses, as seen in hypoploids, is obviously as valid and informative regarding these problems as the test involving overdoses in hyperploids. What Mohr has named the "exaggeration phenomenon" shown by deficiencies is, then, in our terminology, the lesser effect of one dose of a hypomorphic gene than of two doses. By this test the other mutant allelomorphs of scute, in which other groups of bristles tend to be absent, are also hypomorphic, as Agol (1932) found; facet is hypomorphic, as shown by Mohr's deficiencies and Patterson's cases of known losses; and forked is hypomorphic, as shown by my experiment previously cited. In elucidation of the test for forked, it may be explained that in this experiment females were made up which possessed one entire X bearing forked and having attached to its right end an extra piece consisting of the region from Bar to the right end; these females also possessed another X that had contained the scute-8 inversion but that had had the distal ("left") end of this chromosome removed up to a point between forked and scalloped. Hence all regions were present in double dose except a small region between scalloped and Bar, containing the forked locus. These haplo-forked hypoploids were markedly forked, phaenotypically.

Tests thus far indicate that most mutant genes (both spontaneous and induced) are hypomorphs, inasmuch as they show "exaggeration" with deficiencies, as Mohr has pointed out, or at least give a form having about the same degree of abnormality as the homozygous mutant. The latter relation would be expected in cases like white eye, where the mutant gene had nearly reached the bottom of the scale of effectiveness and hence itself had almost as little normal effect as the deficiency had. This latter type of mutant may, descriptively, be called "amorphic."

These hypomorphs and amorphs are just the kind of mutants which the few remaining advocates of the presence-and-absence hypothesis, and the advocates of purely quantitative mutation, require as evidence for their views. It should be noted, however, that their having a lesser effectiveness than the normal allelomorph by no means proves that they themselves involve material losses. They may consist of partial inactivations, or they may give rise to processes that lead in a somewhat different direction, and hence do not work so effectively in the observed direction, or they may involve conflicting tendencies. Moreover, a given mutant allelomorph (whether spontaneous or induced) may be very hypomorphic, or practically amorphic, in regard to one kind of activity of the normal gene, and normal or nearly normal in regard to another kind of activity. This is well exemplified in the scute series, in which each different allelomorph acts hypomorphically only in respect to its own peculiar combination of bristles, and is normal or nearly so in its action on other bristles. Since, in a comparison of different allelomorphs, the amount or intensity of effectiveness may vary separately from the types of effect, and both of these in turn may vary separately from the number or extensity of the effects, advocates of the quantitative view would here be driven to admit the existence of various parts of the gene and to assume that these parts could vary quantitatively more or less independently of one another. This would be a distinct retreat from the simple hypothesis of quantitative variation of the gene as a whole.

Whatever the explanation of hypomorphism may be, it is of interest to observe that the finding that most mutant genes are of this type conforms to Wright's contention (1929; see also Muller 1928b, pp. 259-260) that gene mutations should in the majority of cases involve more or less inactivation of the processes governed by the normal gene, and that these less active genes should more often act as recessives to the normal than as dominants. This implies that one dose of the normal gene usually has an effect more nearly like that of two doses than of no dose. Whether the latter principle is a primary one, however, or is due to the past selection of modifiers, is another question.

On the Compensation of the Effects of Dosage Differences between the Sexes, and on Dominance

In the above connection, it will be worth while to make somewhat of a digression, to consider a curious fact that has emerged from the results concerning hypomorphs. That is, it appears that in the great majority of the cases of hypomorphic sex linked genes, one dose in the male produces about as strong or at times even a slightly stronger effect in the direction of normality than do two doses in the female. This must of course be due to the interaction of other genes in the X chromosome, whose simultaneous change in dosage affects the reaction.[3] In some cases at least it has been possible to show, by studies of the effects of different chromosome pieces, (a) that genes other than the genes for sex are acting as the "modifiers" in question, (b) that the modifiers responsible for the dosage compensating effect on different loci are to some extent different from one another, and (c) that more than one modifier may be concerned for a specific locus.[4] I base these conclusions on various results obtained in work of Offermann, who has been especially active in the study, of Patterson, and of myself.

We may for convenience call these genes "modifiers," but with the reservation that they may sometimes be as important in the causation of the phaenotypic effect as the "primary" gene whose mutations we have available for study. The essential relation is that, in so far as the amount of phaenotypic effect produced by this so-called "primary" gene depends on its dosage, it does not depend at all on the mere "concentration" of this gene in the cell, nor on the relation of its dosage to that of the other genes in general, still less to that of the autosomal genes, but solely on the ratio of its dosage to that of another specific gene or genes which lie in the same chromosome (the X). That a relatively high amount of intra-chromosomal interdependence in regard to dosage expression existed among sex linked genes was realized some time ago (Muller 1930b) and denoted as "intra-chromosomal genic balance." In that work, however, we were dealing with those relatively rare normal genes, or gene-combinations, which have a quite different effect, visibly, in one dose than in two. The present findings go much further, in showing the existence of a far stronger interdependence, and one which applies not just to a relatively few scattered genes but to the great majority of the individual genes in the X which can be sampled.

Now this great system of "modifiers," all acting to give a similar sort of effect, and probably affecting most of the genes of the X chromosome, must have a function. It cannot be that of giving the male *mutant* as strong, that is, as nearly normal, an expression of its mutant gene as the homozygous female mutant has. It must therefore be a system which acts on the normal allelomorph similarly to the mutant, but the action of which is more readily apparent to our eye in the mutant type. In most cases the normal gene gives, so far as our eye can perceive, practically the same effect in one as in two doses. Nevertheless, there must be some difference which, though imperceptible, is important for survival; otherwise this system of genic interaction would not be thus maintained to keep the same optimum degree of effect in both sexes, despite the different doses. It follows that the dominance of the normal gene over its "absence" is really far from perfect, physiologically (that is, that one dose is not really as effective as two), though it may seem so to the casual genetic observer, and that by selection a system of interacting genes has become established such that the expression of the one dose in the haplo X type is like that of the double dose in the two X type. Bobbed, being present in double dose in male as well as in female, is, *as expected*, an exception to this rule of dosage compensation, in *Drosophila melanogaster*. In *Drosophila simulans*, on the contrary, bobbed does show dosage compensation, and here it is found, correspondingly, that the male carries only one dose of the "normal" allelomorph (the Y being sometimes neutral and sometimes actually "antimorphic" in effect—see page 245—as shown by results of Sturtevant [1929]).

The question may here be raised: Why were the normal allelomorphs of most of the sex linked genes other than the bobbed of *D. melanogaster* ever "lost" from the Y chromosome if their absence was so deleterious as to require the subsequent evolution of this complicated compensation system? The case of the Y of *simulans* shows that they can be thus "lost," or, better to say, changed in expression like a loss, and this would seem to point to the importance of *accidental* multiplication, not guided by selection, as an occasional evolutionary process. It may be, however, that most of the genes in the X, unlike bobbed, never were present in the Y, in anything like their present form, at least; that is, that the male has had but one dose of them from the beginning of their existence as such. In that case, they must have arisen either as duplications, as "neomorphs" (see page 117), or both, after the present sex-determining system had already become established. This question might be answered definitely by genetic analysis in a species in which we knew that a part of the X had been derived from an autosome (for example, *D. hydei* or *"obscura"*?).

The existence in the X of "modifiers" of such a specific kind that, by their change in dosage, they modify the amount of effect of other sex linked genes to the extent required to make the male and female alike, indicates that specific modifiers of gene action are plentifully available. In the case of some of the sex linked genes arising in the manner last suggested (so as to have existed in different dosages in the two sexes from the start) it is possible that the dosage compensation did not result from the selection of mutations in these modifiers but that the "primary" genes themselves were so selected at the time of their origination as to be, *ab initio*, adapted in their action to the other, pre-existing genes in the X which we now call "modifiers." And even when the compensation did not thus exist from the start, it is likely that the inter-adaption of primary gene and modifier did not always occur through changes in the modifier alone but also through changes in the primary gene that made the latter sensitive to the modifier (such changes in the primary gene as would be involved in the mutation of eosin to apricot, for example). Thus, where there is only one modifier causing the dosage compensation of a gene that did not have this property to begin with, the chances seem *a priori* to be equal that the dosage compensation arose (if by one step) by a further change in the primary gene itself, or by a mutation in the modifier; the greater the number of modifiers, the larger the rôle that their mutations have probably played in the process, as compared with mutations in the primary gene. We should also remember that mutations could also take place in other genes, for example, autosomal genes, which would serve to bring the primary gene and the modifier into the reciprocal relation with one another which they now have. But, however all that may be, the results do give evidence of the availability of "modifiers," or, to put it more precisely, of mutations which cause certain specific types of nicely adjusted genic interaction, favorable for survival, and not having this survival value too much obscured by pleiotropic effects.

The above conclusion would appear to lend support to Fisher's theory of the origin of dominance, inasmuch as on that theory, too, specific modifiers (albeit of a somewhat different kind), without important other effects of their differences from their own parent genes, are called for. It would also allow us to adopt to a certain extent the suggestions of Haldane, concomitantly. There is, however, an important difference between the mechanism of selection for dosage compensation here studied and that postulated either by Fisher or by Haldane for the modification of dominance. For in the former the selective moment, if I may call it so, exists throughout the population, while in the latter it is supposed to be limited to a comparatively small minority. Thus the difficulty is encountered that the pressure of the selection in question may be too small, as compared with that of mutation, or of the selection for even very weak pleiotropic effects.

I believe that the above difficulty can be avoided and a better case made out for the origin of dominance by selection if we assume that this selection has had a somewhat different mechanism from that previously postulated. I prefer rather to postulate that the mutations favoring dominance—the genes or genetic conditions which tend to make the heterozygote like the homozygote—have been selected and are maintained not so much for their specific protection against heterozygosis at the locus in question as to provide a margin of stability and security, to insure the organism against weakening or excessive variability of the character by other and more common influences—environic and probably also genetic. These modifiers must so affect the reaction set going by the primary gene in question as to cause this gene, when in two doses, to be near an upper limit of its curve of effectiveness,[5] that is, in a nearly horizontal part of the curve, not so readily subject to variation by influences in general, *including* reduction in the dosage of the primary gene. This does not mean that the phaenotype is necessarily made any more extreme, for counter-checks can be set up. That is, the level of the curve as a whole and its shape, as well as the region wherein it approaches a horizontal limit, are also adjustable, by means of modifying mutations that reframe the conditions under which the reaction takes place. Such modification (see Ford 1930), and not merely an increase in potency of the "primary" gene, will be necessary in the numerous cases in which the curve of effectiveness did not, originally, approach the horizontal within physiologically acceptable limits (or did not do so at all).

It should be distinctly understood that the crux of the above view of the origin of dominance lies in the proposition that, where a change in gene dosage causes a perceptible change in its phaenotypic expression (that is, when it is in a noticeably sloping part of its "curve of effectiveness"), it is likely that the degree of expression of the character will be modifiable to an unfavorable extent by environic and by other genetic changes. This seems reasonable, a *priori*, inasmuch as some of the disturbing influences would be expected to act by altering the reaction in a way similar to that whereby the change in gene dosage would alter it, and hence would tend to be similarly effective.

But we need not rely on *a priori* reasoning alone. There is a significant amount of experimental evidence already existing to show that there is considerably more phaenotypic variability in the expression of hypomorphic mutant genes than of their normal allelomorphs. Now, these hypomorphs evidently cause a reaction of a type similar to that of their normal allelomorphs, but a weaker or lesser reaction, one which, unlike that of the normal allelomorphs, is much affected by dosage changes. This variability is true of all the known hypomorphs yet studied: namely, all the hypomorphs of the scute series, the white series, the forked series, and the bobbed series (excluding the amorphs, which afford a converse test of the same proposition). The same variability applies also, as we should expect, to the effect of normal allelomorphs in single dose in those relatively rare cases in which the single dose has a perceptibly different (that is, lesser) effect than two: these cases comprise Notch wings, Plexate venation, and several Minute bristle conditions. All told, the evidence given above may be sufficient to show the truth of our proposition as a usual rule. It is not necessary to claim for it, nor do we believe that it has, the validity of a universal law.

In conclusion, we may call attention to the bearing of a further fact, derived from our study of dosage compensation, on the problem of dominance. We have seen that in all probability many of the normal genes in the X chromosome have this dosage compensation, despite the fact that, even in the female, there is hardly a perceptible difference between the effect of one dose and of two. This indicates that, even though the normal gene produces its effect in what appears to us to be a nearly horizontal region of its curve of effectiveness (where changes in dosage produce little discernible effect), nevertheless there is a distinct influence, unfavorable to the organism and perceptible in its survival rate, if the effect is made either slightly stronger or slightly weaker. The disadvantage of a stronger effect is shown by the fact that, in the female, the strength of effect has become fixed at so low a level as to call for dosage compensation. For in a sense the dosage compensation may as rightly be regarded as a means of keeping the female from having too strong an action of the gene as a means of giving the male a strong enough action. If twice as high potencies in the female were biologically acceptable, this relatively simple change should often have been utilized (that is, have survived) whereby the male would automatically have been provided with a sufficiently high potency to obviate the need for dosage compensation. We must conclude, then, that in the fixing of the conditions determining dominance too, it was not feasible merely to increase the potency of the "primary" gene; instead, the characteristics of its curve of effectiveness had somehow to be altered.

Experimental evidence of a different nature, indicating that dominance is not a primary property of genes but must have become developed by selection, is given in the section on neomorphs (see page 120).[6]

Hypermorphic Mutations

We must now return from our digression, which has perhaps helped us to understand why hypomorphic mutant genes usually show dosage changes better than do the normal genes from which they were derived, and are recessive to the latter. The question next arises: are all mutant genes hypomorphic? This can be answered categorically in the negative.

Since it has been found that there are reverse mutations of hypomorphic mutant genes, such as scute, apricot, and forked, both spontaneously and as a result of irradiation, we must regard the allelomorphs thereby resulting not as hypomorphic but as hypermorphic to their immediate progenitor genes. Whether or not such a change involves a real increase of material is a doubtful question, subject to the same considerations as applied, conversely, to the hypomorphic mutations. Timoféeff-Ressovsky (1929, 1931a), as well as Patterson and myself (1930), has discussed in some detail the varying frequency of such changes for different loci and allelomorphs.

Now if hypermorphic changes of already mutant allelomorphs may occur, resulting in partial or complete reverse mutations, there might well be hypermorphic mutations of normal genes also, resulting in changes of a type opposite to that of our ordinary mutations. Usually these would be difficult or impossible to detect, on account of the fact previously referred to that two doses of the normal gene are already at nearly the maximum point in the curve of effectiveness. Thus such changes would be apt to escape observation. Very likely, however, Nasarenko's (1930) mutant "abrupt" is a hypermorphic mutation of the normal allelomorph of Notch, for it is at or near the Notch locus, and it and Notch deficiency counteract each other instead of showing an exaggeration effect.

Antimorphic Mutations

What evidence have we for other mutational changes than such as could be explained as mere diminutions and increases? The dominant (somewhat variegated) allelomorphs of brown eye in chromosome II are a case in point. When there is one dose of the recessive brown and one of the normal gene, the latter dominates and the phaenotype is red. But, as Glass and I have found (see Glass 1932), when to the above complex a dose of the dominant allelomorph of brown is added, the result is a brownish (somewhat variegated) color. It may be explained that this combination is produced by making up a fly that is a compound of recessive brown and dominant brown, and carries as excess a fragment of the second chromosome derived from Bridges' "Pale" translocation; this fragment contains the normal allelomorph of brown. The resulting brownish color shows us that the addition of dominant brown to a heterozygote of normal and recessive brown has a real effect and involves the addition of some kind of gene material different in its effect from the material in the normal gene. This effect, the color change, lies in the same direction from normal as does that of the recessive brown, as comparison of the colors indicates. This is shown more conclusively by the fact that while a hyper-diploid containing one dose of dominant brown and two of normal has practically normal red eyes, a hyper-diploid otherwise similar to the above but with a dose of recessive brown substituted for one of the normals has brownish (somewhat variegated) eyes—that is, the substitution of recessive brown in place of normal results in a better manifestation of dominant brown. But the recessive brown itself acts practically as an amorph, since the addition of a dose of it, as an extra, has practically no effect either on the incompletely brown color of the heterozygote of dominant brown and normal or on the red color of the heterozygote of recessive brown and normal. Hence the dominant brown represents something that differs from normal, in its effect, in the same direction as a loss does, but more strongly. In a sense, it has an actively negative value. More accurately, it has an opposite action to that of the normal allelomorph, competing with the latter when both are present.

A similar conclusion may be drawn with regard to the mutant gene ebony, of chromosome III. For, starting with a hyperploid containing two ebony genes and one normal (derived from translocation II-III26 — Painter and Muller 1929), as a basis of reference, we find that the subtraction of one ebony makes the color lighter, while the subtraction of the normal makes it darker. I would term such antagonistic mutant genes, having an effect actually contrary to that of the gene from which they were derived by mutation, *antimorphic*.

Abnormal abdomen may now be interpreted to be a member of this class, as shown by results in Mohr's experiments with Notch-8 deficiency. In the first place, it is to be observed that the gene for Abnormal produces a change in the same direction as a loss of the normal gene. This is shown by the fact that if we start with a heterozygous fly having one Abnormal and one normal gene (this is somewhat Abnormal in appearance), the substitution of a real loss (Notch-8 deficiency) for the normal gene in it intensifies the Abnormal abdomen character. But the Abnormal gene, though thus producing a change in the same direction as a loss of the normal gene, acts more strongly in this same direction than a mere loss does. This in turn is shown by the fact that homozygous Abnormal flies are still more Abnormal in appearance than are the compounds of Abnormal and deficiency. That is, the degrees of phaenotypic Abnormality, as found by Mohr, were as follows:

$$\frac{Ab.}{Ab.} > \frac{def.}{Ab.} > \frac{norm.}{Ab.} > \frac{norm.}{def.} = \frac{norm.}{norm.}$$

Since in the first three terms of the series the gene represented below was always the same, the observed differences prove the degree of abnormal effects to be in the order $Ab > def > norm$.

It may be mentioned that a recessive allelomorph of Abnormal has been produced by X-rays. It will be seen that in such cases the recessive mutant, though classifiable as an amorph or possibly a weak hypomorph, probably involves no mere loss of material, since what is apparently a still greater change in the same direction gives a gene which again has a demonstrably active influence.

Unless we make the very improbable assumption that the Y may contain other active genes than bobbed influencing the same character, we may also include among antimorphs the gene existing in the Y of most races of *Drosophila simulans* (see Sturtevant 1929) which (unlike the bobbed allelomorphs reported upon by Stern 1929) actually decreases the bristle length of males containing bobbed in their X. It is also possible that the genetic conditions designated as Minute 1^2 and Plexate include antimorphs—in fact, such is the conclusion which we should ordinarily draw from a recent report; on the other hand, an earlier report interprets these conditions as deficiencies (see Morgan, Sturtevant and Bridges 1927, and Morgan, Bridges and Schultz 1931). Possibly the apparent contradiction is due to the effect of dosage changes of other genes in the added fragments rather than to the genes in question (that is, an intraregional dosage interdependence). Fortunately, this possibility can rather easily be put to the test in these cases (in part at least), since a smaller fragment involving the region in question is available in the Blond translocation, and others can rather readily be manufactured. In the meantime, the "position effect" interpretation is not excluded here, nor is that of gene mutation accompanying breakage.

Neomorphic Mutations

Somewhat different from the negatively acting, competing mutant genes, or antimorphs, is the class which I am provisionally terming "neomorphs." A good example is the dominant mutant, Hairy wing, near the left end of the X chromosome. The homozygous Hairy wing female is about twice as hairy as the heterozygous Hairy wing female or the Hairy wing male (this constituting an exception to the dosage compensation rule for sex linked genes). The relatively low grade hairiness of the heterozygous as compared with the homozygous female, in this case, is due solely to the single dose condition of the gene for Hairy wing and not at all to a possible influence of the normal allelomorph in the heterozygote. For if a small piece containing this region be broken off of a normal X chromosome, and added either to the heterozygous or homozygous Hairy wing female or to the Hairy wing male, there is no diminution of the hairiness. On the other hand, if a small piece containing a Hairy wing gene be added to an individual otherwise normal, Hairy wing will show. The normal allelomorph thus fails to compete. It itself acts like an *amorph*, so far as its detectable effect on the character under consideration is concerned. Yet it is no mere absence; it has a material existence, for Hairy wing has arisen at the same locus several times (including at least twice by irradiation).

We must conclude from the above results that the mutation to Hairy wing does not result from an addition of material transferred from another locus (since the mutation always reappears at the same locus). It must rather be a change in the nature of the gene at the original locus, giving an effect not produced, or at least not produced to an appreciable extent, by the original normal gene. If the effect had been produced to some appreciable extent by the normal gene also, then the addition of a dose of the normal to the Hairy wing individual should have actually increased hairiness.

The fact that normal genes may thus act as amorphs with regard to a particular character affected by their mutations should serve as another warning against regarding mutant genes that seem to be amorphic or hypomorphic as really involving a mere absence or loss of material. The obtaining of reverse mutations from near-amorphs, such as eosin from white, gives further evidence for this conclusion.

The same kind of finding as above noted for Hairy wing—namely, lack of effect on the character when extra doses of the normal allelomorph are added—was observed by Offermann in studying the spontaneously arisen dominant, Blond, of Burkart. This interpretation holds only if we regard Blond as having its locus in the X chromosome. This is uncertain as Blond lies near the break of a mutual translocation involving X and II (see Burkart 1932), but as Blond follows the sex linked rule of dosage compensation it is in all probability in the X. We are, however, making sure of its neomorphism by testing also the effect of adding an extra dose of the suspected region of chromosome II.

Bar eye is a third neomorph. It is well known that Sturtevant has considered Bar as having no normal allelomorph, at least none at the same locus as itself. However, the recently reported finding, by

Dobzhansky (1932), of a second Bar-like mutation ("baroid"), induced by X-rays at the same locus as the old, indicates to me that this locus normally contains a gene that is subject to this particular type of mutation, although Dobzhansky still believes that the normal allelomorph was somehow transported there from another locus, at the time of the mutation. Bridges' original Bar-deficiency of 1915 (published upon in 1917), which we may now interpret definitely as a loss, shows that the absence of the Bar-locus in the non-Bar chromosome of a heterozygous Bar female has the same effect on the Bar eye character as the presence of the normal allelomorph itself, and Sturtevant's work on chromosomes which have lost the Bar locus by unequal crossing over is an indication in the same direction. (There is a possibility that in the origination of Bar a gene became duplicated *in situ*, and that one of the resulting twins mutated at the same time. On this rather special hypothesis the mutation would have been of the neomorphic type. But in that case the normals formed from Bar by unequal crossing over would not represent complete "absence.") On the other hand, increased doses of Bar give the abnormal effect more strongly, just as we find for Hairy wing and Blond, and unlike the situation in the case of hypomorphs.

While Thompson (1929) has raised some objection that we may here be adding and subtracting only a part of the gene, in getting these effects, this possibility is ruled out in some recent studies of Offermann using a strong allelomorph of Bar ("Super-Bar," B^s, found by Stone) that exists in a chromosome fragment. The addition of fragments containing the whole Bar gene had the expected effect of increasing the bar-like character of the eye in a clear-cut fashion. Offermann likewise proved that this result could not be due to the excess dosage of other genes in the piece. Bar, then, is a mutation of a normal gene, giving a gene that produces a new effect, foreign to the original gene, and not competing with the latter. It is very probable, however, that the new effect is in some way related to that of the normal allelomorph. For it is evident that Bar obeys the usual rule of sex linked genes, having the male, with his one dose, much more nearly like the homozygous female, with her two doses, than like the heterozygous female (see also the case of Blond, and note the contrast with that of Hairy wing).

A recently published mention by Morgan, Bridges and Schultz (1931) of the lack of effect of changes in dosage of a fragment containing the normal allelomorph of Bristle on the degree of expression of this second chromosomal dominant leads to the conclusion that it also must belong in the class of neomorphs.

It might yet be possible to evade the obvious conclusion that gene mutations, including those produced by X-rays, involve qualitative changes, changes in the kind of structure and not merely in the quantity of the gene or its parts. For it might be postulated that in all cases of neomorphs there was an imperceptible rudiment of the part which produced the effect in question, already present in the normal gene, and that this part merely became vastly increased in amount by the "mutation." Or it might be postulated that all such changes were "position effects," caused by gene rearrangements. While there are an exceptionally large number of rearrangements both among known neomorphs and antimorphs, there are cases— Hairy wing, Bristle, Dominant eyeless, Abnormal abdomen—which do not involve such changes, unless we suppose the rearrangement to be on such a minute scale as to escape detection. Both these paths of escape into the ultra-small would, however, be pure speculations, the burden of proof for which would rest upon the advocate thereof.

It does not seem to be a coincidence that more loci have yielded hypomorphs than neomorphs, and that even loci which have yielded neomorphs have done so with relative infrequency. These results, if corroborated by more extensive work, would speak for the correctness of the principle put forward by Wright (1929; see also Muller 1928b, pp. 259-260) that mutations having an effect in the direction of losses (that is, those that tend to be disorganizing and inactivating) should in general be more frequent than those causing increased or new effects. But while this principle is necessary as one basis for Wright's theory of dominance, it is not, alone, sufficient for a derivation of the latter; neither is it contradictory to the general viewpoint put forward by Fisher that the usual dominance of normal genes has been developed through natural selection. It is to be noted, further, that the hypomorphs tend to be recessive, and the neomorphs "dominant." This again is in line with Wright's view, but it is also in line with Fisher's (since any given neomorph originates so infrequently that there has been much less chance for selection to have affected its mode of expression), and it is still more in line with the idea previously offered (p.113), that selection has worked primarily towards the stabilization of the reactions of the normal, homozygous genes. (In the latter case, even rather frequently recurring neomorphs would tend to be dominant.)

When, however, we examine into the type of dominance found, we obtain a result of greater apparent significance. For while the recessiveness of the hypomorphs is usually fairly complete, as generally expected, *the "dominance" of the neomorphs is in most cases far from complete, being of the "intermediate" type.* Now this result is exactly what we should expect if dominance of the nearly complete type has been developed by selection (especially, if by the type of selection advocated on page 113), but it is a considerable surprise, in fact, it seems contradictory to the idea that such dominance is usually a primary property of the gene. It will therefore be important to examine further cases with reference to this question.

While we have spoken above of the general trends of the results, it should be emphasized that no absolute rules can be made with regard to the dominance of the different classes of mutants. A known loss like Notch-8, Plexate, and at least three known Minute bristle conditions, may be dominant or semi-dominant in its effect, and therefore an amorph or a hypomorph may be likewise. In these cases one dose of the normal gene has distinctly less effect than two. On the other hand, neomorphic genes may be so "weak" in their effect that two doses are required before they rise to the level of visible manifestation. This was very nearly true in the case of a certain Hairy wing mutant, and in the case of baroid in the female; under certain genetic conditions (for example, in the presence of Zeleny's modifier, called "emarginate") it was true of Bar itself, and under certain environmental conditions it was true of Abnormal abdomen. For the same reason, we cannot make absolute rules regarding the exaggeration of recessives and dominants by deficiencies. If the recessive or near-recessive should be a neomorph, like baroid, it will not show exaggeration by a deficiency; if the dominant should be hypomorphic, as in the case of the absence of coxal bristles in some scutes, it will be exaggerated by a deficiency. But the more usual case is the recessive hypomorph (for example, eosin, facet), which shows exaggeration, the amorph (like white) which shows no effect, and the semi-dominant neomorph (for example, Bar) and antimorph (for example, Abnormal), which show instead an apparent inhibition by a deficiency.

On our interpretation of most gene mutations as qualitative structural changes, even the distinction into classes above outlined is not an absolute one, and reflects rather the gene's final behavior than its real structure. So we may expect to find genes, for example, that are hypomorphic in one respect and neomorphic in another. Possible examples of this are scute-8, scute-12, and scute-M-4 (in deleted X 24); the two latter show certain semi-dominant Hairy wing effects, as well as hypomorphic scute characters, but it is as yet uncertain whether these effects are really referable to the same locus or represent group mutation or possibly effects of changed position.

Multiple Allelomorphs Forming Non-quantitative Series

There are already numerous cases known in which it can be shown that a given mutation has markedly changed a gene only in regard to certain of the effects which the original gene produced, while another mutation in the same gene changed it more pronouncedly in some other respects. This has been shown *par excellence* with regard to the various hypomorphic changes possible in the scute locus in the studies on scute allelomorphs carried on by the Moscow geneticists. One of their most important contributions lies in showing the richness of the different patterns of change possible in a given gene, since thus far very few of the numerous allelomorphs are indistinguishable from one another. That the tendency to certain kinds of groupings of effects on the different bristles is partly an expression of certain real features of gene structure, and will help us to understand the arrangement of gene parts, is also a reasonable conclusion.

Attempts to explain the matter in a simple quantitative way, as in Goldschmidt's criticisms, or by means of developmental relations, as in the Plunkett-Sturtevant-Schultz hypothesis of diffusion of influences from a center, fall in the face of the facts. We do not have time to mention the various logical difficulties which the latter hypothesis encounters in its actual working out. Suffice it here to say that a study of numerous gynandromorphs involving various scute allelomorphs has been carried out in our laboratory, chiefly by Patterson, and that the results show clearly that the development of bristles, in so far as it is under the influence of the scute gene, is not governed by one or a few centers, but is in its major features autonomous at the site of each bristle. On the other hand, later work throws grave doubt on the possibility of grouping all the effects into one exact line (this is equally against both the unmodified sub-gene hypothesis and the theories of Goldschmidt, Sturtevant, et cetera). And the evidence that such a line, if it represents gene parts in a one-to-one correspondence, may be cut without destruction of either piece, is still to be found.

This still leaves the locus of scute the most suitable yet found for the study of multiple allelomorphism and gene structure, and it leaves the sub-gene hypothesis, or some modification of it, as a possible interpretation, although the way is not as clear and easy as before. It will, I think, be profitable to follow the method there used, that of concentrating on intensive studies of the different kinds of mutations possible in individual genes, as induced by irradiation and otherwise.

Such studies as we have carried out on other loci than scute have shown somewhat similar phenomena, and in some respects amplify our view. For example, the cases now known are fairly numerous in which different recessive mutant allelomorphs of the same locus have effects which are to some extent, or almost wholly, different in their character or in their location on the organism. Thus, mutant allelomorph 1 may affect character A very much and B very little or not at all, while allelomorph 2 affects A little and B much. Such allelomorphs, when crossed, usually form a compound that is more normal than either. For, in respect to each character effect or body region, the more normal effect is usually the more dominant; that is, the compound is usually in each respect more like that allelomorph which has a more nearly normal effect on that character or region. This was evident, for example, in Emerson's (1911) allelomorphs giving different combinations (= patterns) of red *versus* white silk, cob, grain, et cetera, in corn. In Drosophila, the first case was that of the truncate series (Muller 1919, 1922b), which concerns not only different regions but different characters, and obeys the same rule throughout. Thus, in this case, the cross of vortex bristles by oblique wings was found to give a compound that was sensibly normal. To explain those members of this series which showed two or more of the effects at once, the interpretation of group mutation of neighboring but physiologically entirely distinct genes was early considered but it was rejected, chiefly because studies on the action of modifying genes as well as of "chief" genes at other loci showed the different developmental effects in question to be physiologically related. In this case, it was also observed that the groupings of effects of different allelomorphs fitted in with no linear series rule. The normal-appearing compound of achaete and scute-1 (found by Dubinin to be allelomorphs) falls under the same category as the vortex-oblique cross. So too may the normal compound of split bristles and recessive notch wings (Glass and Muller unpublished), and also certain effects observed by Dobzhansky (1930a) in the Stubble series of allelomorphs. The list could be considerably extended.

There are, however, exceptional cases, in which the compound is not more like the normal in respects in which the two allelomorphs differ. The best case of this is the appearance of leg-like antennae in the compound between aristopedia, which has such an effect, and its allelomorph spineless, which does not, as found by Sturtevant (1929). A few of the missing bristle effects in scute crosses show a similar tendency; so too does the extra bristle effect in crosses of split bristle and facet-eye (see below).

We now have to report exceptions of the opposite type also, namely, those in which the compound is more like normal in respect to effects in which both allelomorphs are similarly abnormal. One such case is that of lozenge-eye in combination with a particular spectacled-eye allelomorph of it. The compound has a practically normal eye but has the female infertility common to both, and their mutual allelomorphism is further shown by the fact each gives a distinctly mutant eye type when crossed with still other members of the series (see Patterson and Muller 1930, Agol 1930). Another case is that of the ommatidial disarrangement in split bristles and facet-eye. Both of these mutants cause ommatidial disarrangement, yet (as with spectacled and lozenge) the compound has a normal eye (Muller unpublished). Their allelomorphism is shown not only by their linkage but by their behavior with other mutual allelomorphs (notches) and by the appearance of extra bristles in the compound, as in split bristles by itself (see above). In such cases as these, we must draw the conclusion that the two allelomorphs, although acting on the very same body region, and having superficially similar effects on that region, nevertheless attain these effects through the intermediation of qualitatively different developmental processes. Further studies of the relations in such series are needed.

Ultimately, too, we must undertake the still more difficult study of the effects of successive mutations in the same gene, to discover, if possible, principles governing their continued evolution. Such evolution, as I see it, implies the possibility of qualitative change in the gene as a necessary condition. The foregoing illustrations, if taken together, afford, I believe, considerable experimental evidence for the existence of such a phenomenon, both as a natural occurrence and as a result of irradiation. And this conclusion remains likely no matter whether the mutational effects of irradiation are of a direct or an indirect nature.

For the rest, I fear that the present paper has raised far more questions than it has solved. But if some of these questions may thus have been opened to attack, our time may not have been wasted.

The author wishes to acknowledge with thanks the assistance of the Committee on the Effects of Radiation on Living Organisms, of the National Research Council of the United States, in the prosecution of experiments referred to in the foregoing.

Notes

[1]For this reason, eosin cannot legitimately be used as an indicator of sex in such experiments as those of Bridges, in which he sought to demonstrate the female character of haploid tissue. That the haploid tissue was dark eosin, as in a female, was doubtless due to the fact that one dose of eosin, with one dose of all other genes, involves the same ratio as two eosins in a diploid, and was not due to the tissue being female. In the present author's opinion haploid tissue of Drosophila containing but one X should in fact be female, but the matter cannot be demonstrated by the use of eosin as a sex marker.

[2]In a recent publication, Morgan, Bridges and Schultz (1931) include cherry among the strongly sexually dimorphic members of the white series. This was certainly not true of the original cherry (see Safir 1913). The present sexually dimorphic stock, labelled "cherry Abnormal," contains neither cherry nor Abnormal abdomen, but is doubtless an ordinary eosin that either displaced the cherry by contamination or was mislabelled.

[3]We arrived at our main results and conclusions regarding this phenomenon of dosage compensation in the spring of 1930. Although we communicated our results to Doctor Stern at that time (prior to the remarks made by Stern and Ogura 1931, upon this topic), we withheld our preliminary report (Muller, League and Offermann 1931) until after certain checks had been carried through.

[4]Judging by certain results recently reported by Morgan, Bridges and Schultz (1931), the second-chromosome mutation Pale (associated with Bridges' original translocation) has, in addition to a "diluting" effect, an effect on the different eye colors of the white series similar to that produced by lessening from two doses to one the gene or genes in the X chromosome that are responsible for the dosage-compensation of most members of this series (thus, those allelomorphs of white that are lighter in the male are lightened by Pale, but the others are darkened somewhat). This means that the chemical process affected by Pale is the same as, or in its effect similar to, that affected by the dosage compensator(s) of the X; but, since we have seen that there is no reason to identify the latter with the gene or genes in the X that decide sex, we have no reason to agree with the

suggestion of the above authors that "the translocation (Pale) may be closely connected with the sex-determining reaction."
[5]That is, the curve expressing the relation of amount of phaenotypic effect (the ordinate) to the amount or concentration of gene material (the abscissa)—a curve which must usually, in its right-hand portion, rise with ever decreasing slope, approaching a horizontal limit, as seen, for instance, in Stern's studies on bobbed and in ours on scute and apricot.
[6]I am indebted to Doctor C. R. Plunkett for calling my attention to the fact that in a paper (1932) presented independently to the same congress he has espoused what is essentially the same viewpoint regarding dominance as that given in the above section.

A VIABLE TWO-GENE DEFICIENCY PHAENOTYPICALLY RESEMBLING THE CORRESPONDING HYPOMORPHIC MUTATIONS*

H. J. Muller[†]
Institute of Genetics, Academy of Sciences, Moscow

On the Lethality of Previously Known Deficiencies

On the conception of the germ plasm as a stupendously complex system of thousands of interacting genes evolved through the natural selection of accidentally advantageous mutations, it is logically to be expected that each individual gene should itself have undergone a complex evolution involving numerous selected mutations whose effects have in part served as a basis for the effects of selected mutations in other genes and that its removal would therefore usually derange the workings of the entire system in various ways. Whether such removal would usually be so detrimental as to be lethal could scarcely be predicted in advance, any more than it could be predicted in advance of considerable knowledge of its function, whether or not the removal of a particular organ from the human anatomy would usually involve fatal consequences. A lethal effect is not so inevitable as it might seem at first sight, for the organism is not merely a complex system with many interlocking parts, interdependent in function like those of an ordinary machine, but through natural selection, it has developed many spare parts, as it were, or at least partially spare parts of overlapping functions. That is, it has available to it many processes of regulation and compensation

* Journal of Heredity, Vol. 26, 1935.
†Professor of Zoology, University of Texas; guest at Institute of Genetics, 1933-35. Originally transmitted for publication Nov. 22, 1934.

that may be called into action in cases of disturbances of the normal equilibrium, including among the latter even changes that are genetic in origin. Nevertheless, it is not to be expected that the organism could withstand the effects of the removal of many genes at once, just as it could not usually survive the removal of many organs at once.

In judging of the degree of injury to be expected, we should bear in mind the *a priori* principle that, for an organism of given complexity, the less numerous the genes are, the more complex must each individual gene necessarily be and the more essential in the vital economy, and the effects of its removal would be correspondingly more dangerous. On the basis of general considerations regarding the very high complexity of the organism as a whole and of its germ plasm, and an estimate of the number of genes as lying somewhere in the thousands, the author in his discussions with other geneticists has long advocated the view that most ordinary deficiencies, involving an appreciable section of the linkage map, and not compensated for by duplications (either by those of recent origin or by those which had become established in the earlier evolution of the genus), should be clearly lethal, but he has withheld from formulating a prejudgment as to how often the removal of a single gene should be lethal to the zygote. Obviously, however, such zygote-lethal effects should be considerably more frequent than effects which are lethal even to individual cells or groups of cells living more or less independently or administered to by normal surrounding tissue.

Bridges' work on non-disjunction proved the lethality of the absence of the entire X chromosome and likewise of the fourth chromosome (when neither fourth chromosome is present), and both his work and Mohr's extended this conclusion to the forked-Bar deficiency and the Notch-8 deficiency, respectively, neither of which was more than a few units long. Since then other deficiencies have been found, all of which have proved to be lethal. To be sure, these deficiencies were not at the time proved to involve actual absences of chromatin, but, as shown in a parallel paper on the case of scute 19, there is now every reason to conclude that they were really of this nature. In the case of scute 19 the absence of chromatin has been definitely proved, both genetically and cytologically. The region lost here is considerably smaller (including perhaps only four genes in all) than that involved in any of the hitherto known deficiencies that were demonstrated to include more than one locus, and here too, the effect is lethal to the zygote.

Examining some of the earlier cases of chromatin absence, Li found that the deficient individuals always died off in the egg stage, that is, very early in development. This was of course to be expected, and such cases form a contrast to many though not all cases of lethal "gene mutations," as first directly demonstrated in the work of Sivertzev-Dobzhansky. This very early lethal action is of course to be interpreted as in the main a cell-lethal effect, since the cells of the early embryo are able to live with as yet little dependence upon one another. This then affords an illustration of the comparatively high complexity and evolutionary elaboration even of the processes of individual cell metabolism, and of the lack of stored gene-products in the cytoplasm that can suffice for more than a few cell-generations of the embryo.

In some recent communications, giving the results of parallel work, Demerec and Stern each describe cases in which known or suspected deficiencies of portions of a chromosome are lethal to somatic cells or groups of cells, developing amidst normal tissue. In Demerec's work, which was more directly concerned with the problem here in question, 24 cases of this type were studied. In explanation of the method, it may be recalled that Patterson had found that, when a female has its two X-chromosomes differentiated by markers for epidermal characters, such as yellow and singed, twin spots (yellow and singed, respectively) lying next to each other are produced by the somatic segregation of these X's from one another in a dividing larval cell. In Patterson's cases this segregation was induced by X-rays, but Stern (reinterpreting earlier work of Bridges and himself on supposed "elimination" of chromosome parts) finds this segregation to occur even without treatment in flies of certain "Minute bristle" types; he interprets the process as one of somatic crossing over. Absence of one member of the pair of twin spots thus produced indicates a lethal effect of the chromosome in question on the cell or group of cells containing it. In Demerec's experiments five chromosomes carrying known deficiencies of more than one locus all proved to be lethal when thus tested. Of 19 other cases, known to be lethal in their effect on the whole individual but not known to involve more than one locus, all except those (4) involving the locus of "cut wings" were likewise lethal to the cells containing them. Demerec concludes from this that deficiencies of a single gene probably have a cell-lethal action in the great majority of cases.

Unfortunately we do not know which of the latter 19 cases were real deficiencies, nor, in these or the previously proved deficiencies, how many genes were missing. Hence the interpretation of the results must remain in question, though no doubt studies by the new cytological method of Painter will be of service here. Certainly not every mutation that is lethal to the whole individual is a deficiency and so it is quite possible or likely that the cut-lethals were not deficiencies at all. On the other hand, it is also quite possible (contrary to Demerec's opinion) that most of the *other* cases involved deficiencies of sizeable sections that included several genes.[1] We do not hold with Demerec that the ease with which the Bar gene is apparently "knocked out" without a lethal effect can be used as a

Synapsis of X chromosomes in individual heterozygous for ac^8w^aB and y^{3P}:

$1J1^+$ y^+ ac^+	bb^+	B	w^a sc^8 sf

$1J1$	bb^+	B^+	w^+ sc^+ ac^+ y^{3P} sf

Chromosomes resulting from single crossing over in region between B and w^a

(1) Crossover with duplication of loci of y and ac:

$1J1^+$ y^+ ac^+	bb^+	B	w^+ sc^+ ac^+ y^{3P} sf

(2) Crossover with deficiency of loci of y and ac:

$1J1^+$	bb^+	B^+	w^a sc^8 sf

HOW THE DEFICIENCY WAS PRODUCED

Diagram showing synapsis of X-chromosomes in individual heterozygous for w^aBy^{3P}. Crossing over in the region between B and w^a produces either duplication or deficiencies of loci for y and ac. By this means it is possible to obtain individuals deficient for only two genes. These were viable. (Exponent + designates normal allelomorphs; "sf" designates locus of spindle fibre; dotted line represents inert regions.)

criterion to show that in the case of other loci also a single-locus loss is more frequent than that of two or more loci; in fact, Demerec's own data on double-Bar and on garnet deficiencies prove that in both the latter cases one-locus losses are exceptional. It therefore seems premature as yet to draw any conclusions, from this evidence, regarding the frequency with which single loci are necessary to the life of cells. In this connection it may be remarked that Gershenson and Nuzhdin, in collaboration with the present writer and quite independently of the work of Demerec and Stern, have been undertaking some investigations of a very similar nature. The results of these will be presented elsewhere.

The present communication has to report the case of a proved deficiency which is probably far smaller than any previously proved deficiency, and this deficiency is found to be viable. The deficiency in question probably involves the loss of two and only two genes, being the first case in which the actual number of genes concerned in a deficiency, or, for that matter, in any given section of chromatin, has been determined. It proves to be viable not only in single cells surrounded and administered to by normal tissue, or in groups of such cells, but even in the zygote as a whole. And the phaenotypic effects produced by it are of interest from the standpoint of the modern theory of mutation.

The Yellow-Achaete Deficiency Produced by
Recombination of Inverted Chromosomes

The deficiency in question was artificially produced by making up an individual in which the homologous X chromosomes, by reason of previous rearrangement, contained their genes in a slightly different order from one another, not different enough to prevent single crossing over between the chromosomes, and so allowing the production of complementary types of crossover chromosomes one of which had an excess and the other a deficiency of the non-matching regions (see discussion of the formation of such new combinations by the author). The starting point for the production of the particular deficiency here studied had been given by Serebrovsky's well known finding that the chromosome containing the mutation scute 8 contains an inversion in which the left break lies between achaete and scute and the right break to the right of bobbed. Serebrovsky also had obtained deficient and excessive chromosomes as a result of crossing over between this scute 8 chromosome and others (scute 4 and yellow 4) having somewhat different inversions; in fact, it was by the study of the phaenotypes of individuals resulting from just such crossing over that he was led to his interpretation of the structure of the scute 8 chromosome. His accompanying conclusion regarding the separability of achaete and scute has been confirmed by us by means of different methods. But in Serebrovsky's cases the other rearranged chromosomes used were such as to produce, by recombination with the scute 8 chromosome, deficiencies of the active region that were always lethal. In our own work a search was made for chromosomes which might be more favorable for an attack upon the question at issue. It was found that the chromosome containing the mutation yellow 3P provided the necessary material.

This yellow mutation, which has dark bristles and dark abdominal bands like the previously known yellow 3, was found by Patterson and determined by him to contain some kind of inversion. We find that when it is crossed to scute 8 both possible types of single crossovers are obtained in the second generation, not only in the heterozygous females but also in the males. When appropriate markers are present in the heterozygous F_1 individual, as for instance when the genes Bar and apricot are present in the scute 8 chromosome and their normal allelomorphs in the yellow 3P chromosome, as shown in the diagram, both expected crossover types (Bar not-apricot, and not-Bar apricot) appear. The flies of the former class, which contain the left end of the original scute 8 chromosome and the right end of the yellow 3P chromosome, show a normal body color, and show no reduction of bristles. Evidently then the left end of the scute 8 chromosome must contain the normal allelomorph of yellow, and the right end of the yellow 3P chromosome must contain the normal allelomorph of scute (for the scute 8 allelomorph shows some reduction in bristle number, especially on the scutellum). The other crossover class, having the left end of the yellow 3P chromosome and the right end from scute 8, has a clearcut yellow coloration like that in the ordinary mutation yellow, not like that in yellow 3P, which is darker, and it is at the same time extremely achaete in type (lacking the dorsocentral bristles and neighboring microchaetes and sometimes even the supra-alars and inner verticals); in addition it shows that moderate reduction of scutellar and some other bristles which is characteristic of scute 8 itself. Obviously then neither the left end of the yellow 3P chromosome nor the right end of the scute 8 chromosome contain the loci of yellow or of achaete, but the locus of scute 8 itself is in the right end of the scute 8 chromosome.

In the yellow 3P inversion, then, the left break must have been to the left of yellow and achaete so that the latter loci became carried around to the vicinity of the right end, together with the locus of scute as well, while in the scute 8 chromosome the loci of yellow and achaete (containing their normal allelomorphs) remained at the left end, the break occurring between them and scute, which was carried over to the right end and acquired the properties giving rise to the scute 8 bristle reductions. The second class of crossovers is accordingly deficient for the loci of yellow and achaete but not of scute, since the latter has a similar position in both original chromosomes. The right break of both inversions proves to be in the inert region, to the right of bobbed. It was already known to be in this position in the scute 8 chromosome (see work of Serebrovsky and of Gershenson), and the fact that both crossover classes were proved by testing to contain bobbed showed that in the yellow 3P chromosome bobbed must lie in the same position as in the scute 8 chromosome.

The Same Deficiency Otherwise Produced

We have recently obtained individuals with exactly the same loci deficient, by the use of a rather different method. This involved breaking off the entire left end of the scute 8 chromosome by means of x-rays, either by means of an apparently simple break, as was done in some cases, or by means of a mutual translocation with the fourth chromosome whereby the two fragments of the X chromosome were made independent of one another, as was done in another case. The resulting right-hand piece, lacking only the loci to the left of bobbed (see diagram) was then crossed to an individual containing the scute 19 deficiency, in the case of which previous analysis had shown the loci from yellow to some point a little beyond scute to be absent. In the resulting heterozygous female the only loci whose absence was common to both X chromosomes were those of yellow and achaete, and here again we find that the individuals were viable and that they exhibited the characteristics yellow and achaete, just like the crossover individuals previously discussed. The achaete character was somewhat more extreme here, however, as might be expected from the fact that the female must carry one more dose of the dosage compensators for this character than does the male.

A yellow-achaete "mutation" found by Koerner in an irradiated scute 8 chromosome while assisting the author in Berlin in 1933 provides a very probable case of still another deficiency of the same region. In the scute 8 chromosome, the location of a part of the inert region, just to the right of the loci of yellow and achaete, provides a favorable opportunity for the occurrence of a deletion having one of its points of breakage just to the left of yellow and achaete and the other point of breakage in the inert region itself, inasmuch as this region is especially subject to breakage. Hence there is much more chance in the scute 8 stock than in normal stocks for a deletion which removes just these two loci of the active region to occur. The "mutation" in question is non-lethal and is sensibly identical, phaenotypically, with the previously described individuals deficient for yellow and achaete, produced by crossing over between the scute 8 and the yellow 3P chromosomes.

Reality and Extent of the Deficiency

The only escape from the conclusion that the loci of yellow and achaete are really absent in the above cases would lie in the supposition that the scute 8 chromosome has these loci duplicated, one set of them lying at the left end of the chromosome, to the left of the left break, and the other set lying at the right end, in the inverted section (a possibility pointed out by the author to other workers on scute, in 1930). But this would require the further peculiar supposition that both these genes at the right end had simultaneously undergone just such extreme hypomorphic mutations that they could no longer manifest themselves through any visible phaenotypic effect of a perceptible kind, *although* still somehow saving the life of the individuals with the apparent deficiencies. Not only would various very special assumptions be required to account for such a condition of affairs, but an intensive study of numerous cases of inversion and translocation has so far failed to reveal one giving any evidence of such a duplication of loci. Many breaks have been studied which occurred in the general region in question, and if breaks had occurred that involved the duplication of any of the visible genes in the region without at the same time totally removing the visible phaenotypic effects of one of these genes, this fact should have been determined by the methods used. Instead of that, the pieces on the right and left sides of each break were always found to be complementary in their effects. It is not denied that duplications may and do occasionally arise by any one of a number of different methods, but it can be seen on the basis of the above considerations that duplications of the type necessary to explain away the present deficiencies, are no more than a very remote academic possibility that we practically need not take into account here.

In regard to the extent of the deficiency, it should be pointed out that we do not positively know that the genes, yellow and achaete, are really separate genes, since neither a crossover nor a break occurring between them has yet come to light. One cannot pass with absolute assurance from the fact that the phaenotypic effects in question are very different and have arisen by independent mutations, to the conclusion that the loci concerned must be separate. For the case of the truncate series of allelomorphs, for instance, long ago showed such effects to be produceable at one and the same locus. However such cases are obviously much rarer than cases of the familiar type; and even in the truncate case many if not most of the mutations did involve simultaneously both of the two different visible characters concerned. All in all, then, it remains extremely likely that two different loci, yellow and achaete, are included in the present deficiency. If so, later work will undoubtedly settle the question by finding separations between them.

Phaenogenetic Considerations

One point of interest from a phaenogenetic standpoint brought out by examination of the deficient individuals is that they do not show a constant absence of all bristles connected with the usual achaete pattern. They give an impression as though the epidermal superstructures had been wiped off over a somewhat limited area; this area is somewhat variable in its size and position, so that on one occasion or another nearly every bristle can appear, and when it does it has a not very atypical position. This shows that the fundamental bristle pattern is determined by other genes than achaete, even though the achaete locus plays a rôle in assisting the production of bristles over a given portion of that pattern, and in fact over a more or less localized portion. In view of this, it seems rather strange and unnecessary that different allelomorphs of achaete should seem to involve somewhat different pattern-effects themselves; they have not, however, as yet shown nearly as much specificity in this respect as the different allelomorphs of scute, and the conclusions from the work on the latter locus may not yet be applied to them.

A second fact of phaenogenetic interest comes out on comparison of the effects of the deficiency with those of mutations of the same loci. It is evident that, phaenotypically considered, the deficiencies of yellow and of achaete belong in the same series with the mutations of these loci, and constitute extreme representatives of their respective series, apparently not more extreme however, at least in the case of yellow, than some of the mutations themselves. This finding illustrates the correctness of the designation "hypomorphs" which the author had attached to recessive mutations of both these loci, and also the correctness of the criterion whereby such "hypomorphism" was ascertained.

By hypomorphism (see papers of Muller, League and Offermann, and Muller,) is meant that characteristic whereby a mutant gene produces an effect similar to although not so extreme as that of a loss of the normal allelomorph. The criterion of such a condition lies in the finding that a reduction in the dosage of the normal allelomorph produces a phaenotypic effect more nearly resembling that of the mutant gene itself, or, *vice versa*, that an extra dose of the normal allelomorph produces an opposite effect from that of the mutant. Alternatively, the conclusion may be based upon studies of the effects of changes in the dosage of the mutant allelomorph, in which case extra doses should give rise to phaenotypes more nearly approaching, or even transgressing, the normal, while reduced doses give still more extreme deviations in the same direction as already shown by the mutant gene when present in normal dosage. These methods, applied to the cases of yellow and of achaete, lead to the conclusion that the mutations so designated are hypomorphic, i. e., have an effect similar to though not necessarily as extreme as that produced by gene loss. (It is of course not implied here that they actually do involve any loss of material by the genes.)

In the case of yellow, the evidence lay in the finding that one dose of the normal allelomorph in the triploid (even in that containing one deficiency of the locus) failed to produce the full normal "gray" coloration, there being a slight but distinct approach to the coloration seen in yellow flies. In the case of achaete, the evidence rested on the fact that extra doses of an achaete locus containing a mutant achaete gene gave an effect more nearly like the normal than did the normal dosage. The checking up of these conclusions by the present finding that the actual absence of the locus of yellow does give rise to a really yellow color and absence of the locus of achaete to the extreme achaete character, has now provided us with final and direct proof of the similarity between the effects of these "hypomorphic" mutations and those of real losses.

It may be noted that, according to the same terminology, the most extreme mutations of yellow known may be classed as "amorphs" (or even perhaps as "antimorphs" in some cases), rather than as hypomorphs, so far as their phaenotypic effect is concerned. Nevertheless, as is well known, they as well as the hypomorphs may by reverse mutation give rise to the normal gene again, an event which is of course inconceivable in the case of a deficiency having a similar phaenotypic effect. The gene change involved in the hypomorphic mutation is therefore probably in itself qualitative, even though the effect may be described quantitatively.

The question must finally be considered as to why individuals deficient for two loci should be able to live at all. An alternative here would be to admit the sub-gene hypothesis, and to suppose that only a part of each locus had become lost, by reason of the genes in question having both originally been divided internally by the chromosome breaks. We may for the time being, however, lay this hypothesis to one side, firstly, on account of the special assumptions here necessitated by it in order to explain why the whole of the apparent phaenotypic effect of both of these genes becomes lost when this deficiency occurs, and secondly, because of the evidence against the hypothesis provided by the apparently complete identity of positions of the left-hand breaks in the case of scute 19 and yellow 3P, respectively. In our further work on breakages, the proposed possibility must nevertheless be borne in mind, as more evidence as to its truth or falsity should shortly accrue from that work.

Supposing now that the whole of both loci have been lost, we may ask what is the expectation that such a loss should be lethal? Evidence obtained in our recent work, being published elsewhere, indicates the approximate correctness of previous estimates of the total number of genes as lying in the few thousands. This, after all, is not a number of so high an order of magnitude, considering the complexity of the organism, and an individual gene should therefore in most cases have a rather compound as well as a complex rôle to play. Thus, it might seem rather strange that *two* genes which, so far as the purposes of the present problem are concerned, might almost be considered to have been chosen at random, should both, and in fact both together, be so dispensable.

Several explanations are possible, short of radical changes in our conceptions of the rôle of the chromosomes, the number of genes, or the complexity of the organism. One is the principle previously touched upon, regarding the prevalence of compensatory systems and the overlapping of functions in general. Another is the supposition that the particular genes in question are less basic and perhaps simpler in function than most genes—particularly could this be true in the case of a gene having to do with pigment production in an artificially protected organism. A third is the possibility that in the course of past evolution there may have been some duplication of loci, such as might occur for instance, by unequal crossing over or by means of minute insertions (see parallel paper on scute 19[2]) (in animals, be it noted, polyploidy as a means of duplication of loci is ordinarily excluded). Any duplication would, of course, eventually be followed by a mutational differentiation of the duplicated loci as pointed out by the author in 1918 (in fact it may with reason be mentioned that *all* present-day loci, no matter how non-homologous now, were ultimately derived by some sort of duplication and mutation from one original gene), but for a very considerable time the duplicated loci should retain partially overlapping functions and meanwhile the loss of one of them would not be nearly so detrimental to the organism, other things being equal, as would the loss of other genes (most of which would have been far more remotely derived from one another). The apparent similarity in the functions of the loci of achaete and scute make the supposition more plausible that these may in the past evolution of Drosophila have been derived by some such duplication from one original progenitor gene. But it must be remembered that the latter idea is still no more than a possibility.[3]

Addendum

Since all the above was written, a paper by Ephrussi has come to hand, in which the latter brings forward evidence of the viability of small somatic areas presumably deficient for yellow and achaete or yellow, achaete and scute. In one case a scute 8 chromosome with a yellow-achaete deficiency was used, in the other case L. V. Morgan's yellow-scute deficiency; these were "covered" by a deleted X chromosome which had a tendency to apparent somatic elimination, and when the presumable elimination occurred, yellow patches having the deficiency were visible on the abdomen. These patches were apparently too small to allow the autonomous nondevelopment of hairs and bristles that ordinarily is associated with the achaete and scute mutations. If the elimination hypothesis is right, then, specific gene-products from normal cells were penetrating, and perhaps also helping to keep the deficient cells alive. Detailed studies have also been made by Gershenson (as yet unpublished), showing the viability even of fairly large thoracic areas presumably lacking the entire left end of the scute 8 chromosome; these occur frequently in ordinary scute 8 material, as had first been noted by Levit in the Texas laboratory, and they show both the yellow character and the absence of hairs and bristles. It is obvious that if the whole individual is viable when deficient for yellow and achaete, patches of this constitution, surrounded by normal tissue, should certainly be viable. It is not yet quite certain, however, that in any of these cases of mosaics the chromosome region in question is really absent, or more or less inactivated through some "position effect" that might not extend as far as to the free end of the chromosome.

At present it is of greater interest for us to know how many genes such a large patch may be deficient for. Taking together the purely genetic evidence from our own and previous experiments, we must conclude that the region to the left of scute, *i. e.*, that missing in our own scute 8 deficiencies, includes at least 4 genes: lethal *J1*, chlorotic, yellow and achaete. Judging by its cytological size in the salivary gland, taken in connection with the work of Muller and Prokofyeva on the size of the structure representing an individual gene in the salivary gland, this region probably contains about eight genes in all. Of the four genes specified above, even the most extreme known mutations in two of the loci—yellow and achaete—are not lethal; those in chlorotic are semilethal, and that in *lJ1* is almost completely lethal, only one viable fly having been observed where many thousands would have been expected if the viability of *lJ1* had been normal. This viable lethal *J1* individual had rough eyes and was completely sterile, but was active and long-lived, and except for the associated scute *J1* character, it was otherwise normal in appearance; this lethal effect then is obviously confined to the egg or larval stages. Judging by the *a priori* knowledge that there are at least five to ten times as many lethal as visible mutations, it is highly probable that among the other (unknown) loci in this small region there are several whose mutations, and therefore (since most mutations are hypomorphic) whose losses, would be lethal to the whole individual. It is therefore of especial interest to find some evidence for the conclusion that even the loss of all these loci together is not lethal to individual cells, or even to considerable groups of cells, nourished in an otherwise normal soma. This evidence, taken together with the fact of the viability of the whole individual lacking *both* yellow and achaete, would seem to make a reinterpretation of the findings of Demerec desirable, or at least a further comparative study of deficiencies in which the number of genes involved is approximately known.

Summary

1. A deficiency is described, produced by crossing over between two inverted chromosomes—scute 8 and yellow 3P—in which the resulting chromosome lacks the loci of probably two and only two genes, namely those of yellow and achaete.

2. Individuals having the above deficient chromosome, and having no other chromosome containing these loci, are viable.

3. Such individuals show the phaenotypic abnormalities—extreme yellow and achaete—shown by the most extreme members of the series of mutant allelomorphs already known at the loci in question. The correctness of the previous phaenotypic classification of the mutations of these series as hypomorphic, ranging to (or beyond) amorphic, is thus demonstrated. It is also noteworthy that no other phaenotypic abnormalities were to be observed as a result of the total loss of these loci than had already been observed as a result of their known mutations.

4. A deficiency involving the absence of the same genes was also produced in a different way: namely, by making up females containing one chromosome having the scute 19 deficiency and another X chromosome derived from the scute 8 inverted X chromosome but having the left end amputated by x-rays. Flies with this deficiency so produced were phaenotypically similar to those having the same deficiency produced by the other method. A yellow-achaete "mutation" in a scute 8 chromosome, probably involving a deletion of these loci, was likewise phaenotypically like the above deficiencies.

5. It is found that the locus of achaete does not govern the laying down of the fundamental bristle pattern characteristic of the region which it affects.

6. Theoretical considerations are discussed, which are raised by the finding of the viability, not merely of cells but of whole organisms, containing deficiencies of genes.

Notes

[1]Work of Mackensen, of Demerec himself, and of Sakharoff, using the method of Painter, and published or orally announced since the above was written, have shown the above conjecture to be correct. (Note added July 13, 1935.)

[2]In some conversations which the author had with Dr. E. G. Anderson, many years ago (ca. 1918), in which the former insisted upon the inviability of individuals deficient for then appreciable sections of chromatin, the latter pointed out that duplications of chromatin might have occurred in the past evolution, and that these would tend to permit some deficient individuals to be viable.

[3]Since the above was written, the salivary gland work of Bridges (1935) and of Offermann have demonstrated the existence of duplications in the normal Drosophila chromosomes; in connection with these, these authors make speculations similar to our own. (Note added July 13, 1935.)

THE POSITION EFFECT AS EVIDENCE OF THE LOCALIZATION OF THE IMMEDIATE PRODUCTS OF GENE ACTIVITY*

by H. J. Muller
Institute of Genetics
Academy of Sciences of the USSR, Moscow

That apparent mutations of genes located near points of chromosome breakage are only changes in gene functioning conditioned by the alterations of gene groupings ("position effect") has been shown (1) by the dependence of the quality of the allelomorph upon the kind of regrouping (Muller), and (2) by the fact that the apparently changed gene when replaced in a normal gene grouping, by means of crossing over, again functions normally, while, *mutatis mutandis*, an originally normal gene gotten into the abnormal grouping now functions in the abnormal manner (evidence independently obtained by Panshin and by Sidorov and Dubinin, in press). Not only the gene immediately adjacent to the break may exhibit altered functioning but also genes further removed (evidence of Muller, 1930; Dobzhansky and Sturtevant, 1932; Dobzhansky and Schultz, 1934; Muller and Prokofyeva, 1934, 1935; Dubinin, 1935; Panshin, 1935).

It might be supposed that the above results imply that there is a direct influence of one gene upon the conformation or chemical activity of a neighboring gene. Such an influence would at first seem understandable, on the supposition that the genes are bound to one

*Proceedings of the Fifteenth International Physiological Congress (Leningrad-Moscow), 1938, pp. 587-89.

another in line by means of chemical bonds, as for instance on the view expressed by Castle in 1919 that the whole chromosome should be regarded as one tremendous molecule. For the chemical activity of a molecule depends upon its structure as a whole, that is, changes in one of its parts affect the method of functioning of other parts. A little consideration, however, shows such an interpretation of the "position effect" of genes to be very implausible, since direct chemical influences of the type in question could hardly extend over distances so vast, from the chemical standpoint, as are those here in question. Certainly the connections between the genes, even if chemical, are of a different nature (allowing of crossing over) from those within the genes, and must allow of the relative chemical independence of the latter; the individual genes, moreover, are very long, from the chemical standpoint, or else lie far apart from one another (see calculation by Muller and Prokofyeva, 1934, of the approximate number of genes in a given length of chromonema). That, under these circumstances, the direct chemical effect of the substitution of one gene for another should extend, not only to the adjacent gene, so as to affect the latter's function, but even through the latter to one or more genes beyond, is hardly conceivable, unless we postulate some hitherto unfamiliar principle of chemistry, such as might be involved in those forces which are responsible for the synaptic attraction between like genes. The latter are so unusual, and act over such relatively great distances, that the possibility is not excluded that the same forces which, when acting between genes of identical conformation, cause a harmonious attraction, might, when acting between unlike genes, set up differential stresses on their different parts and so cause distortions in their conformation and consequent changes in their chemical properties.

The alternative to the above interpretation is that the "position effect" is an expression of the interaction between the *products* of neighboring genes rather than between the genes themselves. This interpretation was independently offered by the present writer (Muller and Prokofyeva, 1934) and by Offermann (C.R.d. Acad. Sci. URSS, 1925, No. 1) and it seems also to have been implied by Sturtevant (1925) in his first discussion of the position effect on Bar eye. In the production of phenotypic effects the gene must begin by interacting with cellular substances so as to produce a highly specific product or products, which must diffuse out from the locus of activity of the gene and in turn cause (or affect) further physicochemical changes. In the course of one of these chains of reaction, that has its origin in an individual gene, there will be many opportunities for interaction with other chains of reaction present in the complicated mixture; thus, the reactions will really form a kind of multidimensional net, rather than a simple chain. The final phenotypic manifestations lie at the ends of the net furthest removed from the inner gene ends, and their quality depends upon the character and strength (including, of course, speed) of all the intermediate reactions and interactions. Amongst these interactions there will necessarily be some between the products of neighboring genes. Now in cases in which these latter interactions happen to involve the *immediate* products of the neighboring genes, the result may be considerably affected by an alteration in the distances between these genes.

From the locus of each of two genes ("A" and "B") involved in such an interaction, the characteristic immediate products ("A_1" and "B_1") issue forth to diffuse out, and they form some sort of concentration gradient, the highest concentration in all probability being nearest the gene of origin. With increasing distance, the molecules of gene product may not only become more dispersed, but may also become altered into further stages, by undergoing various subsidiary reactions with other substances that they encounter. As a result, the amount of interaction between "A_1" and "B_1," per unit of time, will tend to be less when "A" and "B" lie far apart in the cell than when they are close together. (In this connection it may be recalled that the rate of bimolecular reactions depends, other things being equal, upon the *product* of the concentrations of the interacting substances, so that even the same amount of material would not react so fast when diluted.) Whether the reaction between "A_1" and "B_1" is one of the main reactions in the production of the phenotypic effect studied, or a side reaction, whether it enhances or hinders the effect, whether it adds to or withdraws from the material or the activity of the main phenogenetic process in question, is immaterial in the present connection: the degree or the quality of expression of the gene will nevertheless tend to be influenced to some extent. For some further considerations regarding the character of the interaction—usually involving more specific and less specific substances, and those which have been removed from or brought into one another's neighborhood, etc.—the reader may be referred to the paper by Offermann *(ibid.)*.

If either of the two interpretations here proposed are correct, the degree and the character of gene functioning should also be influenced to some extent by the manner of grouping of the different chromosomes and chromosome regions with regard to each other, i.e., by the (partly accidental) mode of juxtaposition of different portions of the chromonema in the cell. Hence, in different somatic cells of the same individual, there might be some differences in gene functioning, depending upon the way the chromosomes happened to be situated. It is possible that some cases of somatic variegation may be caused in this way. In that case agents, genetic or otherwise, which affected chromosome arrangements, would thereby affect gene expression. A possible case in point might be the influence of the Y chromosome of *Drosophila* upon somatic variegation. The latter possibility acquires more plausibility in consideration of the fact that in all such cases of variegation so far known the affected gene has been brought by rearrangement into the neighborhood of a "chromocentral region"—i.e., a region which is especially disposed to undergo conjugation in the somatic cells, with the corresponding regions of non-homologous chromosomes (see Prokofyeva, *Cytologia*, 1935). Noteworthy in this connection is the fact that the Y chromosome itself is to be classed as "chromocentral." On the other hand, the fact of the transmission of a part of this effect of the Y through the egg cytoplasm ("delayed" or "maternal inheritance") recently discovered by Nuzhdin, speaks against this possibility. However this may be, the question of inter-chromosomal position effect should be capable of experimental testing and a positive answer would decide in favor of an interpretation of the "position effect" as a result of an indirect interaction between genes —either between gene products or via the force of synaptic attraction—rather than as a result of a direct chemical union between the genes themselves.

Those interactions between the products of neighboring genes which are not between immediate products, but between products further removed from the starting points of the reaction chains, cannot be expected to be affected by changes in gene topography (except as a secondary consequence of changes in the immediate products), for the distribution of the substances here interacting must have reached an equilibrium independent of the positions of the genes of origin. In studies of the "position effect," therefore, we are dealing with changes that we know to have had their inception at or very near to the starting point of the gene-character series of processes, but perhaps not in the gene itself. In no other cases, except possibly in those dealing with species-specific and individual specific antigens, do we have valid evidence as to how near or how far from the gene itself, in the series of physiological or morphogenetic reactions, the substances or processes studied really stand.

POSITION EFFECT AND GENE DIVISIBILITY CONSIDERED IN CONNECTION WITH THREE STRIKINGLY SIMILAR SCUTE MUTATIONS*

Daniel Raffel and H. J. Muller

Baltimore, Maryland, and the University, Edinburgh, Scotland

Received February 8, 1940

Background of the Present Work

After the proposal of the subgene theory by Serebrovsky, Dubinin and their co-workers (Serebrovsky and Dubinin, 1929), in interpretation of the relationships observed by them among scute alleles, an attempt was made by Muller and co-workers, first at the University of Texas laboratory and later at the Institute of Genetics of the U.S.S.R., to obtain further scute alleles and to analyse these and the ones previously obtained elsewhere, with a view to further testing the above theory and to further investigation of the curious relationship which he had observed between "gene mutations" and "gene rearrangements" (Muller 1930a, b, 1932). It was soon evident that a high proportion of the scute mutations involved the breakage and reattachment of the X chromosome very close to the locus of scute, but it was not clear whether the phenotypic change represented a "gene mutation" that was near to but, theoretically at least, separable from the rearrangement, or whether it represented the "position effect" of the gene rearrangement itself.

We shall not describe here the work of analysing the position of breakage of these rearrangements of the scute region with respect to each other, reported by Muller and Prokofyeva (1934, 1935a) and briefly mentioned below. Suffice it here to say that the numerous rearrangements, although all appearing to possess one point of breakage and interchange of gene connections in one of four definite positions near scute had their other point of breakage anywhere in the X or other chromosomes, so that the gene arrangements occurring in the neighborhood of scute, after the breakages and re-

*Genetics, November, 1940, 25: 541-83; pp. 541-46 and 574 (part)-82 included.

The authors wish to acknowledge their indebtedness to Dr. N. I. Valivov for the provision of the facilities and opportunities for this work. Practically all of the present paper was written in 1938, its publication having been delayed by circumstances connected with the remoteness of the authors from one another.

attachments had taken place, were in all cases very different from those in the normal chromosome and (with the exceptions to be noted presently) from each other. Correspondingly there was very much diversity in the phenotypic expression of the 'alleles,' although no fixed relation was discernible between the map position of the different chromosome breaks and the kinds of scute phenotype associated with them.

Evidence was, however, obtained that a strong relationship did exist between the type of rearrangement and the type of phenotypic change when two scute mutations that had not previously been studied were subjected to analysis. These were "scute-L8," found by H. Levy in Texas in 1932, and "scute-S1," found by T. G. Sinitskaya in Leningrad in 1934. It was found in genetic investigations of the senior author that these two mutants had their X chromosomes broken at sensibly the same place in the scute region, and had them broken also in the right-hand chromocentral ("inert") region of the X, the part of the chromosome between these two breaks being inverted with respect to the rest. In all these particulars, moreover, these two rearrangements agreed with the already known inversion found in the mutant scute-4. (Tests made later did, however, show some difference in the position of the breaks in the chromocentral region, that in scute-4 being to the left of bobbed and block A, that in scute-L8 between them, and that in scute-S1 to the right of both.) By themselves, these coincidences would not be so very striking, since, in the first place, scute mutations (already known often to be associated with breaks near the scute locus) were being searched for, and since, secondly, breaks in the chromocentral region occur relatively frequently. What made the findings striking was the fact that, to parallel this unusual resemblance in type of gene rearrangement, there was also a similar strong resemblance between the types of phenotypic expression of all three of them. In fact, the phenotypic expressions of all three were more like one another than any of them was like any of the numerous other scute mutations known, just as the gene arrangements were more like one another than any of them was like that of any other scute.

These facts were first known only for scute-L8 and scute-4, and were taken by Muller and Prokofyeva (1934, 1935a) as furnishing, along with other facts, strong evidence for their conclusion that the phenotypic changes caused by the so-called mutations accompanying chromosomal rearrangements are in general, except in so far as they are due to losses or duplications, manifestations of a "position effect" on the genes lying near the points of breakage. The later results on scute-S1, agreeing with those on scutes-4 and -L8, seemed to remove all possibility of the agreement between gene arrangement and phenotype being a matter of coincidence.

In view of the significance of such a relationship for our understanding of mutations, both spontaneous and induced, and in order to learn something more concerning the nature of the so-called position effect, it was decided to make a more accurate study of the phenotypic effects of these three scute mutations, in stocks that were as nearly isogenic as possible. For, despite the phenotypic similarity of these three mutations, certain differences had been observed between them, as well as peculiarities of the recombinational forms, as for example the sterility of crossover males with the left part of the scute-4 and the right part of the scute-L8 chromosomes. These had not been subjected to quantitative study in the earlier work because it was not yet known to what extent they might be due to differences in environmental conditions or in other genes (modifying factors that might lie anywhere in the X chromosome or the autosomes), and to what extent the differences were localisable in and near the gene for scute itself and the right-hand points of breakage.

The expression of scute is known to be rather sensitive to differences in environic factors and modifying genes, and there was no reason to regard the original stocks of the three inversions as containing fewer "invisible" differences in their genes—either in their X chromosomes or autosomes—than most stocks do. In fact, scute-S1 was known to carry a smaller inversion, morphologically somewhat similar to the known inversion called delta 49, in its X chromosome, entirely included within the larger inversion. This same stock of scute-S1 was also known to have an inherited tendency to nicking at the ends of the wings. All this made it the more important to make a comparison on groups of flies which had been made isogenic and in which the effects of environmental differences were minimized. The present paper gives a report of this study on these three scutes. In addition, the effects were studied of the various possible combinations having the left part of one of the inversions and the right part of another, in stocks similarly isogenic.

The results of this investigation show that the phenotypic expressions of these three mutations are, even when subjected to this more exact comparison, very similar to one another but that they are not identical. It is found that both the left and right regions containing the points at which the breaks and recombinations occurred (hereafter referred to as the left and right "ends" of the inversions) appear to affect the development of the bristles. However, while the influences of the left regions (including the "locus of scute" itself) are unquestionable and regular, analysis of the right regions shows them to be much weaker, more uncertain and inconsistent, and it is possible that they do not represent any real effect of the right ends themselves.

The above findings raise important questions of interpretation, concerning the position effect, gene divisibility, etc., which are herein discussed in the light of theoretical considerations and of related work on these subjects.

* * * * *

The real question here, then, is to what extent there may exist, in the scute region of the normal X chromosome, a series of elements that can be separated from one another, without losing their capability of reproduction, and that, at least when in their normal positions, co-operate in the production of the given character (the bristles produced by the normal allele of the scutes). Still another question is that of the possible existence of elements, not capable of reproduction except in their original setting, that are subject to being cut off from their reproductive base by chromosome breakage. It may also be questioned to what extent the functions of these elements differ from one another (as, for instance, to what extent they may affect different bristles), and to what extent each of them may subserve other, differing characters as well. Certainly the "gene" for achaete, just to the left of scute, has some part in this scute complex. And our series of studies on the chromosomal conformation of the other alleles shows that, just to the right of the main scute locus also, there lie one or more genes which (as compared with genes that may be substituted for them by inversion or translocation of other euchromatic regions) exert an appreciable position effect assisting in the production of the normal ("non-scute") bristle characters. At least one of these genes is not immediately adjoining the scute locus but lies to the right of the locus of the lethal which itself is to the right of scute, because the scute character is affected even when the chromosome is broken and rearranged to the right of this lethal locus. We cannot, at present, be sure that between the boundaries so set, or even within the main "scute locus" itself, the genetic material is not still further divisible, in the sense defined, nor know to what an extent it may be thus divisible. Certainly neither our experiments here presented, nor our whole series of studies on scute, give good evidence for the existence of such further divisibility, but it is equally important to note that they do not give convincing evidence against it either, as they might seem to do on first consideration, and, in fact, it is quite possible that a part of the effects here noted are results of such divisibility.

We have laid emphasis on this matter because this question of the further divisibility (without loss of reproductive capacity of the elements) of regions of the chromosome that have, on other grounds, been considered as probably representing single "genes," has recently been brought to the fore by various results in the field of gene mutation and chromosome rearrangement. In the first report of the finding of minute rearrangements, and of the phenotypic changes accompanying them (Muller, Prokofyeva and Raffel, 1935), the suggestion was made that many, perhaps all, of the supposed gene mutations produced by irradiation, and probably some at least of the spontaneous ones as well, represented fundamentally the same phenomenon, although on an even smaller scale than that found in our cytologically demonstrable cases. But at that time we did not believe that gene mutations in general—especially those forming the basis of evolutionary progression—could be of such type, because we did not think of "genes" (as defined by the mutational properties of a given chromosome region) as being further genetically divisible, and we realized that the number of kinds of somatic changes dependent upon the limited position effects of rearranging these relatively large and few units could not be nearly of the order of magnitude necessary to provide for the great evolutionary plasticity and diversity of organisms. Since then, however, considerations of the similarity in expression, and in mode of production, of "gene mutations" and of minute rearrangements, and of the empirical impossibility of drawing a line between them, have led us to question whether or not there may be even minuter rearrangements than those which change the position of "whole genes" (as taken in the older, less flexible sense). For if smaller, linearly arranged parts of those regions which have been considered as genes (by criteria of mutation and allelism) may become rearranged with respect to each other in essentially the same manner as the "whole genes," then, at least by having such parts rather numerous and of a number of diverse kinds, sufficient plasticity of result is introduced to make plausible the conception that most gene mutations might be of this kind.

Among the findings which played an important part in leading us to put the present question, was that concerning the effect of varying the dosage of radiation upon the production of mutations. It had been found by Muller and various co-workers (Koerner, Vogt, Belgovsky, Berg, Panshin and Borisoff), and later confirmed by certain results of Dubinin and his colleagues, that the frequency of rearrangements that are readily detectable as such genetically, that is, "large rearrangements" induced by X rays, is proportional to more than the first power of the dosage (ionizing capacity) of the rays—the value being, for the doses ordinarily used, about half-way between the first and second power. On the other hand, as various workers have shown (Oliver, Hanson, Timoféeff-Ressovsky and others), and as special studies of Raffel have recently confirmed, the frequency of the "gene mutations" is simply proportional to the first power of the dosage of radiation. Here then there seemed to be a rather fundamental distinction between the mechanism of production of rearrangements, which presumably always involve at least two breaks and so may depend more nearly on the second power of the number of ions, and "gene mutations," which conceivably involved (at least in their initial stages) but one chemical substitution.

The possibility had not yet been excluded, however, that *minute* rearrangements might obey the same dosage rule as gene mutations, for they had not yet been tested in relation to this question, on account of the difficulty usually encountered in obtaining enough recognizable cases of them. Studies of Belgovsky, Prokofyeva,

Raffel and Muller, however, showed that, by the use of special stocks, minute rearrangements in or near certain chromocentral regions could be obtained and recognized in sufficient quantities, and it was accordingly decided that the frequency of the production of these rearrangements by different doses of X-rays should be measured. This has been done both by Belgovsky and by Muller and Makki (see Belgovsky 1939, Muller, Makki and Sidky 1939, Muller 1939) and their results have shown clearly that these minute rearrangements vary as the first power of the dosage, just like the supposed gene mutations. This result now breaks down the last empirical distinction that it was possible to draw between "gene mutations" and "chromosome rearrangements" and opens wide the door for considering the former also to result from double or multiple breaks, with reattachment, like the latter, but on an even minuter scale. And this in turn raises questions concerning the limits of what have been called "genes," and the propriety of assuming that "genes" as conceived according to our different hypothetical criteria are necessarily coextensive.

Since the above possibilities were suggested by Muller (1937) some similar suggestions have independently been made by Goldschmidt (1937 a, b, 1938). Although we differ from Goldschmidt in that we regard our suggestions as pointing, as yet, only to possibilities, while he regards his corresponding proposals as representing something highly probable, and although we differ also in various matters of emphasis, implication, and subsidiary interpretations, as well as in what we regard as the more valid grounds for regarding such a conception as plausible, we must nevertheless agree in the more general proposition, central to his theme and ours, that the "gene," in the rather loose sense in which it has so long been taken for granted by most geneticists, may *perhaps* be genetically further divisible, even into many genetically linearly arranged portions of semi-autonomous character (autonomous in the sense of their being able to reproduce when in other linear arrangements), and that, contrariwise, neighboring "genes" often or usually co-act, in a manner made possible by their juxtaposition, so as to produce character-effects that depend upon overlapping regions, somewhat larger than a single "whole gene," as formerly conceived. The idea of a "whole gene" or, more directly, of "a gene" itself, thus comes under scrutiny, and we are at present far from having evidence that the "whole gene" or "the gene" (meaning just *one* gene") would be the same when defined by the various different criteria listed. We should not wish, however, to deny the alternative possibility, that the in some ways simpler-seeming conception of indivisible genes in the older sense (modified, however, by the conception of the position effect) may eventually be found to correspond to the facts, after all. What we do wish to emphasize chiefly is that more work will be needed before the question can be decided.

Whether genetics and cytology themselves will provide methods adequate for solving such remote questions it is as yet too early to say. As an example, however, of a type of genetic study that might conceivably throw light on a question of this kind, we shall mention a study undertaken by Muller, with the aid of Sinitskaya, to determine whether it was possible to induce reverse mutations in scutes of the type reported upon in the present paper. If these scute mutations represented position effects of the rearrangements of "whole genes," in the older sense, then it should much more readily be possible to obtain reverse rearrangements that would restore the original order, and the normal phenotype, than if the scute mutations represented rearrangements the breakages of which had come between smaller parts of the "gene." For in the latter case new breaks would much more rarely (especially when both of them were considered) come between just the same two parts as before—a condition that might well be necessary in the case of so manifestly complex a gene as that for scute. In the latter case, too, there would have been a chance that a part of the gene had been lost when the original mutation occurred, and so could not be restored. On the other hand, in case "whole genes" were concerned, there would be especial reason for hoping that exactly reverse rearrangement might be found within a reasonable time, because it is known that breaks occur much oftener in or near the chromocentral region, and the scute rearrangements here in question are, as we have seen, such that both points of reattachment now adjoin such a region.

In order to increase the chance of breakages occurring near both of the original positions at once, a recombination chromosome was used which had the right end of scute-4, which contains the longest chromocentral region to the right of its right break, and the left end of scute-L8, which contains more chromocentral region just to the right of its left-hand break than scute-4 does, since bobbed is included in this region in scute-L8 but not in scute-4. (Unfortunately at that time it was not yet known that block-A was not in this region of scute-L8, along with bobbed, otherwise the left end of scute-S1, which has both these genes at the left end, would have been used.) Scute males having the above recombination chromosome were then X-rayed with a dose of about 3,000 r, and crossed to females with attached X chromosomes, and their sons were examined for possible reverse mutations of scute to a normal or near-normal phenotype. However, among the approximately 50,000 male offspring examined, none showed such a change.

We can by no means regard this negative result as being in itself of much significance, until the frequency with which breaks in and near such chromocentral regions occur becomes better known, and it will be desirable to have the experiment repeated, with even larger numbers. We present it only to show that the possibilities of investigating the general problems here at issue by means of genetic tests are as yet by no means exhausted.

All in all, we do not wish to give the impression that our results with the three scutes here reported upon actually support the idea of a finely divisible gene. They do, however, give evidence for the position effect, and this phenomenon in itself connotes that the gene, as defined by the mutation-allelism test, extends over a larger region than that defined by breakage, crossing over or self-reproducibility, and that, in fact, the regions of successive genes, as defined by the mutation-allelism test, do not merely adjoin but overlap each other. On the other hand, our present results do not, in themselves, give evidence of a finer divisibility than that found in our more general study of breakage in the scute region, which had indicated the existence of at least four separable genetic constituents ("genes") within the space of one or two visible bands, and which further showed that, if other breakage points than those forming these four parts existed, the elements included between them must be undetectable by ordinary genetic tests. It was, then, not these results, but those of other investigations, especially the recent ones on minute rearrangements and their relation to dosage, those on the phenotypic relations of achaete and scute, and general considerations based on the manner of production of mutations and the nature of the gene, that made it necessary to take up in some detail here the question of finer gene divisibility, and to consider to what extent our present results might be in favor of or opposed to such a conception. As we have seen, they can be interpreted in either way with roughly equal plausibility (aside from extraneous considerations that might affect the plausibility of the divisibility idea). Hence, so far as our present results are concerned, this matter must still be left an open question.

It should eventually be possible to obtain further light on this question through the obtaining of additional scute alleles and their intensive study. The next time an inversion occurs with the left break in the same apparent position as that of scutes 4, S1 and L8, and the right break just to the right or left of *bb* and block A or between them, will it, when made isogenic with whichever of these three scutes whose arrangement it seems to duplicate, also be identical with that scute phenotypically? If so, it is unlikely that the "scute gene" is subdivisible into different parts affecting the bristles. Such work is more or less complementary to the study of the effects of reverse rearrangement above discussed. And, in general, a continuance of intensive work on breakage in the scute region should give more information about the number of possible points of breakage.

There are other considerations bearing on the question of the segmentalism of the genetic material, for which the reader may be referred to another paper (Muller 1940). Among these are the results, obtained by Muller and Mackenzie (1939) since the present paper was written, showing that ultra-violet light produces gene mutations but not gross rearrangements. This and other facts would argue for a more fundamental distinction between gene mutations and rearrangements than that above suggested as one of the alternative extremes.

Summary

1. Analysis of the three scute mutations, scute-4, scute-S1 and scute-L8, produced by X-rays, shows that all three involve an inversion, having its left break close to the right of the "scute gene," and its right break in the proximal chromocentral ("inert") region of the X chromosome. None of the numerous other scute mutations investigated has breaks in both of these positions.

2. Single crossovers of both contrary classes between each of these inversions and each of the others are viable, and phenotypically similar to the original types (except as noted in section 5, following). Hence all three of the left-hand breaks must have been in identical positions or else in positions so close to one another that deficiency of the region between them was neither lethal nor productive of any detected abnormality (except as noted in section 5). Salivary study by Prokofyeva revealed no difference in positions of the left-hand breaks.

3. Genetic testing of the crossover chromosomes for bobbed and cytological testing (in metaphase stage) for block A showed that, while in scute-4 the right-hand break was to the left of both these genes, in scute-S1 it was to the right of both of them, and in scute-L8 between them, carrying bobbed to the left end and leaving block A at the right, a result that had probably been made possible by the occurrence of a further, very minute, rearrangement, whereby these two genes interchanged their positions. If other genes differentiated the positions of the right-hand breakage points, the absence of these from the X chromosome produces no effect detectable by the methods used. Salivary study by Prokofyeva showed that the right-hand breaks were differentiated by only one or two faint lines of the chromocentral region.

4. Phenotypically, these three mutations, and also the recombinations between them, resemble each other, but the exact extent of the resemblance or difference could not be gauged until isogenic groups of all nine of them (the three original combinations and the six possible recombinations between them) were constructed. The methods are given whereby, through a scheme of crosses involving 26 successive generations, the nine lines isogenic for all of the X chromosomes except their very ends were constructed, and whereby, through ten further generations, these nine groups were made isogenic for their major autosomes (again except for their very end regions) at the same time.

5. One of the recombinations between the original scutes (that having the left end of scute-4 and the right end of scute-L8) proved to be sterile, at least in the male, but when the isogenic lines were obtained the same type of recombinant, having the bulk of its X chromosome replaced by that of the standard X used, was as fertile as the other scutes. This shows that complementary genes for sterility had arisen in the X chromosomes of the two scute mutants, lying in different loci, and (at least one of them) separable from and not dependent upon the points of rearrangement of the inversions. Alone, neither caused sterility, but only in combination with one another. This serves to illustrate the mode of origination of genetic isolation in the evolutionary splitting of species.

6. Comparison of the nine isogenic groups shows them all to be much more similar to one another than any of them was to any of the numerous other investigated scute mutations. This, taken in connection with the unusual similarity of all of them to each other in gene arrangement, proves that there is a close connection between type of gene arrangement, that is, between the kind of neighbor genes a given gene possesses, and type of phenotypic effect, that is, the phenotypic similarity must be due to the "position effect" of the genes, and their change of expression, seen as the visible scute mutations, must have been due to the change of gene positions relative to their neighbor genes.

7. Despite the great similarity, there were unmistakable differences between the different types which it is logical to refer to the relatively slight differences in their gene arrangement.

8. Analytical comparisons of the nine classes and of averages between certain groups of them, showed that the left ends of the inversions differed in their effects in a consistent fashion, the order of abundance of bristles of practically all differentially affected types, in the presence of the left ends of the different scutes (with the right end derived from the same scute in all three cases), being scute-4 > S1 > L8. The isogenic lines of the original combinations of left and right ends showed the same order of effects. It is inferred that these differences in the left ends, and in the original scutes as a whole, are caused by the position effects, in connection with the scute gene, of genes that differentiate the present left ends of the chromosomes from one another, and that lie just to the right of the leftmost of these scute breaks. Among these genes may be bobbed and block A, and possibly other "invisible genes" from the original right or left ends, or from both.

9. Although there were also some differences of statistical significance produced by the different right ends (in the presence of a constant left end), these were considerably less than the differences produced by the left ends, were not in the same direction in the case of different bristles, showed no consistency when the results from the different right ends in the presence of one left end were com-

pared with the corresponding results in the presence of another left end, and showed no tendency to be complementary in value to the results from the left ends (as they should if due to a transfer, by the inversion, of different bristle-producing genes, or subgenes, from the original left to the right end). The interpretation accordingly suggests itself that the apparent differences obtained from the right ends might perhaps be really due to a lack of complete isogenicity on the part of the lines studied.

10. The question is raised of to what extent the breakages in the region of scute in this and other cases where they seem identical in position are really identical, or may be separated by parts of a "gene-complex" (or "gene," according to definition) which, although able to reproduce separately, function to produce bristles only, or mainly, when in proximity to one another, and function normally only when in proper arrangement. On account of the extreme reduction of bristles in these cases of nearly identical rearrangement, caused by the position effect, the influence upon the bristles of differences in such hypothetical parts might not be noticeable under these conditions. However, it is conceivable that they, rather than bobbed, block A, or other genes from the right end, are the chief differentiating factors that, by their differing position effects with the rest of the scute complex, cause the differences that have been noted between the effects of the different left ends. Similar considerations apply to other loci, and make it uncertain to what extent our criteria as to what constitutes a single gene, based upon different methods of approach (herein listed), refer to co-extensive structures. These considerations likewise affect our judgments regarding gene size and number. The undoubted overlapping of function of portions of the chromonema distant enough to be separable by crossing over or breakage, caused by the position effect, raises further difficulties in the delimitation or definition of *a* gene. In recent publications Goldschmidt has independently expressed a point of view which is in some essential respects similar to this.

11. The finding of minute rearrangements, with position effects resembling gene mutations, has made the above question more acute, for on the hypothesis of independently reproducing gene-parts or "sub-genes" (or genes within a larger gene-complex), the "gene mutations" *might* simply be rearrangements so small as to lie within a "gene" (or gene-complex). This would agree with the recent discovery by Belgovsky and Muller that demonstrable rearrangements of minute size vary in frequency as the first power of the X-ray dosage, like "gene mutations," and differently from large rearrangements, the variation of which is, for ordinary doses, approximately as the 3/2 power of the latter. However, the question of gene delimitation is as yet far from settled, being as yet in the earliest stage—that of being formulated. Certain genetic avenues of approach to it can be descried, of which one illustration is cited,

which involved an experiment, having negative results, designed to find reverse mutations of one of the recombinational scutes here studied. The failure here would argue for a relatively high divisibility of the genetic material, but is not yet to be taken as more than merely suggestive, especially since other considerations and results point in the opposite direction.

EVIDENCE OF THE PRECISION OF GENETIC ADAPTATION*

H. J. Muller
Professor of Zoology, Indiana University

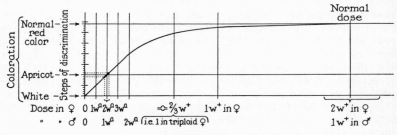

Fig. 5. The relation between eye color and gene dosage or activity in the case of apricot and its alleles, white and normal. The symbol w^+ represents the normal allele of apricot; w^a, as before, represents the apricot allele.

Dosage Compensation as an Adaptation
Developed in Connection with the Normal Type

Turning our attention to the question of the cause of the phenomenon, we must, to begin with, reckon with the at first sight surprising fact that the above cited manifestations of dosage compensation are all exhibited by mutant genes (mainly hypomorphs). It is evident that there could be only the most minimal advantage to the species in

The Harvey Lectures, Series XLIII, 1947-1948, Springfield, Illinois: Charles C. Thomas, 1950; lecture delivered February 19, 1948; pp. 188 (part)–209, 226 (part)–29, and figures 5 and 7, included.

having these mutant genes attain one degree of expression rather than another, in view of the fact that they occur so rarely in the population anyway, and that they are especially rare in that homozygous condition in females in which the compensators exert their characteristic effect. Moreover, it is found in the case of the locus of apricot, and of some others in which several grades of hypomorphic alleles are available, that in general the compensation works as well for one grade of mutant allele as for another, making the female about equal to the male. Now there can hardly be an advantage in keeping the apricot female's color as low as it is if at the same time there is an advantage, in the case of the darker allele coral, in having the grade of the female (though here too kept down to that of its own corresponding male) kept as *high* as it is in this latter case. The effect on the manifestation of the mutant character must therefore be an automatic result of the operation of processes the reason for existence of which lies in their effect in some other connection.

What then is this "other connection?" There can be but one answer here. The compensators must be genes, established in the normal type, which have the effect of equalizing the expressions of the *normal* alleles of the mutant genes which we have been studying, so as to make the female's two doses of the normal gene produce the same degree of development of the given character as does the male's one dose of the same normal gene. And the fact that the phenomenon is so general in its occurrence indicates that this result must entail some advantage to the individual and to the species. This advantage cannot lie in the fact of the resemblance itself, between male and female, that is thereby brought about in the given characters. Rather it must mean that, as regards most features and characters, whatever is the best grade of expression for an individual of one sex is also, and for the same reasons, the best grade for one of the other sex as well. For after all the males and females of the same species usually have much more in common, in their needs, way of life, physiology, ecology, etc., than they diverge in; and, while secondary sexual differences certainly should and do occur, these are, from the standpoint of the total organismic make-up, a comparatively minor part of the whole. But the genes in the X-chromosome are numbered in the hundreds or even thousands, and they concern all sorts of bodily processes and structures. Therefore, in the case of the great majority of them, that grade of development of their effects which is best for one sex is pretty much the same as the best grade for the other sex. Since, however, the female has two doses of each such gene and the male but one, the attainment of that same grade by both would require some special genetic mechanism, one only to be achieved by what we have termed "dosage compensators."

A converse proof of the existence of dosage compensation as an adaptation to the end of equalizing the expression of genes of which the two sexes have unequal doses is provided by an examination of the dosage effects of non-sex-linked genes. Here too we find, mainly from studies involving chromosomes with small sections missing, that most mutant genes are hypomorphs, giving a more normal grade of character as a result of two doses than of one. But here the two doses in the female give an effect like that of two doses in the male, in accordance with the fact that here both male and female do regularly have the same dosage. Thus, the sexes are again usually equal, but, compensators being unnecessary to achieve this result, genes having the property of compensators do not occur.

A still more crucial test of the same point is furnished by the case of the hypomorphic mutant called "bobbed," which reduces bristle size, a case worked out by Stern (1929) before dosage compensation was known. This gene lies in the X-chromosome, but in that small part of it which has a homologue in the Y-chromosome, so that, unlike the vast majority of sex-linked genes, the male has the locus represented in both its sex chromosomes, there being ordinarily one so-called normal allele in the X and, in effect, at least one[1] in the Y. Now the dosage studies showed that in this case, as with non-sex-linked genes, there was no dosage compensation, inasmuch as a male with one dose of the gene for bobbed, and lacking a Y, looked much like a female with one dose of it, while a female with two doses had much better developed bristles than either. A remarkable check on this case, being in a way the converse of the converse, is found in the genetic situation with respect to bobbed in the related Drosophila species *simulans*, as disclosed by data of Sturtevant (1929). Here the Y does not contain an allele of bobbed like the normal allele present in the X, but contains in some strains an amorph (i.e. fails to influence the bobbed character), and in others an allele which, like an antimorph, acts to intensify the abnormality when the mutant gene for bobbed is present in the X. Thus, dosage compensation of bobbed would certainly be expected in D. *simulans*, if it really exists to serve the end of character equalization. And this is in fact found to be the case. For, unlike what occurs in D. *melanogaster*, the *simulans* bobbed male without a Y, having its one dose of bobbed in the X, possesses as well developed bristles as the female with two doses of bobbed. All these cases, then, combine to show that it is not the fact of a gene's being in the X-chromosome, *per se*, which somehow leads to its being subject to · dosage compensation, for this phenomenon appears only in the case of those genes whose normal alleles are regularly in different doses in the two sexes.

Further evidence that the chromosome configuration in itself has nothing to do with the matter is seen in the cases in which a piece of the X-chromosome has become broken off and attached to another chromosome and/or, conversely, in which a part of another chromosome has become translocated onto the X. Whether the pieces are large or small, or derived from one or another chromosome region, the result is the same: the genes, both those originally of the X and those of other chromosomes, still have the same dosage effects as they did in their old positions. Compensation is a chemical mechanism, or rather, system of mechanisms, stably established in the distant past, with reference only to those particular genes which regularly existed in different doses in the two sexes, and so it continues to operate now even when we change the very conditions that must once have called it forth.

If our thesis is correct, dosage compensation is a mechanism normally at work to equalize the expressions of the different doses of *normal* genes present in the X-chromosomes of the two sexes, and it must have become established as a result of the advantage conferred by this regulation of the expression of the normal genes. Why then have we drawn our above cases from the effects observed in the case of *mutant* genes? Quite obviously this is because of the mutant genes' having a level of activity so low that differences in their dosages or activity give an easily observable result, whereas for normal genes, lying as they do near their saturation level, the difference in expression resulting from two as compared with one or three doses are usually imperceptible, as has previously been pointed out. Dosage tests like those above described for mutants have in fact been carried out for the normal alleles of all these mutants. But since the individuals, whether male or female, with one or two or three doses looked sensibly alike in the great majority of cases, no conclusion as to whether dosage compensation was or was not occurring could be directly derived from these observations. The mutants, in other words, were required by us to serve as indicators, or sensitizers, for processes and relations which we would not otherwise have been aware of, but which we cannot avoid concluding must really be present in the normal organism as well.[2]

But although the great majority of normal genes fail to show enough visible dosage effect to make such studies possible on the normal alleles of most known mutant genes, it would be strange if the X-chromosome, containing as it does from one to several thousand separable genes in all, did not include some normal genes that were far enough from their saturation level to be open to such investigation, either singly or collectively. That this is true is demonstrated by the fact that the subtraction of a comparatively small section from one of the X-chromosomes of an otherwise normal female, though it only changes the dosage of relatively few of her normal genes, frequently leads to a visible morphological abnormality (aside from effects on sex and sexual characters), of a type depending on what region is subtracted. The "deficiency," as it is called, is also apt to reduce the viability in some way, and it is certain to cause death if the piece removed is a rather large one, or if it includes any one of a number of particular loci. These results prove several points. It becomes evident, first, that there are a few normal genes whose effect is considerably different in one dose than in two. It is only to be expected, however, that these seldom happen to be the normal alleles of the relatively few visible mutations which we have to work with. Second, it is evident that there are many normal genes whose effect is slightly different in one than in two doses, so that by the reduction to single dose of many at once the combined effect becomes perceptible where the individual effect would not be. Third, the doses that these genes normally have, and their normal relationships to one another, are the ones most advantageous for the organism. And fourth, these normal genes are subject to dosage compensation.

At the risk of laboring our argument, it is important that we see clearly how the fourth conclusion above is arrived at. It depends on the fact that, when we reduce the dosage of the normal genes in a given section of the X-chromosome from two to one, by removing this section from one of the two X's of a female, we establish the dosage of *these* genes which the male normally has. The normal male however does not exhibit the morphological or physiological abnormalities that appear in the females with these deficiencies. This means that in it the normal genes in question, though present in only one dose, attain about as high an effectiveness as is achieved by the two doses of them in the female. This difference in effect can only be referred to the double dose which the females have of genes in other parts of the X-chromosome, that must act as compensators.

Further evidence of the same sort of thing is furnished by studies of the effect of *adding* sections of the X that contain normal genes. This operation too results in definite syndromes of visible and physiological abnormalities (aside from effects on sex and sexual characters), especially if the piece added is large, although, as might be expected from the shape of our curve of effectiveness (Fig. 5), a larger addition than subtraction can be tolerated. But in such cases it is always evident that, while addition of a given piece to a male (leading to two doses of it) results in changes similar in kind to those produced by the same addition to a female (leading to three doses of it in her), the changes in the male are considerably more pronounced. It will be seen that this male, having thereby been given only two doses of the normal genes in question, has, so far as these genes alone are concerned, a genetic composition which the female tolerates with entire impunity. The difference in effect obviously lies in the double doses of compensators for these normal genes which the female possesses. And that the two doses in the male cause even more abnormality than three doses of the same section of chromosome in the female is also to be expected, if the degree of effect depends on the ratio of primary genes to compensators. For the two-dose male has a ratio of these (2:1) which is further from the normal ratio (2:2 or 1:1) than is that of the three-dose female (3:2).

All the above evidence shows clearly that the normal genes in the X-chromosome are subject to dosage compensation, even though we can seldom prove this directly in the case of previously selected loci, containing the normal alleles of known mutant genes, since most normal genes are too near their saturation level to make such observation possible. But the question then arises, should not the very fact that most of these genes are so near their saturation level make dosage compensation unnecessary in their case? We have seen that for the normal alleles of apricot, scute, etc., practically no difference between the effects of one and two doses can be seen in either female or male. Why then would there be a perceptible advantage in going through the motions of equalizing them still further? The answer can only be that since, even for these cases, there is evidence from the mutant alleles that the compensation mechanism does apply to the given locus, we must conclude that there *is* an advantage in it, even when the genes are normal ones.

The Surpassing Precision of Adjustment thereby Implied

Let us now try to estimate how small the sex difference in the character is, which we have thus decided must affect the organism's welfare. We may use here essentially the same method as we applied when we calculated, on the basis of the variability of the mutant, how much variation in the normal character was consistent with survival. We may assume, as a first approximation (though one justified by existing data on multiple alleles), that the amount of effect of the compensators on the mutant genes is ordinarily about the same, relatively to the activity of these genes, as the amount of effect on the normal genes, relatively to the activity of the latter. That is, since we observe that the additional dose of compensators present in the mutant female as compared with the male reduces the effectiveness of the two doses of the given mutant gene which she possesses so as to make them equal to the one dose of the male, we infer that the compensators are likewise, in the normal female, reducing the effectiveness of her two doses of the normal allele to that of the male's one dose, and with at least as great relative accuracy. We may tentatively mark off the amount of activity thereby attained in the normal female as a point on the abscissa of our curve (e.g. in Fig. 5), placed in a region so near that of the saturation level that a point half way from the origin to this point would still give a character not perceptibly (to our unaided observation) different from it.

Now there has necessarily been a certain latitude in the determination of the exact grade of effectiveness of the mutant allele (e.g., apricot), owing to: (1) errors of perception or of measurement of the given character, and (2) variations in conditions that influence it. Moreover, in the case of some mutant genes, there is also some inaccuracy in the compensation achieved, evinced by under- or over-compensation as the case may be. A maximum estimate of the error from all these causes together has been indicated, in the case of apricot, by the dotted vertical lines arising on either side of the ordinate that marks the typical effect of two doses of the mutant in the female or one in the male. (In the given case, these limits represent mainly the degree of coarseness of our powers of observation—i.e., the discrimination thresholds.) But, in harmony with our previous premise, we should, to be on the side of caution, assume that, in its action on the normal character, the process of dosage compensation has an equivalent amount of latitude to that found in the mutant, in the sense that the inexactitude may be as much, *relatively* to the total activity of the normal genes, as it is relatively to that of the mutant genes. This enables us to plot on the abscissa the approximate plus and minus limits of the effectiveness of the genes existing in the normal type (either male or female). Constructing ordinates at these limits, and marking off the points at which they intersect our curve of effect, we may then find (on our vertical axis) the maximum difference in the normal character which could be produced by one dose in the normal male as compared with two doses in the normal female. It will be seen that in the given case this difference, which might be called the maximum inaccuracy of the dosage compensation, is small, even as compared with the difference caused by a change from one to two doses in the same sex.

Stating the above in a somewhat different way, let us first assume a maximal inexactitude of compensation for the mutant gene studied (apricot). This would here be about equal to one step of visual discrimination, since (according to observations of the author but contrary to some statements in the literature which report the male to be slightly darker) no certain difference can be distinguished between the apricot male and female. Now divide this maximal inexactitude (or, more properly speaking, uncertainty) by the amount of visible difference which the compensation mechanism is here working to offset, i.e., by the amount of visible difference between the effects of one and two doses of the apricot gene in the male. This gives a relative value for this maximal possible inexactitude, which turns out to be about one tenth. That is, *at least* nine tenths of the dosage difference has been compensated for but possibly (at most) there is a one tenth under- or over-compensation. To be on the side of caution, we may now assume that there is as great a relative inexactitude of compensation for the normal alleles also—although, on the average, the inexactitude should actually be less for normal than for mutant alleles, on account of the mechanism having been evolved in relation to the normals. This then leads us to the conclusion that, in the case of the normal alleles of apricot, not more than one tenth of the difference between the effects of one and two doses in the male has escaped compensation, while nine tenths at least have been compensated for. But we have seen that the entire difference in question, between the effects of one and two doses of the *normal* gene, whether in male or female, is itself (on the average, at least) imperceptible to our eye. Thus we find that selection has been sensitive to differences at least an order of magnitude smaller than the smallest difference which we can ordinarily see. Hence even subliminal gradations of this fineness are actually of adaptive significance to the organism.

Application of the same method leads to similar conclusions in the case of scute and most of the other characters observed in regard to this point. That is, the compensation mechanism involves a process, or system of processes, that works to a much greater degree of refinement than is visible to us. We have seen, then, that natural selection has in the first place, in the interests of character stability, established the effectiveness of the normal gene at a point on the curve so near to the saturation level that one dose is not visibly different in effect from two, so far as we can see. Yet even this likeness is far from sufficient, for organisms (male *versus* female) that may differ regularly to this seemingly slight degree, otherwise the mechanism of compensation would not have been set up, in addition to this, in the case of the great majority of sex-linked genes, so as to reduce the difference to a tenth or less of even this invisibly small amount!

It is evident too that the required equalization cannot so advantageously be achieved by the simpler method of stepping up the normal gene's effectiveness still more, into a still flatter portion of the curve, otherwise the more elaborate compensation mechanism which exists would not have been needed. That it does exist and therefore was needed shows that a relatively slight increase in the effect, in fact imperceptible to us, brought about in the above way, is disadvantageous, just as an imperceptible decrease in the effect is. In other words, it is as important to keep down the grade of the normal character to the given level in the two-dose female as to keep it up to that level in the one-dose male, and in most cases the gene's activity cannot advantageously be brought near enough to an actual saturation level to obviate this requirement. However, for the lesser variations in effectiveness of the normal gene, caused by fluctuating environmental conditions and by variable genetic "background," the raised stability brought about by the near-saturation level of the gene must be of great value.

There is no doubt, however, that in many cases specific regulatory mechanisms ("servomechanisms") have been evolved, in addition to the above, to achieve an even higher stability in the face of given especially frequent or especially disturbing conditions, as many phenomena both of embryology, regeneration, physiology and pathology show. Moreover, in a relatively small but absolutely huge number of cases, the adaptive reactions go far beyond mere stability, and consist instead of positive changes of an advantageous nature following given types of changes in conditions. These reactions range from the "morphogenic" to the "physiological," there being no essential distinction between the two categories. This however is a topic too large to be entered upon here, since it would launch us upon the entire subject of how the organism works. We mention it here only to set our own problem in its proper limited place in relation to biological phenomena in general.

In order to avoid the conclusion that differences far too small to be evident to us are nevertheless of importance to the organism some might prefer to suppose that selection has rather worked by eliminating the occasional individual in which, owing to special conditions, the character in question had been influenced to a considerably larger degree than usual by the gene difference in question. This possibility has already been discussed in its relation to the character stabilization brought about by raising the gene's effectiveness to near-saturation levels. We have seen that, although this position is tenable, and is doubtless valid to a certain extent, it nevertheless brings us to much the same conclusion in the end, when this is expressed in terms of the *average* amount of character-difference caused by a gene difference which has an appreciable adaptive value. Moreover, there is reason to infer that in many cases there is no actual threshold amount of difference which suddenly emerges as disadvantageous, but that the amount (or the chance) of disadvantage may be taken as roughly proportional to the amount of deviation from the norm, even in the case of minute differences. In such cases, then, the amount of selection involved would be the sum of that occurring for each grade of expression, and that for a given grade would be proportional to approximately the product of the number of individuals with that grade times the amount of their deviation (i.e., the size of the grade, when the normal is designated as zero). A reckoning of this kind will show that here the selection based on relatively low grades of deviation (e.g. those less than the standard deviation) will probably in most cases considerably outweigh that based on the rarer, more extreme deviants. This presupposes, however, for the cases we have dealt with above, that survival affords a considerably more sensitive criterion of the degree of development of the character than does our own eyesight.

An Objection Based on Correlation between Useless and Useful Characters

A different objection which may be raised to these conclusions is that, in studying the above characters of eye color, bristle development, etc., we may have been dealing only with certain unimportant superficial expressions of gene changes which have other, more important, effects, hidden from our casual observation. In other words, characters are often correlated in their development, and we may have studied the less important by-products of the gene-initiated processes. On this view, natural selection may in truth have resulted in the establishment of dosage compensation for the normal gene, because of the advantage of attaining a given level of development of its most important effect. This effect itself, though hidden, might be subject to a very considerable dosage influence. Yet, studying only the side effect, we may have been able to obtain evidence of only a subliminal action of the compensators. Granting this viewpoint, we might avoid the conclusion that. selection has had to deal with extremely fine differences.

It is true that genes do have multiple effects, thus causing correlations between characters, and that in no individual case with which we are dealing can we know that the advantage of the dosage compensation mechanism lies in its influence over that particular effect of the given gene which is obvious to us. However, it would be strange if we had missed the major effect of the gene in such a large majority of the cases, especially since some at least of the genes concerned (the normal alleles of yellow, achaete and white) have been proved physiologically dispensable, i.e., the individual can live in the total absence of these genes. But if we have caught the major effect in any of the cases, then that effect does show the type of compensation at issue—a type so refined as to operate on subliminal grades of the character. Furthermore, we have seen that with but very rare exceptions (relative to the total number of genes) the effects of individual genes, whether in the X or other chromosomes, are so near their saturation level as to make direct discrimination between one and two doses impossible. Since a very wide sampling has consistently given this result, it would be highly unlikely that this relation did not hold for the major effects of genes in general as well as for their minor effects. In fact, if our interpretation is correct it is particularly for the major effects that this aid to stability has been established. But if this is true of the major effects, and if the dosage compensation found is, as the present criticism started out by assuming, also a phenomenon developed primarily for its influence on the major effect, then the main conclusion still remains valid, for the compensation results in much finer grades of difference even than those, already subliminal, which are due to doubling or halving the dose. Thus, in any case, the compensation mechanism must be concerned with the equalization of exceedingly minute differences.

A third point to be considered in connection with the question here at issue is the following: The great majority of characters which a gene affects are not immediate products of it but are end-results of complex webs of biochemical processes, in which a given thread or chain of reactions can, theoretically, be picked out that has its root in the gene in question, and leads from the latter to the character through a considerable series of events (see Fig. 7). Now when the

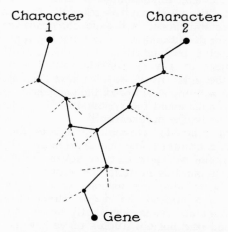

Fig. 7. Diagram of a branching chain of reactions whereby a given gene produces two effects. Each straight continuous line represents some intermediate process between the gene and the characters observed, and each dot represents a new developmental stage or substance, resulting from those processes which lead up to it. Dotted lines represent processes derived from other genes or gene-combinations, or from environmental influences, that impinge upon the processes derived from the given gene and affect the nature of the next stage reached.

given gene has multiple effects, it is evident that the gene either serves as the root of two or more entirely separate chains of reactions which respectively lead to the two or more characters affected, or else that, although but one basal chain of processes has its start at the given gene, this chain somewhere along the line becomes branched, so as finally to diverge to the two or more correlated characters. Owing to the complexity of the whole web of ontogenetic and physiological processes, the branching will, in the case of different genes, occur at different points. In some cases it will happen to occur early, near to or at the gene itself, while in others it will occur late, near the character which the observer examines. This diversity in the position of the branching has been amply demonstrated by many studies in physiological genetics, as well as in other fields of biology and medicine.

Now influences derived from other genes (as well as, ultimately at least, from environmental sources) impinge upon these chains of reaction at practically every link, thus playing their part in the determination of the final characters. Unless we make very unusual assumptions the compensating genes work in this way too. That is, the compensations may be achieved by influences impinging on the reaction chain at any point. And as it is a matter of indifference to the organism at which point this anastomosis of effects takes place, so long as the final advantageous result, compensation, is attained, it will sometimes be above and sometimes below the branching that leads to a given character (Fig. 7), if this character alone is important enough to have compensation established for it. Moreover, in such a case, if the compensation is the accumulated result of a number of influences, derived from different, cooperating compensator-genes, some of these influences, ordinarily, will be brought to bear above, and others below, the point of branching. Only those influences which act below the branching, however, would then affect the secondary characters as well as the important one. For this reason, we should not expect to find dosage compensation to be nearly so widespread or so accurate as it is if we had been studying only secondary characters, such as were of too little importance for the mechanism to have been developed in relation to them themselves. All in all, then, we may reject the objection based on correlation of characters, and conclude that dosage compensation has in fact become established because of its advantage in regulating more precisely the grade of characters whose variation in grade, *even without it*, would be exceedingly minute.

We may here digress to point out that the considerations above set forth concerning the way in which the reactions initiated by genes bifurcate to produce multiple effects (Fig. 7) also throw light on the related question of the extent to which selection for a given important character may be expected automatically to carry in its train a developmentally correlated but not advantageous change in another character. It should rarely happen that two apparently separate characters, especially if they be characters governing only degrees of development or proportions of already present parts or substances, will be so closely connected, with the branching occurring so very near to the distal end of the reaction chain of either of them, that they cannot both be affected separately, by influences impinging beyond the point of branching. Therefore if the so-called secondary effect is a disadvantageous one, it will usually be corrected, without disturbance of the primary effect, by means of a selection acting upon genes which affect the secondary branch but not the main stem. Moreover, it is to be expected—especially in view of our present results—that most visible characters, even those of an apparently superficial nature or of very minor degree, will nevertheless have enough importance in themselves for their variations to be felt in the selective process. For this reason we should be very wary of any interpretations which would explain the existence of a given grade of development of a character as an automatic by-product of selection for a more primary character.

So, for example, the finding that the mutation from the normal grayish-tan to yellow body color in Drosophila results in a cuticle which is not so resistant to environmental changes in dampness in no way explains why the flies do not normally have a yellow body color. For if that color were in itself advantageous it could doubtless be arrived at by selection of mutations in other genes which, though not having the undesirable chemical action, nevertheless gave effectively the same color, or by selection of "modifying" mutations which, with the gene for yellow in question, counteracted the undesirable chemical effect, while leaving the color yellow. In fact, there are other species which normally look rather like the yellow mutant of D. *melanogaster* and it is probable that in them some such arrangement has in fact been attained by selection (without giving them the above mentioned handicap), as a result of ecological conditions which put a premium on such a color.

The organism, then, is genetically highly plastic, at least so far as its proportions and the relative degrees of development of its different features are concerned. Thus we may assume it, in general, to have attained optima in all these respects, largely regardless of developmental correlations. In fact, the correlations normally occurring, such as the observed principles of heterogonic growth, Gloger's rule, etc., have themselves come down through the long mill of selection and hence are themselves in large measure advantageous adaptive reactions. Moreover, they can themselves be changed again by further mutation and selection, as observations of specialists in such fields have shown. Nevertheless, the organism does of course have its grave limitations, causing change in some directions and to some degrees to be more difficult than in others, or even impossible.

The Developmental Mechanisms Involved in Dosage Compensation

In the above discussions we have implied that dosage compensation has, for each sex-linked gene that is subject to it, become established through a natural selection of all available and innocuous mutations in the X chromosome that chanced to result in a compensating action upon the expression of the sex-linked gene in question. (Included here of course would also be such mutations in the given gene itself as furthered its sensitivity to such compensation.) This interpretation would put the method of evolution of this phenomenon in line with that which we have good reason to conclude has been followed in the case of most other functional systems of organisms. It might however be postulated that there are one or more peculiar genes in the X-chromosome which are especially suited to serve as compensators to all others in it, and that the only mutations then needed to achieve compensation are those, perhaps of a simple specific type, in the genes to be compensated, which allow the developmental processes caused by them to become responsive to the influence of these particular compensators. As a plausible guess, it might further be postulated that these compensators are none other than the gene or genes determining sex itself, and that their compensating influence is exerted through processes which form a part of those that differentiate the sexes.

Even though it is now known that, in Drosophila, the turning of the scales which decides which sex is to develop depends upon the cumulative action of numerous sex-differentiating genes of individually small effect, scattered through the X-chromosomes, this would not vitiate the possibility here in question. For the effects of these numerous genes obviously converge to set going one fundamental sex-differentiating process, or "focal reaction," on which in turn most or all of the secondary features of sex differentiation depend (see Muller, 1932a). This is shown, among other things, by the essential similarity of the whole system of results, so far as sex is concerned, whenever any limited group of these sex-differentiating genes comes into play, in experiments in which the dosage of different parts of the X-chromosome is varied. Thus it might well be supposed that either this main sex-differentiating process itself or one derived from it served as the root mechanism for dosage compensation, which would thereby take on the aspect of a secondary sexual phenomenon of fairly familiar type.

This possibility was never thought to be very probable, in view of certain results derived from a study of X-chromosome fragments, to be mentioned presently. It has however been pretty definitely disproved recently, by some experiments carried out in 1946 by the present writer and Miss Margaret Lieb in collaboration, but not yet published (see Lieb, '46). These made use of a mutant gene called "transformer" found by Sturtevant, a recessive lying not in the X but in the third chromosome, which has the effect, when homozygous, of causing flies with two X-chromosomes, which otherwise would have become normal females, to develop into males. Although sterile (even when provided with a Y), these males are well developed in virtually all other respects, so that it can be inferred that the main sex-differentiating process has been initiated in them in very much the same form as it has in regular males. If now the dosage compensation of the Drosophila female is brought about through effects of the female sex-determining process, or system of processes, as such, then these males with two X-chromosomes should not have the dosage compensation characteristic of the female operative in them. If, for instance, they are provided with two doses of apricot, one in each X-chromosome, they should have the rather dark eye color characteristic of the male with two doses, not the compensated color of the female with two doses, which looks like the one-dose male. The test clearly showed, however, that they had the fully compensated color, like that of the female with two doses, even though they were males with two doses. Obviously then, the compensation was caused, as in the ordinary female with two doses of apricot, by the presence of a double dose of compensators, lying in other parts of the X than at the locus of apricot itself, and these worked quite independently of the sex-differentiating genes, since all of the latter, together, although present, were here quite incompetent to cause any visible approach towards the female sex. Tests of several other compensated sex-linked characters than apricot—scute, forked and Bar—with the transformer gene gave this same result quite unequivocally for all.

These findings had been expected because tests performed much earlier, involving the addition of different fragments of the X-chromosome, first by the writer and then by Offermann working in collaboration with the writer, had shown that, in the case of different sex-linked genes, there is a different distribution of sex-compensating potencies throughout the length of the X-chromosome. That is, not only were the fragments taken from different regions unequally effective in the compensation of a given gene (when due allowance was made for their sizes), but their effectiveness relative to one another was not the same when tested with one sex-linked gene as when tested with another one. The different genes therefore had, to a considerable extent at least, different compensators, not one common set of compensators as they would have had if the compensation had worked through sex-differentiating effects. Furthermore, the results for none of the sex-linked genes agreed well with the relative values of the different regions of the X-chromosome in influencing sex-determination itself, as worked out, after some pioneer work of the present author, chiefly by Dobzhansky and Schultz, and by Patterson, Stone, Bedichek and their associates.

A further and more elaborate investigation of the behavior of the different regions of the X-chromosome in compensating for particular genes has been carried out more recently (1946), by the writer and Lieb working in collaboration, and the results from this confirm and extend the earlier conclusions. It would take us too far afield here to describe in detail the technique or the results of these various experiments on the location of the compensators. The method was, essentially, first to produce by irradiation fragments of the X-chromosome taken from different regions, and then to determine to what extent the addition of these fragments to a regular chromosome complement (usually of a female) affected the expression of a given sex-linked character, the locus of which lay outside of the fragment. In most cases the compensation proved to be a complex phenomenon, which could not be pinned down, *in toto*, to a particular chromosome region, nor even regarded as a simple summation of the effects of the different regions. Some regions, however, had distinctly more influence than others in the compensation of a given gene, and there were even cases where a certain region exerted what may be called a "negative compensation," working in exactly the wrong direction, an effect which was however counteracted by means of overcompensation elsewhere. That is, the surprisingly accurate compensation exerted by the chromosome as a whole was a final resultant, brought about only through an integration of individual effects which in detail appear chaotic. And a similar chaos was evident on comparison of the manner of distribution of the effects among different regions, as seen in comparisons of the cases of different compensated genes.

Now this is exactly the sort of result we should anticipate if each gene has had its own separate system of compensators selected for it, and if the compensation for each has in most cases come about by a succession of steps. Some genes could of course have gained a foothold (if we suppose them not to have been priorly present) that even worked the wrong way in the given respect, provided they possessed an advantage lying in some other direction, but even these would ultimately be corrected, by the selection of genes that counteracted such an effect, as we have pointed out in our discussion of correlated characters, and so the final resultant effect would be superior to that of any single interacting gene. The attainment of the accuracy finally arrived at must usually have required many small mutations, which, taken together, increasingly whittled the character into shape, as it were. And while in some cases these mutations may have been successive changes in the same gene, any mutation in the X-chromosome that worked in the advantageous direction would be acceptable, so that in most cases it is to be expected that a fairly complex system became at last established. Since, however, the advantage of the compensation for any single locus is only what might be called a "second-order" one, dealing as it does with such minute, to us subliminal, grades of effect, the establishment of these precisely working systems must have taken far more time than needed for visible "first order" effects. Moreover, there may more often have been setbacks which required repair, and which thus led to still greater complexity.

If we may infer that most of the genes in the X-chromosome have compensation systems like those studied above (an inference to be accepted with some caution since we were dealing only with genes capable of giving conspicuous visible mutations), we would be led to the peculiar conclusion that, since there is usually more than one compensator for each gene of the X-chromosome, and since the compensators are themselves in this chromosome, most sex-linked genes not only have an original or primary function but also serve as compensators for one or more other sex-linked genes. Each individual gene then would be complex in its functioning and also in its potentialities of mutating so as to affect its different functions to different degrees, relatively to one another. Finally, as there are over a thousand sex-linked genes, it will be seen how amazingly complex, in all probability, is the tangle formed by the sex-linked system as a whole.

In conceiving the mode of action of a compensator, or collective group of compensators, for a given sex-linked gene, which we will call the "primary gene," it is easy to make the mistake of thinking that each dose of the compensator or compensators effects a given total amount of reduction of the activity of the primary gene (or rather, gene-product). If this were true however then the female with her two doses of both primary and compensators would show an effect equivalent to twice that produced by the one dose of primary and one of compensators in the male. In other words, there would be no equalization of the sexes. Moreover, in that case compensators acting strongly with hypomorphs would not work properly for genes at higher levels. We must therefore infer that the compensators, when present in any given dose, work in such a way as to effect the same *proportionate* amount of reduction in primary gene activity, regardless (within wide limits) of what the dose or activity of the primary gene is. This would ordinarily be the case if the inhibiting action of the compensator were itself little influenced, in return, by the amount of primary gene-product it had to affect. An example of this would be a situation in which the compensator's "product," determined indirectly by its gene, consisted in some such pervasive condition as a relatively high pH, which the primary gene's product, no matter how concentrated, had little effect on. In such cases, then, the compensators, at a given dose, would tend to reduce the primary action by a given proportion, rather than by a given absolute amount.

Moreover, the relations must be so fixed that the compensators, when themselves in double dose, reduce the effect of a given dose of the primary gene to half of that which would obtain in the presence of a single dose of compensators. For only thus can the effect of the female's double dose be reduced to that of the male's single dose. Such a result would be brought about most simply in a case in which the compensators, when themselves in single dose, reduced the primary effect to half what it otherwise would be, and in which, when their dose was raised, their own effectiveness rose in the usual geometrical manner. For, in such a case, one dose of the primary with one of compensators, as in the male, would have an effect which may be designated as "one half" (i.e. one half that of one uncompensated dose of the primary gene). And two doses of the primary with two of compensators, as in the female, would have an effect equal to the product of two doses (for the primary) times one half (for the first dose of compensators) times another one half (for the second dose of compensators), a product which of course is itself equal to one half, and therefore the same as the effect in the male, i.e., properly compensated. And no matter what the degree of activity of the primary gene might be in such a case (e.g., whether it were the normal allele or, say, a hypomorph having an activity equal only to one quarter of one dose of the normal), the compensation would still work to equalize the effects of the one and two doses of the primary in the two sexes. Whether this simple scheme is usually true can probably be determined definitely through quantitative studies involving several different doses of compensators.

Summary

The attempt to interpret the structures and reactions of living things without reference to their adaptive significance is a consequence of confused thinking, stemming from the opposition to the Darwinian principle of natural selection. As shown by illustrations from Drosophila, mutations provide abundant evidence of the adaptiveness of existing "normal" features, as well as material for determining how these features operate in furthering the life of the individual or the species. Moreover, a study of the effects of changing the number (dosage) of genes, and of the nature of the dominance of normal to mutant genes, leads to the conclusion that not only is each normal feature of adaptive value, in a qualitative sense, but that its exact grade of development, quantitatively considered, represents the optimum value for it under the conditions that prevailed during the period when it attained that value. For the activity of each gene is usually so near its saturation level as to result in a high stability of its effects, despite the presence of disturbing factors. It is this which ordinarily results, secondarily, in its appearing to be dominant over its more weakly acting ("hypomorphic") mutant allele.

Beyond this, a study of the expression of mutant genes which exist in two doses in the female and one in the male (those in the X-chromosome) shows that special genetic mechanisms have been evolved for compensating for the effects of these dosage differences, so as to make the amount of effect in the two sexes much more nearly the same than it otherwise would be. The mechanisms involve the presence of other, modifying genes in the X-chromosome, that may be termed "compensators." These, in their double dose in the female, reduce the activity of her two doses of the "primary gene" so as to make the effect like that of the one dose of primary gene and one of compensators in the male. It is shown that actually these mechanisms must have been evolved for the function of equalizing the effects of the normal genes rather than the mutants, even though we can seldom be aware of this equilization in the case of normal genes, because of their above-mentioned near-saturation level. In other words, the stabilization of expression attained through the high level of activity of the normal gene does not by itself equalize the effects in the two sexes sufficiently to satisfy the organism's needs, despite its giving effects in one versus two doses which are not to us perceptibly different. For the compensating mechanisms which have been evolved serve to equalize them much more exactly.

This shows that differences in visible characters which are of far finer grade than can be detected by our own powers of discrimination are nevertheless of adaptive significance in the organism's struggle for existence, i.e., they are of selective value.

Experiments are cited which show that these compensating reactions are no mere consequences of the sex difference itself, that a given gene usually has a whole system of interacting compensatorgenes, and that the systems for different genes are different from one another. Thus each must have evolved through an accumulation of several or many steps, subliminal to our perception. The second-order magnitude of this selection pressure is illustrated by evidence of Lamy and the writer, indicating the incompleteness of the compensation for genes in parts of the X-chromosome of D. *pseudoobscura* which have more recently been acquired by the X from another chromosome. The objection is considered that, instead of subliminal selection for the characters under observation, the results may be due to the developmental correlation of these characters with other, more important but unobserved characters, in regard to which major differences were caused by the one-dose: two-dose relation of the sexes. It is shown that this interpretation encounters serious difficulties, based on the lack of completeness of developmental correlation. Thus we are led back to the conclusion that selection must in fact have dealt subliminally with the actually observed characters.

Further evidence of the adaptive value of normal characters, and in fact of the value of the precise grade of expression which they exhibit, is found in their frequent persistence virtually unchanged over millions of years, and even in different species having similar needs. It is shown that the frequency of mutation is high enough to have prevented such stability, had selection not actively favored the given norm. The causes of deviations from high stability are considered. A formula is given whereby the strength of such selection can be calculated from the existing variability within a large, persistent and interbreeding population, when the amount of variation arising by mutation per generation has also been determined. Though data of the latter nature are as yet insufficient it can in the meantime be concluded that the prevalent assumption is incorrect which would regard deviations within the so-called "normal range" (e.g., within the central eight or nine deciles of a population) as being of negligible detriment to individuals possessing them.

It is concluded that long persistent morphological, physiological or biochemical features, characteristic of large populations, should in general be assumed to have or to have had adaptive value, under the conditions in which these groups evolved, and that the degree to which they are normally developed is also of adaptive significance. Failure to find this significance, or function, is to be taken as an indication of our ignorance, and of the need for a deeper understanding of their workings. This justifies us in applying a "teleological" viewpoint here, which is in no wise mystical. In medicine, it should, moreover, lead to caution in attempting the alteration of standard bodily reactions, or the extirpation or alteration of structures normally present, until the functions of these parts and processes, and of their normal degree of development, have been well determined. At the same time, it must also be recognized that selection itself has been subject to grave limitations. Some of these have been discussed above. The organism is not perfect in any absolute sense, otherwise there would be no use in medicine, or in any form of artificial "interference" with nature.

Notes

[1]It is probably present in full or nearly full strength in just one arm of the Y (the short arm), and in the form of a weaker allele in the other arm, as Neuhaus first showed. Thus the male would have it represented thrice, but its total dose is probably not much, if any, more than double in this sex, so that the male's dose is not very different from the female's.
[2]More delicate than direct observation of eye color, however, is electrophotometric determination of the relative concentration of extracted pigment. R. M. Valencia, F. Verderosa and the author have, since the above was written, applied this method to the red pigment of eyes having the *normal* allele of apricot. The results show unequivocally that this normal allele does in fact (like apricot but unlike eosin) have dosage compensation, just as had been expected on our theory presented above. (Footnote added in proof, May 14, 1949.)

FURTHER EVIDENCE OF THE RELATIVELY HIGH RATE OF ORIGINATION OF "INVISIBLE" DETRIMENTAL MUTATIONS*

H. J. Muller and Helen U. Meyer

To develop a criterion of relative fitness including both survival and reproductive effectiveness, *Drosophila* X-chromosomes, to serve as "experimental" and "control," respectively, were first made co-isogenic except for a small terminal region differentiated as regards yellow. After experimentals (nonyellows) were subjected

Science, 1959, 130: 1422; paper presented before the National Academy of Sciences meeting at Indiana University, Bloomington, November 18, 1959.

to the chosen influence, each experimental chromosome and its (randomly picked) control were multiplied rapidly. Of each such experimental and control pair about 12 parallel sublines were then established in capacious culture jars, by putting into each jar 600 males, equally divided among experimentals and controls, and 600 females having attached X-chromosomes. In every generation parents were discarded, and offspring, after abundant accumulation, were transferred en masse. Thus the males' X-chromosomes competed severely without interchanging parts. Yellow was meanwhile "covered" by Y-chromosomes containing nonyellow. Anomalous interchange, via triploidy or chromosome detachments, was prevented by sterility genes. After 12 to 24 generations of competition a subline's resultant ratio was ascertained by crossing its males en masse to recessive females having separate X-chromosomes, and then scoring "regular" daughters for yellow.

Disregarding fitness changes of < 10 per cent as insufficiently conclusive, 10 pairs of chromosomes having neither member experimental showed one yellow inferior, also one nonyellow; 14 pairs whose nonyellows had before competitive breeding accumulated spontaneous mutations (evidenced by 10 per cent lethals) heterozygously in females for 53 generations showed four fitness decreases, all nonyellows; 43 pairs whose nonyellows had averaged 16,000r exposure in oogonia (lethal yield, 8 per cent) showed 12 inferior, all nonyellows. These results confirm earlier conclusions that "invisible detrimentals" arise at least 3 to 4 times as frequently as lethals.

3 Gene Theory

See also in this volume:

"Bearings of the Drosophila Work on Systematics," pp. 482-96

"Continuity and Discontinuity of the Hereditary Material," pp. 332-38

"A Further Analysis of Loci in the So-called 'Inert Region' of the X Chromosome of Drosophila," pp. 443-49

"Minute Intergenic Rearrangement as a Cause of Apparent 'Gene Mutation,' " pp. 339-43

"On the Dimensions of Chromosomes and Genes in Dipteran Salivary Glands," pp. 362-67

"The Optical Dissociation of Drosophila Chromomeres by Means of Ultraviolet Light," pp. 344-49

"The Origination of Chromatin Deficiencies as Minute Deletions Subject to Insertion Elsewhere," pp. 350-61

VARIATION DUE TO CHANGE IN THE INDIVIDUAL GENE*

Dr. H. J. Muller

I. The Relation between the Genes and the Characters of the Organism

The present paper will be concerned rather with problems, and the possible means of attacking them, than with the details of cases and data. The opening up of these new problems is due to the fundamental contribution which genetics has made to cell physiology within the last decade. This contribution, which has so far scarcely been assimilated by the general physiologists themselves, consists in the demonstration that, besides the ordinary proteins, carbohydrates, lipoids, and extractives, of their several types, there are present within the cell *thousands* of distinct substances—the "genes"; these genes exist as ultra-microscopic particles; their influences nevertheless permeate the entire cell, and they play a fundamental rôle in determining the nature of all cell substances, cell structures, and cell activities. Through these cell effects, in turn, the genes affect the entire organism.

It is not mere guesswork to say that the genes are ultra-microscopic bodies. For the work on *Drosophila* has not only proved that the genes are in the chromosomes, in definite positions, but it has shown that there must be hundreds of such genes within each of the larger chromosomes, although the length of these chromosomes is not over a few microns. If, then, we divide the size of the chromosome by the minimum number of its genes, we find that the latter are particles too small to give a visible image.

The chemical composition of the genes, and the formulae of their reactions, remain as yet quite unknown. We do know, for example, that in certain cases a given pair of genes will determine the existence of a particular enzyme (concerned in pigment production), that another pair of genes will determine whether or not a certain agglutinin shall exist in the blood, a third pair will determine whether homogentisic acid is secreted into the urine ("alkaptonuria"), and so forth. But it would be absurd, in the third case, to conclude that on this account the gene itself consists of homogentisic acid, or any related substance, and it would be similarly absurd, therefore, to regard cases of the former kind as giving any evidence that the gene *is* an enzyme, or an agglutinin-like body. The reactions whereby the

*In symposium on "The Origin of Variations" at the thirty-ninth annual meeting of the American Society of Naturalists, Toronto, December 29, 1921; published in *The American Naturalist*, Vol. LVI, January-February, 1922. Contribution No. 156 of Dept. of Zoology, University of Texas.

genes produce their ultimate effects are too complex for such infer- ences. Each of these effects, which we call a "character" of the or- ganism, is the product of a highly complex, intricate, and delicately balanced system of reactions, caused by the interaction of countless genes, and every organic structure and activity is therefore liable to become increased, diminished, abolished, or altered in some other way, when the balance of the reaction system is disturbed by an alteration in the nature or the relative quantities of any of the component genes of the system. To return now to these genes them- selves.

II. The Problem of Gene Mutability

The most distinctive characteristic of each of these ultra-micro- scopic particles—that characteristic whereby we identify it as a gene—is its property of self-propagation: the fact that, within the complicated environment of the cell protoplasm, it reacts in such a way as to convert some of the common surrounding material into an end-product identical in kind with the original gene itself. This ac- tion fulfills the chemist's definition of "autocatalysis"; it is what the physiologist would call "growth"; and when it passes through more than one generation it becomes "heredity." It may be observed that this reaction is in each instance a rather highly localized one, since the new material is laid down by the side of the original gene.

The fact that the genes have this autocatalytic power is in itself sufficiently striking, for they are undoubtedly complex substances, and it is difficult to understand by what strange coincidence of chemistry a gene can happen to have just that very special series of physico-chemical effects upon its surroundings which produces—of all possible end-products—just this particular one, which is identi- cal with its own complex structure. But the most remarkable fea- ture of the situation is not this oft-noted autocatalytic action in it- self—it is the fact that, when the structure of the gene becomes changed, through some "chance variation," the catalytic property of the gene may[1] become correspondingly changed, in such a way as to leave it still *auto*catalytic. In other words, the change in gene structure—accidental though it was—has somehow resulted in a change of exactly *appropriate* nature in the catalytic reactions, so that the new reactions are now accurately adapted to produce more material just like that in the new changed gene itself. It is this par- adoxical phenomenon which is implied in the expression "variation due to change in the individual gene," or, as it is often called, "mu- tation."

What sort of structure must the gene possess to permit it to mu- tate in this way? Since, through change after change in the gene, this same phenomenon persists, it is evident that it must depend upon some general feature of gene construction—common to all genes— which gives each one a *general* autocatalytic power—a "carte blanche"—to build material of whatever specific sort it itself happens to be composed of. This general principle of gene structure might, on the one hand, mean nothing more than the possession by each gene of some very simple character, such as a particular radicle or "side-chain"—alike in them all—which enables each gene to enter into combination with certain highly organized materials in the outer protoplasm, in such a way as to result in the formation, "by" the protoplasm, of more material like this gene which is in combination with it. In that case the gene itself would only initiate and guide the direction of the reaction. On the other hand, the extreme alternative to such a conception has been generally assumed, perhaps gratuitously, in nearly all previous theories concerning hereditary units; this postulates that the chief feature of the autocatalytic mechanism resides in the structure of the genes themselves, and that the outer protoplasm does little more than provide the building material. In either case, the question as to what the general principle of gene construction is, that permits this phenomenon of mutable autocatalysis, is the most fundamental question of genetics.

The subject of gene variation is an important one, however, not only on account of the apparent problem that is thus inherent in it, but also because this same peculiar phenomenon that it involves lies at the root of organic evolution, and hence of all the vital phenomena which have resulted from evolution. It is commonly said that evolution rests upon two foundations—inheritance and variation; but there is a subtle and important error here. Inheritance by itself leads to no change, and variation leads to no permanent change, unless the variations themselves are heritable. Thus it is not inheritance *and* variation which bring about evolution, but the inheritance *of* variation, and this in turn is due to the general principle of gene construction which causes the persistence of autocatalysis despite the alteration in structure of the gene itself. Given, now, any material or collection of materials having this one unusual characteristic, and evolution would automatically follow, for this material would, after a time, through the accumulation, competition and selective spreading of the self-propagated variations, come to differ from ordinary inorganic matter in innumerable respects, in addition to the original difference in its mode of catalysis. There would thus result a wide gap between this matter and other matter, which would keep growing wider, with the increasing complexity, diversity and so-called "adaptation" of the selected mutable material.

III. A Possible Attack through Chromosome Behavior

In thus recognizing the nature and the importance of the problem involved in gene mutability have we now entered into a *cul de sac*, or is there some way of proceeding further so as to get at the physical basis of this peculiar property of the gene? The problems of growth, variation and related processes seemed difficult enough to attack even when we thought of them as inherent in the organism as a whole or the cell as a whole—how now can we get at them when they have been driven back, to some extent at least, within the limits of an invisible particle? A gene cannot effectively be ground in a mortar, or distilled in a retort, and although the physico-chemical investigation of other biological substances may conceivably help us, by analogy, to understand its structure, there seems at present no method of approach along this line.

There is, however, another possible method of approach available: that is, to study the behavior of the chromosomes, as influenced by their contained genes, in their various physical reactions of segregation, crossing over, division, synapsis, etc. This may at first sight seem very remote from the problem of getting at the structural principle that allows mutability in the gene, but I am inclined to think that such studies of synaptic attraction between chromosomes may be especially enlightening in this connection, because the most remarkable thing we know about genes—besides their mutable autocatalytic power—is the highly specific attraction which like genes (or local products formed by them) show for each other. As in the case of the autocatalytic forces, so here the attractive forces of the gene are somehow exactly adjusted so as to react in relation to more material of the same complicated kind. Moreover, when the gene mutates, the forces become readjusted, so that they may now attract material of the new kind; this shows that the attractive or synaptic property of the gene, as well as its catalytic property, is not primarily dependent on its specific structure, but on some general principle of its make-up, that causes whatever specific structure it has to be auto-attractive (and autocatalytic).

This auto-attraction is evidently a strong force, exerting an appreciable effect against the non-specific mutual repulsions of the chromosomes, over measurable microscopic distances much larger than in the case of the ordinary forces of so-called cohesion, adhesion and adsorption known to physical science. In this sense, then, the physicist has no parallel for this force. There seems, however, to be no way of escaping the conclusion that in the last analysis it must be of the same nature as these other forces which cause inorganic substances to have specific attractions for each other, according to their chemical composition. These inorganic forces, according to the newer physics, depend upon the arrangement and mode of motion of the electrons constituting the molecules, which set up electro-magnetic fields of force of specific patterns. To find the principle peculiar to the construction of the force-field pattern of genes would accordingly be requisite for solving the problem of their tremendous auto-attraction.

Now, according to Troland (1917), the growth of crystals from a solution is due to an attraction between the solid crystal and the molecules in solution caused by the similarity of their force field patterns, somewhat as similarly shaped magnets might attract each other—north to south poles—and Troland maintains that essentially the same mechanism must operate in the autocatalysis of the hereditary particles. If he is right, each different portion of the gene structure must—like a crystal—attract to itself from the protoplasm materials of a similar kind, thus moulding next to the original gene another structure with similar parts, identically arranged, which then become bound together to form another gene, a replica of the first. This does not solve the question of what the general principle of gene construction is, which permits it to retain, like a crystal, these properties of auto-attraction,[2] but if the main point is correct, that the autocatalysis is an expression of specific attractions between portions of the gene and similar protoplasmic building blocks (dependent on their force-field patterns), it is evident that the very same forces which cause the genes to grow should also cause like genes to attract each other, but much more strongly, since here all the individual attractive forces of the different parts of the gene are summated. If the two phenomena are thus really dependent on a common principle in the make-up of the gene, progress made in the study of one of them should help in the solution of the other.

Great opportunities are now open for the study of the nature of the synaptic attraction, especially through the discovery of various races having abnormal numbers of chromosomes. Here we have already the finding by Belling, that where three like chromosomes are present, the close union of any two tends to exclude their close union with the third. This is very suggestive, because the same thing is found in the cases of specific attractions between inorganic particles, that are due to their force-field patterns. And through Bridges' finding of triploid *Drosophila*, the attraction phenomena can now be brought down to a definitely genic basis, by the introduction of specific genes—especially those known to influence chromosome behavior—into one of the chromosomes of a triad. The amount of influence of this gene on attraction may then be tested quantitatively, by genetic determination of the frequencies of the various possible types of segregation. By extending such studies to include the effect of various conditions of the environment—such as temperature, electostatic stresses, etc.—in the presence of the different genetic situations, a considerable field is opened up.

This suggested connection between chromosome behavior and gene structure is as yet, however, only a possibility. It must not be forgotten that at present we cannot be sure that the synaptic attraction is exerted by the genes themselves rather than by local products of them, and it is also problematical whether the chief part of the mechanism of autocatalysis resides within the genes rather than in the "protoplasm." Meanwhile, the method is worth following up, simply because it is one of our few conceivable modes of approach to an all-important problem.

It may also be recalled in this connection that besides the genes in the chromosomes there is at least one similarly autocatalytic material in the chloroplastids, which likewise may become permanently changed, or else lost, as has been shown by various studies on chlorophyll inheritance. Whether this plastid substance is similar to the genes in the chromosomes we cannot say, but of course it cannot be seen to show synaptic attraction, and could not be studied by the method suggested above.[3]

IV. The Attack through Studies of Mutation

There is, however, another method of attack, in a sense more direct, and not open to the above criticisms. That is the method of investigating the individual gene, and the structure that permits it to change, through a study of the changes themselves that occur in it, as observed by the test of breeding and development. It was through the investigation of the *changes* in the chromosomes — caused by crossing over—that the structure of the chromosomes was analyzed into their constituent genes in line formation; it was through study of molecular changes that molecules were analyzed into atoms tied together in definite ways, and it has been finally the rather recent finding of changes in atoms and investigation of the resulting pieces, that has led us to the present analysis of atomic structure into positive and negative electrons having characteristic arrangements. Similarly, to understand the properties and possibilities of the individual gene, we must study the mutations as directly as possible, and bring the results to bear upon our problem.

(a) The Quality and Quantity of the Change

In spite of the fact that the drawing of inferences concerning the gene is very much hindered, in this method, on account of the remoteness of the gene-cause from its character-effect, one salient point stands out already. It is that the change is not always a mere loss of material, because clear-cut reverse mutations have been obtained in corn, *Drosophila*, *Portulaca*, and probably elsewhere. If the original mutation was a loss, the reverse must be a gain. Secondly, the mutations in many cases seem not to be quantitative at all, since the different allelomorphs formed by mutations of one original gene often fail to form a single linear series. One case, in fact, is known in which the allelomorphs even affect totally different characters: this is the case of the truncate series, in which I have found that different mutant genes at the same locus may cause either a shortening of the wing, an eruption on the thorax, a lethal effect, or any combination of two or three of these characters. In such a case we may be dealing either with changes of different types occurring in the same material or with changes (possibly quantitative changes, similar in type) occurring in different component parts of one gene. Owing to the universal applicability of the latter interpretation, even where allelomorphs do not form a linear series, it cannot be categorically denied, in any individual case, that the changes may be merely quantitative changes of some *part* of the gene. If all changes were thus quantitative, even in this limited sense of a loss or gain of part of the gene, our problem of why the changed gene still seems to be autocatalytic would in the main disappear, but such a situation is excluded a priori since in that case the thousands of genes now existing could never have evolved.

Although a given gene may thus change in various ways, it is important to note that there is a strong tendency for any given gene to have its changes of a particular kind, and to mutate in one direction rather than in another. And although mutation certainly does not always consist of loss, it often gives effects that might be termed losses. In the case of the mutant genes for bent and eyeless in the fourth chromosome of *Drosophila* it has even been proved, by Bridges, that the effects are of exactly the same kind, although of lesser intensity, than those produced by the entire loss of the chromosome in which they lie, for flies having bent or eyeless in one chromosome and lacking the homologous chromosome are even more bent, or more eyeless, than those having a homologous chromosome that also contains the gene in question. The fact that mutations are usually recessive might be taken as pointing in the same direction, since it has been found in several cases that the loss of genes—as evidenced by the absence of an entire chromosome of one pair—tends to be much more nearly recessive than dominant in its effect.

The effect of mutations in causing a loss in the characters of the organism should, however, be sharply distinguished from the question of whether the gene has undergone any loss. It is generally true that mutations are much more apt to cause an apparent loss in character than a gain, but the obvious explanation for that is, not because the gene tends to lose something, but because most characters require for proper development a nicely adjusted train of processes, and so any change in the genes—no matter whether loss, gain, substitution or rearrangement—is more likely to throw the developmental mechanism out of gear, and give a "weaker" result, than to intensify it. For this reason, too, the most frequent kind of mutation of all is the lethal, which leads to the loss of the entire organism, but we do not conclude from this that all the genes had been lost at the time of the mutation. The explanation for this tendency for most changes to be degenerative, and also for the fact that certain other kinds of changes—like that from red to pink eye in *Drosophila*—are more frequent than others—such as red to brown or green eye—lies rather in developmental mechanics than in genetics. It is because the developmental processes are more unstable in one direction than another, and easier to push "downhill" than up, and so any mutations that occur—no matter what the gene change is like—are more apt to have these *effects* than the other *effects*. If now selection is removed in regard to any particular character, these character changes which occur more readily must accumulate, giving apparent orthogenesis, disappearance of unused organs, of unused physiological capabilities, and so forth. As we shall see later, however, the changes are not so frequent or numerous that they could ordinarily push evolution in such a direction against selection and against the immediate interests of the organism.

In regard to the magnitude of the somatic effect produced by the gene variation, the *Drosophila* results show that there the smaller character changes occur oftener than large ones. The reason for this is again probably to be found in developmental mechanics, owing to the fact that there are usually more genes slightly affecting a given character than those playing an essential role in its formation. The evidence proves that there are still more genes whose change does not affect the given character at all—no matter what this character may be, unless it is life itself—and this raises the question as to how many mutations are absolutely unnoticed, affecting no character, or no detectable character, to any appreciable extent at all. Certainly there must be many such mutations, judging by the frequency with which "modifying factors" arise, which produce an effect only in the presence of a special genetic complex not ordinarily present.

(b) The Localization of the Change

Certain evidence concerning the causation of mutations has also been obtained by studying the relations of their occurrence to one another. Hitherto it has nearly always been found that only one mutation has occurred at a time, restricted to a single gene in the cell. I must omit from consideration here the two interesting cases of deficiency, found by Bridges and by Mohr, in each of which it seems certain that an entire region of a chromosome, with its whole cargo of genes, changed or was lost, and also a certain peculiar case, not yet cleared up, which has recently been reported by Nilsson-Ehle; these important cases stand alone. Aside from them, there are only two instances in which two (or more) new mutant genes have been proved to have been present in the same gamete. Both of these are cases in *Drosophila*—reported by Muller and Altenburg (1921)—in which a gamete contained two new sex-linked lethals; two cases are not a greater number than was to have been expected from a random distribution of mutations, judging by the frequency with which single mutant lethals were found in the same experiments. Ordinarily, then, the event that causes the mutation is specific, affecting just one particular kind of gene of all the thousands present in the cell. That this specificity is due to a spatial limitation rather than a chemical one is shown by the fact that when the single gene changes the other one, of identical composition, located near by in the homologous chromosome of the same cell, remains unaffected. This has been proved by Emerson in corn, by Blakeslee in *Portulaca* and I have shown there is strong evidence for it in *Drosophila*. Hence these mutations are not caused by some general pervasive influence, but are due to "accidents" occurring on a molecular scale. When the molecular or atomic motions chance to take a particular form, to which the gene is vulnerable, then the mutation occurs.

It will even be possible to determine whether the entire gene changes at once, or whether the gene consists of several molecules or particles, one of which may change at a time. This point can be settled in organisms having determinate cleavage, by studies of the distribution of the mutant character in somatically mosaic mutants. If there is a group of particles in the gene, then when one particle changes it will be distributed irregularly among the descendant cells, owing to the random orientation of the two halves of the chromosome on the mitotic spindles of succeeding divisions,[4] but if there is only one particle to change, its mutation must affect all of the cells in a *bloc* that are descended from the mutant cell.

(c) The Conditions under which the Change Occurs

But the method that appears to have most scope and promise is the experimental one of investigating the conditions under which mutations occur. This requires studies of mutation frequency under various methods of handling the organisms. As yet, extremely little has been done along this line. That is because, in the past, a mutation was considered a windfall, and the expression "mutation frequency" would have seemed a contradiction in terms. To attempt to study it would have seemed as absurd as to study the conditions affection the distribution of dollar bills on the sidewalk. You were simply fortunate if you found one. Not even controls, giving the "normal" rate of mutation—if indeed there is such a thing—were attempted.[5] Of late, however, we may say that certain very exceptional banking houses have been found, in front of which the dollars fall more frequently—in other words, especially mutable genes have been discovered, that are beginning to yield abundant data at the hands of Nilsson-Ehle, Zeleny, Emerson, Anderson and others. For some of these mutable genes the rate of change is found to be so rapid that at the end of a few decades half of the genes descended from those originally present would have become changed. After these genes have once mutated, however, their previous mutability no longer holds. In addition to this "banking house method" there are also methods, employed by Altenburg and myself, for—as it were—automatically sweeping up wide areas of the streets and sifting the collections for the valuables. By these special genetic methods of reaping mutations we have recently shown that the ordinary genes of *Drosophila*—unlike the mutable genes above—would usually require at least a thousand years—probably very much more—before half of them became changed. This puts their stability about on a par with, if not much higher than, that of atoms of radium—to use a fairly familiar analogy. Since, even in these latter experiments, many of the mutations probably occurred within a relatively few rather highly mutable genes, it is likely that most of the genes have a stability far higher than this result suggests.

The above mutation rates are mere first gleanings—we have yet to find how different conditions affect the occurrence of mutations. There had so far been only the negative findings that mutation is not confined to one sex (Muller and Altenburg, 1919; Zeleny, 1921), or to any one stage in the life cycle (Bridges, 1919; Muller, 1920; Zeleny, 1921), Zeleny's finding that bar-mutation is not influenced by recency of origin of the gene (1921), and the as yet inconclusive differences found by Altenburg and myself for mutation rate at different temperatures (1919), until at this year's meeting of the botanists Emerson announced the definite discovery of the influence of a genetic factor in corn upon the mutation rate in its allelomorph, and Anderson the finding of an influence upon mutation in this same gene, caused by developmental conditions—the mutations from white to red of the mutable gene studied occurring far more frequently in the cells of the more mature ear than in those of the younger ear. These two results at least tell us decisively that mutation is not a sacred, inviolable, unapproachable process: it may be altered. These are the first steps; the way now lies open broad for exploration.

It is true that I have left out of account here the reported findings by several investigators, of genetic variations caused by treatments with various toxic substances and with certain other unusual conditions. In most of these cases, however, the claim has not been made that actual gene changes have been caused: the results have usually not been analyzed genetically and were in fact not analyzable genetically; they could just as well be interpreted to be due to abnormalities in the distribution of genes—for instance, chromosome abnormalities like those which Mavor has recently produced with X-rays—as to be due to actual gene mutations. But even if they were due to real genic differences, the possibility has in most cases by no means been excluded (1) that these genic differences were present in the stock to begin with, and merely became sorted out unequally, through random segregation; or (2) that other, invisible genic differences were present which, after random sorting out, themselves caused differences in mutation rate between the different lines.

Certain recent results by Altenburg and myself suggest that genic differences, affecting mutation rate, may be not uncommon. To guard against either of these possibilities it would have been necessary to test the stocks out by a thorough course of inbreeding beforehand, or else to have run at least half a dozen different pairs of parallel lines of the control and treated series, and to have obtained a definite difference in the same direction between the two lines of *each* pair; otherwise it can be proved by the theory of "probable error" that the differences observed may have been a mere matter of random sampling among genic differences originally present. Accumulating large numbers of abnormal or inferior individuals by selective propagation of one or two of the treated lines—as has been done in some cases—adds nothing to the significance of the results.

At best, however, these genetically unrefined methods would be quite insensitive to mutations occurring at anything like ordinary frequency, or to such differences in mutation rate as have already been found in the analytical experiments on mutation frequency. And it seems quite possible that larger differences than these will not easily be hit upon, at least not in the early stages of our investigations, in view of the evidence that mutation is ordinarily due to an accident on an ultramicroscopic scale, rather than directly caused by influences pervading the organism. For the present, then, it appears most promising to employ organisms in which the genetic composition can be controlled and analyzed, and to use genetic methods that are sensitive enough to disclose mutations occurring in the control as well as in the treated individuals. In this way relatively slight variations in mutation frequency, caused by the special treatments, can be determined, and from the conditions found to alter the mutation rate slightly we might finally work up to those which affect it most markedly. The only methods now meeting this requirement are those in which a particular mutable gene is followed, and those in which many homozygous or else genetically controlled lines can be run in parallel, either by parthenogenesis, self-fertilization, balanced lethals or other special genetic means, and later analyzed, through sexual reproduction, segregation and crossing over.

V. Other Possibilities

We cannot, however, set fixed limits to the possibilities of research. We should not wish to deny that some new and unusual method may at any time be found of directly producing mutations. For example, the phenomena now being worked out by Guyer may be a case in point. There is a curious analogy between the reactions of immunity and the phenomena of heredity, in apparently fundamental respects,[6] and any results that seem to connect the two are worth following to the limit.

Finally, there is a phenomenon related to immunity, of still more striking nature, which must not be neglected by geneticists. This is the d'Hérelle phenomenon. D'Hérelle found in 1917 that the presence of dysentery bacilli in the body caused the production there of a filterable substance, emitted in the stools, which had a lethal and in fact dissolving action on the corresponding type of bacteria, if a drop of it were applied to a colony of the bacteria that were under cultivation. So far, there would be nothing to distinguish this phenomenon from immunity. But he further found that when a drop of the affected colony was applied to a second living colony, the second colony would be killed; a drop from the second would kill a third colony, and so on indefinitely. In other words, the substance, when applied to colonies of bacteria, became multiplied or increased, and could be so increased indefinitely; it was self-propagable. It fulfills, then, the definition of an autocatalytic substance, and although it may really be of very different composition and work by a totally different mechanism from the genes in the chromosomes, it also fulfills our definition of a gene.[7] But the resemblance goes further —it has been found by Gratia that the substance may, through appropriate treatments on other bacteria, become changed (so as to produce a somewhat different effect than before, and attack different bacteria) and still retain its self-propagable nature.

That two distinct kinds of substances—the d'Hérelle substances and the genes—should both possess this most remarkable property of heritable variation or "mutability," each working by a totally different mechanism, is quite conceivable, considering the complexity of protoplasm, yet it would seem a curious coincidence indeed. It would open up the possibility of two totally different kinds of life, working by different mechanisms. On the other hand, if these d'Hérelle bodies were really genes, fundamentally like our chromosome genes, they would give us an utterly new angle from which to attack the gene problem. They are filterable, to some extent isoluble, can be handled in test tubes, and their properties, as shown by their effects on the bacteria, can then be studied after treatment. It would be very rash to call these bodies genes, and yet at present we must confess that there is no distinction known between the genes and them. Hence we cannot categorically deny that perhaps we may be able to grind genes in a mortar and cook them in a beaker after all. Must we geneticists become bacteriologists, physiological chemists and physicists, simultaneously with being zoologists and botanists? Let us hope so.

I have purposely tried to paint things in the rosiest possible colors. Actually, the work on the individual gene, and its mutation, is beset with tremendous difficulty. Such progress in it as has been made has been by minute steps and at the cost of infinite labor. Where results are thus meager, all thinking becomes almost equivalent to speculation. But we can not give up thinking on that account, and thereby give up the intellectual incentive to our work. In fact, a wide, unhampered treatment of all possibilities is, in such cases, all the more imperative, in order that we may direct these labors of ours where they have most chance to count. We must provide eyes for action.

The real trouble comes when speculation masquerades as empirical fact. For those who cry out most loudly against "theories" and "hypotheses"—whether these latter be the chromosome theory, the factorial "hypothesis," the theory of crossing over, or any other—are often the very ones most guilty of stating their results in terms that make illegitimate *implicit* assumptions, which they themselves are scarcely aware of simply because they are opposed to dragging "speculation" into the open. Thus they may be finally led into the worst blunders of all. Let us, then, frankly admit the uncertainty of many of the possibilities we have dealt with, using them as a spur to the real work.

Notes

[1] It is of course conceivable, and even unavoidable, that *some* types of changes do destroy the gene's autocatalytic power, and thus result in its eventual loss.

[2] It can hardly be true, as Troland intimates, that all similar fields attract each other more than they do dissimilar fields, otherwise all substances would be autocatalytic, and, in fact, no substances would be soluble. Moreover, if the parts of a molecule are in any kind of "solid," three dimensional formation, it would seem that those in the middle would scarcely have opportunity to exert the moulding effect above mentioned. It therefore appears that a special manner of construction must be necessary, in order that a complicated structure like a gene may exert such an effect.

[3] It may be that there are still other elements in the cell which have the nature of genes, but as no critical evidence has ever been adduced for their existence, it would be highly hazardous to postulate them.

[4] This depends on the assumption that if the gene does consist of several particles, the halves of the chromosomes, at each division, receive a random sample of these particles. That is almost a necessary assumption, since a gene formed of particles each one of which was separately partitioned at division would tend not to persist as such, for the occurrence of mutation in one particle after the other would in time differentiate the gene into a number of different genes consisting of one particle each.

[5] Studies of "mutation frequency" had of course been made in the Œnotheras, but as we now know that these were not studies of the rate of gene change but of the frequencies of crossing over and of chromosome aberrations they may be neglected for our present purposes.

[6] I refer here to the remarkable specificity with which a particular complex antigen calls forth processes that construct for it an antibody that is attracted to it and fits it "like lock and key," followed by further processes that cause more and more of the antibody to be reproduced. *If* the antigen were a gene, which could be slightly altered by the cell to form the antibody that neutralized it—as some enzymes can be slightly changed by heating so that they counteract the previous active enzyme—and if this antibody-gene then became implanted in the cell so as to keep on growing, all the phenomena of immunity would be produced.

[7]D'Hérelle himself thought that the substance was a filterable virus parasitic on the bacterium, called forth by the host body. It has since been found that various bacteria each cause the production of D'Hérelle substances which are to some extent specific for the respective bacteria.

THE GENE AS THE BASIS OF LIFE*

H. J. Muller

1. The Localization of Genes

What is meant in this paper by the term "gene" material is any substance which, in given surroundings—protoplasmic or otherwise—is capable of causing the reproduction of its own specific composition, but which can nevertheless change repeatedly—"mutate"—and yet retain the property of reproducing itself in its various new forms. There is clear evidence that such material is to be found in the chromatin (where it is linearly arranged), and to some extent in the chloroplastid primordia and their derivatives, and there is no reason to believe that it exists anywhere else within the cell. In this connection it may also be noted that in the most primitive organisms which contain a chlorophyll-like substance the chromosomes do not seem yet to have become distinctly grouped apart from their cytoplasmic surroundings, into a walled-off nucleus; hence the genes more directly associated with the chlorophyll, on the one hand, and the nuclear genes, on the other hand, may well have had a common origin, and may only in later phylogeny have become separated.

2. The Size and Number of Genes

In order first to make our topic as concrete as possible let us now put to ourselves the question: *What is the size of the chromo-*

*Presented before the International Congress of Plant Sciences, Section of Genetics, Symposium on "The Gene," Ithaca, New York, August 19, 1926. This paper was published in 1929 in *Proc. Int. Cong. Plant Sci.*, 1: 897-921. The present text has been copied from the latter publication, with the omission of sections 2a, b and c, since the calculations there given have now been superseded. That in 2a involved a methodological error pointed out by Wright—the omission of a factorial in the denominator of the formula—which resulted in values of maximum gene size about half as great, and of minimum gene number about twice as great as those which should have been obtained; this error has unfortunately been adopted by several authors since that time. However, a more direct method, based on chromosome breakage, has recently been devised which gives even smaller values of gene size, and larger gene number, than those given in the present article. For this see Muller and Prokofyeva, 1934, *C. R. Acad. d. Sci. URSS*, 4: 74-83 (Russ. and English), reprinted 1935 in *Proc. Nat. Acad. Sci.*, 21: 16-26; and Muller, 1935, *Amer. Nat.*, 69: 405-12.

somal gene,—or, if a more pedantic formulation be demanded, what is the size of the smallest portion of protoplasm, separable under some conditions by chromosome interchange, which includes all the substance *specifically* necessary for the transmission of a single given Mendelian *difference?* One way to approach this question is through an attempted determination of the number of genes (taken in this sense), since this number may then be divided into the known bulk of the chromatin containing these genes. The present author, after an attack upon this problem, stated (in a paper written in collaboration with Altenburg in 1919) that the minimum number of genes in the X chromosomes of *Drosophila* must be about 500. (The total haploid number would consequently be about 2000.) From this it readily followed (as I stated in 1921) that the gene is an "ultra-microscopic particle"—though the determination did not yet seem precise enough to warrant an overt comparison with the size of protein molecules, or of other, less familiar, colloidal bodies of the cell, and such comparison was therefore left to the reader's imagination.[1] As I have never explained the method by which these conclusions were arrived at this may be briefly sketched here, together with some recent refinements of it, and the results thereby obtained.

(a) The Evidence from Mutations in Identical Loci. (Text omitted.)

(b) Evidence from Crossover Frequencies. (Text omitted.)

(c) The Evidence from Changes in Bar Eye. (Text omitted.)

(d) Conclusions as to Gene Size.

Taking, provisionally, the figure 600, in the light of our three very different methods, as representing at any rate the minimum number of genes present, and dividing this into the haploid volume of chromatin, from 0.2 to 0.3 cubic micra, as determined by measurements of chromosomes, we obtain a maximum average gene diameter of approximately one-fifteenth of a micron. This is just below the limits of image formation by visible light, and in the range of size accepted for "colloidal" particles, but it might still contain hundreds of typical protein molecules. If, however, the actual number of genes is really much larger, if the gene is highly compound (see next section), or if the genes occupy but a small fraction of the volume of the chromatin—as is probably the case—then the real size of the elementary genetic unit becomes much smaller.[2] It should be pointed out again, in this connection, that the above calculations deal only with the size of that portion of material separable by crossing over, which is responsible for the transmission of an ordinary Mendelian difference. That difference might depend upon just a chemical radical or a single atom, or even upon a single electron position; at the other extreme it would also be possible that the ordinary Mendelian difference in higher organisms was a "regional" chromosome change, of variable extent, which generally covered much more than the minimal amount of substance capable of self-propagation in the nucleus.

Our formula, then, does not give us any direct information concerning the size of the smallest portion of gene material which would be capable of reproduction as such, without the co-operation of other, contiguous gene material. The small size of some "microchromosomes," and of some chloroplastic primordia, shows us, however, that the minimal amount of gene material, in this sense too, at most borders on the ultramicroscopic. We shall see later, moreover, that the primary mechanism of gene-propagation in all forms of life is probably identical with that in the simplest, smallest known organisms, and since in a virus we know this can be crowded into a space about a fiftieth of a micron in diameter the minimal amount of self-propagable substance is seen to be of ultramicroscopic dimensions. The similarity of dimensions of the quantity just mentioned to that above calculated for "maximal gene size" is interesting, although it may be accidental. Reasons will be given subsequently for the view that the smallest self-propagable unit is probably much smaller than this.

3. The Interrelations of Genes in the Chromosome

Although we may speak of genes as units, either in the sense of Mendelian differentiators or in the sense of independently propagable elements, it must be recognized that they may be only *potential* units, and that in the chromosome they may conceivably exist not as separate particles, or even as chemically disunited substances, but in the form of a linearly continuous structure. True, there is a tendency for a given differential to hold together as a unit when it crosses over against its allelomorph in the heterozygous, but we must also remember that in cases of mutation of an entire region, so-called "deficiency," this region, comprising numerous ordinary separable loci, now holds together as a unit too, when crossing over occurs in the heterozygote. In the case of the unequal crossing over of bar eye, however, we can determine that the bar gene holds together as a unit even in the homozygous condition, for the askew crossing over here occurs just to the right or left of it, but never within it. Furthermore, in cases of chromosome breakage, fusion, or inversion of a region, such as is sometimes found in *Drosophila*, if the genetic material in the chromosome did not have some kind of segmental structure, then the rearrangement of its parts, at the point of breakage or reunion, should always be equivalent, in its effects, to what we now call a "gene mutation"; a number of cases are known in which no such effect has been observed, although in others "mutation" has apparently accompanied the rearrangement. More observations will be necessary on this point. Further important observations of Sturtevant on bar eye do suggest that the spatial relations of the genes with their neighbors are of genetic consequence, as well as their internal arrangements. In finding that two bar genes in contiguity in the same chromosome exert more effect than two lying in homologous chromosomes, he discovered that the local pattern of the genes is a fact which may itself become, in effect, genic in its significance. Nevertheless, this does not make improbable a segmental structure of the gene material.

If we accept the inferences, later to be drawn, that the self-propagable material everywhere is fundamentally alike, and that the smallest independently reproducing portion of it is exceedingly minute, then the chromosome must have some kind of linearly repetitive structure. It also would follow from the "gene-element" interpretation of eversporting genes, presently to be discussed, that the gene material at times at least may be non-linearly repetitive in its formation. Finally, the regularity of the mathematical relations observed in linear linkage, with its corollary, interference, proves that the disunion of parts of the chromatin structure from each other (in crossing over) is determined by geometrical and physical factors and not by chemical bonds or affinities of a sort that would differ from point to point according to the atomic configurations within the gene material. This fact too, then, connotes a chain-like, segmental arrangement of those atomic connections that must exist within the "chromatin" thread, allowing of breaks, between these segments, which are governed by "mechanical" circumstances.

Admitting as yet, however, the provisional nature of our conclusions regarding genic discontinuity, it is still quite legitimate to speak of the number or size of "genes," as suggested in the beginning, in the sense of the number or size of linearly connected[3] regions so taken that in them non-overlapping genetic differences, separable by crossing over, can occur, and these differentiable parts fit our conception of genes in being concerned in the propagation of their own specific structure largely independently of what other kinds of genetic material they may happen to be associated with.

4. Is the Gene Compound?

A converse of the above question of gene interrelations is that of its interior composition. If what we call the gene, in the above sense, can be shown to be made up of several or many identical parts (such as like molecules), then our most fundamental genetic unit becomes much smaller and our interpretation of basic genetic phenomena will be much affected in various ways. The work on eversporting, variegated plants, particularly the brilliant studies of Emerson, Anderson, Eyster, and Demerec, have, taken collectively, shown that here at least the gene is in all probability compound, since segregation of parts obviously occurs within it at some mitoses, but it is most important to know whether these cases afford a real glance into the interior of typical genes or are—if I may so put it—"teratological."

I mentioned in 1921 that the question might be solved if we could observe the distribution of mutant genes from the time of their origin, by noting the appearance or non-appearance of the mutant character in cells descended in a known way from the cell in which the mutation had occurred, as might conceivably be done in some somatic tissue. For, if the mutation originally happened in one of a number of interchangeable gene parts, or particles, then, as the particles of the new and the old kind, now existing side by side in the same gene, multiplied and became separated into two groups by chromosome division, followed by cell division, some cells would finally be formed having genes containing particles all of the mutant type, other particles all of the old type, just as, more grossly, green may become segregated from white plastids in leaf development, and—here is the important point—*these differing cells, forming areas of different genetic type, should dovetail amongst each other in the form of an irregular patchwork.* On the assumption of a gene compounded of equivalent particles, there appear only two alternatives to this eventuality, both of which, on analysis, turn out to be spurious.

The first apparent alternative would be that the collection of particles within the gene always divides by a kind of "equation division," so that the two gene-halves destined for the two daughter cells always contain a half of each gene-particle that the original gene had contained. In that case there would be no sorting out whatever, and the mutation, if it could produce any phaenotypic effect at all, could (subject to developmental influences) exert its effect from the beginning, on the whole block of cells derived from the cell in which the original mutation had taken place. In that case, however, with the passage of innumerable zygote-generations more and more of the gene particles within the gene in question would become differentiated from each other, through their separate mutations, until we had, in effect, as many different genes, of one particle each, which were individually capable of showing the typical phenomena of stable, Mendelizing differences. Hence this alternative destroys itself.

The second apparent substitute notion, for avoiding a patchwork effect, if the gene is compound, is that the original particles in the gene become sorted out, in subsequent cell divisions, in the same exact order of dichotomy in which they had originally been formed from one another within the gene. Thus the most closely related gene particles, and the group of particles descended from a mutated particle would come to lie in a group of related, adjacent cells, instead of becoming scattered irregularly in cell inheritance. Examining such a supposition further, we find that it would require an elaborate and orderly dichotomous grouping of the particles, bundle within bundle, in the order in which they had been formed in a hypothetical doubling and redoubling of the gene particles as the gene grew. This is shown in the figure. Now, as the chromosome split for

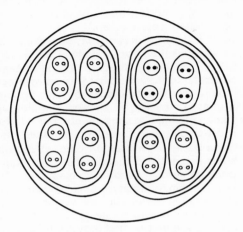

Fig. 1. Cross sectional diagram of chromosome—showing the sort of dichotomous grouping of gene parts which would prevent the descendants of a single mutated gene particle (shown in solid black) from becoming scattered amongst non-contiguous cells.

mitosis, it would have to be supposed to divide first along the line of earliest separation (between the two largest bundles). In the gene growth following this division each particle would have to form exactly two again, and a new, as yet least-marked, line of division would form from between each of these two sister-particles, that became more prominent in each successive cell generation till it became the oldest division line, along which the split occurred. Since this set of conditions would have to apply to all the genes arranged linearly along the chromosome, we should probably have particles of corresponding descent arranged and held adjacent to one another in adjacent genes, so that all genes could undergo the same orderly splitting at the division of the chromosome. This would amount to our having the whole chromosome divided up into strands, bundle within bundle, in the same order as we supposed the gene particles to be grouped within the individual genes. In other words, we should really have, not so much multiple genes, as multiple chromosomes, longitudinally divisible and subdivisible finally into elementary strands. This notion seems to fall of its own weight, if carried beyond the stage of a few strands, but, in any event, within each strand the gene would have but one particle (that is, no repetition of identical parts). Hence we see that the sorting out of descendants of a mutant gene-particle into just one block of cells (consisting of cells all more closely related to each other than to any others) would mean that the individual chromatin *strands*, at any rate, had a non-compound gene structure. A patchwork, on the other hand, would mean a compound gene, provided the cells remained together in order of their relationship.

I had at first thought that *Drosophila*, because of its "indeterminate cleavage," was unsuited for a study of the order in which mutant gene particles might be distributed in the embryonic cell divisions, but it occurred to me later that this feature need not make it impossible to obtain the desired evidence here, for, as the arrangements of parts in gynandromorphs showed, the cleavage nuclei usually preserve their original arrangements after division. Thus, although the first two nuclei sometimes are destined for the formation of anterior versus posterior halves, at other times for right versus left halves, or for somewhat diagonally cut fractions, their respective descendant nuclei seldom become irregularly scattered amongst one another, in the form of a patchwork. If, then, the gene consists of a number of particles, which do not maintain their order in the elaborate manner above detailed, the genetically differing parts of mosaic flies in which a mutation had occurred during early development should be scattered about irregularly in a much larger proportion of instances than is the case with male and female parts of gynandromorphs. But if the different parts do not have such a tendency to be scattered more irregularly than in gynandromorphs we could conclude the converse, that is, that the gene has not more than one particle, or at least not more than one particle in each strand of an orderly group of strands.

A survey of the rather meager number of somatic mosaics in *Drosophila* which had originated by gene mutation then indicated that in all these cases the mutated region seemed to form one complete block, contrasted with the complete block of non-mutated tissue. The clearly bilaterally divided yellow and gray male reported by me in 1920 is a good example of this. This, then, makes it seem likely that, in *Drosophila*, the genes in each chromosome strand are units, in that they do not contain more than one of any given kind of interchangeable, separately mutable, self-propagating molecules (or particles of any order).

In view, however, of the very remarkable results of Demerec, to be reported at the present meeting of the Congress, I must for a time reserve judgment, and admit the possibility that the mutational mosaics which more nearly resembled patchworks simply had not been detected, and that in the ones seen the superficial cells studied were already too far removed in descent from the original mutant ancestral cell to show the interdigitative effects of such intra-gene segregation. Or—as seems more plausible—it might be supposed that there is a partially orderly distribution of "gene elements," which only sometimes becomes irregular. Meanwhile, we must be prepared to watch closely for as many mutational mosaics as we can find, as well as to follow the possible segregations of the gene particles from generation to generation of individuals—though previously it had not seemed to me likely that such segregation would still remain incomplete after an entire zygotic generation.

5. The Gene in Relation to Higher Life Processes

It may be reiterated at this point that there is no good evidence from genetics of any heritable differences between organisms except such as are resident either in the numerous genes of the nuclear "chromatin," or, much more rarely, in the plastid primordia, which may contain a homologous substance. And since our evidence is extensive, and the phenomenon of heritability a highly peculiar one, it is logical to conclude that in all probability all specific, generic, and phyletic differences, of every order, between the highest and the lowest organisms, the most diverse metaphyta and metazoa, are ultimately referable to changes in these genes—chiefly in the multitudinous and very diverse chromosomal genes, to a lesser extent in the plastid genes.

It is, to be sure, still contended, especially by a few paleontologists not familiar with genetics, that the "evolutionary" differences distinguishing species and other more widely separated groups are of another kind from the Mendelian gene-differences dealt with in ordinary crosses. But to these persons we may throw back the question: "Why, then, is it that we never *find*, in our crosses, organisms that differ in these other ways, the ways that are supposed to be of evolutionary significance?" Has evolution suddenly been stopped, somehow frozen, so that within species such differences are no longer accruing; or do the individual smallest steps out of which the larger differences are built always make the organisms so differing uncrossable? How convenient that arrangement would be for avoiding a genetic test of the issue! If so, why is it that the varieties of a species are so seldom found to be uncrossable (more often do we find intra-varietal or self-sterility, following Mendelian lines); do not crossable varieties represent "evolutionary" steps? As a matter of fact, many so-called "species" themselves are crossable, and, when crossed, they too give evidence that their differences are truly genic, of the kind dealt with above but very numerous. Are all such cases, then, to be outlawed, and put in a different category from those in which the species-building is of "true evolutionary significance?" Then indeed would nature have perpetrated a hoax on the geneticist. In that event certainly the correctness of an evolutionist's views would be measured by the extent of the faith which enabled him to hold to them, *despite all evidence to the contrary*. But fortunately such an attitude is now uncommon in science.

And so, even if the genes should not form the basis of the distinction between animate and inanimate matter in general (though I shall try to show later that they do), at least most biologists will now admit that they do form the bases of all the higher developments that distinguish the most advanced from the most primitive forms of life. And by the expression, "they form the bases," is meant that the change in the gene structure was the cause of the more superficially observable morphological or physiological difference, and that this same (thus changed) gene structure, now existing, is somehow necessary for the continued maintenance of these observed properties, forms, and physico-chemical reactions. The genes are, of course, by no means the *only* necessary cause of the characteristics of the organism, any more than the present author is the sole cause of the present paper, but they are the *differential* causes of the specific, generic, etc., differences noted.

Just *how* these genes thus determine the reaction-potentialities of the organism and so its resultant form and functioning, is another series of problems, at present practically a closed book in physiology, and one which physiologists as yet seem to have had neither the means nor the desire to open!

6. The Gene in Relation to More Fundamental Life Processes

If the preceding discussions have seemed to carry us far afield, they are after all closely connected with actual data, the inferences therefrom are capable of concrete expression, the possibilities involved can largely be mapped out, and perhaps subjected to final testing by methods not unlike those we now possess. We may now allow ourselves to enter a realm further removed from our present experimental methods, devoted to basic questions that must as yet be treated in rather an abstract fashion.

We may put the questions: Could there ever have been a time, in the evolution of living matter, prior to the existence of what we may permissibly term the genes, and, at or before the time when genes did arise, how complicated could living matter have been, and what could have been its properties? We shall examine these questions only in the light of the naturalistic interpretation, that the complications of living matter evolved gradually, and that its operations were referable only to physical and chemical processes that were not somehow guided in advance by the relative advantages of alternative outcomes.

To start with, I think that most biologists will agree that we cannot speak of matter as "living" unless it has the property of growth, at least during a part of its career. In physico-chemical terms, growth involves "autocatalysis," inasmuch as the substances that grow must so affect some of the surrounding materials that the latter are transformed into end-products some of which are identical in composition with the former substances. Chemists ordinarily understand by an autocatalytic process any reaction, or set of reactions, in which one of the products formed (called the "autocatalyst") tends to augment the speed of the reaction, and hence to cause the formation, within a given time, of more end-products, including, therefore, more substance like itself, than would otherwise have been produced. Thus, within that time, the "autocatalytic substance" causes an increase in the amount of material of its own kind. (This increase must, moreover, be greater than the amount of its substance used up.) Naturally, it is a not uncommon occurrence for the product of a reaction to influence, at least to some slight extent, either positively or negatively, the speed of that reaction, since few substances act with complete indifference in the presence of others that are undergoing recombination. Hence some degree of autocatalysis in the general sense above defined is by no means rare in chemistry.

In the growth of "living" substances, it is to be observed that a much more peculiar type of autocatalysis occurs than the general type above described, since here it is not merely a question of the autocatalyst happening to affect the *speed* of reactions that are going on appreciably anyway. For "living" matter is not ordinarily produced, at least not to any appreciable extent, unless it is priorly present (else we should have "spontaneous generation"). Here, then, the "autocatalytic" substances—those that grow—may be considered as actually causing those particular reactions to occur whereby they themselves are produced.

When it is remembered that the medium surrounding living matter is necessarily complex, containing constituents that would render it ultimately capable of running through the whole multitudinous gamut of recombinations of organic chemistry, and that, on the other hand, the syntheses of "growth" must in any case be highly specific, it is seen to be a very noteworthy coincidence indeed that any organic autocatalysts should exist which happened to cause, among this array of possibilities, just those reactions which again produced their own particular physico-chemical structure. If, however, the fine distinction be made that possibly these reactions are not "caused" by the autocatalyst in an absolute sense, inasmuch as the reactions may actually be going on otherwise, but at an *inappreciable rate*, it must be observed also that the latter statement would apply equally well to innumerable other reactions, which also would be proceeding, at an inappreciable rate, amongst the substances initially present in a complex medium, but that the autocatalysts here in question must then be considered as specifically *selecting* that one amongst all these series of reactions, to catalyze, which happens to result in the products identical with themselves. Moreover, the addition of other substances to the medium, instead of the specific autocatalysts in question themselves, does not, in any case so far discovered, "cause" (in the above sense) those particular reactions to occur whereby these autocatalysts are produced. This emphasizes the special nature of the latter reactions, and therefore the degree of the coincidence that our growth-autocatalysts should be selectively "causing" just these reactions. It is in line with these considerations that, although autocatalytic reactions in the more general sense first defined are not uncommon in general chemistry, "specific autocatalysts"—which, in the above sense, are specifically necessary to "cause" the production of more material of their own kind,—are highly unusual outside of living matter,[4] since, regarded as a series of chemical events, such autocatalyses represent far more of a coincidence than the former ones.

We must note further that, in all such cases in ordinary chemistry, if we caused a change in the composition of the autocatalytic substance (through some further reaction that occurred after it had been formed) we should practically always render it non-autocatalytic. For the change will either leave the substance still capable of affecting the original reaction in the same way as before—in which case the substance will not be causing the production of material of exactly its own kind any more—or, if the effect of the substance on the original reaction becomes altered, it would be most remarkable if it chanced to be altered in precisely such a direction that the reaction now caused was of just such a nature as to produce this substance in the exact form in which it had become modified. Such reciprocity between the change in the specifically autocatalytic substance and the change in the effect which it had on the substrate would require a special kind of construction in the former, of a sort not yet known to the chemists [see note 4, p. 204], which allowed of variation in certain features of its pattern while at the same time a mechanism was retained which caused that variable pattern to be copied in its present form by the substances being newly formed. A specifically autocatalytic substance of this kind would fulfill our definition of a gene, since it would be able to "mutate" without losing its property of "propagation." If able to mutate thus, indefinitely, it would eventually go through an evolution akin to biological evolution.

Now we shall attempt to show that, in the evolution of living matter, there was probably not a form of protoplasm, ancestral to our present protoplasm, which already had the power of growth (or "specific autocatalysis") without containing genes (that is, without that exceptional form of specific autocatalytic function, as we know a chromosomal gene can). If this is true, it means that "life" did not occur before the gene. And we shall attempt to show, further, that this first material, ancestral to our own, that could grow, probably consisted of little else than the aforementioned gene, or genes.

In the first place, attention should again be called to the fact that the more complicated a given chemical product is, the more special will be the reactions necessary to produce it, and therefore the slimmer and slimmer (in geometrical progression) will be the chance that this product will happen itself to produce just these same reactions, that is, to be "specifically autocatalytic" (unless we either suppose some purposive organization of the external medium in adaptation to it, or suppose a gene-mechanism within it that built up the complications through a series of *selected* mutations). Thus it is almost inconceivable that a whole system of substances as complicated as that which any protoplasm or cytoplasm is conceived to be, should have come together by the chance action of physical and chemical substances, to form just such a structure that the working of this system reproduced that same system again, in all its features—*unless* the whole mechanism of biological evolution, involving reproduction, variations, the reproduction of variations, and natural selection, had long previously been at work building up this system in just the right way from much simpler beginnings, that is, unless substances that may, in effect, be called genes, had existed first.

The difficulty involved in the production of any such system, antecedent to the existence of *mutably* autocatalytic bodies—that is, genes—becomes still more insurmountable when we consider that the highly adapted system thus thrown together would, on one view (1), have to have the property not only of reproducing its protoplasmic portion—growing, if you prefer—but, in addition, it would by chance have to possess in perfected form before their use properties like those of a mimeograph. For when (perhaps much later) the mutable genes came into existence in connection with this protoplasm, the latter would have to have the effect of reproducing these genes too, each after its own mold, somewhat as a mimeograph reproduces forms presented to it. An alternative (2)—if we should still hold to the hypothesis in question that the protoplasm arose without the cooperation of pre-existing genes—would be to ascribe to the composition of the genes themselves most of the mechanism necessary for their mutably specific autocatalytic properties, but such a double origin of the remarkable attribute autocatalysis, in both protoplasm and genes independently, is doubly improbable—or, should we say, improbable as the square, especially in consideration of these two autocatalyses being of fundamentally different types, immutable in the protoplasm, mutable in the genes. Thirdly (3), we cannot well derive the genes from the protoplasm, by some sort of mutation, in order so to explain their specific autocatalytic ability, because we have not supposed the protoplasm to be able to mutate without *losing* its autocatalytic ability. If it had been able to do so, it would itself fulfill the definition of "gene material" and so we should after all have had the genes to begin with. [Moreover, in that case there might be evidence of the existence, even today, of material in the cytoplasm having the potentialities of genes—that is, propagable despite mutation. Any intermediate position between the three hypotheses noted above will simply share, in appropriate ratios, their respective difficulties.]

We are, therefore, practically driven to the conclusion that the extraordinary property of protoplasmic growth, or reproduction—biological autocatalysis—did *not* exist before the property distinctive of the gene existed—namely, before that peculiar form of specific autocatalysis existed which is compatible with change in composition (mutation). The gene, then, arose coincidentally with growth and "life" itself, if our argument be correct.

We shall further conclude that at the time of its inception this mutable autocatalytic system was extremely simple, as compared with forms of protoplasm that have as yet been analyzed, consisting of little or nothing else, in fact, than what may be called the gene. For the more complicated we imagine any chance-supplied companion-structures (corresponding to the general "protoplasm") to have been, which were supposedly necessary in the first place for the operation of the genic autocatalysis, the more we run into difficulty in trying to account for the lucky coincidence that the combined activity of the genes and of these necessary by-standing substances should have caused the reproduction, *not only* of the genes, but also of these other materials themselves. Similar considerations to those followed here also lead us to the view that probably the gene itself was not highly complicated in its essential structure, inasmuch as it had to be specifically autocatalytic in respect to all its parts.

What the structure of the gene itself actually was, in physico-chemical terms, the modern geneticist would like to know—perhaps beyond all other questions of genetics—but as yet he remains in almost complete ignorance of this matter. What feature or features of its structure allowed it to *mutate* without losing this specific autocatalytic ability can only be guessed at most inadequately now, but in these features lay all the promise of life, as distinguished from the inanimate. The mutations must have been, must still be, rearrangements in pattern of one sort which leave unchanged certain other arrangements, of an entirely different sort, which are responsible for the specific autocatalysis. The latter, *stable* arrangements somehow result in the copying of the former, mutable arrangements (as well as their own), by the raw material as it becomes organized, and the character of these mutable arrangements, in turn, is of great moment in determining those *not* directly autocatalytic reactions of the gene with its surroundings, whereby it now organizes its environment in its own interests.

The latter, mutable sorts of arrangements within the gene material have certainly undergone vast changes and complications in the course of evolution, and under their influence, of course, the protoplasm has evolved and changed, but the other arrangements, those features of gene structure which are responsible for its primary autocatalysis—these must still be the same as in the immemorial ages past, before green slime bordered the seas. The secret of this immutable (but mutation-permitting) autocatalytic arrangement of gene parts may perhaps be reached first by an upward thrust of pure physical chemistry, or perhaps by biologists reaching down with physico-chemical tools through the chromosome, the virus, or the bacteriophage. Studies of the nature of gene-attractions may help. This matter lies, as it were, in another dimension from mutation—and perhaps this statement may be true even literally speaking.

When we take this point of view, it is evident that we escape our logical difficulty concerning the origin of present-day protoplasm, with its intricately interlocking parts that all act to further the growth and exact reproduction of the whole. For the origination of this system, just like that of the complicated gross morphology of the higher plants and animals (which was a later accomplishment of the gene), came about gradually, step after tested step, as mutation followed mutation in the primordial autocatalyzing genes. In this process those mutant genes whose by-products (end-products other than their own material, not originally necessary for "life") were most useful in further reproduction differentially survived, multiplied, and mutated again. On this view, then, the view that seems best to stand the tests of ultimate analysis, the great bulk, at least, of the protoplasm was, after all, only a by-product, originally, of the action of the gene material; its "function" (its survival-value) lies only in its fostering the genes, and the primary secrets common to all life lie further back, in the gene material itself.

Even now, in a large cell, which (in diploid) contains thousands of genes, a change in a single invisible one of these ultra-microscopic particles can profoundly affect the physical and chemical properties of the entire mass, and the resultant physiological reaction-systems are distant reflections of the new gene-composition. The mutations of the genes have thus laid the building blocks of the present protoplasm even as they hold hope for its still further improvement.

7. The Attack through Studies of Mutation

How little critical work has been done in the study of these all-important mutations, as compared with the work on what we may now term the superficial aspects of organisms! Through the work on gene mutation we may not only gain knowledge of the mode of occurrence of the changes themselves, leading possibly to some degree of control over protoplasm from its root, as it were, but we may perhaps also gain some insight into those genetic arrangements which are subject to this mutation. As will be explained in the papers of Eyster and Demerec, most instructive work is now being done on "eversporting" plants and animals, which throws light on the possibly compound nature of the gene as it exists in them. I should, however, prefer to call these cases of *eversorting* rather than *eversporting* genes, since we seem to be dealing with a phenomenon of intra-genic segregation of particles already differentiated by mutation. This still leaves open for study the whole problem of the original causation of mutation in whatever may be the elementary gene particles.

On the latter question, that of the causation of the primary mutations, there has—with one exception—been only negative evidence
as yet, all agents tested in the attempt to produce mutation having
visibly failed. The recent experiments of the present author, however—
especially when taken in connection with some prior work done in
collaboration with Altenburg, and some work done with Hanson, have
indicated that a rise in temperature increases the likelihood of mutation in *Drosophila*. This is only a first step in a laborious quest,
but the elaboration of special genetic methods and stocks in *Drosophila* which allow the detection of lethal factors in relatively
great abundance, now makes such work on mutational origins feasible for the first time. The beginning of the pathway to the micro-
cosmic realm of gene-mutation study thus lies before us. It is a difficult path, but, with the aid of the necromancy of science, it must
be penetrated.

We cannot leave forever inviolate in their recondite recesses
those invisibly small yet fundamental particles, the genes, for from
these genes, strung as they are in myriad succession upon their
tiny chains, there radiate continually those forces, far-reaching,
orderly, but elusive, that make and unmake our living worlds.

Résumé

1. The method is explained whereby a minimum estimate of the
number of genes in *Drosophila* may be obtained from data showing
the observed frequency of occurrence of mutations in loci identified
as separate. The (haploid) number based on recent data is about
1150. Both rough and more refined approximation methods are described. It is proved mathematically that the number of genes so
arrived at is truly minimal, probably far below the actual number,
and it is shown that more nearly correct (though still minimal)
numbers might be obtained by such methods if extensive data on
autosomal lethals were at hand.

2. The attempt to estimate the number of genes by dividing the
frequency of crossing over between genes as nearly adjacent as
possible into the total frequency of crossing over is criticized. It is
shown mathematically that the results obtained could have been produced even if the genes were indefinitely more numerous than they
are calculated to be by this method, but other elements of uncertainty, concerning the relative frequencies of crossing over in different parts of the chromatin, and under different genetic conditions,
make possible the other alternative, that the estimate so arrived at
is too large. The number of genes calculated by the method here
discussed is between 1400 and 1800.

3. It is shown that the data on symmetrical and asymmetrical
crossing over between the "genes" for bar eye, obtained by Sturtevant, furnish a special case of the second method, with the peculiar

advantage that the crossing over is known to be between adjacent loci. This method gives a figure similar to that obtained by the second method.

4. When the "minimal number" of genes is divided into the bulk of the chromatin containing them (as measured by Bridges) it is found that the "maximal" diameter possible for the average gene is about a twentieth of a micron, just within the range of size of ultra-microscopic, colloidal bodies. The real size may be much smaller, however, and we have as yet no clue to possible gene chemistry.

5. Various considerations make it probable that the genes in the chromosome are not in the form of a continuum, but occur segmentally, in units the interconnections of which are like one another, and different from their intraconnections. Nevertheless the spatial arrangements of the genes with regard to one another may have some influence upon the effects which the genes produce in the cells.

6. The arrangement of parts in mosaics of *Drosophila* caused by mutation furnishes evidence indicating that the gene is not composed of identical particles which ordinarily may undergo rearrangement in the formation of the daughter-genes. It is therefore indicated that a gene in a given chromosome-strand does not contain more than one molecule of a given kind. However, in the face of the apparently contrary evidence of Anderson, Eyster, and Demerec on eversporting organisms, more data will be necessary to decide whether or not the "typical" gene is composed of a number of identical parts that may *at times* become rearranged.

7. It is pointed out that growth involves a specific autocatalysis, without which life cannot exist. The gene, when in its protoplasmic setting, is known to possess this property of "specific autocatalysis." Still more remarkable, the gene can mutate without losing its specific autocatalytic power. In view of this latter peculiarity of the gene, it becomes a supererogation, and involves improbable assumptions, to suppose that any other portion of the protoplasm, independently of the gene, is specifically autocatalytic; "growth" of the rest of the protoplasm would follow as a by-product of gene activity. Likewise it involves apparently insuperable difficulties to suppose that, in the most primitive living matter, highly organized companion substances to the gene ("protoplasmic" in nature) were necessary to make the gene-autocatalysis possible. Genes (simple in structure) would, according to this line of reasoning, have formed the foundation of the first living matter. By virtue of their property (found only in "living" things) of mutating without losing their growth power they have evolved even into more complicated forms, with such by-products—protoplasm, soma, etc.—as furthered their continuance. Thus they would form the basis of life.

8. Modern work on mutation holds promise of attacking successfully some of the important problems concerning the gene. Such

studies are now feasible for the first time, and a beginning has already been made, in the finding that temperature affects the rate of mutation.

Notes

[1]The estimate of number or size thus made has since been used in a publication by Sturtevant (1921), and later by others (e.g., Morgan, 1922, Morgan, Bridges, and Sturtevant, 1925).

[2]It must be remembered that some sperm heads seem mainly composed of a combination of nucleic acid with protein of a relatively simple, *small* molecule type, with little (but probably enough) room left over for large protein molecules to be present in as great abundance as the genes seem to exist. There is, however, no strong reason to suppose either that the genes are composed of, or contain or form a part of, either simple protein molecules or nucleic acid, just because the major part of the chromosome substance is of this nature; on the other hand, it would be still more gratuitous to deny this possibility. At present any attempt to tell the chemical composition of the genes is only guesswork. It is tempting, for instance, to suppose that genes are enzyme molecules, in special form, and that enzymes are proteins in special form, but while this appears more probable than any other individual guess, its chief merit after all is that it lies in the path of least mental resistance. Just because the molecular basis of the genes *does* multiply is the very reason why it is unnecessary to suppose that, in their reactions upon the cell protoplasm, these molecules, like those of enzymes, do not become used up. They may merely be reproduced as fast as they are used up. And the substances formed in these reactions may eventually *lead to* the production, or the modification, of the real enzymes. This speculation is not here urged as a probability, but merely as a warning against too ready acceptance of definite conclusions concerning gene chemistry. As we shall see later, the act of reproduction itself, which the gene carries out, must be designated as "catalytic," and in this respect it is indeed like the action of an enzyme, but its actual mechanism may or may not be like that of enzymes in general. In fact, "enzymes in general" are not yet known to constitute a chemically coherent group of substances.

[3]See Sturtevant's work on bar and infra-bar for proof that even two directly adjacent "genes" are linearly connected.

[4]In these connections, the analogy of growth-autocatalysis to ordinary crystallization, as drawn by Troland, is suggestive, but it does not go far enough; moreover, if it did hold as pictured, we should expect much more evidence of genelike action in "inorganic" material.

NEW MUTANTS, ADDITIONS, AND CORRECTIONS TO SYMBOL LIST IN DIS-9*

Report of H. J. Muller

dp and its Allels

The allels having different kinds of expressions were not sus-pected of involving the same locus until crosses of the abovesigned (1918+19) showed them all to act as a series of allels, as was an-nounced at the meeting of the American Society of Naturalists, Philadelphia, December, 1919, and mentioned in *Am. Nat.* 56: 32-50, and in *Eugenics, Genetics and the Family* 1: 106-112. The locus has, in accordance with the usual custom, been called "T," after the first mutation (Truncate) discovered at that locus, but the locus has been referred to as "dp" by Bridges. This change would make for con-venience, chiefly because most of the mutations more commonly dealt with at this locus are more usually to be treated as reces-sives, whereas the original mutation, Truncate, being treated as a dominant, was given the large letter. In the 1919 address, cogent reasons which still stand were given for regarding the locus as pleotropic (rather than as a group of loci) and its allels as qualita-tively different (rather than in different loci) and for regarding those, like Truncate, which had multiple action, including a lethal effect, as *not* representing deficiencies. This was one of the reasons why a difference of opinion later developed as to whether the ex-istence of a lethal effect in connection with an allel of a viable, vis-ible mutation should be taken as prima facie evidence of deficiency.

In the case of the truncate series, evidence against the deficiency hypothesis lay in the following: (1) allels affecting combinations of *any* two of the three major characters—vortices on thorax, wing truncation, and lethality—could be obtained, whereas deficiencies of contiguous genes having a linear order should make possible only two of the three conceivable combinations of two effects; (2) the dif-ferent effects were produced in different degrees in different cases; (3) the three major effects are produced together in some of the allels not merely because of the accidental proximity of different loci responsible for the different effects but because the effects are developmentally related. The latter fact is proved by the finding (Muller, 1919) that the chief chromosome-three intensifier of the wing character of truncate intensifies also the vortex character, both of vortex and of truncate itself; moreover, the near-mimic, humpy, found by Bridges (1918) in the second chromosome has a combination of effects similar to that of truncate.

Drosophila Information Service, 1939, 12: 39-40.

FURTHER INFORMATION CONCERNING THE MULTI-LOCUS NATURE OF THE DUMPY SERIES IN DROSOPHILA*

H. J. Muller, Helen U. Meyer and E. A. Carlson
Indiana University, Bloomington, Indiana

Different dumpy ("*dp* ") "alleles" involve any combination of the following diverse effects: *o* ("oblique," shortened or "truncate" wings), *l* (lethality), *v* ("vortex," thoracic eruptions); compounds manifest effects common to both "alleles." On finding this "allelism," Muller (1919-'23) based his inference that these diverse characteristics represent biochemically related effects of one complex gene, rather than a "gene-nest," on the following considerations. (1a) Some intensifiers of *o* intensified *v*. (1b) Mutation of a quite separate gene, $humpy^+$, gave a phenotype both oblique-like and vortex-like. (2) One of the three types of mutations combining two of the three effects must, on a three-locus interpretation, have involved two nonadjacent loci, skipping the middle. However, Fogel (1949, these Records) proved the multiplicity of loci by obtaining crossover combinations. The following observations confirm and extend his discovery. First, *olv* has been obtained from *o/lv*, presumably by crossing over with *o* intensified by influence of *lv*. Second, this *olv* by subsequent crossing over with $o^+l^+v^+$, reestablished *lv*. Distribution of markers *s* and *Sp* proved *o* leftmost here. Third, an ultraviolet-induced $ol^{(v)}$ (superscript indicating faint *v*) produced, from combination $ol^{(v)}/v$, clear cut $o^+l^+v^+$ crossovers. *s-Sp* distribution proved *v* rightmost here. A separate *l* locus remains unproved. Although phenotypic overlaps arose, the above cases proved genetic. Despite locus multiplicity (or doubleness), considerations 1a, 1b and reciprocal cross-influences (positional?) show that *at least* one pleiotropic gene, capable of mutating to change the characteristics differentially, does exist here. Several features of this case weaken consideration 2, however. They raise the possibility of some gene-mutations producing seeming rearrangements of the dumpy components.

Records of the Genetics Society of America, No. 24, 1955.

ANOTHER CASE OF DISSIMILAR CHARACTERS IN DROSOPHILA APPARENTLY REPRESENTING CHANGES IN THE SAME LOCUS*

F. Verderosa and H. J. Muller

Indiana University, Bloomington, Indiana

Like vortex, oblique, and their alleles, which years after their discovery were unexpectedly found to be heteromorphic derivatives of what was shown to be probably one complex locus (Muller, 1921, *Science* 53: 97 *et seq.*), so too the sex-linked recessive small eye, *sy*, found by Bridges as a spontaneous mutant *(Genetics of Drosophila*, 1925) and by Muller (1928) as an X-ray-induced one, and the X-ray-induced recessive outstretched wings, *od* (Muller, 1930), arose separately and, having seemingly unrelated phenotypes, were not suspected of allelism, although Bridges (see Bridges and Brehme, 1944) had placed both at 59.2 on the linkage map. Abrahamson in 1953 discovered an X-ray-induced mutant, termed "odsy" by us, combining both these characteristics. Our crosses between these types showed each "compound" to exhibit that mutant characteristic, and only that, common to both parents. Thus, *od/sy* appears normal. Crossing over was studied in the presence of heterozygous inversions ("Curly" and "Payne") involving all major autosome arms, to promote crossing over. Females with "cis" ("coupling") arrangement, *f car/odsy*, gave no genuine crossovers among 17,498 offspring (apparent crossovers were tested), while those with "trans" ("repulsion") arrangement, *f od car/sy*, gave none in 9,714. Nevertheless the region *f-odsy*, ordinarily giving 2.5 per cent, showed 4 and 5 per cent, and *odsy-car*, ordinarily 3.3, showed 10 and 13 per cent crossing over in cis and trans crosses, respectively. Since it is very unlikely that both *odsy* and *od* or *sy* involve minute inversions, we conclude that these genes are alleles. We propose as their revised symbols *os*, *os^o* and *os^s*.

Records of the Genetics Society of America, 1954, 23: 72; and *Genetics*, 1954, 39: 999.

STUDIES ON THE ACTION OF THE
DOMINANT FEMALE-LETHAL Fl AND OF
A LESS EXTREME ALLELE, Fl^s*

S. Zimmering and H. J. Muller

Tests were made to determine whether the female lethal *Fl* (Muller and Zimmering, 1960, *Genetics* 45: 1001-1002) still acts as a complete lethal when present in pseudo-males having two *Fl*-containing X-chromosomes and two third chromosomes containing *tra* ("transformer of sex," Sturtevant, 1945, *Genetics* 30: 297). It was found that the sex transformation failed to save the lives of these flies. Similarly, in flies heterozygous for *Fl*, the viability of pseudomales (XX, but homozygous for *tra*) was as much reduced by the dominant action of *Fl* as was the viability of their non-transformed sisters that had the same X-chromosome composition but were heterozygous for *tra*.

Tests of the genetic factors determining the dominant female-lethal effect of *Fl* in crosses of our *y v* stock ("b120") have shown that all the major chromosomes (X, II, and III) of this stock play an important and synergistic role in producing the effect. In daughters of females heterozygous for some or all of these three chromosomes little or no dominant lethal effect was produced except when all three of the chromosomes were present together in the given mothers. The effect was a maternal one, tending to kill the heterozygous *Fl* (but not the non-*Fl*) daughters of all classes, provided that the mothers contained these intensifiers in all three chromosomes, in at least single dose. The intensifiers themselves were partially dominant, in that mothers homozygous for them gave a higher lethality of daughters heterozygous for *Fl* than did mothers heterozygous for them. When virgin females carrying the intensifiers are kept at a comparatively high temperature (35°C) for thirty-six or more hours prior to egg laying, the mortality of their heterozygous *Fl* daughters, derived from eggs laid at 25°C within the next three days, relative to that of their brothers, is considerably reduced (in the cases studied, from about 96 per cent to 80 per cent). Little reduction of mortality is produced when the exposure to warmth is allowed to last only twenty-four hours. Other cases of genes that have a maternal effect in killing daughters but not sons have been reported by Redfield (1924, 1926), Gowen and Nelson (1942), Gowen (1949), and Bell (1954), but in these cases there was no finding of a primary female-lethal gene, corresponding to *Fl*,

Drosophila Information Service, No. 34, 1960.

that had to be present in the female that was herself subject to the lethal action.

In the experiment on pseudo-males the stock that had been used to provide the *tra* gene (our stock "j22") had had females with attached X's and males whose single X-chromosome contained w^a. The crosses of this stock unexpectedly showed that the w^a-containing chromosome also carried an allele of *Fl*. We are, for reasons to be given below, denoting this as Fl^s (a symbol superseding our earlier, unpublished designation, Fl^2). It was found that compound females, one of whose X-chromosomes carried *Fl* and the other Fl^s invariably died. However, when crosses were made of Fl^s males to stocks *y v* ("b120") and *w* ("b69"), which on crossing to *Fl* males had given a high mortality of daughters, i.e. a high dominance of *Fl*, no such lethality occurred among these daughters. That is, Fl^s, unlike *Fl*, failed to act as a (partially) dominant lethal. That this difference was not caused by autosomal genes was proved by experiments in which the autosomes were appropriately substituted by the aid of chromosomes having inversions and markers. Similarly, parts of the X far from *Fl* were ruled out.

It was further found that Fl^s, unlike *Fl*, is not lethal even in the female homozygous for it, despite its lethality when "in compound" with *Fl*. It was, however, found to cause complete sterility of the homozygous *Fl* females (hence the superscript *s*). Their abdomens remain unenlarged, like those of homozygous *fes* females, while they appear normal in other outward respects. In regard to its female-lethal effect, Fl^s might be designated as an isoallele of *Fl*. This is not true in regard to its female-sterile effect, however. Like the lethality of *Fl*, the sterility of Fl^s is to a certain extent and under some conditions dominant, inasmuch as heterozygous Fl^s females are found in some crosses to have a high frequency of sterility. It is noteworthy that such sterility has not been observed among heterozygous *Fl* females. Thus Fl^s appears to be qualitatively different in its action from *Fl*.

Whereas *Fl* arose within Inversion 49, Fl^s is in an X-chromosome of normal structure. It must therefore have arisen as a result of a spontaneous mutation independent of that which produced *Fl*. Both these genes have been found by linkage tests to be slightly to the left of *oc*. No crossovers have yet been obtained between either of them and *sn*. Although nine crossovers between *sn* and *oc* that could have involved *sn-Fl^s* crossing over, were it possible to the right of *sn* have been tested for Fl^s, none of these did involve sn-Fl^s crossing over.

Thus far, tests for female lethality have been made in our laboratory, by Robert Baum and by Marcia Henning, of a considerable number of our stocks in which the X-chromosome of the male had been kept confined to males by having them always crossed to females with attached X's. Thus far, no cases of female lethality have been found other than those in which the original Fl allele had been present as a result of the common origin of the Fl-containing region of the given X-chromosome with that of the X-chromosome of the stock in which Fl had first been discovered. These results suggest that mutations of the type in question are comparatively rare.

4 "Spontaneous" Gene Mutations

THE RATE OF CHANGE OF HEREDITARY FACTORS IN DROSOPHILA*

by H. J. Muller and E. Altenburg
From the Rice Institute, Houston, Texas
and Columbia University, New York City

A knowledge of the rate at which hereditary changes of various sorts occur is the necessary groundwork for an adequate understanding of evolution. The wide recognition given to this fact is attested to by the vast amount of literature on the subject of "variation," but, with our new exact knowledge of the Mendelian and chromosomal method of inheritance of the so-called "variations," it is evident that this literature has very little bearing on the real question of how often changes in the hereditary factors, *i.e.*, mutations, actually occur: for the breeding procedures used in the experiments there considered were not of the type necessary for ferreting out the new mutant factors as they arise, and for distinguishing between them and the apparent variations caused by the sorting out of old mutant factors into new combinations. There is, to be sure, enough work to show that the real mutations are "rare"—whatever that term may mean; but, so far as an approximate quantitative determination of the rate of factor change is concerned, it is not possible, from the published work, to determine even its general order of magnitude. Some special scheme of crossing is required for this purpose.

In the present series of experiments with *Drosophila* the X chromosome was chosen as the most convenient one for the detection of mutation, since every hereditary factor in either of the X chromosomes of the female fly stand revealed in the characters of one half of her male offspring, no matter what their father was. Thus, if the female has a new mutated factor in one of her X chromosomes, even though she does not usually show that factor herself, and even though her mate does not contain it, nevertheless one half of her sons are bound to show it and the mutation will thus be recognized. There is reason to believe that by far the commonest type of mutation is that which gives rise to a lethal factor—which kills the organisms containing it—and such lethal factors, also, in the X chromosome of a female, would be revealed; in this case, by the fact that half the male offspring, receiving it, would die before hatching.

Proceedings of the Society for Experimental Biology and Medicine, 1919, XVII: 10-14.

There would thus be half as many sons hatched as daughters, giving a sex ratio of 2 ♀: 1 ♂, instead of 1 ♀: 1 ♂, the usual ratio. In the first set of experiments these lethal factors were looked for primarily, by making a count of the sex ratios.

As a preliminary measure, about ninety females were bred, and the sex ratios of their progeny counted. Those families which gave a lethal, *i.e.*, 2:1, sex ratio (there were three of these) were then discarded, since there was no way of knowing, in this preliminary cross, whether these lethals had just arisen by mutation or were of ancient origin. Females from the normal families (with 1:1 sex ratio) were bred, however, since any lethal later discovered in the descendants of these flies must be due to a really new mutation, inasmuch as the ancestors had been certified as normal. It was necessary, moreover, in selecting females for breeding the next generation, not to breed many females from the same family, but to choose them from as many separate families as possible, in order to be sure that any mutations that might be discovered later had arisen separately, and were not merely sister representatives of one original mutation. By continuing this method of breeding from separate families over five or more generations after the preliminary tests, the sex ratios in 385 families were counted. Thirteen of these were found to be 2:1 ratios; this is a proportion of one new lethal mutant among each thirty females that are bred. This figure is of a far higher magnitude than any which had been anticipated. It should be noted that at the same time as all these lethals arose, no mutations causing ordinary visible character variations were observed.

The correctness of classification of most of the thirteen lethals was verified by further breeding tests, but there were a few doubtful cases, and it was realized that ratios intermediate between 1:1 and 2:1 are sometimes brought about in other ways. Although the possible error due to these cases was not enough to change the order of magnitude of the frequency found, a new set of experiments was undertaken in which a still more definite test of lethal factors than the sex ratio was used—namely, the test of linkage to known factors in the X chromosome. The breeding procedure—having preliminary tests, breeding from many separate families, etc.—was the same as before, but instead of using pure wild type flies for the work, the following cross was made in each generation: $\dfrac{w^e \, v \, f}{W \, V \, F}$ ♀ × $w^e \, v \, f$ ♂. In this case a lethal arising in either X chromosome makes itself known not only by the 2:1 sex ratio, but by the practically total absence of all males containing factors on both sides of the lethal. By noting whether any expected class of males was absent, it could thus be determined whether a lethal was present, and, if so, approximately where it was located in the chromosome. 1,062 families were examined in this way, after the preliminary tests, and twenty lethals were found—a ratio of one in fifty-three. Enough work has been done on them thus far to know that they occurred in at least ten different loci scattered along the X chromosome—but this is a bare minimum. Four of the lethals (perhaps five) are more strictly speaking "semi-lethals," as they occasionally allow the male possessing them to live (and then produce some curious morphological effects in him) but lethal mutations are so much more frequent than the type of visible character variation ordinarily dealt with, that none of the latter were observed in the whole experiment.

The above figure of 20 in 1,062 has a probable error due to chance of about ±3 in 1,062. There can, therefore, be no doubt about the correctness of the order of magnitude of the ratio 1:53, so far as any error caused by random sampling is concerned. The ratio 1:53 is, however, a composite result, for the families were kept in two main lots, one at about 66° F., the other at about 80°. The 445 grown at the lower temperature produced five lethals, or one in ninety; the 517 at the higher temperature produced 13 lethals, or one in forty. The other two were new lethals which occurred in the 100 bottles kept at room temperature, in which the lethals found in the two main series were being tested out. In this connection, it should be pointed out that the high ratio of one in thirty observed in the earlier experiment was obtained in bottles kept at room temperature in the warm climate of southern Texas. Although the absolute numbers of lethals are small, the difference between the two series in the later experiment is probably statistically significant,—at least, it may be calculated that if the lots had really been similar, the chances would have been about twenty to one against a difference of this magnitude occurring between figures of the given size. Taking the figures at their face value, we should obtain Q_{10} for mutation between 2 and 3, as is usual for chemical reactions.

If we accept the one in fifty-three ratio as representing the average frequency for the X chromosome, and if, as there is reason to believe, mutation occurs at the same rate in the other chromosomes as in the X chromosome, then, since the X's form about one fourth of the entire chromosome mass, we may figure that about one fly in every thirteen has a new lethal mutation in some chromosome or other. It is evident that, at this rate, without natural selection to weed out the "unfit," the race would soon become filled with lethal factors. For the X chromosome alone, since each female has two X's, and one female in fifty has a new lethal, we may figure that one X chromosome in every 100 contains a lethal factor just arisen in the present generation. Or, to put the matter differently, each X chromosome would, on the average, tend to contain one lethal factor after 100 generations—which means about four years in *Drosophila*. The rate of change for the X in *Drosophila* is thus about one detectable mutation in four years. This immediately shows us that *Drosophila* must have a different rate from some other organisms— man for example—for if the X chromosome of man mutated at anything like a similar rate, all the X chromosomes in a female would contain several lethal factors by the time she was ready to reproduce, and none of her sons would be viable.

The rate of one mutation in four years is the rate for the whole chromosome. It is of greater interest to know the rate for the individual factors. There is good reason to believe that there are at least 500 factors in the X chromosome of *Drosophila* —probably many times that number. But, taking this undoubtedly much too low minimum figure, it is easy to see that, if 500 factors show only one mutation in four years, each individual factor must on the average show a change in its composition only once in 2,000 years. (Yet this is in the mutable *Drosophila*.) It will be interesting to observe the difference in mutation rate in different organisms and under different conditions.

A STUDY OF THE CHARACTER AND MODE OF ORIGIN OF EIGHTEEN MUTATIONS IN THE X-CHROMOSOME OF DROSOPHILA*

(Abstract)

H. J. Muller, University of Texas
and E. Altenburg, Rice Institute

Since the eighteen mutants found in the experiment of the writers on mutation frequency were nonselected or random samples of (detectable) mutants in the sex-chromosome, a study of them furnishes quantitative data bearing on the nature of mutations. 1) All were lethals or sublethals. Of the five sublethals, four produced morphological abnormalities. 2) All were completely recessive except one mutant of the yellow mouse type. 3) Half of the loci involved are crowded into the 1.5 units space to the left of white eye (the rest being scattered rather evenly). This indicates that this region of the chromosome is really much longer than the map represents. 4) All the lethals gave negative tests for 'deficiency'; hence deficiencies are evidently much rarer than ordinary lethal mutations. 5) Three lethals were allelomorphs of known non-lethal factors, and two of these lethals were allelomorphs to each other. Of the latter one became dominant in its lethal effect when crossed to a non-lethal allelomorph. 6) Lethals very near 'duplicated' loci remained unaf-

Anatomical Record, 1921, 20: 213.

fected by the 'duplication.' 7) Mutation occurs with not markedly different frequency in the two sexes, for seven of the lethals were found in the maternal, eleven in the paternal chromosome. 8) These mutations occur not only near maturation but also in earlier germ cells, in either sex, as shown by the original appearance of some of the lethals in two sisters simultaneously. 9) Two of the original mutant individuals contained two different lethals at once; in one case these were in opposite chromosomes, in the other case in the same chromosome.

MUTATION*

H. J. Muller
University of Texas, Austin, Texas

Beneath the imposing building called "Heredity" there has been a dingy basement called "Mutation." Lately the searchlight of genetic analysis has thrown a flood of illumination into many of the dark recesses there, revealing some of them as ordinary rooms in no wise different from those upstairs, while others are seen to be subterranean passageways of quite a different type. In other words, the term mutation originally included a number of distinct phenomena, which, from a genetic point of view, have nothing in common with one another. They were classed together merely because they all involved the sudden appearance of a new genetic type. Some have been found to be special cases of Mendelian recombination, some to be due to abnormalities in the distribution of entire chromosomes, and others to consist in changes in the individual genes or hereditary units. It seems incumbent upon us, however, in the interests of scientific clarity, to agree to confine our use of the term mutation to one coherent class of events. The usage most serviceable for our modern purpose would be to limit the meaning of the term to the cases of the third type—that is, to real changes in the gene. This would also be most in conformity with the spirit of the original usage, for even in the earlier days, mutations were conceived of as fundamental changes in the hereditary constitution, and there were never intentionally included among them cases merely involving redistribution of hereditary units—when these cases were recognizable as such. In accordance with these considerations, our new definition would be: "mutation is alteration of the gene." And "alteration," as here

*Eugenics, Genetics and the Family, 1923, I: 106-12. (Proceedings of the Second International Congress of Eugenics, New York City, September, 1921.)

used, is of course understood to mean a change of a transmissible, or at least of a propagable, sort.

In thus trimming down the scope of our category of mutation we do not deprive it of the material of most fundamental evolutionary significance. For all changes due to the redistribution of individual genes or of groups of genes, into new combinations, proportions, or quantities, are obviously made possible only by the prior changes that make these genes differ from each other in the first place. It should in addition be noted that changes due merely to differences in the gross proportions of entire groups of genes must be relatively incapable of that delicate adjustment which is required for evolutionary adaptation. And as to the question, frequently raised, whether all evolution is ultimately due to mutation, this is necessarily answered in the affirmative by our definitions of the gene and of mutation, which designate the gene as any unit of heredity, and mutation as any transmissible change occurring in the gene. The question of the basic mechanism of evolution thus becomes transferred to the problem of the character, frequency, and mode of occurrence of mutation, taken in this precise, yet comprehensive sense. And since eugenics is a special branch of evolutionary science it must be equally concerned with this problem.

In choosing the body of data wherewith to attack these questions of mutation, in their new form, it must unfortunately be recognized that the results with the evening primrose, Oenothera, although they formed the backbone of the earlier mutation theory, can no longer be regarded as having a direct bearing on the modern problem, since they cannot be shown to be due directly to changes in the genes. Certain of them, such as gigas, lata, scintillans, etc., have been proved by Geerts, Lutz, Gates, and others, to be due to abnormalities in the apportionment of the chromosomes. Very valuable information on the genetics of cases of this sort is now being obtained, especially in the work of Blakeslee, Belling, and Farnham on much clearer cases of similar character in the Jimson weed, and, finally, in work of Bridges on the fruit fly Drosophila. Most of the other so-called mutations in the evening primrose appear to be due to the normal hereditary processes of segregation and crossing over, working on a genetic constitution of a special type. Evidence for this was obtained in my analysis of the analogous case existing in the fly Drosophila, as follows. It had previously been shown by de Vries, and further elaborated by Renner, that germ cells or individuals of Oenothera bearing certain genes always died, in such a way that all the surviving individuals were heterozygous (hybrid) in regard to these genes. I later showed, through work on Drosophila, that when such a condition (there called "balanced lethal factors") exists, the situation tends to become still further complicated through the presence of other heterozygous genes, which are linked to those which cause death. When one or a group of these non-lethal genes crosses over (separates) from the lethals, as they occasionally do, they may become homozygous, producing a visible effect. Thus new types of individuals appear which may be ascribed to "mutation," whereas they are really due to crossing over. The work of Frost on stocks has shown that a precisely analogous situation exists in that form also, and G. H. Shull is obtaining direct evidence for the same conclusion in the evening primrose itself. In any event, it must be granted that so long as this interpretation cannot be definitely refuted, these variations cannot be used as examples on which to base our theory of gene change. In place, then, of the elaborate system of conclusions which has derived its support chiefly from the results in the evening primrose, it will be necessary for our present theory of gene change to erect an independent structure, built upon an entirely new basis.

The data upon which the new theory must be built consist of two main sorts, which may be called direct and indirect. (1) In the cases giving the direct evidence, the occurrence of the gene change can be proved, and it is possible to exclude definitely all alternative explanations, such as contamination of the material, emergence of previously "latent" factors, non-disjunction, etc. So far, the only considerable body of such evidence is that gotten in the Drosophila work, where mutations have (in this sense) been actually observed in at least 100 loci. Considered collectively, however, there exist in other organisms enough scattered data to afford ample corroborative evidence for the generality of occurrence of mutations like those observed in the Drosophila work. In addition several specially mutable genes have been found in a number of plants (as well as in Drosophila) that are giving highly valuable information along their particular lines. And a number of selection experiments that have been performed on non-segregating lines of various organisms have also given us direct evidence, if not of the frequency, then at least of the infrequency, of mutations. (2) As for the indirect data, these may be gotten by examination of Mendelian factor-differences of all kinds, on the assumption that they must have arisen through mutation. Although this assumption can be shown to be fully justified, these cases cannot provide information concerning the manner of origin of the mutants, nor can they furnish a reliable index of the frequency of mutations, since the mutant genes may have been subjected to an unknown amount of selective elimination or selective propagation before the observations were taken. As for the still more indirect data, derived from studies of phylogenetic series and comparisons between different species, genera, etc., these occasionally give suggestive results, but where crosses cannot be made or where the differences cannot be traced down to the individual genes, such facts can seldom lead to trustworthy genetic conclusions.

On these various data, duly weighted, we may found our new mutation theory. We know nothing, as yet, about the mechanism of mutation, or about the nature of the gene—aside from the fact that nearly all genes hitherto studied behave like material particles existing in the chromosomes. Nevertheless there is already evidence for a number of empirical principles regarding the changes of the genes, some of which may conveniently be listed here in the form of fourteen statements. I shall have opportunity merely to present these principles, without attempting any adequate explanations of how they have been derived from the data.

1. The first and probably most important principle is that most genes—both mutant and "normal"—are exceedingly stable. Some idea of the degree of this stability may be obtained from some quantitative studies of mutation which Altenburg and I have made in the fruit fly Drosophila. It may be calculated from these experiments that a large proportion of the genes in Drosophila must have a stability which—at a minimum value—is comparable with that of radium atoms. Radium atoms, it may be recalled, have a so-called "mean life" of about two thousand years.

2. Certain genes are, however, vastly more mutable than others. For example, a gene causing variegation in corn, studied by Emerson, and another in the four-o'clock, studied by Maryatt, ordinarily have a mean life of only a few years; and that causing bar eye in Drosophila has a mean life of only about 65 years, as is shown by the results of Zeleny. (In expressing these results we are here using the physicists' index of stability, which seems most appropriate for the present purpose also.)

3. External agents do not ordinarily increase the mutability sufficiently (if at all) to cause an obvious "production" of mutation.

4. The changes are not exclusively of the character of losses; this is shown by the well established occurrence of reverse mutations, in bar-eyed and white-eyed Drosophila, in Blakeslee's dwarf Portulaca, Emerson's variegated corn, and probably in a number of other recorded instances. It is known that mutations having an effect similar to that of losses do occur, however, and they may be relatively frequent.

5. The change in a given gene is not in all cases in the same direction, and it does not even, in all cases, involve the same characters. The latter point is illustrated by a series of mutations which I am investigating in Drosophila, which all involve one gene, but which produce, as the case may be, either a shortened wing, an eruption on the thorax, a lethal effect, or any combination of these three.

6. The direction of mutation in a given gene is, however, preferential, occurring oftener in some directions than in others. This is well illustrated in the studies on variegated corn and four-o'clocks, and on the bar eye and white eye and other series in Drosophila.

7. The mutability and preferential direction may themselves be-

come changed through mutation, as illustrated by some of the same cases.

8. The mutations do not ordinarily occur in two or more different genes at once. In only two instances in Drosophila have mutations been found in two different, separated[1] genes in the same line of cells of one individual. But a recurrent case, apparently of this kind, has recently been described in oats, by Nilsson-Ehle.

9. Not only does the mutation usually involve but one kind of gene—it usually involves but one gene of that kind in the cell. That is, the allelomorphs mutate independently of one another, just as totally different genes do. There is evidence for this derived from corn, Portulaca, and Drosophila.

10. Mutations are not limited in their time of occurrence to any particular period of the life history. This has been proved in the above mentioned studies on mutable plants, in Drosophila, and in other cases.

11. Genes normal to the species tend to have more dominance than the mutant genes arising from them. This is very markedly the case in Drosophila, where even the relatively few mutant genes that have been called dominant are very incompletely so, and might more justly be called recessive. In other organisms, the same condition of things is strongly suggested, although the direct data on occurrence of mutations is as yet too meagre to allow of certainty.

12. Most mutations are deleterious in their effects. This applies not only to the organism as a whole but also to the development of any particular part: the delicate mechanisms for producing characters are more likely to be upset than strengthened, so that mutations should more often result in apparent losses or retrogressions than in "progressive" changes. This is both an a priori expectation and a phenomenon generally observed.

13. Mutations with slight effects are probably more frequent than those with more marked effects. This must not be understood as referring to the different mutations of each given gene, but it applies in a comparison of the mutations occurring in different genes. Thus, there are more than a dozen mutations, in different loci, which reduce the size of the wing in Drosophila so slightly as to leave it more than half its original length, whereas only four reduce it to less than half-length. Mutant genes with effects so slight as to be visible only by the aid of specific co-genes seem to arise still more frequently. It is reasonable to conclude that the mutations with slighter effects would more often take part in evolution, because they should usually be less deleterious, and this conclusion is borne out by observations on the multiplicity with which such factor-differences with relatively slight effects are found in species crosses.

14. The range of those mutations which are of appropriate magnitude to be visible is probably very small, in comparison with the entire "spectrum" of mutations, so that there are many more le-

thals than visible mutations, and probably more subliminal than visible.

The above empirical and semi-empirical principles must be regarded as a mere preliminary scaffolding, for the erection of a later, more substantial, theory of mutation. Time does not permit me here to discuss which directions of research, and what methods, seem the most promising for future results. Suffice it to say that it is especially important to obtain accurate data concerning the effect of various conditions upon the rate of mutation. This seems one of the logical routes by which to work towards the artificial production of mutation and consequent more perfect control of evolution. At the same time such results should also give a further insight into the structure of the gene. The way is now open, for the first time, to such studies on mutation rate, first through the finding, by Emerson, Baur, Maryatt, Zeleny, and Blakeslee, of a number of specially mutable factors in different organisms, and second, through certain special genetic methods which I have elaborated in Drosophila, for the detection of lethal and other mutations there.

It has now become recognized that advances in theoretical or "pure" science eventually carry in their train changes in practice of the most far reaching nature—changes which are usually far more radical than those caused by progress in the applied science directly concerned. It may therefore be asked at this point by eugenists: "Are there any applications of the knowledge which has already been gained about mutation in general, to eugenics and to the principles which should govern us in guiding human reproduction?" I think that one such application is already clearly indicated.

In order to understand the nature of this application it will be necessary first to consider the proposition—emphasized by East and Jones in their book, "Inbreeding and Crossbreeding"—that the only way for a genetically sound stock to be formed is by its going through a course of inbreeding, with elimination, by natural or artificial selection, of the undesirable individuals that appear in the course of this inbreeding. The truth of this proposition depends upon the fact that many recessive genes of undesirable character are apt to exist in a population. Since the frequency with which these genes are able to produce their characteristic effects, i.e., to "come to light," depends on the closeness of the inbreeding, it is evident that inbreeding will be necessary in order to recognize the genes adequately, and hence to eliminate them.

Our present theory of mutation, however, carries us further than the proposition just considered. It shows that these undesirable genes have arisen by mutation; in fact, as stated in point 12, the *great majority* of mutations are deleterious, probably even to the degree of being lethal, and it is also known, as noted in point 11, that many—probably the great majority—are recessive. In other words, our mutation theory shows that probably the majority of the mutations that are occurring are giving rise to genes of just the type specified in the above discussion. This immediately shows us that not only are inbreeding and selection desirable for raising the genetic level of a population, but they are absolutely necessary merely in order to maintain it at its present standard. For the same process of mutation which was responsible for the origination of these undesirable genes in the past must be producing them now, and will continue to produce them in the future. Therefore, without selection, or without the inbreeding that makes effective selection possible, these lethals and other undesirable genes will inevitably accumulate, until the germ plasm becomes so riddled through with defect that pure lines cannot be obtained, and progress through selection of desirable recessive traits can never more be effected, since each of them will have become tied up with a lethal. To avoid such a complete and permanent collapse of the evolutionary process, it is accordingly necessary for man or nature to resort to a periodically repeated, although not continuous, series of inbreedings and selections in the case of any biparental organism.

This conclusion is more than a mere speculation, or even a deduction from our principles. The reality of this process of mutational deterioration has been directly proved, in the case of Drosophila, through experiments that I have conducted on lines in which the processes that usually accompany inbreeding and selection were prevented: in these lines there was found an accumulation of lethal genes so rapid that it would have taken but a few decades to have brought about the presence of a lethal gene in practically every chromosome of every fly. Although the same general thesis undoubtedly applies also to mankind we do not yet know the speed of the process here. Its speed depends upon the actual frequency of mutations, which it will be very important—and extremely difficult —to determine in the case of mankind. Meanwhile, no matter what this rate may be, the process remains a real one, which must eventually be reckoned with, and either grappled in time, and conquered, or else yielded to.

I have dwelt at length upon this particular application to eugenics, of some of the mutation studies. I believe, however, that this is but one example of such applications, and that from an increasing knowledge of our theoretical science there will inevitably flow an increasingly adequate technique for coping with our refractory human material. Meanwhile, the crying need is for more of the theoretical knowledge—and for the support of pure science, in its investigation of the processes lying at the root of the germ plasm.

Note

[1]Contiguous genes may be affected in the rare cases known as "deficiencies," found by Bridges and Mohr.

THE MEASUREMENT OF GENE MUTATION RATE IN DROSOPHILA, ITS HIGH VARIABILITY, AND ITS DEPENDENCE UPON TEMPERATURE*

H. J. Muller†

University of Texas, Austin, Texas

[Received October 25, 1927]

Intrepretation of the Findings, and General Considerations

Although these results constitute, in the opinion of the writer, the first demonstration of the effectiveness of any specified agent whatever in influencing the mutations of numerous genes, and probably of genes in general, yet we must be exceptionally cautious in going far from these facts and attempting to draw still more general or remote conclusions from them. The sheer fact of the temperature effect on mutation is worth having, but by itself it stands as an isolated beam in the largely unseen structure of mutation and gene theory. More results gained by similar methods are badly needed. But, in this connection, perhaps the most hopeful feature of the present data is that they show that mutation is indeed capable of being influenced "artificially" — that it does not stand as an unreachable god playing its pranks upon us from some impregnable citadel in the germ plasm; instead, it can be "moved," and its movements detected, studied and "mapped."

It should be repeated here that we do not as yet have any valid evidence on the question of how direct the effect of temperature upon mutation is. We know, however, that in the case of ordinary chemical reactions, the direct effect of a rise in temperature is in the direction of an increase in the speed of the processes, and that the magnitude of this increase is between about 100 and 200 per cent for each 10 degrees centigrade (for ordinary temperatures). We have seen, in the present work, that in the case of mutation rate also the effect of a rise of temperature is in the "positive" direction, and that the magnitude of the effect observed here too seems rather similar to that just stated. These facts, then, certainly suggest that mutation depends primarily on a chemical reaction, and is thus directly affected by temperature; pushing the conclusion further, it would become probable that mutation consists ultimately in

Genetics, July, 1928, 13: 279-357; pp. 343 (part)–51, and table 3, included.

†Department of Zoology, University of Texas, Contribution No. 211.

changes of structure of the general type conventionally designated as "chemical" rather than of one of the types called "physical," (not to speak of such imaginary types as vitalists might postulate). But these points can certainly not be regarded as critically proved, for changes in chemical reactions, dependent on temperature, may in turn cause marked effects on physical processes, and ,*vice versa.*

We know, for example, that the frequency of the semi-mechanical process of crossing over is, in certain chromosome regions, about doubled by a rise of 10° C, at a certain temperature level, and this may quite possibly be brought about through a primary chemical effect of temperature, that in turn influences some "physical" property like chromosome plasticity. In some similar way it might be supposed that mutation, though itself a "physical" process (that is, not involving changes in intra-molecular attachments), could be influenced by a chemical change or complicated series of changes occurring outside of the genes. If a series of changes was involved, the initial process (the effect of temperature upon which was ultimately responsible for the changes in mutation frequency) might even be outside of the organism itself, since as has before been pointed out, we cannot absolutely exclude such, possibilities as that a change in composition of the food, or in some other cultural condition, itself somehow dependent on the temperature, secondarily affected the mutation rate. We may return to the point, however, that in the case of any sorts of indirect action such as those pictured above, the facts that the effect of a rise in temperature was positive in direction, and was of apparently the same magnitude as are the direct effects on chemical reactions, would have to be regarded as in the nature of a "coincidence." And coincidences do not form good postulates.

One of the points to be remembered in considering the possible mode of action of any agent in changing the structure of a gene is that we are not necessarily dealing here simply with an alteration in the composition of pre-existing gene material, but we may instead, or in addition, be dealing with some kind of interference, by the agent in question, with the process by which the pre-existing gene forms new gene material. The pre-existing gene may remain unmutated, and the "mutation" may consist in the fact that, for some reason, the new gene material built up at that particular time was not just like the old. In that case, the more rapidly gene growth occurred (that is, the more gene material was formed in unit time) during the time that the "interfering agent" was able to act, the greater would be the number of mutations that occurred. Since an ordinary rise in temperature, during stages when cell growth is occurring, usually increases the rapidity of that growth, this by itself would then lead to a direct effect of temperature on mutation frequency, even if other effective factors remained constant. Evidence on this question might be gained if we found that the effect of temperature on mutation rate varied in direct proportion to the rapidity of gene growth that was going on in the germ plasm at the time when temperature was applied. For example, on this hypothesis, warmth applied to mature spermatozoa should produce no such effect. It was because of these considerations that the series of cultures involving the aging of spermatozoa was carried on, but it will be recalled, the mutation rate was too low in that experiment to permit the securing of results. Similar work, with the aid of the newer methods, should be more informative.

There is at least one path of indirect action of temperature that might, on *a priori* grounds, have been postulated as a mechanism whereby mutation rate could be influenced, which can be categorically eliminated as a cause of the effects observed in the present experiments; that is, the possibility that the mutation rate was affected through the known effect of temperature upon crossing over. Such an idea may have already suggested itself to the reader in view of the peculiar relationships found to exist between crossing over and bar eye "mutation," by Sturtevant, on the one hand, and between crossing over and reddish mutation in *D. virilis*, by Demerec, on the other hand. Fortunately for a decision on this point, crossing over could not occur in the present experiments, in those chromosomes in which mutation was looked for. Furthermore, most of the mutations occurred in chromosome regions the crossover frequency of which is affected little or not at all by ordinary temperature changes. The mutations observed, then, were not phenomena of exchange between homologous chromosomes. They may well have been affected, however, by some of the same forces (for example, those exerted in synaptic attraction) as also influence the process of crossing over.

An attack on such questions as the above, also, does not now seem so remote. Whether or not, or how, certain synaptic occurrences are associated with mutational changes in general is one of the topics that may be investigated by modifications of our present metods. An intensive mutation study, in which given conditions, known to affect another process in question (for example, synapsis), are concentrated at crucial stages of the life cycle, could scarcely fail to yield evidence regarding such a point.

In the light of the new "gene-element" conception further and perhaps even deeper problems are raised by the present study. Accepting, that is, for purposes of discussion, this new theory, it is not clear whether the effect of temperature here detected would be due to a greater rate of sorting out of "gene-elements" already heterogeneous in the gene before the experiment started, or to an actually greater rate of "gene-element mutation," or both. Various indications, however, would point to the rate of mutation in whatever are the primary gene particles as having itself been increased. One of these indications is the usual lack of grouping in sister lines of those identically located lethals which were found in most of the experiments,—although the latest experiment on the X here seems to form an exception. Another indication is the finding of apparently as great an effect of temperature on mutation frequency, per generation, in the experiments involving many generations as in those involving few, whereas if merely the rate of sorting out of elements had been hastened the supply of differing elements would have dwindled away in the course of time. On this point too, however, the results are only "suggestive." The methods here used are, however, capable of application to this problem too.

Evolution theory and practical breeding must in part follow in the wake of mutation study. Evolutionists would doubtless eagerly make use of the notion that mutation happens more frequently, per unit time, and also probably per natural generation, at warmer temperatures. And if this were constantly true it could scarcely fail to be an important factor in the rate of evolution, since mutations seem to be so rare that their rate may often be the *limiting* factor in the rate of evolution, and the latter process will then be directly proportional to the former (other things being equal). But it must be pointed out that the significance of the results here presented, for evolution, must largely depend upon the answer to some of the problems previously raised. Take, for example, the problem last discussed, as to which hypothetical part of the process of mutation has been accelerated: The change in the ultimate gene elements, or in their postulated rate of sorting out (and, possibly, in their differential rate of multiplication) to form manifestly different genes. If the former process has been speeded up, the effect would indeed be important in the long run, and therefore of consequence in evolution; if the latter process only is involved, the effect might be evanescent, since the rate of supply of new "gene-elements" would not be increased. It must be remembered, too, that "other things" are not equal, in nature, and that other factors (including those of selection) differentiating warmer from cooler climates may, on occasion, be vastly more influential than an effect of temperature upon mutation rate itself. This too, however, is within the pale of investigation.

In practical breeding, any factor should be of importance that can affect mutation rate, even if for only a few generations. The implications of the present study for the improvement of organisms whose germ cells can be subjected to controlled temperatures are therefore obvious, and need not be dwelt upon here further. Conversely, cold might be used as an aid in maintaining genic stability in already standardized races.

In conclusion, it may be repeated that, while the effect of temperature on mutation here observed seems of interest, more speci emphasis should perhaps be placed on the opening up of the methods here set forth, and on the proof that these methods c used successfully in attacking problems which hitherto hav inaccessible. Temperature is merely one of a great numbe ditions—external and internal—the effect of which upon mutation can be studied in various ways. And, as the present work demonstrates, some of these other conditions, or at least one, certainly do exert an influence upon mutation rate far greater even than that of temperature. As to what these conditions, or this condition, consist of, the present experiments give little hint, though they varied markedly from experiment to experiment. This in itself presents an alluring problem, which likewise seems capable of approach through the present methods. Thus, through attacks of this kind, we may perhaps hope for the study of mutation eventually to pass from its earlier observational and speculative stage to one of quantitative and controlled study, from which exact knowledge, and principles not now to be guessed, may finally emerge. The "factor theory" itself awaited intensive quantitative study before its structure could be soundly established, so did the chromosome theory, and so, probably, will the future theory of mutation.

It may appear as though experiments of this type are too cumbersome to be prosecuted. They are not nearly so cumbersome as they were when the first results were obtained with them, and still better methods are, it is hoped, being developed. Since, however, the methods can be successfully used at all, then, for the very reason that they do require effort, it becomes all the more needful for a larger corps of investigators to step into the work thus provided, to make still further improvements, and to gain further data on the important problems that abound in this new field. Each plant-generation in the earlier work on Mendelian inheritance required a year, and much labor, and an experiment required several years; yet through such work biology made relatively rapid strides. And the mutation work is now only in its early years.

Summary

1. The development is traced of methods of obtaining valid data on the frequency of gene mutations under varying conditions. The ...ds fall under two general groups:
... the X-chromosomes. These again fall into two sub-
... sex ratio counts of each test-culture, and
... of the presence or absence, in
...ses of males from mothers hete-
... genes."
...ks containing balanced lethal or
...low the accumulation of mutant
... selection, and the tests, involv-
...ved in the second generation, are
...-culture of each of the numerous

ries" was kept constantly. It is therefore likely that warmth is effective in influencing mutation when applied specifically to the stages mentioned.

11. It should be noted that both the direction of the effect of temperature on the time-rate of mutation, and its approximate magnitude, are the same as in the case of its effect on the time-rate of ordinary chemical reactions.

12. Possible interpretations of the findings concerning temperature are discussed, and their bearings on other topics are pointed out.

13. It is believed that the methods by which these results have been obtained open up a new field of genetics—the quantitative study of gene mutation, as occurring throughout one or more entire chromosomes under purposely varied conditions.

AGE IN RELATION TO THE FREQUENCY OF SPONTANEOUS MUTATIONS IN DROSOPHILA*

by H. J. Muller

Pursuant of the question whether, as sometimes held, "spontaneous" mutations accumulate in the germ plasm of individuals in proportion to their age, studies were made of the frequency of sex-linked lethals in offspring of Drosophila aged for different periods and in different ways. To make possible the obtaining of sufficiently large-scale data for significant comparisons, special stocks were constructed which, in the test crosses of offspring, (1) allowed the use of non-virgin females, (2) disclosed lethals in both the X-chromosome of maternal and that of paternal origin, and (3) guarded readily against non-disjunction. In this way some 200,000 X-chromosomes were tested.

Regarding the paternal chromosomes, it was found that, instead of the newly hatched males giving rise to a lower proportion of mutant offspring than those a week older, they give two to three times as high a proportion, provided the young males used are virgins and the older ones have previously expended their first week's supply of spermatozoa. This must mean that at some period or periods mutations take place with a lower frequency in one group of germ cells, those destined to form the sperm used during the second week after hatching, than in another group simultaneously present in the

*Year Book of the American Philosophical Society, 1945, pp. 150-53.

same male, namely, those to be used during the first week. And this effect must be caused by some physiological difference or differences between these groups of cells that strongly affect their mutability, i.e., their sensitivity to mutation-inducing factors normally present.

In contrast to these results, tests of the offspring of spermatozoa that had been stored for different lengths of time while mature showed that in them mutations decidedly do accumulate during their aging, to such an extent that spermatozoa aged several weeks in the female may contain several times as many mutations as they originally had. It might be supposed that the above mentioned higher mutation frequency in the sperm of newly hatched males as compared with older ones could be explained on the same basis, i.e., by accumulation of mutations in stored sperm, since there is storage of spermatozoa in the pupae. However, the difference is too pronounced to be accounted for in this way. As for the question whether there is an accumulation of mutations in spermatozoa while stored in the male, like that in the female, the results with still older males make it probable that this is the case. However, neither the latter question nor that of the amount of accumulation of mutations in the immature germ cells of the male, as aging proceeds, could be studied critically here because of the infrequency of copulation of older males and the uncertainty regarding how long their sperm had been kept in the mature condition before ejaculation.

In the study of mutation in females there was little difficulty of the above sort, and the results were, within the statistical limits, surprisingly constant. The frequency of mutations inherited from the mother was sensibly the same in offspring derived from eggs laid at any time from the first through the sixth week after hatching; moreover, delay in laying the eggs did not appreciably affect the result. In some series the females, while being aged, were kept mated and well supplied with food throughout their adult life, so that there was a continuous active proliferation of their germ cells, while in others the process of egg production had for most of this time been practically halted by inadequate feeding, and sometimes also by virginity, but both methods of aging yielded substantially the same mutation frequency.

These relatively uniform results show that most of the mutations must arise during one or more particular stages in the life cycle of the female's germ cells, stages which are gone through similarly, and are of similar duration, both in the case of the lines of cells that produce the early eggs and in those that produce the eggs of latter life. In contrast, far fewer mutations occur during the major period of the germ cells' existence, that in which the "primary germ cells" or gonia must spend most of their time as the adult is growing older. For the great variations in the length of this period in the different cases had no appreciable effect on the mutation frequency. As in the male, then, there is a particular stage or stages of relatively high mutability, but, unlike what is found in the male, the frequency of mutations arising therein is approximately the same in the lines of germ cells that are to be used earlier and in those used later. That one of these especially mutable stages is early "cleavage" is indicated by the comparatively large number of "group" cases, where the same mutation appears in a high proportion of an individual's offspring. It seems probable that another mutable stage occurs late in the germ track, i.e., during or near maturation, but more evidence is needed here.

Corroboration of these conclusions was afforded by the mutation frequencies found in chromosomes derived from parents, whether male or female, that had been maintained two or three weeks longer than normally in the larval condition by larval underfeeding. For here too the frequencies were similar to those of the controls, not precociously aged, and failed to show that increase to be expected if, during this aging, mutations had been arising in the immature germ cells at as high a time-rate as that obtaining during the remainder of the germ cycle.

These relations, if general, would in part at least explain why species with longer life cycles do not seem to have mutation frequencies proportionately higher than those with shorter cycles, although no doubt selection also tends to work in this direction.

A study of part of the material, with cytological examinations of detected cases by T. Dobzhansky and most of the linkage tests by L. Goldstein, showed that spontaneous structural changes in chromosomes arise with an appreciable frequency, all told, but one far lower than that of gene mutations.

THE FREQUENCY OF SPONTANEOUS MUTATIONS AT INDIVIDUAL LOCI IN DROSOPHILA*

H. J. Muller, J. I. Valencia and R. M. Valencia

Spontaneous visible mutations involving nine "chosen" sex-linked loci (prune, white, ruby, carmine, singed, raspberry, vermilion, garnet, forked) were looked for among approximately 60,000 nondisjunctionally produced daughters of females having one Y-chromosome, one X-chromosome with all these genes mutant and one

*Records of the Genetics Society of America, 1949, 18: 105-6 (with corrections).

with inversions but all these genes normal. Nine verified "gene-mutations" and an estimated eight that were not analyzed arose at these loci, scattered as though randomly. Thus the frequency of spontaneous gene-mutation in the female here was 1 in 32,000 ($=3.10^{-5}$) per locus. But since females of the parental stock gave nearly 0.7 per cent sex-linked lethal mutations, a rate almost quadruple the usual, the frequency of gene-mutations at the nine loci would *ordinarily* average between 10^{-5} and 7.10^{-6} per locus in females. In a different stock, homozygous for cinnabar to facilitate detection of eye color changes, L. and E. Altenburg found none among 50,000 sons. Allowing for inviability here, this falls significantly below 3.10^{-5} but not below 10^{-5} per locus. In our own material, miniature and cut mutations were detectable also. However, low viability rendered miniatures unreliable (none appeared). Nine cuts, those analyzed being cytologically invisible lethals, probably gene-mutations, arose among the 60,000, i.e., $1.5 \cdot 10^{-4}$. In addition, eighteen to twenty-one mosaic mutations involving one of the "chosen" nine loci, four involving miniature (more viable when mosaic), and four cut, were found. None proved transmissible. Hence most had arisen during enbryogeny. No gross rearrangements were found. Three mutants (all white lethals) were designated presumptive deficiencies. Two were examined cytologically, one proving invisible, the other obviously deficient....

INFLUENCE OF AGEING AT TWO DIFFERENT TEMPERATURES ON THE SPONTANEOUS MUTATION RATE IN MATURE SPERMATOZOA OF DROSOPHILA MELANOGASTER*

Helen L. Byers and H. J. Muller
Indiana University, Bloomington, Indiana

Although earlier work demonstrated that higher temperature applied throughout life increases the mutation rate, the possible dependence of this result upon differences in rate and kind of cell multiplication, growth, and metabolism remains unclear. Experiments were accordingly undertaken to study the influence of tem-

*Records of the Genetics Society of America, 1952, 21: 14-15; and Genetics, 37: 570-71.

ARTIFICIAL TRANSMUTATION
OF THE GENE*

Most modern geneticists will agree that gene mutations form the
chief basis of organic evolution, and therefore of most of the com-
plexities of living things. Unfortunately for the geneticists, however,
the study of these mutations, and, through them, of the genes themselves, has heretofore been very seriously hampered by the extreme
infrequency of their occurrence under ordinary conditions, and by
the general unsuccessfulness of attempts to modify decidely, and in
a sure and detectable way, this sluggish "natural" mutation rate.
Modification of the innate nature of organisms, for more directly
utilitarian purposes, has of course been subject to these same
restrictions, and the practical breeder has hence been compelled to
remain content with the mere making of recombinations of the material already at hand, providentially supplemented, on rare and
isolated occasions, by an unexpected mutational windfall. To these
circumstances are due the wide-spread desire on the part of biologists to gain some measure of control over the hereditary changes
within the genes.

It has been repeatedly reported that germinal changes, presumably mutational, could be induced by X or radium rays, but, as in
the case of the similar published claims involving other agents
(alcohol, lead, antibodies, etc.), the work has been done in such a
way that the meaning of the data, as analyzed from a modern
genetic standpoint, has been highly disputatious at best; moreover,
what were apparently the clearest cases have given negative or
contrary results on repetition. Nevertheless, on theoretical grounds,
it has appeared to the present writer that radiations of short wave
length should be especially promising for the production of mutational changes, and for this and other reasons a series of experiments concerned with this problem has been undertaken during the
past year on the fruit fly, Drosophila melanogaster, in an attempt
to provide critical data. The well-known favorableness of this
species for genetic study, and the special methods evolved during
the writer's eight years' intensive work on its mutation rate (including the work on temperature, to be referred to later), have
finally made possible the finding of some decisive effects, consequent upon the application of X-rays. The effects here referred
to are truly mutational, and not to be confused with the well-known
effects of X-rays upon the distribution of the chromatin, expressed

*Science, Vol. LXVI, No. 1699, July 22, 1927, pp. 84-87.

by non-disjunction, non-inherited crossover modifications, etc. In the present condensed digest of the work, only the broad facts and conclusions therefrom, and some of the problems raised can be presented, without any details of the genetic methods employed, or of the individual results obtained.

It has been found quite conclusively that treatment of the sperm with relatively heavy doses of X-rays induces the occurrence of true "gene mutations" in a high proportion of the treated germ cells. Several hundred mutants have been obtained in this way in a short time and considerably more than a hundred of the mutant genes have been followed through three, four or more generations. They are (nearly all of them, at any rate) stable in their inheritance, and most of them behave in the manner typical of the Mendelian chromosomal mutant genes found in organisms generally. The nature of the crosses was such as to be much more favorable for the detection of mutations in the X-chromosomes than in the other chromosomes, so that most of the mutant genes dealt with were sex-linked; there was, however, ample proof that mutations were occurring similarly throughout the chromatin. When the heaviest treatment was given to the sperm, about a seventh of the offspring that hatched from them and bred contained individually detectable mutations in their treated X-chromosome. Since the X forms about one fourth of the haploid chromatin, then, if we assume an equal rate of mutation in all the chromosomes (per unit of their length), it follows that almost "every other one" of the sperm cells capable of producing a fertile adult contained an "individually detectable" mutation in some chromosome or other. Thousands of untreated parent flies were bred as controls in the same way as the treated ones. Comparison of the mutation rates under the two sets of conditions showed that the heavy treatment had caused a rise of about fifteen thousand per cent in the mutation rate over that in the untreated germ cells.

Regarding the types of mutations produced, it was found that, as was to have been expected both on theoretical grounds and on the basis of the previous mutation studies of Altenburg and the writer, the lethals (recessive for the lethal effect, though some were dominant for visible effects) greatly outnumbered the non-lethals producing a visible morphological abnormality. There were some "semi-lethals" also (defining these as mutants having a viability ordinarily between about 0.5 per cent and 10 per cent of the normal), but, fortunately for the use of lethals as an index of mutation rate, these were not nearly so numerous as the lethals. The elusive class of "invisible" mutations that caused an even lesser reduction of viability, not readily confusable with lethals, appeared larger than that of the semi-lethals, but they were not subjected to study. In addition, it was also possible to obtain evidence in these experiments for the first time, of the occurrence of dominant lethal genetic changes, both in the X and in the other chromosomes. Since the zygotes receiving these never developed to maturity, such lethals could not be detected individually, but their number was so great that through egg counts and effects on the sex ratio evidence could be obtained of them *en masse*. It was found that their numbers are of the same order of magnitude as those of the recessive lethals. The "partial sterility" of treated males is, to an appreciable extent at least, caused by these dominant lethals. Another abundant class of mutations not previously recognized was found to be those which, when heterozygous, cause sterility but produce no detectable change in appearance; these too occur in numbers rather similar to those of the recessive lethals, and they may hereafter afford one of the readiest indices of the general mutation rate, when this is high. The sterility thus caused, occurring as it does in the offspring of the treated individuals, is of course a separate phenomenon from the "partial sterility" of the treated individuals themselves, caused by the dominant lethals.

In the statement that the proportion of "individually detectable mutations" was about one seventh for the X, and therefore nearly one half for all the chromatin, only the recessive lethals and semilethals and the "visible" mutants were referred to. If the dominant lethals, the dominant and recessive sterility genes and the "invisible" genes that merely reduce (or otherwise affect) viability or fertility had been taken into account, the percentage of mutants given would have been far higher, and it is accordingly evident that in reality the great majority of the treated sperm cells contained mutations of some kind or other. It appears that the rate of gene mutation after X-ray treatment is high enough, in proportion to the total number of genes, so that it will be practicable to study it even in the case of individual loci, in an attack on problems of allelomorphism, etc.

Returning to a consideration of the induced mutations that produced visible effects, it is to be noted that the conditions of the present experiment allowed the detection of many which approached or overlapped the normal type to such an extent that ordinarily they would have escaped observation, and definite evidence was thus obtained of the relatively high frequency of such changes here, as compared with the more conspicuous ones. The belief has several times been expressed in the *Drosophila* literature that this holds true in the case of "natural" mutations in this organism, but it has been founded only on "general impressions"; Baur, however, has demonstrated the truth of it in *Antirrhinum*. On the whole, the visible mutations caused by raying were found to be similar, in their general characteristics, to those previously detected in non-rayed material in the extensive observations on visible mutations in *Drosophila* carried out by Bridges and others. A considerable proportion of the induced visible mutations were, it is true, in loci in which mutation apparently had never been observed before, and some of these involved morphological effects of a sort not exactly like any seen previously (*e.g.*, "splotched wing," "sex-combless," etc.), but, on the other hand, there were also numerous repetitions of mutations previously known. In fact, the majority of the well-known mutations in the X-chromosome of *Drosophila melanogaster* such as "white eye," "miniature wing," "forked bristles," etc., were reobtained, some of them several times. Among the visible mutations found, the great majority were recessive, yet there was a considerable "sprinkling" of dominants, just as in other work. All in all, then, there can be no doubt that many, at least, of the changes produced by X-rays are of just the same kind as the "gene mutations" which are obtained, with so much greater rarity, without such treatment, and which we believe furnish the building blocks of evolution.

In addition to the gene mutations, it was found that there is also caused by X-ray treatment a high proportion of rearrangements in the linear order of the genes. This was evidenced in general by the frequent inherited disturbances in crossover frequency (at least 3 per cent were detected in the X-chromosome alone, many accompanied but some unaccompanied by lethal effects), and evidenced specifically by various cases that were proved in other ways to involve inversions, "deficiencies," fragmentations, translocations, etc., of portions of a chromosome. These cases are making possible attacks on a number of genetic problems otherwise difficult of approach.

The transmuting action of X-rays on the genes is not confined to the sperm cells, for treatment of the unfertilized females causes mutations about as readily as treatment of the males. The effect is produced both on oöcytes and early oögonia. It should be noted especially that, as in mammals, X-rays (in the doses used) cause a period of extreme infertility, which commences soon after treatment and later is partially recovered from. It can be stated positively that the return of fertility does not mean that the new crop of eggs is unaffected, for these, like those mature eggs that managed to survive, were found in the present experiments to contain a high proportion of mutant genes (chiefly lethals, as usual). The practice, common in current X-ray therapy, of giving treatments that do not certainly result in permanent sterilization, has been defended chiefly on the ground of a purely theoretical conception that eggs produced after the return of fertility must necessarily represent "uninjured" tissue. As this presumption is hereby demonstrated to be faulty it would seem incumbent for medical practice to be modified accordingly, at least until genetically sound experimentation upon mammals can be shown to yield results of a decisively negative character. Such work upon mammals would involve a highly elaborate undertaking, as compared with the above experiments on flies.

treatment, before fertilization, causes no noticeable alteration in the frequency of detectable mutations. Therefore the death rate of the mutant sperm is no higher than that of the unaffected ones; moreover, the mutations can not be regarded as secondary effects of any semi-lethal physiological changes which might be supposed to have occurred more intensely in some ("more highly susceptible") spermatozoa than in others.

Despite the "negative results" just mentioned, however, it is already certain that differences in X-ray influences, by themselves, are not sufficient to account for all variations in mutation frequency, for the present X-ray work comes on the heels of the determination of mutation rate being dependent upon temperature (work as yet unpublished). This relation had first been made probable by work of Altenburg and the writer in 1919, but was not finally established until the completion of some experiments in 1926. These gave the first definite evidence that gene mutation may be to any extent controllable, but the magnitude of the heat effect, being similar to that found for chemical reactions in general, is too small, in connection with the almost imperceptible "natural" mutation rate, for it, by itself, to provide a powerful tool in the mutation study. The result, however, is enough to indicate that various factors besides X-rays probably do affect the composition of the gene, and that the measurement of their effects, at least when in combination with X-rays, will be practicable. Thus we may hope that problems of the composition and behavior of the gene can shortly be approached from various new angles, and new handles found for their investigation, so that it will be legitimate to speak of the subject of "gene physiology," at least, if not of gene physics and chemistry.

In conclusion, the attention of those working along classical genetic lines may be drawn to the opportunity, afforded them by the use of X-rays, of creating in their chosen organisms a series of artificial races for use in the study of genetic and "phaenogenetic" phenomena. If, as seems likely on general considerations, the effect is common to most organisms, it should be possible to produce, "to order," enough mutations to furnish respectable genetic maps, in their selected species, and, by the use of the mapped genes, to analyze the aberrant chromosome phenomena simultaneously obtained. Similarly, for the practical breeder, it is hoped that the method will ultimately prove useful. The time is not ripe to discuss here such possibilities with reference to the human species.

The writer takes pleasure in acknowledging his sincere appreciation of the cooperation of Dr. Dalton Richardson, Roentgenologist, of Austin, Texas, in the work of administering the X-ray treatments.

H. J. Muller

University of Texas

THE PROBLEM OF GENIC
MODIFICATION*

H. J. Muller
University of Texas, Austin, Tex.
(With 4 text-figures)

For nearly three decades geneticists have been engaged in studying the distribution, localization and expression of the genes—that
is, in universalizing the discoveries of Mendel, in proving correct
the early inferences of Roux regarding the linear arrangement of
determiners in the chromosomes, the later suggestion of Janssens
concerning their exchange by chiasmatype, and the *a priori* conceptions of Naegeli that each character is the resultant of multiple
determiners and environic factors interacting in manifold and de-
vious ways. The rare exceptions to normal gene distribution—involving chromosome misplacements, breakages, fusions—have
served chiefly to prove these same old principles. And from these
principles are utlimately derivable most of our complex modern
genetic and phaenotypic ratios, provided we treat the genes as immutable entities. That we can do so, for most purposes of short
range prediction, has been shown by the combined work of Johannsen
and numerous others. In this sense, then, the oft-quoted saying
originated by Weinstein in 1916 is true, that "the problem of heredity has been solved."

Yet, given all the above principles, and only them, scarcely one
step could have been taken in the long epic of evolution whereby
modern organisms were derived from the most primitive protoplasm. For the genes cannot be, and are not, immutable entities.
Accumulating evidence of the same three decades, most of it happened upon as a by-product of work having a different primary
object, has made it clear that the basis of heritable variation lies
in very infrequent, sudden changes in individual genes. And so,
parallel with our knowledge of heredity proper, a body of fact has
gradually grown concerning this negation of heredity—gene mutation,—this more deeply underlying process whose almost imperceptible action eventually results in the momentous transformations
of biological history. But so far our knowledge concerning gene
mutation has been of a different order from that concerning heredity itself, consisting mainly of scattered, fragmentary observations
under largely uncontrolled conditions, not susceptible to that quantitative analysis which made the ratios of Mendelian recombination

*Verhandlungen des V. Internationalen Kongresses für Vererbungswis-
senschaft, Berlin, 1927, Supplementband I der Zeitschrift für induktive
Abstammungs-und Vererbungslehre, 1928, pp. 234-60.

In examining these P_1 -F_1 cultures, it was soon noticeable that their productivity decreased progressively with increasing treatment of either parent, although, as had been expected, the fertility of the females was much more affected in the first brood than was that of the males. In the later brood, the females partially recovered fertility, but the males did not. When the F_1 flies hatched they were subjected to close scrutiny and among somewhat over two thousand examined in all the treated series eighty-one having distinguishable (though often slight) morphological abnormalities were observed, while among about the same number of controls there were only about nineteen that seemed correspondingly abnormal. Among these abnormalities there must of course have been included modifications not genetic in their basis.

The F_1 flies, not necessarily virgin, were then mated together in pairs, brothers by sisters as far as possible. (They then formed the P_2.) One thousand and eleven cultures containing control females, and one thousand and fifteen from the various treated series, distributed as shown in table 1, were started, in as many separate half-pint bóttles. These matings had the formula

$$\frac{\text{sc v f}}{\text{bb}} \, ♀ \times \frac{\text{sc v f}}{\underline{}/} \, ♂$$

The multiple heterozygous condition of these P_2 females made it possible to discover and to locate any lethal or visible mutant gene lying in either of their sons (the F_2). In the case of a lethal, sons showing the non-crossover combination of genes lying on either side of the lethal would be missing from the F_2 aggregate, and the per cent of the crossover classes would show the location of the mutant gene more exactly.

As the F_2 generation of these cultures began to be examined, certain facts soon asserted themselves forcibly. The controls were consistently showing an extremely low rate of mutation, similar to what had been observed on some previous occasions; in fact, only one lethal was found in the 947 fertile control cultures, comprising twice this many tested control X chromosomes (two for each mother). But the treated series just as consistently showed a rate of mutation far in excess of anything previously known, and it was evident in addition that, where the P_1 male only had been treated, lethals and other mutations were present in the bb-bearing chromosome, derived from him, and very seldom in the sc v f-bearing chromosome, whereas, where the P_1 female only had been treated, these relations were exactly reversed. (The figures are shown in table 1). It appears quite clear, from these statistics, that mutations are produced by X rays, in *Drosophila* and furthermore, that they are produced both by treatment of the mature sperm, and of the eggs. In the case of brood 2 of the t-2♀ series the cells must have been in relatively early oögonial stages at the time of treatment, yet here too mutations were unquestionably produced, and the mutant genes were transmitted to the viable eggs laid after the partial return of fertility. This result runs counter to the assumptions made by some X ray practitioners in justification of some of their practices in ovarian therapy.

Table 1
$P_2 — F_2$ cultures in "First Experiments"

Series	Cultures started	Cultures hatched	Lethals		Semi-L.		Visibles	
			Mat.	Pat.	Mat.	Pat.	Mat.	Pat.
C	1011	947	0	1	0	0	0	0
t_1	30	25	*0*	*1*	*0*	*0*	*0*	*0*
t_2♀ BR. 1	68	56	*6*	0	*1*	1	*0*	0
t_3♀ BR. 2	168	160	*7*	1	*3*	0	*1*	1
t_2	86	65	0	*10*	0	*1*	0	*1*
t_3	136	72	0	*8*	0	2	0	*4*
t_4BR. 1	315	217	0	*34*	0	5	1	6
t_4BR. 2	212	188	2	*20*	0	5	0	7
Tot. t	1015	783	*13*+2	*73*+1	*4*+0	*13*+1	*1*+1	*18*+1

note: mutations in treated chromosomes are shown in italics. Among the semi-lethals and visibles a few inconspicuous mutations are here included that were not detected till the next generation ($P_3 —F_3$).

As usual, the numbers of recessive lethals (shown in the table) furnished the most extensive and the most definite test of the mutation rates, but there was no question that mutations having various other forms of expression had also been produced. Directing our attention first to other recessive effects on viability, we find a much smaller, but still noteworthy number of "semi-lethals," all chromosomes but one in the treated. We may define these, somewhat arbitrarily, as genes which ordinarily reduce the viability to about a half to ten per cent of the normal, and which therefore may often be mistaken for lethals, in counts based on one culture. A large proportion of the semi-lethals detected produced visible effects, in those males containing them which survived; hence this class highly overlapped that of the visible mutations. As was to have been expected, some semi-lethals, as well as some relatively inconspicuous visibles, escaped detection till the following generations (F_3 and F_4) were examined, but this did not signify that they had not arisen before that time. Beyond the semi-lethals, there was also no doubt that there had arisen, in the treated X chromosomes, a rather abundant class of recessive mutant genes that produced only a slight reduction of viability. Of course it is well known that visible mutant genes commonly, though not always, have such an effect on viability, and this relation was observed in the present experiments as well, but it was also noticeable that in very many cultures of the treated series in contrast to the controls, the sons bearing one of the X chromosomes (the treated one) tended to run behind the sons of the contrary class in numbers even when they showed no discernible abnormality. The obtaining of definite counts, in order accurately to measure and follow up this phenomenon, would have been very time-consuming, however, and was therefore precluded in the present experiments, in view of the other matters that required attention. It may be observed that the genes here in question fall into the same phaenotypic category with the numerous recessive genes for reduced vigor depicted in the prevalent theory of heterosis.

Significant numbers of visible mutations also were obtained, and again, with rate exceptions, they occurred in the treated chromosomes. These visibles may roughly be classified into the "conspicuous" and the "inconspicuous," though of course the line of division will vary widely according to the observer, the conditions of observation, and the mode of application of the term. Despite this difficulty, we may say that at least half of the visible mutations here observed were such as would have been regarded by *Drosophila* workers in the early years, and by all but the most practised to-day, as inconspicuous. (See table 2). Most of these would have been likely to have passed unnoticed in the present work, had they appeared in single individuals only. It was the fact that an entire group of individuals bearing the mutant gene could be observed that made it possible here for a comparatively large proportion of them to be recognized. This corresponds with published observations of Baur on natural mutations in *Antirrhinum*.

Table 2
Mutations in "First Experiments"

	Lethal		Sem.	Weak	Vigor.
	cr. o. mod.	cr. o. norm.	$(\frac{1}{2}—10\%$ viab.$)$	$(10—70\%$ viab.$)$	$(70—"100+"\%$ viab$)$
± conspic.			7	3	6
∓ inconspic.	} 23	} 68	5	6	5
nvis.			5	many ?	?

On the whole, the visible mutations in the treated chromosomes were similar in general type to what had been observed before in previous *Drosophila* work. Of the twenty not classified as semi-lethals seven were similar both in appearance and at the same time in locus, to previous described mutations. These were (in order of their locus) white eye, facet eye, tan body, tiny bristle, small wing, small eye, and a fertile mutant called "cleftoid" resembling in appearance and locus the sterile "cleft" described by Weinstein. Of these mutants, white, tan, small wing, and small eye were crossed to stock of the original mutants, and the apparition of the mutant character in the offspring showed that the X ray mutants were really allelomorphs of the old mutants. In addition, vermilion eyes appeared in a sterile F_1 female, which, barring mutation in her treated chromosome, should have been only heterozygous for this recessive gene. In view of the reappearance, then, of the five verified and three probable well-known mutations in the treated X chromosome, among fewer than 1014 females, whose parents were known not to contain them, it seems impossible to avoid the conclusion that changes of the same kind as those unhesitatingly described as "gene mutations" in other *Drosophila* work were now being produced by the X rays.

The visible mutations that were not allelomorphic to previously known ones were of diverse kinds — three characterized chiefly by ommatidial disarrangements, four by various wing pecularities ("expanded," "mussed," "arc" and "splotched"), one by "ruffled hairs," one by a combination of small size and melanism (called "pigmy") and two rather diffuse in their effects ("wee" and "deacon"). Among these, "splotched" was clearly dominant. There were also among the lethals and semi-lethals several at least partially dominant for visible characters — including "stumpy," "mosaic bristles" and "cloven thorax."

The relative numbers of induced gene mutations located in different chromosome regions are shown in figure 2. Like the mutations previously known, they seem to occur in all regions, but there is a sharp maximum in the density at the left end, followed by a minimum, and there is another, somewhat lower, maximum about twelve units from the right end. The absolute numbers are large enough to allow us to be fairly certain of this much. In addition they make it rather probable that there is another minimum, to the left of the second maximum. Now, all these same features may be distinctly seen in the standard *Drosophila* map that shows the position of the previously observed spontaneous visible mutations in the X chromosome. It is likely that these apparent unevennesses in density are due to a kind of false perspective, and indicate variations in the frequency of crossing over per physical unit — i. e., in the relation between map distance and actual distance, — rather than real variations in the frequency of mutations or of genes in different portions of the chromonema.

Mutations in autosomes, if they were ordinary recessive lethals, could not have been detected in this set of experiments at all; if they were recessive visibles, they would not have shown until F_3 and, even then only one quarter of those existing in F_1 would ap-

ficiency involving bobbed, a mutant non-lethal condition that rendered the chromosome possessing it likely to become eliminated at the reduction division, and another case of rearrangement of loci in the X chromosome, yielding visibly abnormal crossovers.

In addition, it was observed that, in the formation of the females of the F_1 generation, three of the four mutant genes already existing in the non-treated chromosome,—namely, vermilion, forked, and bobbed—each arose again (in separate cases) in the treated chromosome, resulting in three females that were homozygous for and manifested one of these recessive characters. Two of them were sterile, but from the other a stock of the new forked, viable and fertile, was derived.

To obtain further data concerning the origination of visible mutant genes another set of crosses was resorted to. In these, normal-appearing males containing bobbed were mated to yellow females of the stock containing the two X chromosomes attached to each other, and a supernumerary Y chromosome. The F_1 males receive their single X from the paternal gamete and their Y chromosome from their mother; hence they can reveal at once, on inspection, visible mutations that occurred in the sperm from which they were derived. The P_1 males were divided at random into two lots, receiving the t-2 and t-4 treatments, respectively. These two series had to serve as checks against each other. Had time permitted, non-treated controls would have been reared also, but all previous *Drosophila* work (including extensive breeding and examination, in the present work, of the stock from which the P_1 males were obtained) has shown visible mutations to be exceedingly rare—certainly not more frequent than of the order of one in the thousand, in the X chromosome. This cross and its results are shown in figure 4 and table 4.

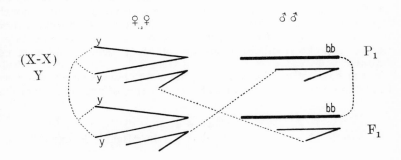

Fig. 4. Scheme of crossings in "Double X Experiment"

(Note: y represents mutant gene for yellow body located in the X-X, or double X chromosome. Y represents Y chromosome)

Close scrutiny of 1,490 sons in the t-2 series showed that 61 had some sort of visible abnormality. In the t-4 series, in a total of 1,150 sons examined, 86 were found to be visibly abnormal according to the same standards. Some dominant autosomal abnormalities showed in the females and there were probably four and certainly one female, grey in color and abnormal in venation, which contained a translocated fragment of the paternal X chromosome in addition to their maternal double X. Among the abnormalities in the males there were many quite definite in their expression, that would in ordinary *Drosophila* work anywhere have been taken for mutations, and these included various cases that appeared identical with previously known mutants. Thus, one fly had all the distinct peculiarities of rudimentary wing, one those of broad, one was like cross-veinless, one like vermilion eye, two others had garnet or ruby-appearing eyes, white eyes appeared three more times, and wings like miniature three times—twice in a form more extreme than previously known. If, now, we run through the list of "best approved" sex-linked mutations, agreed upon by *Drosophila* workers, we find that the majority of these, or, if not these, then at least mutants looking just like them, have reappeared in the present combined experiments. Though, in the experiments involving the double X, several circumstances prevented the testing of the apparently recurrent mutants against the genes which they resembled, the presumption is in favor of their identification being in most cases correct, since in the preceding experiments those mutants that were tested all turned out to have been correctly identified.

Up to this point we have confined our attention to mutations having a mode of expression familiar in genetic work—namely, dominant and recessive "visibles" and recessives affecting viability. We may now consider two other possible categories—namely, mutants that are dominant for lethal (inviability) and for sterility effects. Though these may not, individually, be subject to the breeding test, if they arise in sufficient numbers they may produce decided effects en masse, and so indirect evidence of their occurrence may be obtained.

In the case of dominant lethals, the most obvious effect of a considerable number of them would be a reduction of productivity of the

Table 4

Visibly abnormal sons of rayed ♂ ♂ in "Double X Exper."

	♂ tot.	♂ mut.
t$_2$BR. 1	1071	*48*
t$_2$BR. 2	419	*13*
t$_4$(all BR. 1)	1150	*86*

cultures. As before mentioned, this was observed, even when only the males had been treated. Secondly, it would be found that this lowered productivity was caused by failure on the part of eggs laid to develop to maturity. This too was observed to be the case, in a new series of experiments in which sample counts of eggs laid and mature flies hatched in control, t-2 and t-4 cultures were compared.[1] Thirdly, and this constitutes the most crucial evidence, if these failures of the treated sperm to form viable zygotes were due to dominant lethal changes that might occur separately in the different chromosomes, as mutations may occur, there should result a depression of the ratio of females to males, since such lethals in the X chromosome would kill the daughters only. We assume here, of course, that the Y need seldom be taken into account in the case of such effects, just as is known to be the case for many other effects, with the exception of male fertility. Now, when the sex counts were added up, it was found that this depression of the sex ratio probably did exist in the treated series, as compared with the controls, and that it was stronger, (not quite twice as strong) in the t-4 than in the t-2 series. (See table 5.) A practically complete check on this explanation can be obtained when the depression in viability of non-disjunctionally produced females can be compared with that of the others.

Table 5.
Sex-Counts in F_1 in Part of "C_1" experiments

	♀	♂	$\dfrac{♀}{2♂}\ (= S)$	$\dfrac{St}{Sc}$	Depres.
C	1496	685	1.09	—	—
t_2	1162	596	0.976	.896	.104
t_4	603	338	0.893	.818	.182

Now, if these dominant lethals occur at random in the chromatin, one such change being independent of another in a different chromosome, then there would be a calculable relation between the amount of depression of the sex-ratio (s) and the amount of depression of egg viability (v). The former quantity would be caused by dominant lethals in the X, the latter by those in the chromatin in general, and so this relation would depend upon the ratio (r) which the total haploid chromatin including the X bears to the X alone. The formula turns out to be as follows:

$$r = 1 + \frac{\log v_c\ ♀ - \log v_t\ ♀}{\log s_c - \log s_t}$$

(That is, the logarithmic depression of egg viability is the $(r-1)^{th}$ power of the logarithmic depression of the sex ratio.)

It should be explained that v♀ here represents the proportion of eggs laid that develop into mature females, in the c or t series and s is the number of mature females divided by males. A larger volume of data must be secured before this formula can be adequately tested out, but the data so far obtained indicate strongly that the randomness of lethal changes assumed in this formula does not generally hold. That is, if dominant lethals occur independently throughout the chromatin with only the frequency, per unit, with which they occur in the X (as indicated by the depression of the sex ratio), then many more eggs would have developed than actually did. This is especially true with the heavier dosage. Thus an additional damaging effect (besides independent mutations) probably comes into play, that tends to involve the sperm or its chromatin as a whole, or at least tends to involve more than one chromosome at a time. Such effects of X rays, not necessarily mutational in nature, were long ago described by the Hertwigs and others on the basis of cytological and embryological investigations.

Dominant genetic changes causing sterility in the male were also frequent in the offspring of rayed fathers, as the first table shows. The female appears to be less often so affected. Tests of several batches of F_1 males by control females in the experiment involving Cl further showed that the frequency of such sterility varies with dosage. The irregularity of the sterility results in the first set of experiments was due to the fact that here the F_1 females were allowed to mate with more than one male, and the extent to which this was allowed to happen varied in different series. Whether this ♂-sterility is mainly due to breakages of the Y chromosomes, like those recently found by Stern, or to gene mutations elsewhere, remains to be studied by tests of its method of transmission through the fertile female. In the crosses involving the double X the males did not receive a treated Y and many of them too were sterile, but their sterility may have been caused by recessive genes in their treated X. It is also to be observed that, in general, flies of mutant character were especially likely to be sterile; in fact about half of the visibly mutant males in the double X experiment failed to breed. The same phenomenon has often been noted sporadically in the case of "natural" mutations in *Drosophila*, but its frequency there has not been studied, in view of the scattered character of the observations. The ♂-sterility tests are summarized in table 6.

Having now passed in review the different kinds of mutations for which direct or indirect evidence was obtained in these experiments, we are in a position to draw certain conclusions concerning the effects as a whole. On the basis of the proportion (16.5 per cent) of recessive lethals and of visibles produced by the t-4 treatment in the X chromosome, we may calculate that there were probably about 47 per cent of germ cells containing such a mutation in some part of the chromatin. But, calculating from the depression of the

would appear. Which type, mutant or normal, would more often give rise to the other, would depend upon the degree of "dominance" of the normal as opposed to the mutant members inside the gene, but, under the conditions postulated, one or the other type of "eversporting" tendency would be found to occur for awhile.

The appearance of the visibly mutant F_1 zygotes from treated parents gave evidence regarding the first point—i.e., the mode of distribution of the mutant genes among the cells (in this case the somatic cells) of the first generation receiving them. The first series of experiments provided some of this evidence, concerning dominant mutations, but the crosses involving the double X provided the bulk of it, as was expected, since here even recessive sex-linked genes from treated sperm could show at once in the sons. It was found to be indeed true that, ordinarily, in a so-called "mutant" F_1 individual not all the tissue was mutant in nature. For mosaically mutant individuals formed a very large proportion of the total of mutants. In fact, it is a question whether all the seeming non-mosaics did not really contain unmutated tissue too, located in some part of the body not subject to the manifestation of the mutant character. Thus the effect of the X rays, in most cases at least, is "fractional," in that it is exerted on only a fraction of the treated gene, or at any rate on only a fraction of that gene material which is derived from a treated gene. This means that the treated gene was to some extent compound, not all its members being transmuted, or else that the mutation did not occur at the time of treatment, but as an after-effect, during or subsequent to the division of the gene, and then only in one of the two or more counterparts of it that should have been formed.

When now we examine the arrangement of the mosaic tissue we find that nowhere was there any evidence of its consisting of an irregular crazy-quilt pattern at all, as the usual compound gene theory would lead us to expect, but, so far as could be determined, it involved just one apparently clean-cut separation, as between right and left halves of the body. (We may of course occasionally expect some irregularities, due to "wanderings" of cleavage nuclei, with the same frequency as this occurs in gynandromorphs). Thus, if the effect is not an after-effect, on an originally unitary gene, there seem at any rate to be not numerous parts, subject to sorting out, but only two or less probably four parts, as though the gene in the treated sperm cell were precociously split in anticipation of one or two succeeding cleavage divisions. Possibly the chromosome as a whole is thus split, invisibly, as some cytologists would have us believe. It would take us too far afield to discuss here possible ways of obtaining evidence to decide between these alternatives. One fact already gained, bearing on the question of an after-effect, may however be mentioned. Mosaics were produced by sperm that effected fertilization more than six days after treatment just as by those functioning within the first day. It will also be recalled that the frequency of mutants from these two classes of sperm seemed the same.

In harmony with the finding of somatic mosaics, it was also found that the germinal tissue of F_1 mutants very often does not correspond in composition with their mutant somatic tissue, even when they are not visibly mosaic. For most of the fertile "mutant" males from double X mothers did not transmit their mutant gene to their offspring.

This brings us to an examination of the second and third points previously mentioned—those concerning the stability, in later generations, of the normal and mutant-seeming genes derived originally from treated genes. This question was tested as extensively as was possible under the circumstances, in the first set of experiments. From each P_2 culture (containing F_1 as parents) that produced F_2 flies, another, or P_3 culture, having the same genetic formula as before, was made up, to secure an F_3 generation, and from as many of the latter as possible a P_4 culture was similarly made up. From cultures in which mutations had been found, several new cultures were always started. Unfortunately, however, in the case of the non-mutant cultures, circumstances made it impossible to make up nearly as many P^4/s as P^3/s.

Table 7. P_3—F_3 cultures in "First Experiments"

	Total cultures hatched	Let.[3]	
		Mat.	Pat.
C	876	3	1
t_1	23	*0*	*0*
t_2♀ BR. 1	50	0	*0*
t_2♀ BR. 2	132	0	*0*
t_2	49	*2*	0
t_3	48	*0*	0
t_4BR. 1	151	*1*	0
t_4BR. 2	137	*2*	0
Tot. t	590	*5*	0

Turning our attention first to the derivatives of non-mutant F_2 cultures of the treated series, we find that, of 590 fertile cultures, 5 showed lethals in the treated chromosome. (Table 7.) This apparent production of a significant number of new lethals, a generation late, does not imply a sorting out of numerous gene members, as might first be supposed, for the mosaic nature of the P_2 flies would be expected sometimes to apply to the germinal tissue as well. In that case, such a P_2 fly would not be recognized as lethal-containing, for some of its offspring carrying the treated chromosome would not carry the lethal; some daughters, however, would carry it, and these P_3 would breed as regular heterozygous lethals. The real breeding test of the compound gene problem thus does not arise until the generation after, in the P_4-F_4 cultures (table 8). Here it was found, amongst 263 cultures derived from non-mutant parent cultures, and descended from treated P_1 males, that there were no lethal or other discernible mutations whatever; in 141 corresponding cultures descended from treated females, 2 lethals and no other mutations were found—a number which of course has little significance by itself, but speaks for the desirability of further data.

Table 8. P_4—F_4 cultures in "First Experiments"

	Total cultures hatched	Let.	
		Mat.	Pat.
C	552	0	0
t_1	15	0	0
t_2♀ BR. 1	36	0	0
t_2♀ BR. 2	90	0	2
t_2	30	0	0
t_3	36	0	0
t_4BR. 1	101	0	0
t_4BR. 2	81	0	0
Tot. t	389	0	2+0

The cultures derived from F_1 flies that bred as mutants showed the mutant gene to remain stable in succeeding generations. In only a very few cases did a fly which was expected to have received a lethal fail to carry it, and these few cases were to have been anticipated because of the chance of occasional crossing over between the lethal and the genes used to mark its place. The visible mutant genes served better than the lethals to test the point (not having been selected for stability already and because homozygous or non-crossing-over stock of them could be established). In these visible mutant cultures, there was no evidence of reversion. Some of them, of course, overlapped the normal phaenotypically, but here tests showed the genes to be mutant still. On the other hand, in the majority of cases the mutants could, by careful inspection, be identified positively, and here the mutant characters always behaved as though perfectly stable in their inheritance. Most of them were followed through the fifth, sixth, or later generations.

On the whole, then, we may conclude that the results of the breeding tests are against the idea of many interchangeable parts in the great majority of genes in *Drosophila*, although further breeding tests are admittedly to be sought. The evidence from the visibly mosaic F_1 flies, which is much stronger than the breeding test evidence so far obtained, leads to the same conclusion. This is, that the gene in the sperm cell is not multiple in structure, but that it not improbably is in two divisions, in preparation for mitosis.

Whatever may be the cause of the fractional effect of raying on the genes, one result of it may be deduced with considerable assurance, provided the fractional effect is true of cells in general. It is evident that, if the induced mutations really occur previous to cell division, rather than as an after-effect, then, since the original treated gene separates later into mutated and non-mutated material, the mutated material in the original treated cell had to "compete" against a much greater amount of non-mutated homologous material than in the succeeding daughter cell that it entered. Hence the induced mutation would often be unable to reach nearly as full expression before division of the treated cell as afterwards. But, since most mutations are lethal or at least deleterious, this means that daughter cells, derived by division of treated cells, will be more apt to be adversely affected by the raying that occurred previously, than the original undivided treated cells were. This would explain why, even if no abnormal distribution of chromosomes occurs at mitosis, tissues which undergo repeated cell division—such as embryonic, lymphatic, epidermal, germinal, and cancer tissue—would be more damaged by raying than tissues like adult nerve, muscle and most gland tissue, that undergo few or no mitoses.

Before closing, we may direct our attention to some further problems concerned with gene structure that may now be attacked through experimental modification of the gene. One of these is the question of the number and size of the genes. As I pointed out some years ago, evidence on this matter can be obtained through an extensive tabulation of the number of recurrences of mutations in identical loci, as compared with uniquely occurring mutations. Obviously, if mutations can be produced in quantities, this method will become far more feasible and more accurate. It will also be of interest to study intensively both the kinds, and the numbers of different kinds, of mutations producible in a given locus. The frequency with which mutations in general can be produced is high enough to permit such a study. It can then be determined, too, how these mutant allelomorphs in their turn can be changed, and whether, for example, they can be caused to mutate back to normal. Certain fundamental questions are involved here. The fact that an allelomorph like white eye apparently occurred four times, and that many of the induced mutations were seemingly identical with those previously known—

despite the supposed complexity of the gene—would suggest that many both of our artificial and natural mutations involve some sort of inactivations of the gene[4], including at times actual "losses." Not all natural mutations can be of such nature, however, else the genes could not have differentiated from one another in the first place. And as for the effect of X rays in this respect, be it noted that, in ordinary substances, they are known to produce chemical changes of all kinds—not simply "break-down processes." However, the "breakdowns" may occur oftener, as is true in general, in harmony with the second law of thermodynamics. The investigation of these questions should at least be attempted and, though these specific problems may not be solved thereby, other leads are sure to open up as the work progresses.

Are "natural mutations" due to "natural X rays?" We must attempt to exclude them and then measure the mutation rate. We must also renew the investigation of the possible effectiveness of other agents, utilizing our knowledge of decreased productivity as an index of an increased mutation rate. Professor Altenburg, in preliminary experiments which he has given me the privilege of referring to here, has obtained evidence that ultra-violet light, in exposures sufficient to cause complete sterility in a majority of treated males, does not cause mutations in the non-sterilized ones treated likewise—at least the rate of mutation can not be increased to anything like the extent to which it is increased by sub-sterility doses of X rays. Preliminary experiments of my own, in which males were subjected to semi-lethal exposures to heat, that sterilized a majority of them, led to the same conclusion as that reached by Altenburg for ultra-violet light.

In the present address, I have purposely discussed various matters that are admittedly subjects of conjecture, not in order to indulge in idle speculation, but to suggest that in the new line of work here described there may be means of obtaining actual experimental evidence regarding some of these matters at least, if only we direct our efforts with due reference to these possibilities. In conclusion, however, it will be well to return to the facts more directly founded on the present data:—namely, the effectiveness of X rays in inordinately raising the rate of gene mutation, both in sperm and in eggs, and in ovarian cells which, after the partial return of fertility, will form eggs; the fact that the intensity of this effect varies with the dosage; the production of sterilizing changes, and probably of dominant lethals; the causation of frequent heritable rearrangements in the linear order of the genes; and the fractional effect of X rays on the genes. It is to be hoped that there may be further developments in the study of the causation of these phenomena, but, whatever these developments may be, it should at least be possible to take advantage of the effects that may be produced, as aids in experimental breeding and in studies in heredity and evolution.

Notes

[1]e.g., from 1,307 fertilized control eggs laid, 990 adult flies were produced; from 569 eggs fertilized by t-2 sperm, 163 flies developed.

[2]Includes sterility due to ♀.

[3]Inconspicuous semi-lethals and visibles first noticed here might have been present in F_2 and hence were included in Table 1.

[4]This suggestion was made to the writer by Altenburg.

THE EFFECTS OF X-RADIATION ON GENES AND CHROMOSOMES*

(Abstract)

This paper reported the author's experiments of the past fifteen months on the hereditary effects of X-rays applied to the fruit fly, *Drosophila melanogaster*. By means of special crosses, the discrimination of mutations in individual genes from genetic recombinations of various sorts (due to segregation, non-disjunction, etc.), was facilitated, and lethal as well as visible changes were rendered detectable. Results in the second and later generations, based on several thousand cultures, showed that gene mutations had occurred in the most heavily treated germ cells at about 150 times the frequency of those in the controls, derived from the same source, while in germ cells less heavily treated the result was intermediate. Germ cells in all stages studied were susceptible to the effect; these included oögonia, ova, spermatozoa shortly before fertilization, and spermatozoa when rayed either in the male or in the female receptacles six or more days prior to fertilization.

The induced mutations resembled spontaneous ones, inasmuch as: (1) The great majority were lethal; of the rest most, but not all, reduced viability or fertility. (2) Recessives greatly outnumbered definite dominants. (3) Many of the visible effects were relatively inconspicuous. (4) Though "new" mutations were somewhat more frequent, there were also numerous repetitions of familiar mutations. (5) All regions of the chromatin were affected, but the induced mutations were more densely distributed in those regions of the linkage map in which more spontaneous mutations have occurred. (6) Multiple allelomorphism occurred. (7) So also did reverse mutation of genes already mutant when treated. The two latter facts argue against the effects always being complete losses or inactivations. (8) Though point-mutations were the rule, there was an occasional "line-mutation" involving a row of neighboring genes, as if

Science, Vol. LXVII, No. 1726, 1928, p. 82.

be protoplasm or air. Thus the figure of 1.8×10^{10} ions per cc. for potassium in air may be taken as substantially representing the maximum "effectiveness" of the radiation from the potassium in the protoplasm also (although in the protoplasm not as much of the energy absorbed may actually be expended in the specific form of ionization). On the other hand, the energy absorbed from the artificial radiation (and from the greater proportion of the natural radiation from outside sources) varies with the coefficient of absorption of the medium. The absorption, when air and protoplasm are compared, is nearly proportional to their respective densities. Hence we must multiply the figure 7.2×10^{12} (the number of ions per cc. produced in air by the artificial radiation) by 800, representing the ratio of the densities of protoplasm to air. This gives 5.8×10^{15} as the figure representing the "effectiveness" (in the sense used above) of the artificial radiation in the protoplasm. It will be seen that the ratio of the "effectiveness" of the potassium to that of the artificial radiation is $\frac{1.8 \times 10^{10}}{5.8 \times 10^{15}}$, or $\frac{1}{3.2 \times 10^{5}}$, which is only $\frac{1}{2100}$ of the ratio (1:150) of the natural to the artificial mutation frequencies. The maximum radiation from the potassium then is even less adequate than that from the outer environment to account for the observed natural mutation rate.

The ionization produced by uranium (chiefly by its alpha rays) is of the order of a thousand times that produced by an equal weight of potassium. Therefore 1/2 gram of uranium per 100 cc. would be 1000 times as effective as 1/2 gram of potassium per 100 cc., and hence this concentration of uranium would be of the right order to give the observed natural mutation frequency. Such a concentration of uranium as this is, however, practically out of the question in the case of a living organism. Similar considerations apply to thorium. Direct measurements are, however, called for to determine whether more highly radioactive materials are present in sufficient amounts to explain the mutation frequency.

IV. The Paucity of Radiation from Other Sources.—Measurements were accordingly undertaken of the total radioactivity of the flies and of their food (standard banana-karo-agar). About two and a half grams of recently killed *Drosophila melanogaster* (approximately 5000 in number, comprising various stocks mixed together) were desiccated in an oven at 120° C. for three days and then ground to a powder. This powder was spread over an area of 36 sq. cm. in a standard type of ionization chamber. The ionization current, produced by an accelerating potential of 270 volts, was measured by means of a quandrant electrometer.

In order to determine the sensitivity of the apparatus, the ionization chamber was calibrated by measurements of the activity both of a potassium chloride surface and also of a small uranium standard. The current obtained from the empty ionization chamber was also measured directly and was found to be 2.5×10^{-15} amperes, representing an effect due to "natural" radiation. The probable error of this determination (based on repeated measurements) was found to be such that a change in this current of about 9 per cent would be three times the probable error of the difference and hence would have been detectable. The smallest detectable activity then corresponds to a current of 9 per cent of 2.5×10^{-15} amperes, or 2.25×10^{-16} amperes. Since the area was 36 sq. cm., this corresponds to an activity per sq. cm. of 6.25×10^{-18} amperes. It is known that one sq. cm. surface of uranium oxide (U_3O_8) gives 5.8×10^{-13} amperes. Comparing these two figures, and allowing for the fact that the uranium oxide is itself only 85 per cent uranium, we see that in our experiment we could have detected a concentration of uranium of $\dfrac{6.25 \times 10^{-18}}{5.8 \times 10^{-13}} \times 0.85$, or about one part uranium in 100,000 parts of the dried fly material or food. An equal amount of activity on the part of other radioactive substances would have been similarly detectable, of course. The direct measurements on the current produced in the presence of the uranium and the potassium salts were in substantial agreement with this determination of the sensitivity of the apparatus.

Numerous measurements were made of the ionization in the presence of the fly powder, and no evidence of any effect of the material on the ionization current was found. Similarly negative results were obtained in tests of the dried and ground fly food. We can, therefore, conclude that the tested materials had a radioactivity corresponding to less than one part in 100,000 of uranium. It will be recalled that about one part of uranium in 200 parts of the fresh fly material, or one in 50 parts of the dry fly material, would have been necessary to account for the mutation frequency. This required amount is 2000 times the amount we could have detected; hence there can be no doubt that any radioactive material present was entirely inadequate in quantity.

An article has recently been published by Vernadsky[2] in which he reports finding that in various organisms, both plants and animals, a considerably higher concentration of radium is present than in the water with which they come into contact, and he consequently regards organisms as collectors of radium. The proportions of radium which he finds are nevertheless very low, of the order of 1:50 of the lowest values that we could have detected. They are, therefore, quite negligible for our present purposes, even if it be supposed that other radioactive substances are stored similarly to the radium.

If the "natural" radioactivity from all terrestrial (including internal) sources combined is thus inadequate, there is no possibility that the cosmic radiation could play a significant role either, since the ionization produced by it (even at high altitudes) is considerably less than that produced over the land by the radiation from terrestrial sources.

V. Consideration of a Possible Alternative. — The only escape remaining from the conclusion that causes other than high-energy radiation are responsible for the production of the great majority of the mutations in untreated *Drosophila* would now lie in the assumption that the germ cells or tissues immediately surrounding them are specific absorbers of radioactive material, and store it in a concentration exceeding by over 1000 times the concentration present in the organism as a whole. Such tissue would have to form a very small proportion of the fly since even if its weight formed as little as 1:1000 of the total, the consequent rise in radioactivity of the whole mass would have been detectable. We find by measurement that the male germ cells (mostly mature) form, at a very conservative estimate, over 1:100 of the total volume of the fly, and the eggs considerably more. The mature germ cells, therefore, cannot themselves be receptacles of the postulated amount of radioactive material, and it would have to be supposed that the cells in the gonad kept passing the material along, as they divided, so that it remained condensed in the immature cells.

A possible biological test of such a special hypothesis might be provided by a study of the effects of feeding the flies small measured quantities of highly radioactive material, such as would not raise the mutation frequency appreciably if uniformly distributed, but would if stored near the germ cells. The amount of increase of the concentration of radioactive substances in the flies, as a whole, so produced, could then be measured directly, and compared with the increase, if any, in the frequency of mutations. Thus it could be determined whether or not the tissue in the neighborhood of the germ cells stored the material to a much greater extent than the fly as a whole did.[3] Such tests would have to be made with various highly radioactive materials, since these differ in their chemical properties. Unfortunately, a negative result from such tests would not in itself be demonstrative, since it might be held that the concentration was automatically fixed at a certain amount, beyond which it was not allowed to rise. (Thus Vernadsky finds that organisms of each species have their own characteristic concentration of radium.) We believe, however, that the assumption of such an extremely high concentration of radioactive material as would here be necessary, confined to the immediate vicinity of the germ cells, is *per se* very implausible, especially in consideration of the fact above referred to that the mature germ cells do not carry any such concentration themselves.

VI. Conclusions. — It is accordingly probable that natural radioactivity is not the major cause of mutations, and of organic evolution, but that most mutations come about as a result of other causes.

The search for these causes must continue. It would still remain true that a certain number of mutations in untreated flies must be caused by natural radiation, but the ratio of these to all the natural mutations is probably smaller than one per 1000, so that it is not likely that more than one or two, if any, among all the hundreds of mutations so far observed in the different species of Drosophila have been caused in this way. At the same time, the gene mutations resulting from irradiation are indistinguishable from those otherwise caused, and this method of artificially producing them in quantities, the only one at present known, may be used to advantage in the study of the mechanism of mutation and of the properties of the genetic material.

Notes

[1] At the instance of the Committee on the Effects of Radiation on Living Organisms, of the National Research Council, this instrument was supplied at cost by the Victoreen Company. The expenses in connection with this investigation were defrayed by a grant from this committee.

[2] We are indebted to Dr. Timofeëf-Ressovsky for translating Vernadsky's paper for us. Dr. Timofeëf-Ressovsky informs us that he has been making an investigation similar to our own. We have also received a communication from Dr. Vernadsky, calling attention to recent measurements of Brunovsky, which show that the concentrations of radium in organisms are really lower than the preliminary results indicated.

[3] Direct measurements of the radioactivity of different gonadic tissues could be made in the case of larger animals, but in the absence of knowledge of their mutation rates, naturally, and when artificially irradiated, such information would be of little value for our present purposes.

TYPES OF VISIBLE VARIATIONS INDUCED BY X-RAYS IN DROSOPHILA*

By H. J. Muller

(University of Texas)

Summary

1. The induced visible variations involving only "point mutations" give every evidence of being the same in their nature as the spontaneous visible variations due to point mutations. Some of the former are sensibly identical with the latter, others form with the latter, and with each other, multiple allelomorphic series. Among these are certain cases of extreme lethal allelomorphs, dominant in their visible effect. Inconspicuous visibles, overlapping the nor-

*Journal of Genetics, Vol. XXII, No. 3, July 1930, pp. 299-334; summary, only, included.

12. In order to determine definitely whether reverse mutations, from forked to non-forked, could be produced by irradiation, experiments were carried on on an extensive scale with flies carrying tinged eyes and forked bristles. Both larval and adult stages, and both sexes, were rayed, in different divisions of the experiment, and an approximately equal number of non-treated flies were bred in the same way, as controls. In all, eight cases of mutation to or towards non-forked (seven being of certainly independent origin) were observed among progeny of treated flies, and none among progeny of controls. In seven of the cases, the mutation involved the germ tract of the progeny in which it was found, and in the other case (derived from treated sperm) the mutation involved part of the soma only, being of a "fractional" nature.

13. Tests of the seven heritable mutations showed all of these to be "point mutations" that had occurred at the locus of forked; they were therefore true reverse mutations of the forked gene.

14. The chance of obtaining all seven independent reverse mutations in the treated and none in the control group would have been only one ·in 128 if the irradiation had not been effective in producing these mutations.

15. Similar experiments were then undertaken with stock of tinged non-forked that had been derived by reverse mutation from forked, to determine whether this could be caused to mutate again to forked. Two inheritable mutations to forked and two "fractionals" confined to the somatic tissue of the flies showing them (the latter derived in both cases from treated spermatozoa) were observed in a count of 58,817 progeny of treated flies. None were found in 34,798 controls. In previous irradiation experiments three other mutations to or towards forked had been detected among 12,482 progeny of treated males, and none in over 10,000 controls. The results suggested, though they did not prove, that mutations from non-forked to forked may be more readily obtained by treatment of the adult males than of the larvae, and that mutations from forked to non-forked may be more readily obtained by treatment of larvae than of adult males. Both these results would be expected if there is a "germ cell selection" among primordial and gonial germ cells, by reason of a faster multiplication rate of non-forked than of forked-bearing cells.

16. Tests of the above two heritable mutations from the later experiment, and of the three other mutations to or towards forked that had been found previously in the progeny of irradiated flies, showed all of these to be allelomorphic to the known forked.

17. The occurrence of these five heritable and two fractional (probable) mutations to forked in radiated material, when considered in connection with the extreme rarity of such mutations in non-radiated material, furnishes convincing evidence that the irradiation was the cause of the mutations in this direction also.

18. The above demonstration that mutations can be produced by

irradiation in both of two opposite directions at the same locus, and that, in fact, a cycle of mutational change can be completed, is irreconcilable with the view that all mutational changes by X-rays consist of losses.

19. There are also grave objections cited in the text against interpreting these results as involving mere increases and decreases in the amount of genic material at the locus in question, or as involving displacements of portions of the chromatin. The non-quantitative relationships shown by the multiple allelomorphs produced after irradiation at the locus of white and possibly at that of scute bear witness to the same conclusion.

20. Comparisons of the viability of flies carrying forked with those carrying non-forked that were produced from this forked showed no significant difference in this respect. There was, however, a noticeably higher speed of development on the part of the non-forked flies. In this sense, the X-ray mutation to non-forked had caused an increase in vigor.

21. These results in general lead to the same conception as arrived at by consideration of the nature of the physical action of radiation, namely, that the induced point mutations are changes in the chemical composition of the genes, that they may be of varied kinds, and that they probably are, through the possibility of the accumulation of such changes, endless in their eventual potentialities. In other words, so-called "progressive" mutations can probably be produced by artificial irradiation in cases where there is the possibility of their occurring at all.

RADIATION GENETICS*

H. J. Muller
Austin, Texas

As the progress of genetics depends upon the study of the origination and behavior of such hereditary differences as may be found between crossable organisms, the ability to produce such differences by radiation has raised to a new level the possibilities in all branches of investigation in genetics and related fields. So comprehensive are the results which have thereby been obtained, that it is only feasible, in the brief time here at our disposal, to confine ourselves on the one hand to a consideration of a few of the more salient advances in genetics made in the past two years by the aid of the radiation technique, and on the other hand to such results of

*Proceedings of the Fourth International Radiologen Kongress, 1934, 2: 100-102.

radiation genetics, since its inception, as are of more especial interest to medicine.

1. Technical genetics

A continuation of the study of chromosome abnormalities produced by radiation has now made the evidence more convincing that in the origination of these there occurs an entanglement of chromosome strands, rather than simple breakage, and this sometimes involves more than the simple interchange of broken ends occurring in crossing over. Decisive evidence has now been obtained that so-called "deficiencies" of minute regions arise in the same way as the other chromatin interchanges, and sometimes involve a transference of a minute section from one region to another. Intensive comparative study of independently arising breaks within a limited region is yielding further information regarding the manner of segmentation of the chromosome into genes or "sub-genes," and of the functional interrelationship of these, known as the "position effect." There is now little doubt that the latter is responsible for the apparent "mutation" of genes located near chromosome breaks. These studies are now being carried out in conjunction with the far finer method of cytological analysis of the chromosomes recently discovered by Painter in his work on the chromosomes of the salivary glands. In this way the mode of cytological manifestation of the gene is determinable and a series of new problems is opened up. Proceeding in another direction, recent studies of the genotypic and phaenotypic effects of chromosome abnormalities have greatly enhanced our knowledge of the synaptic properties of chromosomes and of problems concerning the interrelationship of genes in their expression (dominance, dosage compensation, sex genes, etc.).

2. Medical and practical applications

The work of Snell in Texas has demonstrated that chromosome rearrangements, resulting in hereditary diminution of fertility, are produced by radiation as readily in mammals as in flies, and this implies that in all probability ordinary gene mutations (which were harder to detect by his technique) are similarly produced in mammals. In view also of the simple proportion existing between the frequency of induced mutations and the total energy of the radiation absorbed regardless of its time-distribution or quality (recently confirmed by Timoféeff-Ressovsky), the conclusion now becomes greatly strengthened that human beings have mutations produced in their germ cells when their reproductive organs are exposed to radiation, exactly in proportion to the total amount of radiation they have received from birth until the time of the reproduction in question, there being an accurate accumulation of the genetic effects over an indefinitely long period. Viability of a germ cell is no indication that it contains no mutations, nor does a return of fertility following a temporary partial or complete sterilization imply that the germ cells in the period of returned fertility contain a germplasm less damaged than that of the cells which were more strongly affected physiologically. There is a similar danger of producing mutations in somatic çells by radiation, which, in the case of tissues in which mitosis occurs, may result in cancers, leukemia, etc.

The mutations produced in the generative cells are incapable of demonstration by any present medical statistics that could be obtained, because of the recessive nature of most of them (requiring the meeting of like abnormal genes from the two parents). Nevertheless they remain as obnoxious, from the point of view of ultimate contamination of the racial inheritance, as if their effects were less insidious and more immediate. Recent studies of Kerkis, in which the author co-operated, show that the commonest type of mutation produced by radiation is that which, from a medical and eugenical standpoint, would be the least desirable of all, in that it neither presents a visible mark or sign of its existence (even when the recessive has been received from both parents), nor does it conveniently eliminate itself in a clean cut way by causing the certain death of the individual, as in the case of the great class of "lethal" mutations hitherto dealt with, but its effects are discernable only through the more or less diminished viability of the individual. This diminished viability manifests itself, in the case of some of these mutations, as much or more under what would ordinarily be optimal conditions of existence as under unfavorable conditions; in other cases it manifests itself only under some sort of unfavorable conditions. It is important not to multiply these vague hereditary weaknesses, weaknesses which it may be impossible to recognize in the individual possessing them.

In the breeding of improved races of plants and animals, where the radiation technique may give some possibilities of the obtaining of wanted mutations (though necessarily with a tremendous expenditure, due to the far larger number of harmful mutations) it will now be seen to be advisable to subject any desired forms thus obtained to a series of outcrosses with non-irradiated stock, in order to minimize the danger of obtaining at the same time invisible mutations of the above-mentioned kind, which diminish viability.

Since mutations occur, even without radiation, similar to those occurring as a result of radiation, though with less frequency, it becomes particularly evident, in view of the findings concerning the relatively high frequency of "invisible" genes causing low viability, that to prevent genetic deterioration of any race some sort of genetic prophyllaxis, necessarily involving a certain amount of inbreeding and selection, is eventually indispensable. This applies to man as well as to other animals and plants, and is a fact which will

SOME PRESENT PROBLEMS IN THE GENETIC EFFECTS OF RADIATION*

H. J. Muller
Department of Zoology, Indiana University,
Bloomington, Indiana

Summary

1. The frequency of the primary genetic effects of ionizing radiation, gene mutations and chromosome breaks, is proportional to that of the ionizations produced, and, within wide limits, it is independent of wave length, and of the time-intensity distribution of treatment.

2. It is not however independent of the genetic and environmental conditions accompanying treatment. For this and other reasons the "Treffer hypothesis" appears inappropriate for measuring the size of the gene or chromonema or that of some postulated "sensitive volume."

3. Since gross rearrangements of chromosome parts require two or more chromosome breaks, which in the case of x- and gamma rays are usually independent, their frequency follows a higher power of the dose than one. In *Drosophila*, but probably relatively little in most organisms other than *Diptera*, these rearrangements are accompanied by changes in the functioning of genes, often including lethal effects, near the sites of breakage. The case remains valid, and is in fact today more secure than ever, for interpreting these changes in gene functioning as effects of the changes in their position relative to the genes near them in line. New evidence is given against the views, recently revived by Catcheside and Lea and by Herskowitz, (1) that these alterations, instead of being position effects, result from some gene alteration associated with the chromosome breakage, and (2) that those gene mutations which are unaccompanied by chromosome rearrangements were also produced in association with a breakage of the chromosome, but that in these cases the chromosome afterwards restituted.

4. The question is considered why the frequency of lethals appears to remain proportional to dose even at high doses, despite the existence at such doses of a considerable class of lethals caused by the position effect of rearrangements whose increase in frequency follows a higher power of the dose than one. It is pointed out that this is probably because the rise in lethal frequency which would be caused in this way is at least partly compensated for by the presence of another kind of lethals, due to small rearrangements, espe-

Journal of Cellular and Comparative Physiology, Vol. 35, Supplement 1, June, 1950, pp. 9-70; summary, only, included.

cially deficiencies, which as the dose rose would increasingly come into combination with gross rearrangements and so become in part irrecoverable and in part lost to view as separate lethals. Not enough is yet known about the preferences of broken chromosome ends for one rather than another type of union to permit reliable calculations to be made of the expectations for different types of lethals at high doses, where there is much competition for union. It is therefore invalid to upset our established conclusions concerning the mechanisms of gene and chromosome mutation on the basis of relatively slight deviations between the observed frequencies at high doses and those calculated on necessarily simplified assumptions.

5. Examples of some of the as yet unsolved problems concerning the manner of origination of chromosome changes are given together with some new evidence concerning them. It is shown that a high proportion of induced small deficiencies must result from two breaks in the same chromosome or chromatid, followed by deletion of the interstitial piece, rather than by exchange of unequal segments between sister chromatids. Evidence of the high frequency of cases of restitution is presented, based on data from ring chromosomes, but the total frequency of restitutions is still unknown. Grounds are given for concluding that the distinction between chromosome structural changes, even small ones, and gene mutations, is valid, despite the fact that these processes are in some ways related.

6. Some of the outstanding gaps in present knowledge of the factors basic to estimating the amount, character and time distribution of the genetic effects of radiation on populations are reviewed. Particular attention is called to the need of data on the following three questions:

(a) The relative frequency of mutations which are neither fully lethal nor characterized by readily detectable visible effects, as compared with the ordinarily observed "lethals" and "visibles." An effort should be made to extend the range of detectability of these "detrimentals" so as to make possible a much closer estimate than at present of the total frequency of mutations of all grades, and their approximate distribution among different grades. It is pointed out that those with very small effects are in the end as much or more damaging to the population than the complete lethals.

(b) The average frequency of mutations at individual loci, and the approximate distribution of such frequencies, as determined for specific loci that serve as samples. Not only the induced but, far more difficult, the spontaneous frequencies should eventually be determined for these loci. This is necessary for ascertaining the time distribution of homozygous manifestation after irradiation.

(c) The average grade of dominance of mutations belonging to different categories, including more especially those ordinarily classed as recessives. Evidence of varied kinds is presented which shows that these usually have an important degree of manifestation in the heterozygote. It is shown that this is probably the chief factor in determining their frequency and rate of elimination in the population, but until the necessary quantitative data for calculating these values have been obtained these estimates of them may be wrong by a factor of as much as ten times.

Although the pilot work on the above problems must be carried out on those higher organisms which are best adapted to genetic work (e.g., *Drosophila*), efforts must be intensified to extend the key findings as rapidly as possible to mammals. Among these, mice furnish the best preliminary material.

7. Some problems are considered concerning the amount and the mode of manifestation of radiation damage to the genetic material of the somatic cells of an exposed individual.

(a) Although gene mutations appear to be about as frequent as in germ cells of gonial stages this source of damage seems of but minor importance except on the relatively rare occasions where dominant genes of malignant expression, and therefore favored in intercellular selection, have been induced in strategically situated cells of a proliferating type of tissue.

(b) Cell damage and destruction caused by gross chromosome changes that entail the loss of chromosomes and major chromosome parts and the production of chromatin bridges, are shown to be, ordinarily, a far more conspicuous effect. Some principles governing the production of these changes, and their relation to dose, as deduced in part from effects of exposure of *Drosophila* spermatozoa, are reviewed. It is explained why such effects are more readily induced by treatment of spermatozoa than of ordinary interphase cells, and why cells in mitosis are similarly susceptible. These conclusions are then applied to explain the law of Lacassagne, that growing organisms and tissues (including malignant tumors) are more particularly susceptible to radiation damage. It is pointed out that, although there are very important effects of radiation, even at low dosage, upon other protoplasmic constituents than the genes and chromosomes, nevertheless evidence of varied kinds converges in pointing to the genetic damage to the somatic cells as the source of most of the delayed and the long-term injury to tissues and to the body as a whole. It therefore becomes necessary to reexamine the whole subject of the general biological and medical effects of radiation on the soma in the light of this interpretation.

The hitherto unpublished results mentioned in the course of this discussion were obtained by aid of grants from the American Cancer Society, given on recommendation of the Committee on Growth of the National Research Council.

THE LOCALIZATION OF THE
MUTAGENIC ACTION OF
NEUTRON-INDUCED IONIZATIONS
IN DROSOPHILA*

H. J. Muller and J. I. Valencia
Indiana University, Bloomington, Indiana

The frequency of translocations induced by fast neutron irradiation of Drosophila spermatozoa was found to vary linearly with dose even at doses sufficient to produce multiple proton tracks per sperm. This shows that broken chromosome ends derived from different breaks caused by the same track undergo recombination with one another much oftener than with those of different tracks. Our interpretation is that breaks caused by the same track tend to occur near together, this proximity favoring union between the broken ends. Thus the pieces would usually unite before greatly changing their relative positions. It must further be inferred that in this material a break usually occurs close to the point of origin of the ionization that induces it, i.e., that remote breakage effects, resulting from migration of ionization-induced, relatively stable mutagens over microscopically appreciable distances, are uncommon. Further evidence for this conclusion is provided by the finding that loci, like that for white eyes, which with X-rays give "visible mutations" seldom accompanied by a lethal effect unless there is a microscopically visible deficiency or other rearrangement, give with neutrons "visible mutations" that *are* usually accompanied by a lethal effect, even when there is no cytologically demonstrable alteration. This concatention of two mutagenic effects in close proximity (whether in these cases usually breaks or gene mutations or both is not yet decided) would result from the crowding of ionizations in proton tracks, *provided* the mutagenic action of the ionizations remained narrowly localized.

*Records of the Genetics Society of America, 1951, 20: 115-16.

THE STANDARD ERROR OF THE
FREQUENCY OF MUTANTS SOME OF
WHICH ARE OF COMMON ORIGIN*

H. J. Muller

Indiana University, Bloomington, Indiana

When the mutation frequency, p, must be determined from tests of cells which underwent varied amounts of proliferation, uncorrelated with their mutation rate, between the times of mutation and testing some of the mutants have a common origin, occurring in "runs" of different sizes. It is then illegitimate to apply the ordinary formula for s_p, the standard error of p, $s_p^2 = \frac{q \cdot p}{n}$, or $\frac{q \cdot P}{n^2}$, where q = (1 - p), P is the absolute number of mutants (= p.n), and n is the total number of tested germ cells. However, this formula can be modified, to suit cases where mutants of common origin can be identified as such.

Let r denote the size of a given run and I_r the number of independent mutations manifested in runs of that size. The number of mutants found in these runs is then $r \cdot I_r$, and P represents the sum of all the $r \cdot I_r$ products. What we wish to find, then, is the standard-error[2] of P/n, i.e. of the sum of $r \cdot I_r / n$. Assuming I_r itself to arise randomly, its standard-error must be the square root of $q \cdot I_r$. As the standard-error of $r \cdot I_r$ is r times that of I_r, the standard-error[2] of $r \cdot I_r$ is $r^2 \cdot q \cdot I_r$. Then, since P is the sum of all $r \cdot I_r$ values, and these are assumed independent, its standard-error[2] is q times the sum of all $r^2 \cdot I_r$ values. As p is P/n the desired formula is $s_p^2 = q \cdot \text{Sum} \ (r^2 \cdot I_r)/n^2$.[1]

This method has been applied to results from irradiation of early germ cells (Meyer and Muller, Edmondson and Meyer, these Records).

*Records of the Genetics Society of America, 1952, 21: 52; and Genetics, 37: 608.
[1]Through a typographical error, the article as originally printed had the last term in the concluding formula represented as n instead of n^2. This mistake has been corrected in preparing the present version.

A NONLINEAR RELATION BETWEEN X-RAY DOSE AND RECOVERED LETHAL MUTATIONS IN DROSOPHILA*

H. J. Muller, I. H. Herskowitz,
S. Abrahamson and I. I. Oster
Department of Zoology, Indiana University,
Bloomington, Indiana

Received March 3, 1954

Summary

When 1000 r of X-rays were applied to adult males of *Drosophila melanogaster* which had hatched not more than 24 hours previously, and offspring derived from sperm ejaculated by these males 7 to 9 1/2 days after irradiation were tested, a frequency of 6.5 per cent ± 0.3 per cent of induced recessive lethals was found in the exposed X chromosomes. This frequency, being more than double that ordinarily obtained, confirms Lüning's finding that germ cells at the given period (i.e., that of 7 to 9 1/2 days prior to ejaculation, in newly hatched males) are especially susceptible to mutagenesis by ionizing radiation. However, a dose of 4000 r, under otherwise identical circumstances, resulted in only 9.3 per cent ± 0.6 per cent of induced recessive lethals. This marked flattening of the lethal frequency-dosage curve at high doses is interpreted as an effect of selection, operating more strongly at higher doses to kill off preferentially, by chromosome breakage, the descendants of the more susceptible germ cells, in which recessive lethals had been induced at a higher frequency. It is inferred that the germ cells of the period in question are heterogeneous in their susceptibilities, and that there is a strong positive correlation between susceptibility to the chromosome-breaking and that to the recessive-lethal-inducing effect of X-rays.

It is pointed out that heterogeneity of a similar kind probably exists, to a lesser extent, in the germ cells of a period shortly before ejaculation, when older males are used, and that it may even be present to some extent in the germ cells of that period in young males. In view of these considerations, and the fact that in most earlier work the importance of exactly controlling paternal age and germ-cell stage was not realized, the significance of earlier data purporting to show the continuing linearity of the lethal frequency-dosage relation at high doses becomes uncertain, and conclusions

Genetics, Vol. 39, No. 5, September, 1954, pp. 741-49; summary, only, included.

based on a supposed linearity in this dosage region should be held in abeyance until more definitive data can be obtained, on material of maximal homogeneity.

THE RELATION OF NEUTRON DOSE TO CHROMOSOME CHANGES AND POINT MUTATIONS IN DROSOPHILA*

H. J. Muller

Indiana University, Bloomington

I. Translocations

The frequency of translocations induced by neutron irradiation of Drosophila spermatozoa within the period of 0 to 6 days before their discharge from mature males is linearly proportional to dose, within the frequency range studied (that of 2 to 10% for translocations connecting chromosomes II and III). Assuming the inference (based on biological and physical considerations) to be correct that at the higher doses used a considerable proportion of the surviving spermatozoan nuclei was traversed by more than one proton track, this linear relation would signify that the broken ends arising from different tracks fail to form interconnections. This in turn would mean (a) that the breaks are produced in close proximity (within about a micron or less) to the site of origination of those activations which instigate them, (b) that the broken ends ordinarily unite only with other broken ends that arise within that distance of them, (c) that the chromosomes overlap in their positions along the length of the sperm head. Neutron-induced translocations involving all three chromosomes studied (Y, II, III) arise more frequently than with mutagenically comparable doses of X-rays, and more frequently than would be expected on a random distribution of breaks. This result also indicates the multiple effect of one proton track, and the overlapping of sperm chromosomes. No significant differences were found in the frequency of translocations produced per n-unit of dose by neutrons from the ORNL pile and those from the ORNL 86″ cyclotron, the frequency of II-III translocations being approximately $170 \times 10^{-6}/n$. For the cyclotron (at least) this represents about $52 \times 10^{-6}/rep$. Comparison with results from sperm X-rayed in mature males shows the cyclotron neutrons to have been about 1.84 as effective, per rep, as 4000r X-rays in inducing translocations in such sperm. However, since the translocation-inducing effectiveness of X-rays on sperm irradiated in the inseminated fe-

*The American Naturalist, 1954, 88: 437-59; abstract submitted in October, 1954, to Biological Abstracts.

male is more than twice as great as on sperm irradiated in the male (Abrahamson and Telfer, 1954), and since this is probably not true for neutrons (judging from related results of the same authors, unpublished), the neutrons here used are probably less effective than 4000 r X-rays in inducing translocations in spermatozoa irradiated while in females. With decrease of dose, the per rep effectiveness of neutrons relative to X-rays rises (inversely) as the square root of the dose.

CHARACTERISTICS OF THE FAR STRONGER BUT "SPOTTIER" MUTAGENICITY OF FAST NEUTRONS AS COMPARED WITH X-RAYS IN DROSOPHILA SPERMATOZOA*

H. J. Muller
Indiana University, Bloomington, Indiana

Experiments of 1953, done with cooperation of Herskowitz, Abrahamson, Oster and others, taken in conjunction with earlier work with the Valencias and others (see these *Records*, 1951), establish frequency of translocations connecting second and third chromosomes at approximately $68 \cdot 10^{-6}$/rep, practically independently of dose, for neutron from either Oak Ridge cyclotron or pile, applied to mature spermatozoa in young males. This effectiveness is 2.4 times that of 4000r X-rays, varying with X-ray $(dose)^{-\frac{1}{2}}$ —NXE (neutron: X-ray effectiveness) in inducing male exceptions, lacking either paternal sex-chromosome or its marked portion, was 3-5. However, subtraction of partial losses, estimated by tests, indicated that NXE for complete losses, presumably representing isochromatid bridges derived from individual breaks, was about 7. Note agreement between these results and those on dominant lethals (Russell *et al.*, 1953; Baker and von Halle, 1954), all obtained independently. Causes of lower NXE for eucentric rearrangements than for individual breaks are: (1) neutron rearrangements contain more complications; (2) they are therefore oftener aneucentric; (3) neutron-

Records of the Genetics Society of America, 1954, 23: 58; and *Genetics*, 1954, 39: 985.

Please note the modifications of the above values occasioned by newer measurements, cited in the abstract of the paper "The Relation of Neutron Dose to Chromosome Changes and Point Mutations in Drosophila, I. Translocations," p. 303, in this volume.

induced fragments probably have slower joining because multiple neighboring breaks ("shattering") must impede unions between major pieces, resulting in isochromatids.

NXE for producing separately registered sex-linked recessive lethals was 2.4. However, for all visible changes of expression of specific loci NXE was about 4, as it was for proved "point-mutations" of these loci (this holds also for female germ cells). This difference from lethals is caused by multiple neighboring effects with neutrons, which hide some third of point-mutational lethals, yet cause neutron-induced rearrangements to affect more loci (hence, to give more "visibles") than X-ray-induced rearrangements.

PRINCIPLES OF BACK MUTATION AS OBSERVED IN DROSOPHILA AND OTHER ORGANISMS*

H. J. Muller and I. I. Oster
Zoology Department, Indiana University,
Bloomington, U. S. A.

Comparison of the rate of reversion of forked here obtained in the treated male germ cells with that of direct mutation of non-forked to a forked allele, as found in work of our own and other groups, shows these two rates to be not very different from one another, unlike what is true for most loci. The spontaneous rates of back and direct point mutation of forked also seem to be very similar, so far as can be judged. However, we are here using only the very meagre figure of two spontaneous direct point mutations to forked among some 529,000 chromosomes derived from male germ cells, as found in data of Bonnier and Lüning and of our colleagues Frye and Schalet (unpublished), and this rate is therefore subject to large error.

As for the other loci investigated in our material, only one case of a reversion that proved fertile and was inherited was found. This was a spontaneous change of ivory eye (w^i) to normal red in cross (c). There were also two changes that appeared to be of the same kind in the treated material of this cross, but both of these mutants were sterile. Since, on the other hand, most of the loci here dealt with other than forked have been shown in earlier work of our group (Valencia and Muller, 1949) and in that of other authors to have direct rates of point mutation, after application of X-rays, comparable with that of forked, it is evident that forked has a frequency of in-

*Proceedings of the International Conference of Radiobiology, Stockholm, 1956, pp. 407—13; part of p. 13, only, included.

duced reversions much more nearly equal to that of its direct mutations than most loci do.

All in all, it may be concluded that in *Drosophila* as in *Neurospora* mutations of the same general types, including back mutations, can be produced by ionising radiation as arise otherwise, and that these mutations include cases of chemical change, of the same categories as those that constitute the material for evolution.

ADVANCES IN RADIATION MUTAGENESIS THROUGH STUDIES ON DROSOPHILA*

By H. J. Muller†

Zoology Department, Indiana University,
Bloomington, Indiana, U. S. A.

Of major importance in assessing the amount of genetic effect produced by ionizing radiation is, first, knowledge of the relation between the mutation frequency, especially the "point mutation" frequency, and the radiation dose and, second, knowledge of the differences in frequency produced by given doses in cells of different types or under different conditions.

1. *Frequency-Dose Relation at Low and Moderate Doses*

In the case of recessive lethal mutations induced by irradiation of *Drosophila* spermatozoa it has been demonstrated by a large amount of work carried out during the first two decades of such studies, 1928-1948, that the relation of frequency to dose is substantially linear over a very wide range (see the table, Series VI). The range was extended down to 50 r or even 25 r by Stern and his co-workers, thus attaining a more than 100-fold amplitude. This being the case, it is likely on theoretical grounds that the linear relation holds all the way down to zero dose.

Progress in Nuclear Energy Series VI, Vol. 2—Biological Sciences, London: Pergamon Press, 1959; (Geneva Conference Paper P/893, 1958).

†Contributors: I. I. Oster, Zoology Dept., Indiana University; I. H. Herskowitz, Biology Dept., St. Louis University; Helen V. Meyer, Zoology Dept., Indiana University; A. Schalet, Biological Laboratory, Cold Spring Harbor, L.I.; S. Abrahamson, Biology Dept., Rutgers University, Newark, N. J.; Sara H. Frye, Zoology Dept., Indiana University; E. A. Carlson, Queen's University, Kingston, Ontario. The cited work of all these contributors was carried out while they were at Indiana University. It was supported by a grant from the U. S. Atomic Energy Commission.

At doses lower than 3000 r more than two-thirds of the recessive lethals are associated with no cytological visible structural change, and this fraction increases with decrease of the dose, as shown by Valencia working at the Indiana laboratory. Hence the linearity principle found for recessive lethals may be inferred to apply primarily to point mutations. Since, however, structural changes induced in the spermatozoa have at moderate and high doses a frequency approximately proportional to the 1.5 power of the dose and constitute a considerable fraction of the recessive lethals arising at high doses, it has been somewhat of a paradox that even at high doses the total frequency of lethals has seemed to remain linearly proportional to the dose: We shall revert to this question in a subsequent section.

Reliable studies on the frequency-dose relation for other animal material than *Drosophila* sperm have not been available until, at the 1955 Conference on the Peaceful Uses of Atomic Energy, Russell made the statement that he had obtained an approximately linear relation for the visible mutations at specific loci induced in his irradiations of mouse spermatogonia, when results from doses of 0, 300 and 600 r were compared. During the past 12 months Oster has extended the study of the frequency-dose relation to comparable cells in *Drosophila*, namely, oogonia, irradiated in third-instar larvae. Possibly included here also was a small minority of early oocytes, but these are known to have induced mutation frequencies, and a distribution of mutational types, similar to those of oogonia. In both these types of cells, the great majority of induced mutations, even at high doses, are of "point" nature. The results of this experiment are shown in the table, Series I.

As the table shows, the frequency of recessive sex-linked lethals induced in these immature female germ cells by the lower dose, 600 r, is even lower than the spontaneous frequency. By reason of the large number of tests carried out at this dose, however, it was possible to attain a relative accuracy almost as great for this induced frequency, after subtraction of the spontaneous frequency, as for that induced by the higher dose, 2400 r. The frequency per roentgen, shown in the 9th column, turns out to be substantially the same for both doses, i.e. the relation is linear. Since the two doses differ by a factor of 4 the statistical errors indicated are less important in allowing possible deviations from linearity than they would have been if one dose had been only twice the other. Thus if we calculate, for example, what the expectations could have been if the frequencies of the lethals had actually been proportional to the 1.5 power of the dose, as those of structural changes are, we find that the observed data depart far too much from these expectations to represent a random sample derived from any such material. It is evident, then, that the present results not only give no indication of a threshold but also no indication of a reduction in the mutagenic effectiveness of the radiation as the dose is reduced to levels at which the induced frequency is lower than the spontaneous one.

These data also make it clear that the induced mutations have here been *added* to the spontaneous ones. That is, the total mutation frequency found at any given dose does not represent some sort of exaggeration, magnification, or multiplication of a "natural" frequency: an exaggeration that becomes proportionately more pronounced as the dose is increased. Instead of this, the total mutation frequency found is made up of two separate components: (1) the spontaneous mutations that would have arisen even without the radiation, plus (2) a contingent of radiation-induced mutations that are of entirely independent origin from the spontaneous ones, even though the mechanisms of origination of the two categories may well have been related in kind. Similarly, the induced mutations themselves are mutually independent.

It was thought desirable to extend our knowledge of the frequency-dose relation not only in the direction of cells having a much lower susceptibility to radiation mutagenesis than spermatozoa but also, contrariwise, to those having an unusually high susceptibility. The work of a number of authors, to be mentioned subsequently, had pointed to the spermatid stage as the most susceptible. This inference was confirmed by direct comparisons in which Oster found that at least twice as many recessive lethals were induced in spermatids as in the most susceptible spermatozoan stage, that present in inseminated females. Oster has therefore made a special investigation of the frequency-dose relation for recessive sex-linked lethals arising in spermatids. For convenience and repeatability in treating the spermatid stage, Khishin's procedure was followed, of irradiating pupae 48 hours after their pupation and, after emergence of the males, utilizing them as parents for not more than the next three days. The doses used were purposely kept low (250 r and 1000 r) so that even at the higher dose the great majority of the lethals found would represent point mutations.

The results are shown in Series VIII of the table. The frequencies obtained after subtraction of the control frequency are again seen to conform satisfactorily with a linear relation, and we have calculated that they are not to be reconciled with the postulate of proportionality to the 1.5 power of the dose. On the other hand, a parallel experiment showed that the frequencies of gross structural changes of chromosomes, represented by translocations between chromosomes II and III, did conform clearly with the 1.5 relation expected on the basis of earlier findings on translocations arising from irradiated spermatozoa. The present data on translocations, derived from the same groups of treated spermatids as the lethals, were as follows: 45/3421 for 250 r and 148/1533 for 1000 r (no controls being necessary since their spontaneous frequency is known to be so low that it need not be taken into account in such work). These results for translocations show that there were no peculiarities of the conditions such as might have tended unduly to reduce the frequencies observed at high doses below those that had actually been produced. Finally, the present results for lethals, similarly to although less strikingly than those for oogonia, show that the induced mutations arise independently of the spontaneous ones and are added to them.

As there are grounds for regarding all the above results for lethals as having reference mainly to point mutations it was thought desirable to get additional evidence concerning the frequency-dose relation for very minute rearrangements. Although earlier work had provided evidence of linearity, for such tiny deficiencies as are usually met with inside of or bordering on heterochromatic regions, doubts and seeming counter-evidence had been raised. Using an X-chromosome of the scute-8 type, that has heterochromatin in the neighborhood of its left end, in which lies the normal allele of yellow-body color. Sara Frye has during the past two years tested the frequency of mutants showing yellow body, among the daughters of untreated males and of those irradiated with 1000 r and 4000 r, respectively.

As is to be seen from the table, Series VII, the large-scale results fit well with the expectation for linearity. These data represent the totals for female offspring derived from four successive two-day broods of eggs, that had been fertilized by sperm ejaculated from the second to fourth day after irradiation. The data from the individual broods show the same results in principle but with somewhat lower frequencies and a slight tendency (here to be expected) to a sub-linear relation in the first two broods. Analyses of the mutants showed that the great majority of them involve losses of at least three loci (those of a lethal, yellow, and achaete) and constitute minute deficiencies. It is true that some cases of "half-translocation" were also present, and that these must have been derived from two widely separated breaks and have had a frequency dependent on the 1.5 power of the dose at these doses. But since such cases could be reckoned to constitute fewer than 20 per cent of all the mutants scored their inclusion did not perceptibly affect the linear relation observed for the totals. In contrast, most deficiencies that are readily visible in euchromatin have their breaks further apart than those here usual, and accordingly follow the 1.5 power rule.

It should be added that two loci in the main euchromatic region of the tested X-chromosome, those of white and forked, were simultaneously scored for mutants in Frye's experiment. These mutants, which were in large majority point mutations, also showed frequencies closely conforming with a linear relation to dose, the counts being 1/263,694 for the controls, 17/180,942 for 1000 r, and 13/41,310 for 4000 r. The per-locus induced frequency here, $0.4 (\pm 1) \times 10^{-7}/r$, is as expected far lower than that of about $8 \times 10^{-7}/r$ found for the yellow deficiencies involving a break in heterochromatin, but distinctly higher than the frequencies of point mutations induced in female germ cells (Series III).

2. Different Susceptibilities of Different Cell Types

Space precludes a historical treatment here of the evidence gathered in the last six years, first by Lüning and his co-workers, then by Auerbach and her student Khishin, by Baker and von Halle, and in the last four years by our own group also, showing that the postgonial stages of *Drosophila* germ cells not only are much more susceptible than the gonial stages to mutagenesis by ionizing radiation, as had long been known, but differ greatly amongst one another in susceptibility. The identification of which stages in the germ cell development of the male correspond to the differing susceptibilities found has been made by Auerbach and Khishin by a combination of genetic and histological methods. On the basis of their comparative results, checked and added to by our own and those of the other workers mentioned, the sequence of varying susceptibility for the production of recessive lethals (that is, the relative frequencies produced by a given dose) may be roughly indicated as follows for the male germ cells: (A) spermatogonia and early spermatocytes 1, (B) meiotic division stages 8, (C) spermatids 12, (D) spermatozoa more than a day before their ejaculation 3, (E) spermatozoa within a day of their ejaculation 4 to 4 1/2, (F) spermatozoa within inseminated females 5 to 6; and for the female germ cells: (A′) oogonia and early oocytes 1, (B′) late oocytes (last 3 to 4 days) 2 to 3.

The X-ray-induced point-mutation frequencies throughout the life cycle have been approximately represented in our figure, by means of the continuous-line graphs. Of course the lengths of time spent in the given stages may vary widely, according to circumstances, from those here shown.

We now have to add to the above story our results on the stages immediately after fertilization, recently obtained by Oster. These show a very low rate, perhaps even lower than in gonia, in the interphase-like nuclei of the first 10 to 25 minutes after egg-laying, but an extremely high rate, equal to or higher than that of spermatids, in the immediately following stage of rapid nuclear divisions. This last result was also obtained, independently and simultaneously, by Ulrich, who reported it at the International Congresses of Radiation Research and of Genetics just held at Burlington and Montreal, respectively. So far, his data and ours for this stage apply only to the chromosomes derived from the father, present in the female zygote, but it seems probable that the principle holds for chromosomes from both parents in zygotes of both sexes, and we have so represented · it in our figure. In this representation, the abscissa has had to be magnified about ten-fold for the period just following fertilization, in order that the observed variations in frequency might be rendered visible.

As illustrations of data relevant to these graphs, the reader may be referred, for stages A′ and C, to Series I and VIII of our table. However, the values found for a given stage and dose often differ by a factor of nearly 2 among different experiments. Thus the frequency for A′ or A (chosen as the unit in the sequence of relative values listed above) may vary between 50 and 100 × 10⁻⁷ induced sex-linked lethals per roentgen. As for Series VI of our table, although the induced value here given has often been used for reference it is now evident that it represents a compromise between D and E (somewhat nearer to E), since it is based on work done before the distinction between these stages was known. Undoubtedly differences would be found to exist between still finer subdivisions than those of the present series if there were means of studying them separately. This is illustrated by Oster's finding that a distinctly higher frequency is evinced by oogonia if they are irradiated while halted in mitosis by colchicine or acenaphthene.

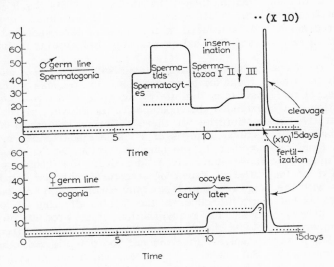

Fig. 1. Frequency of sex-linked recessive lethals.
Continuous lines = induced mutations × 10⁶ / roentgen.
Dotted lines = spontaneous mutations × 10⁶ / hour.

A recent example of a comparatively fine distinction in stages is given by the data of Whiting and Murphy. These show that in the wasp *Habrobracon* recessive lethals are produced at about the same rate per roentgen (if we make the assumption, not contradicted by the data, that the effect is approximately linear at the dose studied) in spermatozoa irradiated in the male and in eggs irradiated at meiotic metaphase I, whereas in eggs irradiated at prophase I a dose nine times as high is required for the same effect. Here, as in the *Drosophila* results, there is a correlation between the amount of chromosome condensation and the degree of susceptibility. However, the existence of additional factors is shown in *Drosophila* by the much higher susceptibility of spermatids than of spermatozoa, despite the somewhat lesser condensation of chromosomes in the former than in the latter stages.

Whatever the factors differentiating the susceptibilities of different stages may be, it is unlikely that the pattern found in *Drosophila* is unique. Thus, in mice, to add to the long-existing evidence that in them as in *Drosophila* there is a far higher production of translocations and dominant zygotic lethals in spermatozoa than in spermatogonia, we have a recent statement by Russell that the mutations at specific loci studied by him are produced at "approximately two to four times" the frequency in male germ cells irradiated between 19 and 23 days before mating than in spermatogonia. This result agrees quantitatively with the relative frequencies of point mutations and of total recessive lethals induced at the probably corresponding *Drosophila* stages A and D. Tazima has reported similar findings in *Bombyx*.

The comparative susceptibilities dealt with above are, as previously mentioned, those for point mutations, in the sense of changes on a scale too small to be definitely detectable by microscopic examination of the extended chromosomes of the salivary glands. The comparative susceptibilities of these different stages to having demonstrable structural changes of a viable kind induced in them differ from one another in the same direction, on the whole, but much more than those above given. Moreover, the frequency-distribution of the different types of structural changes found also varies with the stage irradiated. Not only chromosome breakability differences but also differences in the factors affecting the joining of the broken ends and the recoverability of the products of union play important parts in the determination of the observed frequencies of structural changes, in a manner too complicated to be entered into here. But there are grounds, which will be mentioned subsequently, for inferring that these other factors are not relevant to the production of the point mutations. We may also infer that even at the most susceptible stage, that of spermatids, the recessive lethals remain a valid criterion, at low and moderate doses, of point mutations.

3. The "Doubling Dose" and the Spontaneous Frequency

The doubling dose for point mutations, *i.e.* the dose inducing as many as arise "spontaneously" in the course of one generation, is subject to enormous variations (see the table). Thus if the spontaneous rate is held constant, the induced rate and with it the doubling dose can vary by a factor of at least 12, depending upon which stage is irradiated. If on the other hand the induced rate is held constant, the spontaneous rate and with it the doubling dose can vary by a factor of at least 70, depending upon the genetic composition of the stock and the history of the germ cells used. Accordingly, if neither rate is held constant the doubling dose can vary by the product of these factors, *i.e.* by at least 840. And by alteration of conditions (such as oxygen tension) its variation can be still further increased.

There has long been evidence that differences as great as ten-fold in the spontaneous point-mutation rate, caused by differences in genetic factors, since termed mutator genes, are not uncommon in *Drosophila.* And even with the same stock, the spontaneous rate, typically represented by 0.2 per cent of recessive sex-linked lethals in the first spermatozoa released by the newly emerged male, is reduced to 0.06 per cent in the spermatozoa released subsequently to these, but if the spermatozoa are stored in the female their rate is increased by about 0.06 per cent per week over their original rate; meanwhile, however, the eggs of all periods show an approximately constant rate of about 0.17 per cent.

The paradoxically higher frequency found among the earlier released spermatozoa is probably to be referred to the longer duration of the post-gonial, pre-spermatozoan period which they spent in the pupa, as compared with the corresponding period spent in the adult by the later released sperm, if we grant that the cells of this period are not only unusually susceptible to ionizing radiation and some chemical mutagens but probably susceptible likewise to some of the mutagenic agents naturally present. Whether or not this interpretation is correct, it is evident that different groups of spermatozoa from the very same individual may show spontaneous frequencies differing by a factor of 7: *e.g.* from 0.06 per cent in second-week sperm engaging in fertilization within a few days to 0.44 per cent in first-week sperm stored in the female for a month. The doubling dose therefore has a meaning only in relation to given stocks bred under given conditions and when the radiation has been applied to given stages in a given manner. However, one may speak of average values for given circumstances.

A considerable source of error that sometimes hampers the determination of the spontaneous rate lies in the inordinately high mutability of the stage that includes fertilization and the nuclear divisions of the newly formed zygote. Evidence for this is found in (1) the disproportionate prevalence of large "clusters" of mutants of common origin among the offspring of given individuals, (2) the high frequency of mutationally mosaic offspring, and (3) the strong influence of maternal genotype on the frequency, in chromosomes of paternal origin, of mutations common to the entire germ track of an individual and hence scored as having arisen in the father. Estimates based on the first effect indicated a spontaneous mutation rate per unit of time at this early stage of the order of several hundred times that obtaining in the germ cells throughout the major part of the organism's life. It was the high spontaneous mutability of this stage that led us to carry out the aforementioned tests that showed it to have a high radiation mutability also. The extremely high mutation rates of this stage lead in several ways to large errors in the determinations of frequency and of doubling dose.

In our figure, the dotted lines represent a rough estimate of the usual spontaneous rate at different stages, in terms of recessive lethals arising per million X-chromosomes per hour. These estimates are based on extensive experiments involving ageing that were carried out by me while at Amherst College. The widely different spontaneous frequencies are here seen roughly to parallel the induced frequencies in their manner of variation, except that the cleavage-stage spontaneous frequency rises so high (to 600 or more) that it cannot be shown on the scale. The prolongation, by ageing, of a relatively mutable stage, such as that of spermatids or spermatozoa, can result in a several fold increase of the total spontaneous mutation frequency. On the other hand, ordinary ageing, that prolongs the very slightly mutable gonial period, produces no detectable effect on the frequency—a phenomenon that helps to explain why longer lived organisms do not have spontaneous frequencies proportionately higher than those of shorter lived organisms.

The large-scale experiment by Schalet that included the observations on mosaics above referred to was primarily undertaken to determine the frequency of spontaneous mutations involving specific loci that arise in chromosomes derived from the father (Series IV of the table). The results gave an average for point mutations per locus that was just within statistical range of the higher value previously obtained from chromosomes derived from the mother (Series III of the table), after allowance had been made for the different mutation rates of the stocks used, as ascertained by the lethal tests. It turns out that for a stock with an arbitrarily assumed standard rate of 0.2 per cent for sex-linked lethals the per-locus point-mutation rate is of the order of 0.3×10^{-5}.

The relation of the point-mutation rate induced at a given stage to the spontaneous rate, when the latter is converted in the manner mentioned into the value it would have for an arbitrary standard of conditions, is (so far as may be judged from present data) about the same for mutations detected by the specific locus method as for recessive lethals, as may be seen by a comparison of Series III and I or by our unpublished comparisons of corresponding data obtained by irradiation of spermatozoa. This result may be expressed by saying that the "standard" doubling dose for either specific-locus point-mutations or recessive lethals induced in oogonia is about 350 r while that in late spermatozoa is about 75 r. There are indications (Series V) that for back-mutations the doubling dose in spermatozoa may be higher than for the more usual types, but this is uncertain since no standard values were established here by tests of lethal rates.

For small structural changes (mainly deficiencies) the spontaneous rate, like that induced in gonial cells by low doses, is smaller than the corresponding point-mutation rate by one or two orders of magnitude. However, the data obtained in the scoring of specific-locus mutants give the spuriously high ratio of about one such structural change to three point mutations. This is because the likelihood of detection of a structural change by this means is proportional to the average number of loci that are lost or changed by it.

4. Mutational Mechanisms and Conditions

Among studies on the production of chromosome aberrations recently carried out by our group have been a number on oocytes. Despite the rarity of *recoverable* gross aberrations from oocytes their chromosomes are readily broken. But the broken ends, except when restitutionally united, usually remain free until, presumably after forming dicentric and acentric isochromatids, they occasion the death of the ensuing zygote. Even in those cases where a broken end succeeds in uniting with another one, derived from a different break, union of the reciprocal broken ends seldom occurs. Thereby a half-translocation is formed which except in special instances results in a lethal degree of aneuploidy in a zygote that receives it.

The types of structural changes induced in oocytes that are oftenest to be detected in viable offspring are (1) those that have involved interhomologue exchanges in the heterochromatic region ("pseudo-crossovers" that seldom act as recessive lethals), and (2) deficiencies, acting as recessive lethals. We infer the deficiencies to have usually been caused by two breaks in the same homologue. For they do not have a tendency to be associated with crossing over. Moreover their frequency varies more steeply than the dose and falls off if the dose has been given in a much protracted or fractionated form, thus following the pattern of multi-break changes. This inference fits in with an observation of Lüning's that more Minute-bristle changes (known to be usually deficiencies) arise after irradiation of oocytes than of spermatozoa.

This exception to the rule of a linear relation between dose and recessive lethals raises anew the question of why, after irradiation of spermatozoa, the relation appears linear even at high doses. For lethals thus produced include a sizeable proportion of deficiencies and other multi-break structural changes. Our interpretation is that this linearity at high doses is a synthetic product of two oppositely acting factors: (1) the presence of multi-break deficiencies and positional lethals that cause the total frequency to rise above the straight line, and (2) the operation of selection in eliminating, via dominant-lethal chromosome aberrations, the offspring of more of the germ cells that at irradiation were in a more susceptible stage. The latter factor, causing a depression of the frequency ever further below the line at higher doses, could mask the influence of the first factor. When irradiation is applied to groups of germ cells known to be highly heterogeneous, the second factor predominates and there can be a marked drop below linearity when high doses are applied to post-meiotic male germ cells. It is to be expected that the more homogeneous in its susceptibility the material is, the more evidence there will be of a rise above linearity, as appears to have been the case in experiments of Edington on *Drosophila* spermatozoa. It is quite possible that oocytes are usually of more homogeneous susceptibility than spermatozoa. Moreover, for doses giving the frequencies of recessive lethals in question, fewer dominant lethals are produced and there is correspondingly less opportunity for selective elimination among the products of irradiated oocytes than spermatozoa.

On the above interpretation, lethal and other induced point-mutations do not ordinarily represent restitutions of breaks that occurred at or near the affected locus. Were that the case not nearly so many recessive lethals should be induced in ring than non-ring chromosomes, because of the greater difficulty of exact (non-torsional) restitution of broken rings, yet recent retests of this question performed by Oster confirm the fact that at low and moderate doses applied to spermatozoa as many lethals are produced in the rings as in the non-rings. At very high doses, to be sure, the frequency in the non-rings does become greater. But this is to be expected in any case because of the inclusion in the non-ring data of many cases of structural change which, had they happened in rings, would have formed aneucentric, inviable combinations.

If we grant the above thesis that point mutations, unlike structural changes, do not involve "effective" chromosome breaks (*i.e.* breaks, the ends derived from which are capable of union with ends derived from distant breaks), then it is also to be inferred that those accessory conditions, such as oxygen tension, that influence the production of both point mutations and structural changes in the same direction and to the same degree, exert their effect on the primary mutational processes of point mutation and breakage, which are obviously related, rather than on the process, subsequent to breakage, of union between "effectively" broken ends. Whether or not an influence in question *is* of the same degree for these two general categories of mutations can be determined by the method used in the following example. In Oster's tests of sex-linked lethals induced in the spermatozoa of late pupae, their frequency after irradiation in oxygen was 2.5 times that after irradiation in nitrogen. For translocations the corresponding figure was 3.8 times. Since the lethals vary with the dose and the translocations with its 1.5 power, an agent that increased lethal production by 2.5 times would, if it affected translocation production to the same degree (*i.e.* that of a dose 2.5 times as great), increase translocations by $(2.5)^{1.5}$, that is, by 3.9 times. This result is in good statistical agreement with the one obtained.

Turning now to the results on the irradiation of spermatids in these two kinds of atmosphere, one finds the effect on lethals much larger than before, namely, about 6 times. This gives an expectation of (6)$^{1.5}$, that is, of 14 times, for the translocation enhancement in spermatids. Again the calculated ratio is in good agreement with the observed one, of 11 (±2) times.

Complications can arise in the interpretation of the mode of operation of accessory conditions when, as in the case of oxygen tension, they are able on occasion to affect more than one step of the mutational process. Thus, in Abrahamson's work on the production of two-break structural changes (detachments of attached X-chromosomes) in oocytes, the oxygen tension existing at the time of irradiation had an effect of the kind above noted. However, a reduction of oxygen tension following irradiation or between two irradiations caused an enhancement of the frequency, presumably by delaying unions between broken ends and thereby making restitutional unions less likely.

The difference in the mechanism of origination of point mutations and structural changes does not justify the conclusion that the former are immediately and irrevocably completed at the moment of irradiation. The conception of a "recovery" process for chromosome breaks in spermatozoa contained in the male, which has been founded on evidence supplied by Baker and von Halle and by Lüning's group, may well prove applicable even to point mutations, as indicated by work of Nordback and Auerbach. In microorganisms evidence of such a phenomenon had already been obtained by Stapleton et al., followed by others. However, a stage of completion and stability of the mutation is finally reached. Except in the special cases where germinal selection operates, these finished mutations must accumulate accurately as a result of repeated or chronic irradiation.

Despite the conditionality of the mutational process and the great influence exerted by genetic, developmental and extrinsic factors in the origination of both "spontaneous" and radiation-induced mutations, there seems in many respects to be a remarkable agreement between these phenomena in *Drosophila* and mammals, except for the far higher per-locus radiation susceptibility of the mammalian genes tested. Selection has apparently been at work to produce a similar overall spontaneous mutation rate per generation in the two groups, in the face of their great differences in life span, DNA content, and other respects, and has likewise resulted in similarities in the mode of expression of their genes. Support for these inferences is to be derived from the fact that recent analyses of human mutational load lead to mutation-rate estimates like those earlier based on a quite different type of extrapolation from *Drosophila* than those here made use of. This agreement attests to the significance of the studies on *Drosophila* in relation to the problems of the genetic effects of radiation on man. At the same time, however, mammals have a frequency of X-ray-induced mutations some ten or more times that of *Drosophila* according to Russell's results on mice. In conclusion, it should also be emphasized that in all the critical work on *Drosophila* the prevailing detrimental character of both induced and spontaneous mutations is very evident.

Ser.	Ref.	Stage of germ cells and indiv. at irradiation	Type of mutation	Dose in r	Mutations found/ chrom. tested	Frequency per chrom. or locus ($\times 10^{-4}$)	Ind. freq. per chrom. ($\times 10^{-4}$)	Ind. freq. per chrom. or locus for 1 r and error ($\times 10^{-4}$)	"Doubling dose" inducing freq. = stand. ♂ spont. observ. spont.	stand. ♂ spont.
I	11 and this art., Oster	oogonia, larvae oogonia, larvae ♀ controls	leth. in X chrom.	2400 600 0	33/2056 117/16,064 49/11,630	161·0 73·0 42·0	119 31 spont. l.≃2·1×♂-stand.	50±12 51±15	830 r	400±75 r
II	This art., Meyer	gonia, adult ♂ sp'zoa, adult ♂ ♂ controls	leth. in II chrom.	3000 3000 0	7/373 248/960 6/1274	190·0 2580·0 47·0	143 2533 spont. l.=♂-stand. for II	48±25 ≀44±55	1022 r 56 r	1000±500 r 60±4 r
III	12, 48 and unpub., Muller and Valencias	gonia, adult ♀ cytes, adult ♀ ♀ controls ♀ controls	nonleth. visible 8 loci, X leth., X	4600 4600 0 0	42/94,380 6/8865 9/62,000 19/2615	0·56 0·84 0·18 79·0	0·38 0·66 (per locus spont.≃45±15×10⁻⁷ at stand. rate) spont. l.=4·0×♂-stand.	0·083±023 0·143±075	2170 r 1260 r	550±230 r 320±190 r
IV	45, 46, Schalet	♂ controls ♂ controls	nonleth. visible 10 loci, X leth., X	0 0	18/490,000 32/8706	0·037 37·0	(per locus spont.≃21±9×10⁻⁷ at stand. rate) spont. l.=1·75×♂-stand.			
V	49, Oster and Muller	cytes, adult ♀ ♀ controls sp'zoa in ♀ ♂ controls	back-mutation of forked†	3200 0 3200 0	6/118,642 3/975,108 8/75,110 4/315,102	0·51 0·03 1·06 0·13	0·48 relation to stand. undet. 0·93 relation to stand. undet.	0·15±·065 stand. undet. 0·03±013 stand. undet.	200 r 430 r	
VI	many, e.g., 2, 44	sp'zoa, adult ♂ ♂ controls 1st wk.		many doses, many experiments, consensus: 275; most usual spont. 20.					73 r	
VII	17, 18 and this art., Frye	sp'zoa, adult ♂ sp'zoa, adult ♂ ♂ controls	defic., etc., of y+ in sc⁸	4000 1000 0	126/41,310 148/180,942 3/263,694	30·50 8·17 0·11	30·39 8·06 relation to stand. undet.	7·64±0·69 8·06±0·67 relation to stand. undet.	14·5 r	
VIII	11 and this art., Oster	sp'tids, pupae sp'tids, pupae ♂ controls	leth. in X	1000 250 0	130/1859 195/8978 19/2392	699·0 217·0 79·0	620 138 spont. l.=4·0×♂-stand.	620±64 552±96	130 r	32±3 r

† The set-up made partial back-mutations of less extreme type visible when derived from ♂ than from ♀.

MUTATION BY ALTERATION OF THE, ALREADY EXISTING GENE*

by H. J. Muller, Elof Carlson and Abraham Schalet†

Summary

1. Earlier studies on *Drosophila*, indicating that natural influences acting on non-replicative stages (spermatozoa, spermatids) result in an increased frequency of spontaneous gene mutations, made it seem probable that these additional mutations consisted of changes in the already existing genes. So did the studies showing that treatment of these stages with ionizing radiation also increased the frequency of gene mutations. The experiments on *E. coli* by Novick and Szilard showing that retardation of replication, brought about by an insufficiency of materials needed for gene synthesis, fails to reduce the spontaneous mutation rate provided further evidence of the same general nature. But all these cases seemed open, in addition, to the alternative interpretation that substances or conditions had been produced, or had gradually accumulated, which later caused "errors" in gene replication.

2. This objection has been removed, for the case of gene mutations induced by exposing haploid male germ cells of *Drosophila* to ionizing radiation, by studies—especially the definitive recent ones of Altenburg and Browning—showing that the great majority of the resulting visible mutants are of the whole-body type.

3. The seeming identity of the mutant gene throughout the body in these cases indicates that the two complementary strands of the given chromosome that were present in the spermatozoon became altered in equivalent, i.e. complementary, fashion. It is proposed (by Carlson) that this situation resulted from an exchange, at the given point in the chromosome, of complementary parts of the two strands, and further proposed (by Muller) that the parts exchanged consisted only of the pair of bases present at that point. The latter process would entail the breakage of only the two bonds that had attached these bases to their sugar groups, while they still remained connected with one another by their hydrogen bonds. We are referring to this proposed exchange as "rotational substitution."

4. Schalet's studies on spontaneous visible mutations found in

Genetics, Vol. 46, 1961; (contribution No. 696 of the Zoology Department, Indiana University).

†Of the Zoology Department, Indiana University; the Zoology Department, University of California at Los Angeles; and the Biological Laboratory, Long Island Biological Association, Cold Spring Harbor, Long Island, New York.

Drosophila X-chromosomes that had spent several weeks in spermatozoa stored in the female ("aged" series) or that had been present in the unusually mutable spermatids of the early pupal male ("unaged" series) indicate that in both series the great majority of the mutations arose as a result of influences acting in the two respective stages. Yet the great majority appeared as mosaics, and these seemed to be predominantly of the half-and-half type. In these cases, unlike those obtained after irradiation, the whole of the preëxisting gene could not have been caused to mutate; hence the mechanism proposed for the radiation-induced cases does not apply here. Yet, for those in which the half-and-half diagnosis was correct, one of the two strands of the preëxisting gene in all probability did mutate, since otherwise it would be expected that only a quarter-mutant would have been produced. The spontaneous mutations here under consideration appear to constitute a large proportion of all the spontaneous mutations that arise in *Drosophila*.

5. The foregoing evidence of the high proportion of mutations, whether radiation-induced or spontaneous, that arise by a permanent change in the preëxisting gene, should not be construed as casting doubt on the occurrence of other mutations through missteps in the assemblage of daughter genes.

point has sometimes been supposed to be the center of the chromosome). Thus, all the genes "to the left" of this point on the map are here found to be completely linked in the male to the genes in the second linkage group, while those "to the right" still undergo recombination with the latter. In other translocations we have found shorter pieces of these chromosomes involved. In several instances the piece has been too short, physically, for the loss or gain to have been demonstrable with certainty, although a considerable number of units of a "sparse" region of the map (a region sparsely dotted with known genes) was involved, thus illustrating that a unit in a "sparse" region is not physically as long as in another region.

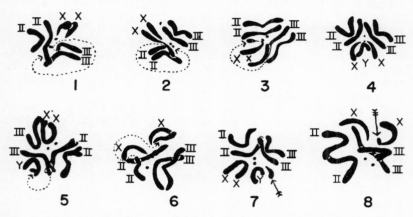

A number of translocations have been found in which, as genetically determined, the donor group has been II or III and the recipient group I (the X). Thus in the case shown in Fig. 2 ("Curly to X translocation a," of Altenburg), the translocated section, belonging to group II, is linked genetically with the "right hand" (the spindle fiber) end of group I, and, as the cytological view shows, one of the second chromosomes has been broken very close to the point of spindle fiber attachment and the whole arm has joined to the X chromosome at its proximal (spindle fiber) end, producing a large V-shaped element. Superficially the chromosome picture here gives the appearance of a normal complex in which the usual arrangement of the elements is altered, because there are still two pairs of large V-like chromosomes and two rod-like elements. However, in the large number of cells which we have studied there is a marked tendency for the X-chromosome arm of the newly constructed V to lie next to the free X chromosome, and similarly the autosomal arm of this V, and the rod-like piece with which it had previously been connected, both tend to assume their normal positions next to the unbroken homolog. Another case is shown in Fig. 3 ("Dichaete to X translocation" of Altenburg). Here a small piece of chromosome III has become attached to the spindle fiber end of an X chromosome.

We have various cases in which a fragment of one of the large autosomes has become attached to the Y chromosome. In the case illustrated in Fig. 4 (III to Y translocation 2) the genetic evidence shows that a considerable number of units from the right-hand end —a somewhat sparse region—has become attached to the Y. The cytological picture, however, gives no distinct evidence either of a loss from the third or a gain by the Y chromosome, although the figures examined are exceptionally good. Either the piece concerned is physically much smaller than the number of units would indicate, due to a high frequency of crossing over in this region, or else a fragment of the Y has undergone interchange, becoming simultaneously attached to the third chromosome—a matter difficult to determine genetically in the case of the relatively functionless Y chromosome. In Fig. 5, on the other hand, a case is shown (III to Y translocation 1) in which a small piece of the third chromosome is attached to the short arm of the Y, producing a small V-shaped element (in addition to the large attached X's, which were introduced by crossing with the yellow attached-X stock).

In a number of cases analyzed genetically a part of the second or third linkage group has become attached to the fourth. One of these cases, involving group II, has been analyzed cytologically also (Fig. 6). Here it can be seen that the second chromosome has broken a little beyond the point of spindle fiber attachment and the fragment appears to be free. There is, however, only one chromosome IV present in a considerable number of critical figures studied, although two IV's are present genetically; hence we conclude that the fragment is really joined to one of the IV's, having thus acquired the spindle fiber necessary for its continued existence. In one or two cells a small knob appears on the proximal end of the fragment; this probably represents the attached fourth chromosome. In the ovaries of just one fly examined two fourth chromosomes were consistently present, with the fragment lying close by; this agrees with the genetic finding that this translocation results in occasional non-disjunction of the fourth linkage group.

In numerous instances following irradiation flies have been found which gave genetic evidence for the presence of an extra portion of group I in addition to the entire X or X's which they possessed. The extra piece usually behaved as a separate element, but in one case showed linkage to group III. On genetic analysis these fragments are found to differ from one another in size, and to be made up of a block of genes from the "left hand" or free end of the map of group I, joined in some instances at least to a small piece of the right hand, or spindle fiber end, with the whole intervening block of genes missing. The sex-differentiating gene or genes are absent in the cases of this kind thus far found. A typical chromosome complex in which this "deleted" sex chromosome lies free is shown in Fig. 7 ("X deletion 2"). Here the other X's of the female were from an attached-X race. In flies of this same stock, by means of a second irradiation, we have gotten this fragment joined to the spindle fiber end of a single X, the latter having resulted from a simultaneous breaking apart of these attached X's. The case was first analyzed genetically as being of this character, and again, as shown in Fig. 8 ("X duplication 1"), the cytological observations conform with the new linkages found. It may also be mentioned that the fragment of an X behaving as attached to group III has been found cytologically to be attached to chromosome III.

In all the figures the large autosomes have been numbered because the translocations studied have allowed us to reach definite conclusions for the first time regarding the relative appearances of chromosomes II and III under the microscope. Chromosome II contains more chromatin than III and typically appears as longer, or, when relatively condensed, as thicker. However, it is not always possible to distinguish between the two because these studies also show that the rate at which the chromosomes of different pairs in a given cell contract is subject to a good deal of individual variation. The positive identification of the second as the largest of the autosomes is in agreement with the recent tentative expression by Bridges on the same subject (Morgan, Sturtevant and Bridges, 1929, Carnegie Inst. Yearbook No. 27, pp. 330-335).

In all the cases so far found in which the cytological picture has disclosed that a section of a chromosome has become broken off from its original connection, and either lost or reattached elsewhere, and in which at the same time a genetic analysis has been made, it has been found not only that certain genes have lost their original linkage relations with others in one of the linkage groups, in fact, in that particular linkage group which is ordinarily taken as corresponding with the chromosome here seen to be broken, but also that the genes involved form a "block," that is, *they constitute a coherent section of the linkage map*. Thus, in the "Star-Curly translocation" of Fig. 1, all the genes investigated that lie to the left of a given locus ("46") in group III behave as though separated from all the genes to the right of this point (although those to the left are still linked as closely as they ever were to each other, as also are those to the right). There is no escape, then, from the conclusion that the previously constructed genetic map represented the genes as correctly distributed with respect to the two sides of the breakage point, in that all those which had been shown by the map as lying to the left of this point were actually on one side of it, and all those shown on the right of the point were really on the other side of it—regardless (for the time being) of whether or not the more detailed arrangement of the genes on a given side with respect to each other was also correct. If, however, the more detailed arrangement, on each side, were not also correct physically, it would have been a strange phenomenon that there should have been any such point at all, with respect to which the map distribution of genes, to right and left of it, should have been physically correct, and still stranger that the breakage should have occurred at exactly this point.

Since, now, breakages at various points have been found to occur, and the same phenomenon as above described has been encountered, wherever genetic analysis has been made, with regard to each of these *sample points*, we are driven to conclude that the *entire arrangement* is correct, *i.e.*, the order of genes on the linkage map is the same as their actual physical order in the chromosome. Previous genetically determined cases of small inherited deficiencies (Bridges, Mohr) and Stern's genetically determined cases of two kinds of large deficiencies involving group III in somatic cells had of course pointed in the same direction, as had also the earlier findings that in normal group interchange ("crossing over") whole blocks of the genetic map were concerned (Sturtevant, Muller), but since in none of these cases parallel cytological evidence of an actually broken or interchanged chromosome could be obtained, direct proof that the loss or exchange of the block of genes of the map was really due to the loss or exchange of a morphological section of the chromosome was still lacking. That direct proof is now provided. In some of the present cases, too, we have the further cytogenetic parallelism that the fragment has become visibly reattached at a particular place on another chromosome—*e.g.*, the spindle fiber end of the X, as in Figs. 2, 3 and 8—and that genetically the translocated map segment is now linked most closely to that portion of the map of the other group which, on the theory of the physical validity of the map arrangement, corresponds to this point. There can, therefore, no longer be room for doubt that the arrangement (that is, the order, but not necessarily the relative distances) of the genes as given in the linkage maps is the same as their actual, physical arrangement.

In view of this, it follows too that the interchange which occurs between homologous groups of genes prior to segregation is an interchange of entire morphological sections of the homologous chromosomes, since it is well known that genetically the linkage maps then exchange entire blocks of genes (hence, as we now see, sections of chromosomes), rather than individual units. But to say this is to say that the so-called "mechanical theory of crossing over" is correct—the theory which holds that the chromosomes, in their normal process of interchange, become broken at one or a few points, and reattached to their linear sequels of the previously homologous members.

But while the order of the genes in the linkage maps thus stands confirmed, the same can not be said of the relative distances there shown. Thus, some translocations involving over thirty units of a relatively "sparse region" are not readily visible under the microscope (*e.g.*, Fig. 4), while conversely a fragment may appear of considerable size (as in Fig. 7) when it represents only a few units

ANALYSIS OF SEVERAL INDUCED GENE-REARRANGEMENTS INVOLVING THE X-CHROMOSOME IN DROSOPHILA*

By H. J. Muller and W. S. Stone
University of Texas

(1) The rearranged X-chromosome termed "delta-49" undergoes practically no crossing-over except near the right end, but considerable non-disjunction, with a normal X, and much crossing-over but little non-disjunction with another "delta-49." For analysis, it was repeatedly X-rayed. Known genes (or allelomorphs) so obtained were found to have the linkage arrangement sc-pn-w-ec-rb-*fw-m-lz-cmn*-f. Genes italicized have inverted arrangement. Crossover frequencies are as expected for this arrangement.

(2) A "ClB" chromosome, on irradiation, became partially re-inverted, so that it again crossed over freely with normal X's. Crossovers having their left end from normal, right end from re-inverted X, are phaenotypically unaffected, but contain, inserted in right region, a duplication of loci *sh* and *ct*, derived from left region. Hence both breakages of re-inversion were to left of respective "ClB" breakages. Left breakages on both occasions were between *cv* and *sn;* right breakages are being located. Lethal of "ClB" arose at left breakage only. Effects of insertion on crossing-over are being studied.

(3) A phaenotypically unmodified X-chromosome showing reduced crossing-over with normal proved to have a section translocated to the fourth ("translocation X⟶IV 1"). This section was non-terminal, but the left and right remainders became reunited, forming a deleted X-chromosome. Left break was between *lz* and *v*, right between *car* and terminus. Zygotes with one entire X plus either fragment die but females or "superfemales" with two entire X's plus either fragment live and breed. Right fragment "dilutes" Bar. Position of sex-differentiator (s?) is being studied through crosses of this stock to triploids and resultant production of "intersex-plus" individuals.

*Anatomical Record, December, 1930, 47: 393-94.

CONTINUITY AND DISCONTINUITY OF THE HEREDITARY MATERIAL*

By H. J. Muller and A. Prokofjeva

Granting that the genetic material is not set together in a mechanical fasion, but forms an organic system in which the interrelation of the "units" is as important in its way as the inner composition of the latter (these two features being in fact mutually dependent), it is the task of genetics to attack in a concrete way the problems of the actual nature of this system, the manner in which it is built up of parts, and these of sub-parts, their visible cytology in relation to their functional genetic expression, how and to what degree these parts may be separated and the effects of such separation, and, conversely, the effects of the connections that normally exist between them. One method of attack upon these problems lies in the possibility of producing breaks in the chromosomes by irradiation and in the subsequent analysis of the results. We have endeavoured during the past year to determine, by analysis of a selected lot of breaks that had been so produced, to what extent the chromosome was sub-divisible by this means, and the consequences of such division. The results already throw some light upon the series of problems first mentioned.

Attention was concentrated upon a highly restricted region of the chromatin, in which as many cases of breakage as possible were analysed with reference to one another, in order to determine what limitations there might be in regard to the positions and manner of breakage. The basis for selection, i. e., the criterion that the break lay within the narrow limits desired, consisted in the phaenotypic effect, accompanying breakage, which was produced on one of the characters (scute, achaete, or yellow), affected by the region in question. The essence of the method of analysis consisted in making recombinations between the various cases of breakage, taken two at a time, with the resultant production of individuals containing the portion of the chromosome to the left of one of the two breaks, together with that to the right of the other break. If the first break was to the left of the second one, this recombinational individual would necessarily contain a deficiency for the region lying between the two breaks, and would hence tend to die or be abnormal, while the complementary recombinational individual (containing the portion of the chromosome to the left of the second break, and that to the right of the first break) would carry a duplication of the genetic material lying between the two points of breakage, a circumstance not nearly so upsetting to the soma. *Mutatis mutandis*, if the second

*Comptes Rendus de l'Académie des Sciences de l'URRS, Vol. IV, No. 1-2, 1934; genetics by H. J. Muller, cytology by A. Prokofjeva.

break were to the left of the first, the reverse phaenotypic relations would be observed. If the two breaks were in identical positions or in positions so nearly identical that a deficiency of the region between them was without detectable effect on the soma, then neither of the complementary classes of recombinations would give the appearance of having a deficiency. In the actual working out of this method many complications arose, the details of which cannot be mentioned here; these depended on the fact that the breakages involved reattachment of the broken fragments at another point in the chromatin than before, and this was nearly always another point of breakage; thus deficiencies and duplications arose in the region of this other breakage as well, and had to be overcome in some way.

Thus far seven breaks in the region in question have been analysed with reference to each other (and an eighth break has been analysed with reference to six of the former seven). Among these seven cases, only four perceptibly separate positions of breakage have been found. In other words, three of the breakages were either in exactly the same positions as previously studied breakages, or in so nearly the same position that a complete deficiency of the region between the two points of breakage was without detectable phaenotypic effect. Nevertheless, the other breakages were far enough apart, so that a deficiency of the region between any two of them was productive of a drastic phaenotypic effect (lethal in all cases but one). The conclusion therefore becomes probably that there are only certain definite points at which the chromatin may ordinarily be broken by irradiation, and that, by the methods here used, it is possible to discover the totality of these points within a region circumscribed in the way explained. The blocks of material between these points may be regarded as "genes" and, if this is true, the distances apart of the breaks studied in an experiment of this kind are of the same order of magnitude as the individual genes, and thus the absolute number of genes contained within the restricted region is determinable by prolonging the experiment until it has become probable, by reason of the number of recurrences, that each point has been represented by at least one breakage. The present experiments are being continued with this objective, but in the meantime it is evident that the number of the genes in the region between the two most distant breaks found in the experiment is at least of the same order of magnitude as the number of blocks thus far found, and probably not much more than twice that number. At the same time no evidence has appeared that a gene—even the mooted gene for scute—can be divided within the limits of its own structure, in such a way as to permit the continued life of both separated portions. The results also show that even at the present level of fineness of resolution, the genes are arranged in line, i. e., in single file, inasmuch as all the recombinations gave results consistent with one another in showing the same gene order.

A further line of evidence for the conclusion that the distances

between the breaks in question were of the order of magnitude of individual genes emerged from the finding that one of the deficiencies
of a region between two nearby breaks was not lethal in its phaenotypic effect, but produced conspicuous visible abnormalities corresponding to previous inferences regarding the visible effects which
would be produced by absence of just two specific genes (those for
yellow and achaete) lying in the region in question. Here then there
is little doubt that the two breaks considered were separated by the
space of just two genes.

The total cytological extent of the entire region studied in this experiment was determined by Prokofjeva through observations of the
chromosomes in the salivary glands. She found that the whole region
occupies only a portion, about three fourths, of one chromatic ring
or node (the second) as seen in this material. Estimating the proportion which the region in question forms of the total material
present in all the chromatic rings, we can thus already arrive at a
tentative approximation of the number of genes in the chromatin; it
is of the order of a few thousand. This agrees with some previous
estimates of the senior author (1916, 1919, 1922, 1926), using totally different methods. The differences in position of the different
breaks were also discerned cytologically by Prokofjeva, pieces of
obviously different thickness having been taken off the second ring
in the different cases. The relative amount removed in each case
corresponded with that to be expected on the basis of the genetic
findings, as indicated in the schematic diagram herewith presented
of the region in question (the free end of the X chromosome). Even
the difference in position of the two breaks that were separated by
the space of only two genes was visible, though nearly on the limit
of microscopic resolution (being of the order of one tenth of a micron). Genetic and cytological maps agreed throughout, and were
linear. Very thin rings are about the size thus found for one gene.

The results then show that it is the region of the chromatic nodes
(rings or bands of the chromosomes of the salivary glands), rather
than the region of the non-staining internodes, that contains the
genes, and that some at least of these nodes contain clusters of
genes rather than individual genes. Since crossing over is known to
occur between yellow and scute, which are both in the cluster here
studied, it is clear that the internodal regions are not to be identified with necessary positions of crossing over. As yet, their function remains unexplained. According to the theory of Koltzoff, which
we accept, the nodes or rings of the salivary gland chromosomes
represent chromomeres, inasmuch as an entire chromosome in a
salivary gland cell is a hollow cylindrical bundle of uncoiled and
parallel-lying chromonemata, formed by the repeated division and
conjugation of the single chromonemata in two original homologous
chromosomes, and since homologous chromomeres of all the chromonemata of a bundle would lie apposed, they would give the appearance of rings or cross-striations. Transferring then our con-

clusions from terms of nodes to terms of chromomeres, we see that the chromomeres contain in some cases at least whole groups or clusters of genes, the individual members of which are separable from one another both by breakage and by crossing over.

The genes of a cluster are capable of forming new clusters by synthesis, for cases were found in which a fragment broken off from one node (cluster) became attached in another region of the chromatin in such a way as to become directly joined on a portion of another node (cluster), to form a new compound node. It should further be noted that this process of breakage can occur simultaneously at two different points within the limits of the very same node, with the deletion of the tiny region between the two points of breakage and its insertion into another region of the chromatin; this has been determined both genetically and cytologically (case of scute 19). Thus we see that even though a few genes are removed from the associate genes on either side of them, they can still maintain themselves and reproduce in their new surroundings, and are in that sense independent of one another.

The above work indicates the potentially discontinuous character of the hereditary material, in that it is divisible into definite blocks capable of self-propagation in any new arrangement, and it also indicates that this divisibility has definite limits of size. On the other hand, studies of the phaenotypic effects produced in the presence of these rearrangements have brought us strong evidence that the genes are, from the point of view of their functions in determining the characters of the organism, not discontinuous, in that neighbouring genes enter into special relations with one another, with the resultant formation of a gene-system of a specific pattern, the joint functioning of which, as such, is necessary for the normal development and maintenance of the somatic characters.

Several years ago Muller had found that changes in gene arrangement were usually accompanied by changes in the phaenotypic effects of genes lying near the points of rearrangement, and suggested (1930) that the general explanation of this result might lie in localized influences between propinquitous genes, such as Sturtevant (1925) had demonstrated in the special case of the Bar gene, but, as Muller pointed out (1930, 1932), it was also conceivable that the results might be due to mutations or losses of genes occurring concomitantly with and caused by the same disturbance as the chromosome breakage. Dobzhansky and Sturtevant later showed (1932) that phaenotypic changes accompanying breakage could be demonstrated rather regularly through the weakenings of dominance in cases of small duplications. Dubinin has recently shown (1934) that in the case of the locus of "cubitus interruptus" in chromosome IV, when there is a change in the gene arrangement nearby (translocation), an alteration often occurs in the mode of expression of the originally normal gene, which is visible only as a weakening of dominance, and since this sort of change has not hitherto been encountered often among "gene mutations" (see, however, such cases as those of "nick" of Bridges, 1919, and of "ebony 12" of Stern, 1926), he brings it forward as evidence that ordinary gene mutation has not occurred here, but that it is the change in gene propinquities' which is responsible for the effect observed. However that may be, we have now found in our present work crucial evidence from another direction for the same conclusion. The scute character, the pattern of which is usually so different in the case of different allelomorphs, is in general affected if a break and rearrangement occur near the scute locus, but it is affected in all sorts of different ways in the case of different rearrangements. When, however, as in one case observed in our present work, practically the same rearrangement recurs, we find that practically the same phaenotypic change also has been produced (cases of scute 4 and scute *L*8). That the very case of such a rare phenomenon—the recurrence of phaenotypically the same scute mutation—should be accompanied by this other still rarer phenomenon—the recurrence of a case of double breakage in almost the same two positions—is a virtual proof that the nature of the phaenotypic change was dependent upon the nature of the rearrangement. In view of the fact that different phaenotypic changes of scute accompany different rearrangements near this locus, and in view of the essentially similar phenomena observed at other loci, we may then arrive at the broad conclusion that, in general, apparent mutations accompanying breakage are really resultants of the change in gene propinquities (position effect). Some "mutations" result from minute rearrangements.

Most scute mutations, be it noted, are accompanied by some rearrangement, although the point of rearrangement lies outside of the scute gene itself, and can be several genes removed from the latter, and therefore the phaenotypic changes in these cases are not results of the loss or mutation of groups of sub-genes, as had formerly been hypothecized. The influence of gene propinquities no doubt is exerted according to an orderly system, in which certain genes play more important roles than others in the production of given effects, so that their removal and the bringing near of other specific genes have definite effects on the characters in question. In general, the influence, although it reaches across several genes, extends perceptibly over only a small distance, fading out at larger distances. In this connection it may be observed that the position effect on the cubitus interruptus gene, which we also, following Dubinin, have observed, but which on the basis of our own work we (unlike Dubinin) believe to be usually associated with a break in the fourth chromosome, probably extends over a distance of considerably more than one node. Thus we cannot identify the range of the position effect with the node, chromomere, or gene cluster, as an otherwise rather prophetic article of Brink in 1932 would lead us to do.

Whether the effect of propinquity is a direct one, of one gene on the structure or activity of the other one, or an indirect one, due to a higher degree of interaction between locally more concentrated products of gene activity than between more distantly produced and hence more diluted or changed products, cannot yet be stated. However that may be, we see that the basis of genetic determination of the characters of an organism cannot be stated completely by a mere listing of the individual genes which the organism contains; the arrangement of these genes also counts. In other words, this arrangement is itself, in effect, genic in nature, and the genetic material is in this sense a continuum.

Papers giving photomicrographs and details of this work are in press.

Institute of Genetics,
Academy of Sciences of the USSR.
Leningrad.

Received
4. X. 1934.

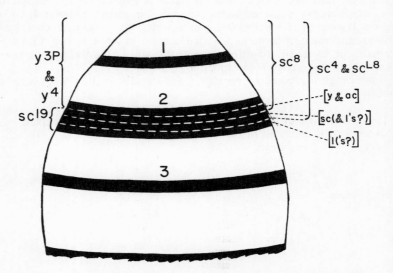

Fig. 1. Diagram of extreme left end of *X* chromosome of *Drosophila*, showing points of breakage in region of the second ring. The brace indicates the section removed in each case. The breaks of *y⁴* and *sc* ᴸ⁸ were determined genetically, while all the others were determined both genetically and cytologically, the results agreeing. Normally the second ring may appear somewhat as if double, but does not appear further resolvable by ordinary cytological methods. Genes lying between the breaks are indicated in brackets.

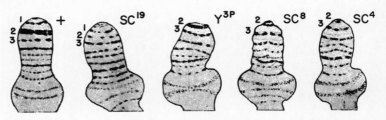

Fig. 2. A typical series of cytological observations of the cases on which Fig. 1 was based. Compare ring 2 with rings 1 and 3 in each case.

MINUTE INTERGENIC REARRANGEMENT AS A CAUSE OF APPARENT "GENE MUTATION"*

By H. J. Muller, A. Prokofyeva and D. Raffel
Institute of Genetics, Academy of Sciences of the
USSR, Moscow

When it was discovered that chromosome breakage and reattachment usually entail effects resembling those of gene mutations located at or very near the point of breakage, it was suggested, as one alternative interpretation of this phenomenon, that the change in position of genes near the breakage point, with respect to other genes in their immediate vicinity, might in itself be the cause of their altered mode of reaction upon the organism (Muller, 1930). This was an extension of the "position effect" principle which had previously been proposed for the special case of the bar genes, two of which had been. found to have a greater effect when in the same chromosome than when in opposite chromosomes (Sturtevant, 1925). Since 1930, numerous further illustrations have been found, by various investigators, showing the comparative regularity with which effects resembling those of gene mutations in nearby loci accompany breaks, but there has been little or nothing in their evidence that would serve to test the probability of the "position effect" interpretation as opposed to the alternative conception that the disturbance involved in the process of breakage was of such a nature as to be likely simultaneously to upset and alter (once for all) the inner composition of genes in the vicinity. The senior author has now, however, obtained definitive evidence (see Muller and Prokofyeva, 1934) of the correctness of the "position effect" interpretation, through the finding that different rearrangements involving the scute locus in *Drosophila* in the great majority of cases result in phenotypically different "allelomorphs," whereas nearly identical rearrangements (scute 4 and scute L8) have given sensibly the same "allelomorphs."

The general question thus arises, what proportion of apparent mutations are only intergenic "position effects" rather than autonomous intragenic changes? Of twenty-seven scute and achaete mutations investigated which have been produced by irradiation, it has so far been possible to demonstrate in eighteen cases that there was a breakage and re-attachment close to the scute or achaete locus. Some or all of the remainder also are probably intergenic rearrangements, for it has been found in this investigation that the rearrangements tend to fall into two categories, gross and minute,

*Nature, 1935, 135: 253-55.

the latter being of such a nature that a genetic discrimination between them and true intragenic mutations would be very difficult, or in many cases even impossible.

One example of a minute rearrangement is scute 19, in which only a fraction of a single chromomere (or chromatin "ring" number 2, as seen in the salivary gland) has, as shown both by genetic and cytological evidence (see Fig. 1), become deleted, by a break on each side of it within the same chromomere, and inserted into another region of the chromatin (within the left arm of chromosome 2). We accept here Koltzoff's explanation of the structure of the salivary gland chromosomes, as bundles of practically uncoiled chromonemata the adjacent chromomeres of which form the "rings" or "discs" (see also Carnoy, 1884, and. Alverdes, 1912, 1913); our work, however, shows definitely that the genes—usually more than one per chromomere—are contained within these chromomeres. Special genetic and cytological methods explained elsewhere have shown that the displaced section of the chromomere here in question includes only about six (four to eight) genes. This case does not illustrate a method of origination of recognisable "deficiencies" alone. If such a deficiency included but one or two genes, instead of six, it would in some cases be viable and resemble in its heredity an intragenic mutation, as other work of Muller (in press) has shown. On the other hand, the inserted section, without the deficiency, could be mistaken for a simple genic " suppressor," especially since, having been weakened in its activity by the effect of its changed position, it could appear as a recessive (unlike most recessives, however, a duplication of the region in which it lay would not serve to counteract it). These changes might or might not be detectable cytologically, depending on their size. If, finally, instead of having been lost or inserted into another region, the minute section dealt with in the case of scute 19 had only been inverted, while remaining otherwise in its place, the change would not only have behaved genetically like a gene mutation, but also it would have been impossible of recognition as a rearrangement, even by the new cytological method.

The existence of minute inversions of the general type above mentioned was at first only an inference from the above and other cases of insertion, but soon actual proof of them was found. The first case in point was that of scute J1. Here cytological examination (see Fig. 1) proved that an only slightly larger section than the above, involving only two chromomeres or "rings," 1 and 2, had become inverted (*in situ*). This was precisely the result which the senior author had been led to expect on the basis of this mutation having involved the simultaneous alteration of the effects of two nearby loci: those of lethal J1, normally to the left, as proved by genetic analysis of chromosome fragments broken between the two loci, and of scute, normally to the right. The seeming "double mutation" here, as probably in most other cases, was simply due to

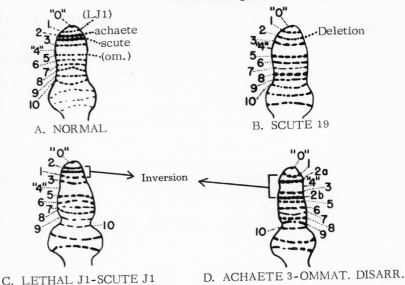

A. NORMAL   B. SCUTE 19

C. LETHAL J1-SCUTE J1   D. ACHAETE 3-OMMAT. DISARR.

Fig. 1. Appearance of extreme left end of X-chromosome of *Dro-sophila melanogaster* as seen in the salivary gland, in normal material and in the case of three minute rearrangements. The exact or approximate ( ) positions of the gene loci concerned are shown in the figure for the normal. All four drawings are from typical specimens and show only the terminal twentieth ($\pm$) of the entire active region of the X-chromosome.

In "A" the line of apparent optical separation within ring 2 does not necessarily separate the loci of ac and sc, and is not necessarily identical with the break within ring 2 shown in "D."

In "C" the upper break may have been within or just below ring 1, and the lower break correspondingly higher and within ring 2; hence the numbering given . represents only the longest inversion here possible.

In "D" the brace indicating the inversion should end just *below* 2a.

the two different position effects occurring at the two different (but nearby) points of breakage and reattachment.

Another case in which the genetic expectation of a minute inversion, based on "double mutation," was similarly confirmed by the cytological finding, was that of achaete 3 (= scute 10). Here the mutation other than that at the achaete locus was the ommatidial disarrangement "om," which was proved to lie slightly to the right of achaete by the same method of analysis of fragments as that used before (analysis by crossing-over being virtually precluded in this as in the other two cases by reason of the small distances involved). In correspondence with this genetic situation, it was found that one point of breakage and reattachment lay within chromomere (= "ring") 2, near the point in this chromomere where previous cytogenetic analysis by Muller and Prokofyeva (1934) had shown the achaete gene to be, while the other point of breakage and reattachment lay just to the left of or just within chromomere (= "ring") 5, the region between these two points of breakage being exactly inverted (see Fig. 1).

Since double breaks and reattachments are not all thus accompanied by a *discernible* position effect in two demonstrably separate loci, this genetic criterion of a minute rearrangement is only sometimes provided. It is therefore evident that a minute inversion involving only a few genes (or sometimes only one gene?) would often be not only cytologically but also genetically indistinguishable from an intragenic mutation, by any methods at present in use.

C. A. Offermann has directed our attention to the fact that there is evidence from another direction that a considerable proportion (if not all) of the apparent "gene mutations" produced by X-rays are really the effects of changes in position caused by minute intergenic rearrangements. This evidence lies in the fact that the frequency of production by X-rays of readily demonstrable (gross) gene rearrangements is vastly greater in spermatozoa than in other cells, and that, corresponding with this, the frequency of production of apparent "gene mutations" is also considerably raised in spermatozoa, as compared with other cells—although not nearly as much raised as is the gross rearrangement frequency (see Muller and Altenburg, 1930). Now exactly such relations are to be expected, if most of the induced "gene mutations" are fine rearrangements, and if we accept the very probable hypothesis that rearrangements, like cross-overs, require contact between two chromonemata (or two portions of one chromonema). For the chromosomes are very much more crowded together and are more condensed in spermatozoa than in other cells. The much greater degree of crowding together would give vastly more chance for juxtaposition of parts that ordinarily lie widely separated, and so would lead to a far higher frequency of gross rearrangements, while the greater degree of condensation would give more chance for contacts on the part of the very fine loopings that would be responsible for the minute rearrangements.

As our studies of mutations in the X and other chromosomes have shown that apparent replicas of practically all known "natural mutations" in *Drosophila* may also be obtained by X-rays, the further question is raised as to what proportion of "natural mutations" in *Drosophila* may really be minute rearrangements. This question is of moment because the range of possibilities of phenotypic change through intergenic rearrangements alone must be far from adequate for any indefinitely continued evolution. The latter must depend for the most part upon intragenic change, and hence it is important for the study of evolution, though at present seemingly so impossible, to be able to distinguish some at least of the intragenic mutations from the minute intergenic types of rearrangement. The matter acquires a greater urgency for geneticists when it is realized that they may now expect to have to meet attacks from orthogeneticists and Lamarckians, who may see in the present uncertainty regarding the "building blocks of evolution," an opportunity of reintroducing teleological notions of evolutionary causation.

In this connection, it must not be forgotten that all the cytogenetic investigations of species-crossing have agreed in showing that species differences in general reside in chromosomal differences and are therefore fundamentally *Mendelian* in their inheritance. When the chromosomes in species-crosses are able to undergo reduction, the species differences show spread of variation and eventual return to either parent species, whereas, when chromosome segregation is prevented—whether by asexual reproduction, by division of chromosomes at both maturation divisions (as in butterfly hybrids), or by the somatic origination of allotetraploidy —the hybrids breed true. Now Mendelian differences have been found to originate only by a sudden process—mutation. Since mutations involving intergenic changes are necessarily inadequate to provide most of the material for species divergence, it logically follows that a part of the mutations must be intragenic. It is only to be expected that many of these would be similar, in their phenotypic consequences, to effects of intergenic origin, and that discrimination between the two classes of change would present considerable difficulties. Such discrimination must, however, be eventually attempted.

THE OPTICAL DISSOCIATION OF DROSOPHILA CHROMOMERES BY MEANS OF ULTRAVIOLET LIGHT*

By J. Ellenhorn, A. Prokofjeva, and H. J. Muller
Corresponding Member of the Academy

The Problem

In recent studies of Muller and Prokofjeva it has been shown that the transverse rings or discs visible in the chromosomes of the salivary glands of *Drosophila melanogaster* may have a genetically compound structure (in the direction longitudinal to the chromosome) even when—as in the case of the ring investigated, No. 2 of the X-chromosome—they appear single or at most double, as seen or photographed by ordinary optical methods. On the theory of Koltzoff, these chromosomes of the salivary glands consist of many conjugated identical chromonemas, extended to their full length and having their corresponding chromomeres lying side by side and often optically confluent.[1] This morphological analysis of the structure of these chromosomes into parallel threads with apposed nodes was in fact described and figured by Carnoy as early as 1884, although of course he did not realize the significance and method of derivation of the threads.[2] The rings, then may be said to represent chromomeres and a compound structure of the rings (in a direction longitudinal to the chromosome) implies a corresponding compound structure of the chromomere in the individual chromonema.

The demonstration of this compound nature of the chromomere in *Drosophila* was affected by a combined genetic and cytological study of cases of chromosome breakage which had been selected—by reason of their having position effects on the same or nearby genes —to lie very close together in a highly restricted region of a chromosome (that of yellow and scute). A genetic map of the relative positions of seven cases of breakage was made (this has now been extended), by means of a special genetic method involving the investigation of individuals representing recombinations between all the cases of breakage taken two at a time. It was shown that these seven breaks lay in only four main positions—if there were a greater number of different positions than this, these other positions lay so near to the former that the absence of the chromonema in the interval between caused neither death nor any easily distinguished morphological effect. Thus it became very improbable that there were many more possible positions of breakage such that

*Comptes Rendus de l'Académie des Sciences de l'URRS, Vol. I, No. 4, 1935, pp. 234-42.

Observations

Investigation of the microphotographs obtained by the use of ultraviolet light and comparison of the structures appearing in them with those seen or photographed by visible light, gives the following results. All the discs seen as units or at most as double (or doubtfully double) in the left end of the X-chromosome of *Drosophila melanogaster*, except disc *O* and possibly disc *4*, which have so far appeared to be simple, are seen by ultraviolet light to consist of several very fine subdiscs arranged close together. The second disc consists of at least four of these fine subdiscs (lettered *a* to *d* in the photograph), of which subdisc *d* appears the thickest. The third disc also consists of four fine subdiscs. The fifth disc consists of three subdiscs. The remainder of the first nine discs— namely, discs *1*, *6*, *7*, *8*, and *9*—each consist of two subdiscs. In addition, a faint single disc is just discernible between discs *3* and *4*, and other faint discs are seen elsewhere in what previously seemed internodal regions, for example, in the anterior portion of the bulb.

It is very probable that by the use of light of still shorter wave length at least disc *2d* and other relatively heavy subdiscs would become dissociated into finer structures. There is genetic reason, referred to in our opening section, to conclude that disc *2* is compounded of somewhat more than four genetically separable parts, but there are not likely to be very many more. It is possible, therefore, that the finer subdiscs may serve to mark the locations of individual genes (although we do not imply here that the chromatin is a necessary component part of the gene). Continuation of the method of genetic analysis of breaks near together accompanied by a cytological study, should make this question soluble in the not very distant future. In the meantime it is interesting to observe that the subdiscs are more uniformly distributed through the length of the chromosome than are the coarser discs distinguished by visible light.

While, so far as the discs seen by coarser optical methods (visible light) are concerned, it is correct to say that genes lie within the region covered by them, it is seen now to be probable that they are also contained within the less deeply chromatic regions that have been referred to as internodes. At the same time the question must now be raised whether, on the scale of fineness of ultraviolet resolution, the fine dark lines represent the positions of the genes or (following Koltzoff's suggestion in "Science," which however was framed with reference to the coarser discs seen with visible light) whether the fine dark lines represent the positions of joints between the genes.

In some regions of our photographs the compound nature of the discs in the transverse direction was also quite evident and it could be seen that the "disc" or "ring" really consisted of about sixteen elements in the field of vision (with an equal number probably on the other side of the chromosome; this would make about 32). There was a suggestion moreover of each of these elements being paired (in a direction transverse to the longitudinal axis of the chromosome), in harmony with the conception that chromonemas primarily attract one another two by two. As there was no further resolution of the elements in a transverse direction, this would make 64 chromonemas present in the chromosome altogether, 32 derived from each original homologue, by a process of five successive doublings. It is hoped to investigate this question in more detail subsequently, our present interest having been concentrated chiefly upon the compoundness of structure in the longitudinal direction.

Institute of Genetics, Academy
of Sciences of the USSR, Moscow,   Received
and State Optical Institute, Leningrad.   Jan. 1, 1935.

Notes

[1]According to a report in "Science Service" (printed in 'Science', October 5th, 1934) Bridges has recently come to the same conclusion on the basis of observations of his own. Koltzoff's theory was described to us by him and sent to press in April, 1934.

[2] Attention may be directed at this point to the fact that Kostoff in 1930 suggested that the succession of transverse striations in the salivary gland chromosomes might be an expression of the linear arrangement of their contained genes.

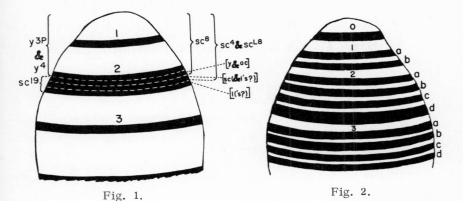

Fig. 1.   Fig. 2.

Fig. 1. Diagram showing compound structure of the second disc in the left
end of the X-chromosome as determined by a cytogenetic study of cases of
breakage (after Muller and Prokofjeva).
Fig. 2. Diagram showing compound structure of the second disc in the left
end of the X-chromosome as determined by a study of microphotographs in
ultraviolet light.

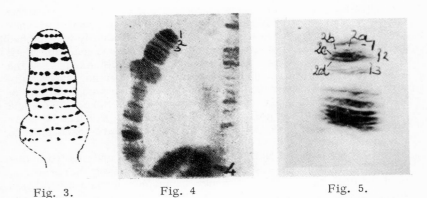

Fig. 3.   Fig. 4   Fig. 5.

Fig. 3. Drawing of left end of X-chromosome. Note that the second disc
appears double.
Fig. 4. Microphotographs of left end of normal X-chromosome in salivary
gland of *Drosophila melanogaster* as seen by visible light (of approx. 600 μ
wave length *N ap* 1.3. Magnification 1600 diameters).
Fig. 5. Microphotographs of left end of X-chromosome, taken by means of
ultraviolet light of 280 mμ wave length, *N ap* 1.25. Note evidence of the
compound structure shown in Fig. 1 and not visible or only very partially
visible in Fig. 4 & 5. Magnification 5000 diameters.

THE ORIGINATION OF CHROMATIN DEFICIENCIES AS MINUTE DELETIONS SUBJECT TO INSERTION ELSEWHERE*

By H. J. Muller†

Institute of Genetics, Academy of Sciences, Moscow

(Received for Publication December 8, 1934)

I. Earlier Work on the Nature of Interstitial "Deficiencies"

The phenomenon of so-called "deficiency," that is, genetic deficiency of a minute, interstitial (i.e., non-terminal) region of a chromosome map, was first met with by Bridges in the case of the forked-Bar region of the X-chromosome of *Drosophila*. It appeared as a spontaneous reversion of Bar to non-Bar accompanied by a lethal effect, and at the suggestion of the present author that the cause might lie in the loss of a piece of the chromosome, which would allow recessive mutant genes in the homologous chromosome to manifest themselves and would prevent crossing-over, the necessary tests were made by Bridges and showed that these effects were in fact produced. Unexpectedly, however, it appeared that the terminal (right-hand) region of the chromosome was present and normal, so that a simple breakage would not explain the results. As the phenomenon of deletion was not yet known, and seemed at the time a rather special assumption, it was deemed doubtful whether the region that appeared lost had really been physically lost, or had been inactivated or caused to undergo simultaneous mutation of all of its genes, chain-wise, to recessive mutant allelomorphs. At the same time (as was suggested by the present author) the results furnished evidence, from a new angle, of the physical validity of the linear arrangement of genes shown in the linkage maps, and indicated too that the normal allelomorph of Bar produced no other effect on the character concerned than did the mere absence of the mutant Bar gene.

The second case of deficiency, Notch 8, found and studied in detail by Mohr, was, in regard to the essential principles pertaining to it, similar to the first, although in another chromosome region and entailing a character effect (Notch wings) dominant to the normal. Here too it remained equally difficult to decide whether there was a real loss or inactivation or chain mutation, nor did the cytological methods of the time avail in reaching a decision. Similar considerations apply to the other natural interstitial deficiencies reported by Bridges since that time (Plexate, Minute 1, etc.).

Genetica, XVII, 3/4, pp. 237-52, 1935.

†Professor of Zoology, University of Texas; Guest at the Institute of Genetics, 1933-35.

With the coming of the X-ray technique and the direct proof through cytological evidence paralleling that of genetics, that deletions could occur which involved a breakage of the chromosome at two places, accompanied by reunion of the terminal pieces and loss of the middle piece from the combination, a mechanism was provided whereby the loss of non-terminal pieces could take place. This raised anew the question whether small deficiencies like the above, and others since found, had been caused in such a way. The cytologically demonstrated deletions, however, all involved the loss of the very large pieces; owing to the nature of the technique used, others would not then have been detectable. It was by no means a foregone conclusion that very small deletions also could take place. In fact, if an analogy were drawn from the process of double crossing over, such an extrapolation of the evidence from large deletions to small ones would not be justified, for in double crossing over it is well-known that two points that are far apart in the chromosome may readily have simultaneous breakage and reattachment, but not two points that are close together. It was therefore desirable to get further evidence concerning the nature of the small interstitial deficiencies, and this was forthcoming from several sources.

As one line of evidence, the author made an examination of several cases that had been obtained by Patterson, which seemed, from genetic evidence, to involve the loss, by simple breakage, of most or all of the left-hand terminal region of the X-chromosome, extending to the right beyond the locus of Notch. (It may be remarked, however, that there was no real proof that the losses did extend entirely as far as the left end and so the cause might not have been a simple breakage). The data showed that these supposed losses had genetic effects like those of Mohr's Notch 8 deficiency (and, of course, the additional lethal effect due to the absence of Patterson's "viability gene" or genes, which had to be compensated by the addition of a partly complementary fragment, called "Theta," from the extreme left end). It was hoped that cytological proof could be obtained that in these cases, giving phaenotypic effects like those of previous "deficiencies," there was a real absence of a section of chromatin, but unfortunately the cytological attack failed, because the pieces involved were too small to be demonstrable by the methods then available. It must of course be conceded that, even if the real absence of a terminal piece had been cytologically demonstrable in these cases, this line of evidence for the loss interpretation of interstitial deficiencies must have remained an indirect one, since it could only show that the original deficiencies of Mohr, etc., gave genetic effects phaenotypically like those of these losses. Similar indirect proof from a converse direction was afforded by the author's studies of the effects of cytologically demonstrable extra pieces of the X chromosome, in which it was found that the phaenotypic results were opposite in character to those produced by the original "deficiencies," thus indicating that the latter comprised absences of the corresponding regions.

Another line of evidence lay in the analysis of cases of inversions and translocations, in which it was found that two breaks in the same chromosome might occur that were at distances from one another considerably smaller than was usual in the case of double crossing over, although cases were not yet known in which the distance was so small as to be comparable in size with those of previously studied "deficiencies."

While the above investigations were in progress, cytological work of McClintock on maize did reveal cases in which there was actual absence from a chromosome of a comparatively small interstitial region. It would, to be sure, have been difficult to determine the lengths of these deficiencies in genetic units and to compare them quantitatively with the lengths of the *Drosophila* deficiencies, but the general principle, so far as it applied to maize at any rate, was directly established.

The same principle has now been established in *Drosophila* by genetic methods in the case of scute 19, here to be described. In addition, after these findings on scute 19 had been made, and the present paper nearly completed, the new cytological method of Painter became available, whereby through a study of the uncoiled and reduplicated chromonemata in the salivary glands (as Koltzoff has shown them to be), differences of the degree of fineness of many interstitial deficiencies would be directly visible. By this means, as Mackensen has reported in a recent abstract, the fact that these deficiencies involve real absences has been clearly demonstrated. The same has likewise been deomonstrated in later cytological work, following the method of Painter, that has been done by Prokofyeva at the Institute of Genetics (Muller and Prokofyeva, in press), as well as in such work by Kossikov and Muller (in press). At the same time it still seems worth while to publish the account of the genetic investigation of scute 19, not only because this had led to the independent establishment of the same conclusion from the genetic side, but also because a number of significant facts are brought out in this case that are not to be gained simply by the cytological analysis of cases of deficiency.

II.   The Scute 19 Translocation—First Results

In a number of laboratories translocations have been extensively studied that involve the mutual interchange of terminal pieces between non-homologous chromosomes, and, where these pieces are small, the aneuploid offspring resulting from recombination taking place in parents heterozygous for these translocations are frequently found to be viable and to show phaenotypic effects similar to those in individuals having "deficiencies" of the same region as that which the aneuploids are known to lack. Hitherto, however, such

dumpy, that is, at about locus 13. The crossing over between the markers was not perceptibly reduced, nor in any wise abnormal, the piece evidently being too small to affect crossing over appreciably. While it cannot be categorically proved that the case is not one of side attachment, this becomes very unlikely in view of the apparent great rarity of the latter phenomenon, if it exists at all, [1] combined with the fact that the attached piece had been broken at both its ends. Insertion is the only probable explanation here.

V. The Genetic Size of the Deleted and Inserted Section

It becomes of interest at the same time to examine more exactly the genetic extent of the fragment that had been thus deleted and inserted. Since, as shown in a parallel paper, achaete and scute are now known to be separate, there must be at least three genes in the fragment, namely yellow, achaete and scute. Yellow and achaete have not, as a matter of fact, yet been separated by crossing over or breakage, but their dependence upon separate genes is extremely probable in view both of their very different phaenotypic effects and of their usually separate mutations.

Further examination of what loci may be present in the piece was aided by an intensive study which the author has been carrying on into the limits of divisibility of the region of the chromosome in question. This entails a comparison of the position of the breaks in various translocations, inversions, etc., of the region. Without going into the details of this matter here, it must be stated that the work thus far has demonstrated at least one more locus, lying to the right of scute, in the region included by the scute 19 fragment, a locus whose absence is lethal in its effect. It is quite possible, and indeed probable, that there are more of these loci, which further study may demonstrate. The existence of the locus just mentioned is demonstrable if crosses are made between flies with the scute 4 and scute 9 inverted chromosomes. A crossover chromosome thereby obtained, which has the left portion of the scute 4 chromosome and the right portion of the scute 9 chromosome, is lethal in its effect upon a male, unless the scute 19 fragment, attached to chromosome II, is present in addition; in the latter case, the male lives. The left-hand breaks of scute 4 and scute 9 are both to the right of scute, but that of scute 9 must be some distance further to the right than that of scute 4, so that in the crossover chromosome the region between these two breaks is missing; but this missing region is supplied when the scute 19 fragment is added. This region, then, must contain at least one gene necessary for life.

Similar studies are being carried out in the attempt to divide the region still further if possible. In this way it is hoped eventually to be able to form some estimate of the actual number of genes in the scute 19-containing fragment. The hope of being able to make such a determination is raised by the fact that the left-hand limit has already been precisely determined. Whatever the answer may be, however, the fragment should physically be a very small one, since it could not be shown to cover any other visible genes than those mentioned, in spite of the fact that all deleted chromosomes previously tested, that extended to the right of scute, covered at least the locus *om*, even when they did not cover Patterson's "viability gene."

VI. Discussion

The reasons have been presented in another paper (Muller, 1932) for considering the two breaks in cases of double breaks as not independent of one another, but as both dependent upon some process that accompanies chromosome contact under special conditions, such as X-rays may bring about. The process may in some ways be compared to crossing over, involving as it does reattachment at the point of contact, but being a kind of illegitimate crossing over between non-homologous regions that ordinarily do not touch in this way. A further difference from crossing over is now demonstrated clearly in the fact that two points of breakage in the same chromosome may under these conditions be so near together, thus being free from the operation of the principle of interference demonstrated by the author in 1912 to hold in the case of crossing over. Interference, so far as present knowledge goes, is apparently explained most plausibly by considerations of chromosome rigidity obtaining under ordinary conditions. Why such interference should not operate in the case of these breaks and reattachments between non-homologous chromosomes is a new problem. As mentioned in a previous section, there were already indications that the rule did not operate normally in such cases, based on the comparatively short distance between the two breaks in some already known cases, but in no case known was the distance of the order of minuteness of that in scute 19. It would be of interest to know if such cases may be actually of higher frequency of occurrence (in relation to the number calculated on the basis of no interference) than those in which the breaks are somewhat further apart.[2]

Another respect in which the present case shows the operation of a principle different from that found in crossing over, lies in the fact that there was here no real exchange of parts, inasmuch as one chromosome was only donor and the other only recipient. The first chromosome broke at two points, the second at not more than one point. This could not have come about through a mere exchange of attachments, at points of breakage coinciding with points of contact, unless the first chromosome had been looped upon itself in a most minute loop, and the second chromosome had rested against the first at *precisely* the point of crossing of this loop. Offermann has suggested that this apparent coincidence might have occurred through the second chromosome having slid along until it naturally came to rest in the notch of the first. At any rate, it is not a case of the simple crossing at two points, of two threads, A and B, followed by their breakage and reunion, for in that event if one part of A becomes attached to one part of B, the other part of A must become attached to the other part of B, as happens in crossing over. The latter test of the translocation, inversion and deletion hypothesis of Serebrovsky and Dubinin, suggested in a recent paper of the author (1932), therefore receives a negative answer. Nevertheless, because of the possibility of contact of three strands at one point, above discussed, this can no longer be regarded as invalidating the very probable idea that chromatin contacts are a causative factor in the recombination process.

The question now arises, are all deficiencies of non-terminal regions produced in essentially the same way as scute 19, by the deleted region having become entangled with another chromosome region? Certainly in some cases at least deletions could arise this way, in which the piece deleted out was never found, for the latter would have a chance to become lost at the subsequent mitotic division, if the process had occurred at a stage when the chromosomes were split, and it would at any rate have another chance at a subsequent meiotic division. On the other hand the piece, although deleted out by contact with another region, might conceivably fail to become attached to any portion of the latter. Again, the mere looping of a single chromosome upon itself, after the manner of an inversion, might have sufficed to entangle its parts sufficiently to cause the deletion, and the part deleted out might, at least at times, have its ends join one another to make a ring; this would lack a fibre attachment point and would therefore be incapable of mitotic transportation. The loopings here in question probably correspond to the very fine spirals described by Vejdovsky in 1911.

If these cases can occur, then it is also possible that equally minute inversions may occur, which could scarcely be recognised by the test of reduced crossing over, but which might nevertheless involve apparent mutations, dependent upon the "position effect" of the rearranged genes. This involves us in the question of how many supposed gene mutations may really be of this type. We are now studying this matter by means of tests of a special kind. The answer to it is critically bound up with the whole problem of gene mutation.[3]

A further point of interest brought out in the scute 19 case is the viability of the individuals homozygous for the small extra fragment attached to the second chromosome, when they already have this region represented in normal X-chromosomes. Such individuals live comparatively well and can be bred, and no doubt could be brought practically to normal viability by selection of "modifying" genes. They show a somewhat darker colour and tendency towards extra bristles, due to the extra doses of the loci concerned (of yellow, achaete and scute), but the piece is so small that it is easily conceivable that such duplications could become established in natural evolution. This then is one method by which the number of genes could become increased. Aneuploidy caused by the addition of whole chromosomes is usually too detrimental to play such a role (except where polyploidy has preceded it). Following such duplication, it is to be expected that the redundant loci will come to have divergent mutations established in them in the course of evolution, and so gradually will become more differentiated, until they can finally be regarded as quite non-homologous genes. In the meantime, however, they would show some ability to produce parallel or "duplicate" mutations and some synaptic affinity.

While such duplications of regions might sometimes become placed in non-homologous chromosomes, as in the scute 19 case, it is to be noted that the likeliest point of attachment, ordinarily, would be in a nearly homologous position in a sister or homologous chromosome, since these ordinarily lie so close together in the cell. Here, then, a localized duplication of materials could be produced, giving rise to an effect similar to that produced by unequal crossing over. Of course this conception is rather speculative, but the possibility of it is of interest in connection with other questions raised by the study of the achaete-scute complex.

Attention may hereby be called to the paper by Muller and Prokofyeva, in which cytological examination of the scute 19 deficiency is made, with the object of determining the method of cytological expression of the genes in the chromosomes of resting nuclei (salivary glands). It may be stated here that the results fully confirm the genetic finding of the deletion of an extremely minute interstitial region of the X-chromosome, located near its left end.

Summary

1) The scute 19 translocation involved the breakage of the X-chromosome, under the influence of X-rays, at two points very near together. Between these points there were located the loci of yellow, achaete, scute and at least one other gene, whose absence acts as a recessive lethal.

2) The minute region between these two breaks was deleted from the X-chromosome, the remainder of which joined together again.

3) The region thus deleted became attached to a non-terminal region of the second chromosome, close to the right of the locus of *dp*, probably by breakage of the second chromosome and insertion of the deleted piece between the resulting pieces of the second chromosome, accompanied by chainwise union of the three pieces.

4) The translocation was not mutual, for no genes became transferred from the second chromosome to the X. The explanation of this fact seems to require the meeting of three threads at one point, presumably by one becoming caught in the notch made by the crossing of the other two.

5) The X-chromosome with the small missing section, when in a

combination containing normal second chromosomes without the inserted fragment, gives the results typical of a so-called "deficiency."

6) On the other hand, individuals having the second chromosome with the attached fragment, but normal X-chromosomes, exhibit the phenomena typical of so-called "duplications," although, unlike what is found in most cases of duplications involving larger regions, individuals homozygous for these duplications can live and breed.

7) One method of origination of minute interstitial "deficiencies" is thus illustrated, and it is proved that these deficiencies involve real absence. Problems connected with the method of formation of such minute deletions are discussed.

8) The question is raised of to what extent supposed gene mutations may consist of similarly minute inversions, arising by a similar process.

9) It is pointed out that the ability of such minute portions of chromatin to become transferred to other regions makes possible also the origination of reduplications of gene material, that are viable and that might become established in evolution.

The results of cytological examination of the scute 19 case are presented in a parallel paper by Muller and Prokofyeva.

Notes

[1]Since the above was written, evidence has been obtained by Kossikov and Muller (paper in press) that even the supposed classical case of side attachment—"Pale" translocation—in fact involves insertion instead.

[2]Evidence to this effect has since been obtained.

[3]Since the above has been written, proof of the occurrence of such inversions has been obtained by Muller, Prokofyeva and Raffel (in press).

ON THE DIMENSIONS OF CHROMOSOMES AND GENES IN DIPTERAN SALIVARY GLANDS*

Professor H. J. Muller†

Institute of Genetics, Academy of Sciences of the
USSR, Moscow

The theory of Koltzoff (1934), afterwards developed independently by Bridges[1], that the so-called giant chromosomes of Drosophila salivary glands are hollow bundles of chromonemata, formed by the side-by-side proliferation and apposition of one original chromonema (or of two conjugated homologues), at once brings our conception of these structures into harmony with the known cytological and genetic facts concerning chromosomes in general. But the question is still asked by some: "Why should it be that these structures develop and are visible in the gland cells of Drosophila and other Diptera and do not seem to have been noted elsewhere?" The answer appears to be a very simple one and in fact, by the simplicity of the explanation it provides, it really constitutes a further corroboration of the Koltzoff-Bridges theory itself.

The answer is that, as was shown long ago by Stevens (1908) and others, Diptera differ from other organisms in the exceptional strength of the synaptic force acting between their homologous chromosomes and chromosome parts in non-meiotic stages. Whereas, in other animals and plants, the tendency of like genes to come together is little evident except at meiosis, in Diptera either this tendency remains stronger, or counter forces do not develop so strongly, so that, wherever the chromosomes are visible, whether in somatic or germ cells, they show a strong tendency to conjugate. In the case of the salivary glands and other cells in which, through reduplication, numerous identical chromonemata have been formed, this synaptic affinity would tend to hold all these homologous parts together in groups (with their corresponding chromomeres in apposition so as to give the appearance of cross-striations).

It is probable, in accordance with the conception of the author (1922, Amer. Nat., 56: 32-50) concerning the nature of the attractive force, and in accordance with the well-established findings and theories of Darlington, that this attraction is primarily two-by-two and is exerted more strongly along a certain plane. This would tend to result in primary, secondary, tertiary, etc., two-by-two associations, all in the same plane. But as the residual force between more and more distant, less directly conjugated strands is pro-

*The American Naturalist, September-October, 1935, LXIX: 405-11.
†Professor of zoology, University of Texas, Austin; on leave for 1935-36.

gressively weaker, this plane can bend sufficiently to allow its edges also to come into contact, *i.e.*, the strands must tend to arrange themselves endlessly around the periphery of a hollow cylinder. This periphery, then, represents the plane of the strongest attractive forces.

There is every reason to believe that essentially the same type of elongated chromonemal filaments as are seen in the "giant chromosomes" of Diptera exist also in the resting cells of other forms, although in these other forms the one important condition necessary for the grouping of these filaments into bundles is absent: namely, an attraction between like genes strong enough (despite insulating and repelling forces) to effect their apposition. Ever since the work of Bonnevie (1909) and of Vejdovsky (1911), there has been definite evidence that the uncoiling spirals (chromonemata) seen in the chromosomes at anaphase and telophase retain their continuity and persist in almost completely uncoiled condition throughout the resting stage, to reform the coils which are seen again in the prophase chromosomes. The reason this did not receive earlier general recognition is because the irregular staining, extreme fineness and great length (with consequent repeated folding back) of these uncoiled chromonemata make it extremely difficult to follow out the course of the individual threads in the resting nuclei of ordinary fixed preparations, while in living material the refractive index of the threads is virtually identical with that of the nucleoplasm. As was pointed out by the present author in 1916 (Amer. Nat., 50: 291), the newly discovered genetic facts of the persistence of the genes in unchanged linear order, throughout the entire reproductive life of the individual, and the evidence that even homologous loci do not undergo any exchange of positions until the meiotic period arrives, made it necessary to postulate the existence of the same structure as that observed cytologically by Bonnevie and Vejdovsky, inasmuch as it had to be concluded that the genes are arranged in the form of a long fine persistent thread, and in order that such a gene-string might be present within the chromosomes at mitosis (as the genetic and cytological evidence combined in proving to be the case) it had necessarily to be coiled somehow. There was, therefore, no alternative to the geneticists, from accepting the chromonema theory of the more advanced cytologists.

On this now orthodox interpretation, then, the chromosomes in the resting stages of cells in general must have essentially the same structure as that seen in the salivary glands of Diptera, except that the chromonemata need not have become reduplicated, and have not become apposed. In regard to the matter of the reduplication of the strands, the distinction is not everywhere applicable. For it is probable that such a reduplication often occurs, in the somatic cells of other forms as well as of Diptera, especially when these cells are not destined for further division but (as so-called "noble cells") attain a large size in adaptation to some specific physiological function. As Koltzoff points out, evidence of such polyploidy has been obtained by Jacoby (1926) in the case of mammalian liver cells. In other forms than Diptera, however, the existence of such polyploidy must only increase the tangle of separate chromonemata winding about through the nucleus and thus make an identification of the individual chromosomes even less possible, whereas in Diptera the active synaptic affinity leads to an orderly grouping of strands which allows us to recognize the chromosomes (or rather, the groups of chromonemata) as such. We see, then, that if the Bonnevie-Vejdovsky theory is right, the observed fact of a somatic conjugation in Diptera should lead us to expect the formation of the giant structures which we see, without our assuming any other unusual property of Diptera or of gland chromosomes.

We are now in a position to judge in what sense the chromosomes seen in the Drosophila salivary glands may really be considered "giant chromosomes." We have seen that their exceptional thickness is explained by the fact that they are compounded of a group of parallel identical chromonemata, and not merely compounded, but arranged in a *hollow* bundle so as to greatly increase the thickness of the group as a whole. Each individual chromonema, however, is probably no thicker in the "giant chromosome" than in the mitotic chromosome, though it may of course have accessory material around it. Nor is there ground for supposing that the individual chromonema is finer in the "giant chromosome," or in resting stages of cells in general, than it is in the mitotic chromosome: it appears thicker in the mitotic chromosome, but the existence of smaller coils within the larger coils, which would lend apparent thickness to the coiled threads of the mitotic stages, had been noted even by Vejdovsky. The same fact of coiling (coarser and finer) also explains readily the far greater apparent length of the strands in the salivary glands of Diptera, and in the resting stages of cells in general, than at mitosis. Hence there is no basis for postulating that the salivary gland chromosomes are really of a very different length than the chromonemata of the mitotic chromosomes (except, of course, when they have artificially been put under tension).[2] It is probable, then, that the "giant chromosomes" are giant only in appearance: essentially, they are chromonema-bundles, in which the structure of the individual chromonema is simply made more manifest by its (for us) convenient uncoiling, reduplication and accurate aggregation.

A few calculations regarding the sizes of the chromonema parts, based upon the premises stated above, may be of interest here. If we assume that the entire mass of the active region of the X chromosome of *Drosophila melanogaster*, as seen at metaphase in the oogonial cells, consists of tightly coiled chromonemal material, filling up all the space, and that this chromonema retains its same length and thickness in the salivary gland chromosome, then, by measurements of the chromosomes in these two stages and by a few simple calculations, it can easily be shown that (with some correction for shape) the average diameter of the chromonema, including that of the gene, in a direction transverse to the longitudinal axis of the chromonema, can not be more than 1/50th of a micron (.02μ). (We say "average diameter," since it is improbable that the "breadth" and "thickness" of the chromonema are exactly equal). The above result is reckoned as follows:

> Volume of X at metaphase = length $(2\,\mu) \times$ breadth $(\tfrac{1}{4}\,\mu) \times$
> thickness $(\tfrac{1}{4}\,\mu) = \tfrac{1}{8}$ cu. μ.
> Volume of active region $= \tfrac{2}{3} \times \tfrac{1}{8}$ cu. μ. $= \tfrac{1}{12}$ cu. μ.
> Length in salivary gland (after Bridges) = 200 μ.
> Let average diameter = x.
> Since volume = length $\times$ (dia.)^2, we have $\tfrac{1}{12} = 200 \; x^2$
> $$x^2 = 1/2400$$
> $$x = \text{(approx.)} \; 1/50 \; \mu. \; \text{or} \; .02 \; \mu.$$

If, on the other hand, we assume that the metaphase chromosome does not have its entire volume occupied by the chromonema, but that the latter is tightly coiled about the periphery only, then the chromonema would have a thickness, in the direction parallel to the surface of the coil, of only 1/250th of a micron *(i.e.,* 0.44μ). In this case we have reckoned as follows:

> Diameter of coil in metaphase chromosome = thickness of metaphase
> chromosome $= \tfrac{1}{4}\,\mu$.
> Length of one coil in metaphase chromosome $= \pi \times$ diameter of coil
> $= 3.14 \times \tfrac{1}{4} = .8\,\mu$ (approx.)
> Number of coils, each $.8\,\mu$ long, in whole chromonema, 200 μ long,
> $$= \frac{200}{.8} = 250.$$

Since 250 coils must be crowded side by side within a distance of one micron (the approximate length of the active region at metaphase), the width of one coil must be about $\frac{1}{250}\,\mu$ or .004 μ.

Probably the truth lies in between these two calculations, but nearer to the first, in view of the fact that there are probably both primary and secondary and perhaps other coils. If the chromonemal coils are not in actual contact, however, their diameter must be correspondingly less.

We may proceed from the above to some tentative calculations concerning the genes. Suppose that the genes are as densely spaced (in the longitudinal direction) throughout the chromonema of the active region of the X as they have been found to be in the "second" band (Muller and Prokofyeva, 1934, 1935; Ellenhorn, Prokofyeva and Muller, 1935). The width *(i.e.,* chromonemal *length)* of that part of the "second" band containing the genes yellow, achaete, scute and the lethal to the right of scute is approximately .5μ (as seen best in the ultraviolet photographs). There are probably very few, if any, other genes within the segment in question. This gives a length of approximately 1/8 micron for one gene, supposing—as seems probable, despite Belling—that there is little or no intergenic material in the longitudinal direction. According to this reckoning, then, the gene length would be between 6 and 30 times as great as its diameter (according to which of the above two estimates of the diameter is chosen). This is in agreement with the fact that proteins and other complex organic molecules in general are chainlike, being much longer in one dimension than in the other two. We must, however, be careful of accepting these preliminary figures as coming even near to the actualities, in so far as we must bear in mind that several of the premises used in calculating them are by no means established and that the correctness of the conclusion as a whole depends upon the correctness of all the premises simultaneously. We are, however, on safer ground in taking the maximal figures for length and breadth as giving the maximum possible gene and chromonemal dimensions. And we see that, even taking these maxima, the *volume* of the gene is much too small to allow it, by itself, to give a visible image—although, on account of its tenuity, its *linear* extent may be just within the visible range. This agrees with the conclusion expressed by the author in 1922 (Amer. Nat., 56, *ibid.*).

The chromonema, too, turns out to be too fine to give an image, except by diffraction or by aid of the accumulation of accessory material about it. We have in the above calculated it to be between 1/50 and 1/250 of a micron in diameter. But the salivary gland X-chromosome has a periphery of about $12 \ 1/2\mu$ (3μ diameter $\times \pi$). If, as we should judge from the appearance of ordinary preparations, by visible light, there are only 16 fibrils in it, this gives a space of $3/4 \mu$ for the diameter of each fibril, together with its accessory material. The above calculated fineness of the individual fibril, however, makes it impossible to say, on the basis of simple observation, how many actual fibrils may be represented within one apparent fibril, and, if there is a basic two-by-two grouping, this would be expected to give an appearance of secondary fibrils, similar in arrangement to the individual ones. Ultra-violet photographs, as well as studies of nuclear growth, may throw some light upon this problem; the former have already indicated a more compound structure than was evident in visible light, but can not yet be regarded as conclusive, since in such light, too, diffraction images may occur.

Notes

[1]Professor Koltzoff visited the Institute of Genetics in Leningrad in March, 1934, and at that time gave a lucid exposition of the essentials of his theory of the structure of the chromosomes in the salivary glands to members of the institute. The present author, convinced by Koltzoff's formulation, thereupon found a supporting fact in the longitudinal fibrilla-

tion which he had already noticed in Ellenhorn's photographs of the Drosophila salivary gland chromosomes, and pointed out that the number of elements visible in them in the transverse direction seemed to be a power of two (2^4). Koltzoff's paper on the subject, which was sent in to press in America in April, 1934, was read by the present author at the time of sending.

[2] Even though the chromosome contraction for mitosis may involve some folding and coiling within the molecule itself as deomonstrated by Astbury for keratin fibers, nevertheless the molecule itself is essentially a chain structure the length of which may be considered as its extended length with the secondary connections undone, and it is the length in this sense which we are considering in the above discussion.

INVALIDATION OF THE GENETIC EVIDENCE FOR BRANCHED CHROMONEMAS, IN THE CASE OF THE PALE TRANSLOCATION IN DROSOPHILA*

K. V. Kossikov and H. J. Muller
Institute of Genetics, Academy of Sciences, Moscow

Status of the Problem

One of the most firmly established principles of biology is that of the linear arrangement of genes in the chromosome and of the linearity of the chromonema which (as the second author stated in 1916), must form the physical basis of the linear linkage map. Expressed in terms of the individual gene, this means a bipolar gene structure, with a consequent bipolar method of attachment of the genes to one another. That the unidimensional arrangement of genes holds even on the finest genetic scale possible, i.e., in the case of directly adjacent genes, can be deduced in the case of Bar genes from the results of Sturtevant's experiments on unequal crossing over and is substantiated by recent work of Muller and Prokofyeva on the arrangement of genes in the region of the scute locus.

There has for a long time, however, existed one apparently contrary genetic finding, which challenged the universality of the linear principle. This is the case of "Pale translocation" in *Drosophila melanogaster*, which has been interpreted as probably involving a

Journal of Heredity, Vol. XXVI, No. 8, August, 1935, pp. 305-17; transmitted for publication November 22, 1934. It should be explained that the present work was carried out in May, 1934, and written up soon afterwards, though publication was delayed by a number of circumstances. (Present version includes all of original text, with figures 6-13.)

branched chromosome structure. In this case, the first translocation known to genetics, it has been concluded—to quote from the
last account given of Pale translocation, by Morgan, Bridges and
Schultz, in December, 1932—that: "The original Pale-translocation
(1917, 1923) involved a break of chromosome II at about the locus
of plexus, and the lateral attachment of this terminal fragment to
the third chromosome at about the locus of Hairless." The translocated piece was thus supposed to be attached to the side of the
third chromosome, in a non-terminal position, and presumably it
was attached at its point of breakage. The attachment, whatever its
nature, was found to be quite stable in that the piece does not tend
to become lost from the chromosome to which it is affixed. The door
having once been opened, by this case, to the principle of branching,
another case recently found in Drosophila, which seems genetically
similar to the first, has been interpreted in the same way.

It will be seen that if any interpretation involving the conception
of some sort of side-attachment in these cases is correct, the
principle of bipolar gene connections and of a linear gene order
must be violated at the locus or loci where the branch is attached to
the main part of the chromonema. For this locus, the radically new
principle must be admitted, that a gene may somehow develop an
extra attachment point. The gene must then be supposed, not only to
be capable of self-duplication in this new form, but to be capable of
just the right kind of self-duplication in order to insure that the
other new genes in the daughter chromonema that is formed will
also have the same method of tripartite attachment to one another
at this locus as in the mother chromonema. In terms of chromosome "division," this is equivalent to saying that the plane of "division" must pass exactly through the point of side-attachment; more
accurately, we should say that the plane of self-duplication must be
parallel to the plane passing through all three points of gene attachment of a tripolar gene. Further than that, in the separation of the
two branched structures from one another, there must be no tendency to breakage. If, now, such tripartite or multipartite structures
can exist and be thus inherited in quite stable fashion, it is hard to
see why they should not, in the course of evolution, have become
more and more numerous, until at the present time the chromonemal structure should have become many-branched or netlike, or
have lost all semblance of linearity. Since the latter has not been
the case, we should be all the more cautious about accepting the
interpretation of a stable branched structure.

In recent years a series of cytological observations has been
reported (see Darlington, Levan, Mather) in which branched chromosome structures have actually been seen, and they have been
interpreted (especially the case of Levan's) according to the precedent set by Pale translocation. For the reasons stated above, it will
be very important to push the analysis of such cases further, so as
to demonstrate conclusively the existence of an actually branched

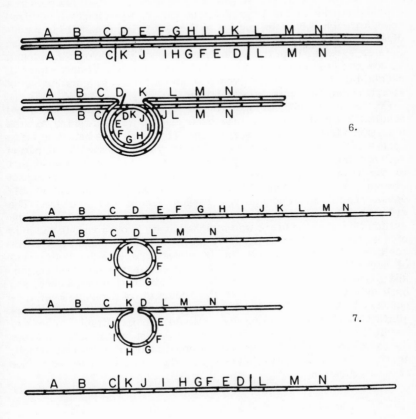

6.

7.

Figs. 6 and 7. Conjugation of normal and inverted chromosomes.

These drawings show schematically the results of conjugation of two chromosomes, one of which carries an inversion in the central region (D-K). The lower half of Figure 6 shows in diagram this material as it appears in the chromosomes of the salivary gland. Figure 7 shows schematically how these chromosomes produce the results shown in Figure 6. The two loops differ in that one of them might be called a "direct loop" and the other an "inverted loop." When these two loops are fused they result in a configuration in which each band in one chromosome is paired with its homologue in the other chromosome just as is the case when two normal chromosomes conjugate without the formation of a loop.

location was discernible on the lengths of both the second and the third chromosomes, but at the same time he reversed his previous conclusions as to the lengths of the latter, when normal, with respect to each other. In regard to the last point, the still later conclusion of Dobzhansky disagreed with his, while that of Muller and Painter agreed. Thus the whole matter was again thrown into doubt. If, however, the length of the third chromosome was visibly affected, as claimed by Bridges, it would seem that the case must be one of insertion rather than side-attachment.

On the other hand, Bridges (in the report of Morgan, Bridges and Schultz) soon afterwards announced genetic results which, on the insertion view, would be surprising. The work was based on large counts of progeny of individuals heterozygous for the translocation and for markers in the region of the second chromosome subject to the translocation. The counts showed that a minute amount of crossing over does occur between the attached piece and the homologous region of a normally arranged second chromosome. The crossover combinations observed were such as to agree with the assumption that the piece was attached at its broken end, to the side of the third chromosome. If it were inserted, these crossovers could only be explained as double crossovers, in which both points of double crossing over had occurred within the inserted region, and since the latter was normally only six to eight units long, and here much less on account of the reduction of crossing over frequency in individuals with heterozygous translocations, the possibility of double crossing over would, at first sight, seem one hardly to be entertained. These results, then, would seem to make the case strong again for the idea of non-linear arrangement, which, as our earlier quotation shows, was the one then accepted by the group in question.

The Cytological Resolution of Pale Translocation

It was thought that all these questions might be decided definitely and simply if a study of the structure of this translocation were made in the chromosomes of the salivary glands which, according to the well-known work of Painter, show the details of chromosome morphology about 100 times more extended than do the ordinary metaphase chromosomes. For this purpose it was advisable to use individuals heterozygous for the translocation, since the figures formed by the synapsis of the homologous regions of the translocational and non-translocational chromosomes would then more clearly show the structure of the rearrangement. It was also desirable to have some sign by which the right half of the third chromosome could be specially marked, cytologically, in order that attention might be focussed on this most critical region. A balanced stock was therefore made up, in which the right arm of one of the third chromosomes contained the well-known inversion,

"CIIIP" (=InP), but not the attached piece of Pale translocation, and the other third chromosome contained the attached piece but had an otherwise normal arrangement of genes, while the second chromosomes were heterozygous for the Pale deficiency but otherwise had normally arranged genes. As a result of the heterozygous inversion in the right arm of the third chromosome, we should expect a loop to be formed on this arm. The formation of a loop, attached by a kind of chiasma figure in one region to the rest of the chromosome pair, is a regular occurrence resulting from the presence of heterozygous inversions in the chromosomes of the salivary glands, since this is the necessary consequence of a conjugation of all homologous loci. The reader may convince himself of this on perusal of Figure 6, which shows in purely schematic fashion the complete conjugation, such as occurs in the salivary glands, of two chromosomes, one of which carries an inversion. The expected loop was, in fact, found in our CIIIP material, and served readily to mark the right arm of the third chromosome as desired.

It was to be expected that within the loop representing the inversion, or not far from it, the attached fragment would be found, either as a side-attachment or as a piece interpolated in one of the homologues and not found in the other. It was found, as a matter of fact, at a point almost opposite the right (distal) end of the inversion, and so near to the attachment of the loop as ordinarily to come within the chiasma-like figure formed by the shifting of partnership of the chromosomes (see Figures 8 and 10). It is clear in all the figures examined that this extra piece is not attached to the side in any way, but forms an integral part of the chromosome in which it lies, which thereby becomes quite noticeably lengthened. This leaves no doubt at all that the insertion hypothesis is the correct one.

On the other hand, the inserted piece is so small, relatively to the whole chromosome, that we do not believe it would ordinarily make a detectable difference in the length of the chromosome, as seen in metaphase figures. This helps to account for the mutually contradictory character of Bridges' two sets of reported results concerning the relative lengths of the second and third chromosomes, based on the idea that Pale translocation could be used to mark them. In metaphase figures, moreover, the chromosomes may vary so much in their relative condensation that the normal second chromosome sometimes appears larger than the normal third, and sometimes smaller.

One difficulty with the insertion hypothesis not above mentioned had been the fact that it seemed in this case to require that one of the surfaces (or "points") of fracture of the third chromosome became attached to the unbroken right hand terminus of the second chromosome, while the deficient second chromosome meanwhile acquired a new termination, coinciding with one of its own surfaces of fracture. More recent evidence indicates that the attachment of

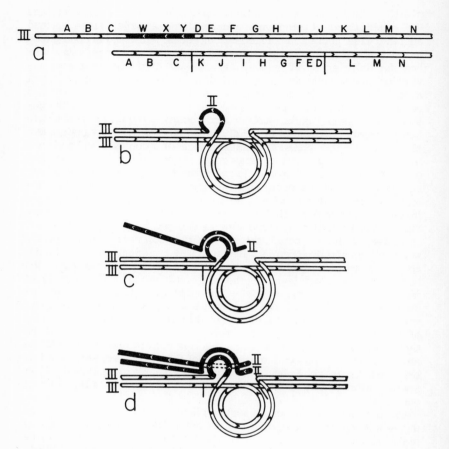

Fig. 8. Conjugation of "pale translocation."

In the pale translocation a portion of the second chromosome has been transferred to the third chromosome. This is shown schematically at *a*, in which the translocated region (W-Y) is black. When a strain heterozygous for this pale translocation is mated with a strain containing the well known " CIIIP" inversion a situation is produced at conjugation in which a double loop is formed as shown at *b*. In this the translocated part of the second chromosome is not synapsed and represents an unpaired strand. An actual case of this type as seen under the microscope is shown in Figure 10. At *c* is shown a more complicated situation in which the normal "right arm" of chromosome II is in conjugation with the homologous region inserted as the "pale translocation" into the third chromosome. An actual case of this type is shown in Figure 11. At *d* is shown conjugation further complicated by the fact that the second chromosome is paired, one member of the pair being normal and in part conjugated with chromosome three as in *c* and for the rest conjugated with the deficient second chromosome. This results in synapsis of all homologous parts of the chromosomes in question, and is

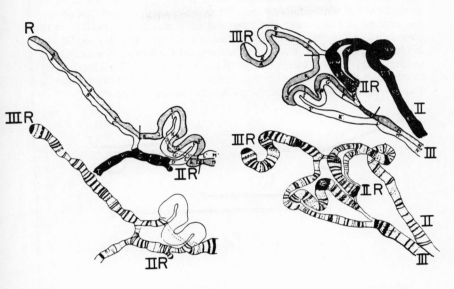

Fig. 11.

Fig. 12.

Fig. 11. This situation is shown diagrammatically in Figure 8c. The lower part of figure 11 shows a drawing of the actual microscopic preparation and above an interpretation of this in diagrammatic form. Here the part translocated from the normal second chromosome is in synapsis with the second chromosome, while the inverted part of the third chromosome is represented by a large loop distinct from the loop due to the pale translocation.

Fig. 12. The lower figure is a drawing of the microscopic preparation and the upper figure is a diagrammatic interpretation of this. The situation is shown in schematic form in Figure 8d. In this two pairs of second and third chromosomes are involved—the third chromosomes, carrying respectively a "CIIIP inversion" and a "pale translocation," and the second chromosomes being normal and "pale deficient." Unless the genetic situation were understood such a figure would seem meaninglessly complicated. It is possible by the use of salivary gland chromosome material to observe under the microscope the types of configuration expected on the basis of genetic presuppositions, and thus to obtain direct observational evidence regarding the correctness of one or another genetic interpretation.

scute 19, where it is certain, on genetic grounds, that no active material was transferred from the second chromosome to the X, although a piece deleted from the X became inserted into the second. In obviation of the difficulty created by the non-mutual character of these insertions and by the consequent inference that three chromosome regions must have met at one point, it has been suggested by Offermann that two of the regions may have happened to lie across one another at first, and that the third strand may then have slid along them until it became caught exactly in the notch made by the crossing of the first two, thus allowing the occurrence of the complicated interchange of the type found. The alternative is to suppose the breaks to have occurred independently of one another, and for the contacts and reunions to have occurred later.

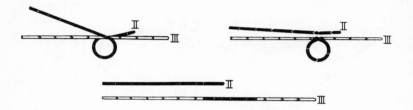

Fig. 13. Suggested mechanism for producing deletions and translocations.

This figure shows a schematic representation of the manner in which a deletion-insertion such as the "pale translocation" might occur. The same result as that here shown might, alternatively, have been produced if the chromosomes had not originally been looped as shown, but had accidentally become broken at the same points as those here indicated (i.e., at the points here represented as intersection points) and had at a later time come into contact and adhered together at their points of fracture, so as to give rise to the new arrangement of segments. Which of the two possible mechanisms is correct we do not yet know.

Bearing on Other Cases and Discussion of Related Problems

The above proof of the insertional character of Pale translocation carries a number of implications which have a bearing on any similar cases supposed to involve side-attachment. For the present case has been the best studied one of this type. Its disproof of side-attachment thus calls very seriously into question the validity of the side-attachment interpretation of any other cases which have only been studied genetically. Genetically it is now not enough to show that a region which *seems* to include the end of the genetic map of one chromosome has become attached to another chromosome in a non-terminal position, since this was true in the case of

Pale. The translocation described by Dobzhansky and Sturtevant as a case of side attachment had, to be sure, the feature that some crossing over occurred between the genes of the translocated piece and those of the homologous region of the normal chromosome; these were of such a nature (including cases where only the originally more terminal genes of the fragment had separated from the other genes, and never cases where only the proximal genes had separated from the others) as to indicate that the piece was attached only at its broken end. It will be recalled, however, that very similar results had also been reported by Bridges in the case of Pale translocation, and must now be interpreted as due to rare double crossing over. That interference is unusually low in the end regions of chromosome II is indicated by results of Spencer. Since, moreover, in just the case of Sturtevant and Dobzhansky here under discussion, the authors state that their numbers were small and irregular and they do not give the exact data concerning their findings, it is hard to see how crucial this evidence was. A reexamination of this case would now be highly desirable.

The cytologically reported cases of branched chromosomes are of course on a different footing. Levan's case seems to be particularly well founded. Yet here too it would seem desirable to pursue the analysis further in several directions: (1) what is the state of the actual chromonema, at the supposed point of branching, as seen in stages when the chromosome is extended? (2) what happens to the branched region during the pachytene and diplotene stages? (3) how stable is the structure through mitosis and in general, through sexual reproduction? It must be realized that there is no genetic precedent here, and that the finding and intensive study, both cytologically and genetically, of actually branched chromonemata, would, for reasons stated in our preliminary discussion, be of exceptional theoretical interest, because of the bearing of such facts upon questions of the structure of the gene. Among these questions are: to what extent may the gene depart from a bipolar structure, and how may such a departure interfere with the gene in its self-duplication and other normal operations.

We already know, of course, that the genes which form the natural free termini of the chromosomes act as unipolar. There is reason, however, based on certain translocations being studied by us, to believe that in some cases at least this unipolarity covers a latent or potential bipolarity, since a portion of the chromonema derived from elsewhere may apparently become attached to the very end of a chromosome. The converse of this seems also to occur occasionally, though very rarely: namely, that an interstitial gene, with bipolar attachment, becomes terminal and thus unipolar. In the case of loci within or bordering on the inert region, the latter sort of change occurs much more frequently (results of Levit, quoted by Muller, and since corroborated in experiments of the latter).

A further fact of interest concerning the two attachment poles of the gene is that they are of the same general nature, that is, not opposite in sign or having a "lock and key" relationship. This is shown by the occurrence of inversions, for if the two poles of a gene had different signs ("north" and "south"), then, at the points of breakage and reattachment of the inversion, north pole would have had to become joined to north pole, and south to south, so to speak.

Though the gene is so minute, it must ultimately be considered on a much magnified scale, and it must be recognized that it has not only poles but different "faces," the properties of which must certainly differ from one another. There is already reason to believe, from the two-by-two method of conjugation which chromatids usually follow at synapsis, that a specific face exercises a specific kind of attracting force, and that the chromatids probably conjugate face to face. Otherwise it would seem that they would be able to conjugate in indefinite succession. In the salivary glands, where the chromatids do practically line up in indefinite succession, in the curved surface of the periphery of a cylinder, it has been noticed by Muller that there is nevertheless some indication that, at times at least, they are grouped in pairs within this surface. This would mean that, besides the specific attraction exerted directly between the faces of major attractive force, there is (especially in Diptera) considerable residual attraction, exerted in the same plane; the latter must operate upon (or, at any rate, through) the "back" surfaces (i.e., those opposite to the surfaces of strongest attraction).

Presumably the most direct attraction operates between the mother gene and the daughter gene that is constructed in the image of the former. Strange to say, this does not seem to result in a mirror image, for if it did there would exist allelomorphs, and in fact whole chromosomes, of two opposite signs. In conjugation, these would react differentially with one another—especially in triploids. The lack of such a distinction shows that, if face-to-face attraction is really the rule, then there can be no differentiation of the attractive forces, or of their determining structures, in a direction transverse to the chromonema (at right angles to the longitudinal and the front-to-back directions).

Although such questions are not directly touched on by the present work, which concerns only the "polar" connections, i.e., those between adjacent non-homologous genes in the same chromonema, nevertheless this whole complex of problems is closely interrelated, and they must eventually be considered in connection with one another, if we are to arrive at an adequate understanding of gene structure.

Summary

1. Proof has been obtained that, in the case of Pale translocation, the fragment which was removed from the second chromosome did

not become attached to the side of the third chromosome, as had been supposed, but became inserted within the length of the third chromosome without any disturbance of the principle of linear gene arrangement.

2. The fragment of the second chromosome in question was not a terminal fragment, but was deleted out of the second chromosome, near the end, by means of two breaks of the second chromosome; the very end segment became again attached to the remainder of the chromosome. The deleted piece became inserted into the third chromosome, in inverted position, at a point where the latter had become broken. Thus attachment took place only between broken ends ("surfaces of fracture").

3. The observations of the chromosomes in the salivary glands, which enabled proof of the above points to be obtained, showed conjugation (varying in degree) between all homologous regions of the normal and rearranged chromosomes, resulting in the complex figures to be expected for such rearrangements.

4. Despite the transfer of material from chromosome II to III, there was no perceptible reciprocal transfer of material from III to II, as happens in double crossing over. This indicates that at precisely the point of breakage three chromosome regions met one another. The latter condition seems to require the assumption of the catching of strands at points of crossing of other strands; as Offermann suggests, such an effect might be mechanical. Alternatively, we should have to suppose that breaks occurred independently of contacts, and that reattachment occurred subsequently.

5. The cytological evidence presented extends the hitherto known limits of the second chromosome, by proving the existence of a section of it lying to the right of the rightmost gene hitherto known (balloon).

6. The crossovers which had seemed to show that the translocated fragment was attached at only one end must therefore have in reality been double crossovers in which both points of crossing over occurred between the two points of attachment of the fragment. As the latter are not more than eight units apart (when in the normal chromosome), these double crossovers span a much shorter distance than was hitherto thought possible for double crossovers in any regions lying entirely on one side of a spindle fibre attachment.

7. In view of the fact that the genetic evidence for side-attachment in the present case appeared to be stronger than that in any other known case, great caution should be exercised in drawing conclusions of side-attachment in other cases that have been investigated only by genetic methods and show similar peculiarities in their heredity. At the same time, apparent cytological cases deserve especially searching investigation, since any which really involved a branched structure would illustrate new possibilities of gene behavior that might be significant in considerations of gene structure.

8. Various problems concerned with the polar attachments and the facial attractions between genes are discussed.

THE REMAKING OF CHROMOSOMES*

Dr. H. J. Muller

Institute of Animal Genetics, University of Edinburgh

I. The Problem of Structural Change in Chromosomes

It is a biological commonplace that species differ in the number of their chromosomes, and in the shapes and sizes of their chromosomes, and that even individuals of the same species may differ somewhat in these respects. For example, Metz's studies of chromosome configuration in species of Drosophilidae showed differences of all these kinds. Occasionally, in passing from one species to another, a given chromosome would seem to have changed its size; in rare instances it might change its shape; oftener two rod-like chromosomes would seem to have fused into one V, or *vice versa*; and sometimes a chromosome would seem to have disappeared entirely.

Until the last decade, the number and kinds of steps involved in the formation of any of these observed chromosome differences could only be guessed at for their actual origination had very rarely been observed. Cytology was in fact very vague even about the nature of the observed differences, for the minuter details of chromosome structure were as yet rarely a subject of sufficiently accurate comparative analysis. Thus we could not tell, in the comparison of Drosophila species, whether the shape change, involving as it did a difference in spindle fibre locus, or "centromere" as Darlington calls it, together with the disappearance of the old one, or in the shift of just this locus from one place to another, or in some sort of rearrangement of a larger part of the chromosome, containing the centromere. Again, we could not tell whether the small chromosome had really gone out of existence when it seemed to disappear, or whether it had somehow been swallowed up in some other part of the chromatin complex. And we could not tell, in the change of rods to V or *vice versa*, whether or not the process was unidirectional, whether it involved mere fusion of whole chromosomes, or mere breakage; whether the centromeres themselves fused, or somehow became split, or were formed *de novo*, or whether one of them, or a whole chromosome region containing them, became lost or reduplicated.

The Collecting Net, 1938, 8: 182-95, 198. This article was the basis of a lecture given at the Marine Biological Laboratory on September 1, 1938.

A few cases—that had necessarily been imperfectly analyzed—were, to be sure, known chiefly in Drosophila, which had led to a number of rather crudely mechanical views regarding the nature of chromosome changes. Among these was the belief that chromosomes might undergo simple breakage, perhaps with loss of the fibreless ("acentric") piece or pieces, but with survival of the other one at any rate. This was supposed to have occurred in "Plexate," in Stern's Y″, and in "Pale" translocation. It was also thought that the detached fragments thus formed might sometimes become attached to the ends as well as to the sides of other chromosomes, or of other parts of the same chromosome. Supposed cases in point were Stern's XY′, "Pale," and Sturtevant's supposedly terminal inversions. And it was further believed that bodily fusions of one whole chromosome to another one might occur, as in attached X's. On the basis of such interpretations, as well as on Sturtevant's more accurately worked out conception of inversions—which, however, still included the idea of terminally attached inversions, as above noted—Drosophila workers and others attempted to picture the changes of chromosome structure that had occurred in evolution, and that were occasionally found distinguishing individuals. In the earlier X-ray work too (1927-1930) the author must plead guilty of attempting to picture the chromosome changes found in largely the same terms.

While, as we shall see, time has shown that these earlier interpretations were wrong in certain features, they were nevertheless right in some very important essentials, and especially insofar as they tried to make their picture conform to the principle long ago laid down by McClung, chiefly on the basis of his comprehensive studies in Orthoptera, "that numerical variations involve only rearrangements of the persistent chromatin aggregate" (cited from McClung, 1921). One important principle that is included in this general idea of the continuity of the component parts as such, is McClung's (1914) concept of the persistence of the centromere, or acromite as he terms it, and of the necessity of the latter for chromosome persistence. But the work of the past decade had made it possible to extend this principle of the preservation of the individuality of chromosome parts in some rather unexpected ways, so as to bring under one general scheme all the different types of alteration of chromosomes that had been separately dealt with in the earlier work under the various special conceptions above noted.

These more recent advances in our knowledge of chromosome evolution have come about through the convergence of a number of lines of investigation. For one thing, the X-ray technique has provided a wealth of material illustrating the origination of multitudes of chromosomal changes, of diverse sorts. In Drosophila, the more exact analysis of these findings has followed, on the one hand, from the elaboration of more refined genetic methods and, on the other hand, from the amazing technique of observation of the chromosomes in the salivary glands inaugurated by Painter. Among the cases so investigated there have been enough of spontaneous origin (including intraspecific differences found in nature) to show that the same principles apply to them as to the products of irradiation. Meanwhile, too, the improvement of cytogenetic method and interpretation in plant material, due especially to the work of Stadler and McClintock and of Darlington and his school, following upon the earlier advances by Belling and Blakeslee, have led to a series of findings in maize, Tradescantia, Datura and other plant forms that are in some essential ways similar to those of the Drosophila work. But as there still remain some important differences, susceptible of alternative interpretations, I shall base my present discussion mainly upon the Drosophila findings.

If we should pass in review, in detail, all the findings concerning chromosome rearrangements which have been made in Drosophila in the past decade, we should see that all of them unite in supporting the proposition that structural changes in chromosomes consist, in general, not of simple breakages or fusions, by themselves, but of *exchanges* in the linear attachments of sections of chromosomes. That is, as in crossing over, a section of chromatin becomes disconnected at some point from the section to which it previously was attached, and, connected, at the same point, to a point on another section at which the latter likewise has become (or becomes) disconnected from its previous association. Thus at least two breakages are necessary, and, as in crossing over, there must be reattachment, and this must occur between the broken ends, not between originally free ends, or between a broken and a free end, or between any end and a free end, or between any end and the side of a chromosome (giving a branched structure). Unlike what occurs in crossing over, however, the two points of interchange are not homologous, and the process has therefore been referred to as "illegitimate crossing over," a term used by both Darlington (1932) and the author (1932) independently. (Whether or not the process involves touching or close juxtaposition of the parts broken, previous to their breakage, as in crossing over, is a matter which we shall consider later.) Since the time when Stadler and the author put forward this principle as a general interpretation of structural changes in chromosomes (at the Genetics Congress, 1932), the evidence for it, in Drosophila at least, has become far stronger, and the various types of apparent exception to it there have received their explanations in accordance with it, especially when it is considered in connection with the interesting facts concerning the so-called "inert" or chromocentral regions which have come to light in recent years.

II. Special Properties of the So-Called "Inert Regions."

The realization that there were special regions of the chromosome complex in which, for a given length of chromosome as seen at mitosis, there were relatively few active genes, goes back to the evidence, to which Metz and I long ago called attention (see Muller, 1914), that the Y chromosome of Drosophila, though apparently large, acts as though virtually "empty."[1] The cause of the apparent emptiness was only in part understood in 1914, however, as it was not realized that any other factor entered in than that of degeneration by mutation pressure under the influence of permanent heterozygosity. Much later, Painter and I (1932) unexpectedly found that the X chromosome has a homologous "inert region," of similar apparent emptiness, and both Heitz and we noted indications that the other chromosomes might have similar regions in the neighborhood of their centromeres.

Our findings on deleted X-chromosomes (1929, 1932), and on translocated autosomes and Y chromosomes, and Oliver's results on inversions of the X-chromosomes, led us, further, to the conclusion that breakage occurred in these "inert regions" with a frequency as great, for a given length of chromosome as seen at mitosis, as in the so-called "active" regions. This high breakability has also been found in the studies of Patterson *et al* (1934) on translocations. It was for this reason that we were at first inclined to regard the actual chromonema in the "inert regions" as being as long, for a given length of mitotic chromosome, as that in active regions.

However, in a review of studies carried on in collaboration with Painter and with Gershenson, it appeared (Muller and Gershenson, 1935) that these breakages in the "inert region" had occurred only at two or three specific points, so far as the chromosome as seen at mitosis was concerned. That is, the regions between these points must be regarded as large genetically indivisible "blocks," produced by individual genes, and so the number of genes and the actual length of breakable chromonema in these so-called "inert regions" that include blocks must be far smaller for a given length of mitotic chromosome, than in active regions. This was in itself a clue to their apparent inertness. But, this being the case, within a given length of this chromonema, or for a given number of genes outside of the "blocks," breakage must occur with far greater frequency in the "inert" than in the "active" regions of the chromosomes. The above conclusions in turn agreed with and explained the finding of Painter (1933, 1934) that in the salivary gland chromosome the "inert regions" were apparently absent, modified by the later finding by Prokofyeva and myself (1935) that they were indeed represented, but only by very short regions, containing about one or two dozen faint bands (and hence probably somewhat more genes) located within and near the chromocenter.

In fact, the chromocenter itself consists, as Prokofyeva first showed (1935), merely of these parts of the chromosomes clumped together, and it has a structure essentially like that of the rest of the chromosomes. It had been far more difficult than the rest to disentangle only because of the fact that these regions of all the chromosomes tend to conjugate into one mass and because in these regions, as a secondary consequence, the disc structure is less clearly arranged and there is a lesser aggregation of nucleic acid. This conjugation of these regions of different chromosomes indicated an at least partial homology between them, and further evidence for this was obtained in the finding of occasional crossing over between the X and both arms of the Y chromosome, when present in the female (Philip, 1934; Neuhaus, 1936, and in the presence of bobbed in both arms of the Y as well as in the X (Neuhaus). Especially pertinent in this connection is Gershenson's recent finding (1936, unpublished) that the chromocentral region of the X, as exemplified by an X chromosome with the "active" portion deleted, tends to segregate from the single fourth chromosome in the meiosis of "haplo-fourth" individuals.

It is tempting to think that this homology is caused, in part at least, by a common derivation of the regions near the centromeres of different chromosomes, a derivation not inordinately remote in time because of the occurrence, in evolution, of transplantations of whole chromosome arms from one of these regions to another, as explained below. At any rate, there is evidence that the genes which do exist in such a chromosome region of any individual chromosome pair are on the whole more dispensable than those in ordinary regions, i.e. their loss, as well as their duplication, causes less functional disturbance, just as would be expected if their functions were being in part subserved by similar genes in the corresponding regions of other chromosomes. But, whatever the explanation, it seems clear that this fact of their comparative dispensability is of importance in the alteration of the chromosome number in evolution.

The chromosome regions in question are thus seen to be peculiar not only in respect to their including a centromere but also in a number of other respects. Chief among these are the following. (1) Their inclusion of the large "blocks" seen at metaphase, rich in nucleic acid, and each dependent only on one gene. (The function of the blocks is as yet unknown, but Gershenson's studies indicate their relative unimportance in segregation.) (2) The mutual and multiple attraction of these genes for one another, no matter what chromosome they lie in, with resultant formation, in resting stages, of a "chromocenter," with its various morphological and physiological peculiarities. (3) The high tendency of these regions to breakage, which includes, as we (Muller, Belgovsky and Raffel, 1936, 1937) have recently found, a tendency to two or more breaks near to one another, with minute rearrangement, as well as to gross rearrangement. Moreover, it extends to neighboring regions, that have, through structural rearrangement, come to lie near the originally chromocentral ones. This tendency to breakage is possibly a resultant of the other peculiarities connected with multiple attraction. (4) Their relative dispensibility in cell functioning, above dis-

as the X and the fourth in *D. melanogaster*. As for their appearance at metaphase, we could hardly expect the centromere, being so near the end as the salivary chromosome work shows it to be, to result in a chromosome distinctly different from a rod, as seen at mitosis. In fact, however, the minute observations of mitotic chromosomes carried out by Prokofyeva and by Heitz have strongly suggested a non-terminal, that is, a sub-terminal, position for it. And agreeing with this is Prokofyeva's observation of small "heads," as she calls them, on the right distal ends of both the X and the fourth chromosomes in the salivary glands. These "heads" resemble somewhat the left distal ends, being not as thoroughly chromocentral as the region slightly to the left of them, which she supposes to contain the centromere itself.

This conception of the existence of another terminal chromocentral region, beyond the centromere of the apparent rods, and having the high breakability characteristic of other chromocentral regions, also affords a ready explanation, consistent with the other known facts regarding chromosome rearrangements, for the frequency with which, in translocations, sections of other chromosomes can be attached beyond the centromere of the X and fourth chromosome, to give rise to chromosomes that are obviously J or V shaped. Thus Panshin, in 1937, and Stone, in 1938, have both found "mottled" fragments, from the left end of the X, attached to the right of the centromere of the fourth chromosome, to give tiny medially attached chromosomes, both arms of which were approximately the size of the normal fourth. Similar attachments of pieces of other chromosomes to the right of the centromere of the X, forming a J or V shaped chromosome, were reported by Muller and Painter in 1929 and have since been seen frequently. Evidently what happened in such cases was the breaking off of the dispensible terminal region lying to the right of the centromere, and its replacement by the larger section from the other chromosome, so as to give a structure which now is obviously non-terminally attached, and which bears witness to the originally more cryptic sub-terminal nature of the attachment in the so-called "rod" chromosome. A rigorous proof of this point awaits a more exact salivary analysis of the chromocentral regions in question in the translocated chromosomes, as compared with the normal ones. Meanwhile, however, the cases certainly do not stand opposed to our general conception of chromosome structure and of chromosome alteration.

III.   Types of Conformation of Chromosome Rearrangements.

Despite the differences above noted between the properties of the chromocentral and free regions of the chromosomes, there is no reason to believe that they differ in regard to those fundamental features of chromosome make-up which determine the mechanism whereby structural rearrangements take place. That is, both regions undergo structural change by means of *exchanges* of linear connections at given points, involving both breakage and reattachment, only these exchanges occur more readily, or at least more frequently, in the chromocentral regions than elsewhere. And, as we shall see, the differences between the regions do affect to some extent the subsequent fate of the reconstituted chromosomes.

Accepting, for purposes of exposition at least, this principle of exchange, let us now see what different kinds of alterations it will result in, according to the topographical accidents of how many points of breakage there are, where in the chromatin they lie, and just which broken ends become attached to one another. We may consider first the situation in the simplest possible cases, that is, when there are only two points of breakage. The first case we may examine here is that in which these two points of breakage lie in the same chromosome. In this particular case, if the broken ends of the two distal sections each unite with that broken end of the interstitial section which was originally attached to the other distal section, an *inversion* results. If the breaks were to one side of the centromere, the inversion may be termed *"paracentric,"* and it will be noted that the proportions of the two arms, and hence the general shape of the chromosome as seen at mitosis, is not changed. But if the breaks included the centromere between them, being *"pericentric,"* the mitotic chromosome will have the relative sizes of its two arms altered, except in the special case in which the two distal sections are sensibly equal in size. The union of the broken ends of the two distal sections with one another results in the formation of a *deleted* chromosome, while the two ends of the interstitial section unite together to form a ring.[3] In the case of paracentric breaks the ring includes no centromeres and hence cannot be transported at mitosis and is eventually lost, while in the case of pericentric breaks it is the other fragment which is "acentric," and becomes lost, while the ring has a centromere (being "monocentric") and may persist for a time. Rings tend to be lost eventually, however, because of the abnormal chromosome types that, for purely mechanical reasons, they give rise to at crossing over (see L. V. Morgan, 1932) and, in some plants, also at mitosis (McClintock, 1933).

The breaks may be near together, so that the inversion or deletion formed is minute. In fact, a curve showing the frequencies of breaks different distances apart, in relation to the frequencies to be expected on a random distribution of breaks, would undoubtedly show a considerable peak for breaks that were close together—a fact the cause of which we shall inquire into later.

As a kind of opposite to the cases of minute rearrangement we have another, also disproportionately abundant class of cases, in which one of the breaks occurred in a chromocentral region, say, that next to the centromere—and the other break occurred either in a so-called "active" region (better to say, "free" region) or in another chromocentral region—say, that at the end of a chromosome. Here then there is a tendency for the included interstitial sections to be larger than expected on a random distribution of breaks, and not infrequently nearly the whole arm of a V-shaped chromosome, or nearly the whole of a rod-like chromosome becomes deleted or inverted.

Continuing our perusal of types of chromosome rearrangement, we may next consider what happens when the two breaks occur in different, non-homologous chromosomes. The process is mutual translocation, and the resultants can survive in the case in which those fragments have united which are complementary with respect to possession of a centromere, but not in other cases, in which only acentric and dicentric parts are formed.[4] Since breakage occurs oftener in chromocentral regions, especially centromeric ones, there are not infrequently exchanges of whole arms between V-shaped chromosomes, and exchanges between one arm of a V and the main arm (that is, virtually the whole) of a rod-shaped chromosome. There are also exchanges between two rods, resulting in one large V and one minute chromocentral V, the loss of which latter could probably be tolerated without difficulty.

Any change involving an increase of chromosome number, such as the change of a V to two rods, is more complicated, except where the Y chromosome serves to supply the extra centromere. For in other cases a disadvantageous amount of duplication of other regions would be entailed unless, secondarily, they were removed by deletion. For this reason the Y has probably served more often as "anchorage" to various chromosomes, in their process of origination as independently attached chromosomes (as proposed by Muller and Painter, 1932). This situation would of course work towards an increase in the homology of the chromocentral regions of different chromosomes.

There is also the equivalent of mutual translocation, occurring between homologous or sister chromosomes. The result here, when viable at all, is usually the formation of a deficiency, equivalent to a deletion, in one reconstituted chromosome, and of a duplication, or as Bridges aptly terms it, a "repeat," in the other one. The duplicated section immediately follows its prototype, and the two sections have their genes lying in the same direction, as in the well-known bar-eye duplication. I am provisionally terming this type of repeat a "joined tandem." Unless they are rather small, duplications, by causing an "overdose" of some genes in relation to others, give individuals with low or even zero survival powers, especially when they are homozygous. Small duplications, however, becoming established in a species, can eventually increase its evolutionary potentialities by providing it with more genes which, though at first alike, later become different through mutation. This is in fact *the* method of increase in gene number.

When, as not very infrequently happens even in spontaneous rearrangements, three breaks occur at once, the possibilities are considerably more numerous. Three breaks in the same chromosome, in addition to giving us obvious combinations of the changes obtained from two breaks, such as two adjoining inversions, or deletion and inversion, also give us another type. In this a section, large or small, has, as it were, been excised or deleted from one place, the broken ends on either side of which are joined together again, and inserted into another position, either in the original or opposite direction (this is a "shift").

When two of the breaks are in one chromosome and the third in another chromosome, a piece may be deleted by the two breaks and inserted into the space made by the break in the other chromosome, thus constituting an "insertional translocation." Here the translocation of material is not mutual, but unidirectional, purely from the former chromosome to the latter. As opposite extremes of proportions for such cases we may mention the case of scute 19, in which a piece consisting of only about four genes became deleted from the X chromosome and inverted into a long autosome (the second), and on the other hand, translocation X-IV1 (or "W 13"), in which a piece comprising about half the X, and cut off, on its right end, within the chromocentral region, became inserted into the tiny fourth chromosome. Other modes of reattachment, following three breaks, of which two are in one chromosome, can give mutual translocations, in which there is an inversion or deletion adjoining the point of chromosome exchange.

When the two chromosomes engaging in triple-break rearrangements are homologous the piece which was inserted constitutes a repetition of some part already in the recipient chromosome, and so it results in the presence of a "repeat," either (1) shifted away from the original position of such a section, or (2) adjoining the latter if two of the breaks in the homologues were at identical points (owing perhaps to a chromosome breaking before its division), or (3) within the latter. The two like sections may then be either in inverted position with respect to each other, forming a "reflexion," or facing in the same direction, forming a "tandem."

Finally if the three breaks are all in different chromosomes, if no two broken ends that were formerly attached together rejoin as before, and if the fragments that unite are in each case complementary with respect to possession of a centromere, a type which may be termed a "triple mutual translocation" results.

Virtually all of the viable types of two-break as well as three-break rearrangements above referred to have been found. As for the different types of more complicated rearrangements producible with more than three breaks, it would take us too far afield to follow them through here. But some of these too have been found, as, for example, Stone's six-break "translocation 12," in which, for one thing, the life of an acentric ring, formed by deletion, was saved by having it broken at another point than that at which it had become joined together, and having these broken ends serve for its insertion, as a straight piece, into the space formed by the break of another chromosome (the fourth). At the same time this ring had a minute piece (containing the locus of "cut wing") deleted from out of it, at an adjoining place, and inserted into still another chromosome (the second). Nor should we take time here to note the various "aneuploid" types, that is, types having excesses or deficiencies of chromosome sections, or both, formed secondarily in later generations by crossing over or chromosome recombination occurring in germ cells heterozygous for one or more rearrangments. As before noted, such individuals with excesses, and especially those with deficiencies of genes, tend to be inviable, especially when homozygous, except in special cases.

In presenting the evidence, six years ago, for the proposition that structural changes in chromosomes, in Drosophila at any rate, were, in general, caused by exchanges, conforming to the principles mentioned above, I had to make the qualification that a small number of cases did exist which seemed to disobey these principles. The cases then outstanding have now all been satisfactorily explained. Some (like scute 19) then thought to be terminal translocations have been found to be insertions. So have the supposed cases of attachment to the side of a chromosome, outstanding among which was "Pale translocation." Other cases, apparently terminal translocations or inversions, have been found to involve breaks near the end. The formation of attached X's, as well as their detachment, are seen not to be mere fusions of rods into a V and *vice versa*, but cases of crossing over with a Y chromosome. Ring X-chromosome formation is found to involve the loss of a minute amount of terminal chromatin, thus enabling the sticking together to occur. And the apparent cases of simple breakage, with loss of the terminal fragment of certain special chromosomes, have recently been shown by Belgovsky, Prokofyeva, Raffel and myself to represent minute rearrangements of the chromocentral region, of which a considerable amount exists here in a subterminal position. A paper of Raffel's at the present meeting gives further evidence of this.

Meanwhile, a very few new cases have appeared, that have been interpreted as terminal deficiencies, not involving reattachment of other chromatin at the breakage points, and certain others that have been interpreted as simple fusion of unbroken rod-shaped chromosomes, at their proximal, that is, centromere-bearing ends. But, considering all the deficiencies examined, it is to be expected that two or three of them would have involved distal breaks in the terminal chromocentral regions, so close to the end that the presence in them of the terminal gene could not be demonstrated. For, as Prokofyeva and I have shown, single genes are at or below the limit of vision, particularly in such regions, and breakage is especially frequent there. On the other hand, an active search which we conducted for such cases failed to yield any, while giving numerous cases of obvious exchange of connections. And as for the apparent fusions of rods, they fit very well into the scheme of mutual translocation, involving breakage in the centromeric chromocentral region of both chromosomes, the breakage in one chromosome being at the base of the long arm, and in the other in the rudimentary arm. The minute size of the latter, in the mitotic chromosome, is no objection here, in view of the known high tendency to breakage of minute regions of this kind.

We cannot, of course, rigorously prove the universal negative, that no cases contrary to our principles occur. But, in view of the considerations given, and our experience with the earlier cases that challenged us, it seems better, as William of Occam would have agreed, not to involve further principles to account for structural chromosome changes, until really cogent evidence has appeared for the inadequacy of those already found.

IV.   On the Mechanism of Rearrangement.

What is the order of events when the exchange between non-homologous chromosome parts takes place? Nine years ago two general possibilities with regard to the mechanism of chromosome change had presented themselves that seemed to be alternative (Painter and Muller, 1929). Two chromosome parts that were to undergo rearrangement with one another might come into contact, perhaps even fuse first, at the points where they were to undergo breakage, and then break, the breaks thus having a common cause, as must be true in crossing over. Or they might break first, perhaps independently of one another, and the broken ends, being somehow adhesive, might later find and fuse with the parts which they were to be attached to. Six years ago Stadler advocated the latter view, but I opposed it, in favor of the former one, on the ground that the rearrangements produced by radiation were not proportional to the square of the dosage of the latter, as they should be if they were the product of two independent breakages, the chance of each of which, singly, was proportional to the dosage itself. Today, for several reasons, I believe that there was probably truth in both views.

It is well known, since the work of Oliver, Hanson, Timoféef-Ressovsky, and many others, that gene mutations vary in frequency directly with the dosage of radiation, that is, with the number of ions formed, regardless of the time distribution of these ions or their type of distribution in space (as determined by the hardness of the rays). And this furnishes good evidence for the conclusion that the individual mutations are caused by individual ionizations, that happened to be favorably situated. If rearrangements of chromosome sections followed the same law, a single rearrangement, with its two or more breaks, would likewise have to be judged to depend on one favorable ionization, that acted as common cause to both breaks, and so the breaks would have been somehow connected. This could hardly have occurred unless both points of breakage had at the time lain near together. But, as above mentioned, if the breaks were independent, each depending on at least one separate ionization, the coincidence of two breaks, necessary to allow an exchange of the broken ends, would vary in frequency as the square of the dosage.

The indications from the earlier work (especially Oliver's in 1930 and 1932) were that rearrangements did not vary in frequency as markedly as the square of the dosage; hence the conclusion which I first drew. Yet Oliver's results did suggest a higher rate of variation of frequency than that of the dosage itself (i.e., than its first power), so further experiments were called for. The first of these, carried out in Berlin in 1933, are presented herewith. It will be seen that these two-break deletions vary in frequency at a rate greater than the first power of the dosage, and yet less than the square. This seemed hard to believe, but Belgovsky in Moscow has tested out the same question on an extensive scale, using translocations, and has consistently gotten the same result. For the doses used, the rearrangements vary in frequency about as the $3/2$ power of the dosage. And Berg, Panshin and Borisoff, in Leningrad, have found the same thing for inversions. Confirmations have now been obtained by Dubinin's co-workers also.

Of the various possible explanations of this peculiar result, I incline to the view that some of the two-break rearrangements are the product of two separate breakages, caused by two separate ionizations—in these cases the broken ends must find and fuse with each other later, and that others—a comparable number—depend on two breakages both of which resulted, secondarily, from the same original ionization. Where is Occam's razor now, it may be asked. The answer is that there are further reasons in support of the existence of both of the processes postulated.

In support of Stadler's thesis that breakage may occur without contact of the parts concerned in reunion, it is now possible to apply the result of a test which I proposed in 1932, as to the mode of exchange of the broken ends. If, as in crossing over, chromosome threads make cross-connections only with the parts which they have been touching, at the time of breakage, then if the broken end which we shall call A_1, lying to the left of a certain breakage point, A, becomes joined with the broken end which we shall call B_2, lying to the right of breakage point B, the segment of thread at which these breakages occurred must have been in contact here, and hence the broken end, A_2, lying to the right of breakage point A, can undergo union only with B_1, which lies to the left of breakage point B. That is, the relation must be a reciprocal one. A_2 cannot, in that case, unite with a different broken end, call it C_1, that was formed by a third breakage, unless we suppose that the third piece of chromosome thread also had touched the other two, and not only touched them, but touched them at exactly the point where they themselves touched one another. This requires a precise three-way cross.

Although Offermann has, to be sure, suggested that such a triple contact might be produced by the mechanical process of the third thread sliding along until it came to rest in the notch of the other two, it would seem far-fetched to explain many cases in this fashion. And all the varied types of triple-break rearrangements—of which not a few have been found—would require this same explanation. Moreover, Dubinin and his co-workers have found that even in rearrangements derived from more than three breakages the type of exchange is apt to be such as would require, on the contact-breakage scheme, the meeting of four or more threads at exactly the same point. Hence he has given up this hypothesis of accounting for rearrangement, which he had earlier championed.

The independence (or comparative independence?) of the frequency of rearrangement in relation to the time over which the total treatment is protracted, in mature sperm—a point on which we are now engaged in obtaining better evidence—likewise argues for the breakage-first scheme. For it is difficult plausibly to explain how the effects of the past ionization can be stored up for weeks, so as to influence the effect of a later ionization (as the $3/2$ power rule implies in such cases), unless we suppose that each breakage, occurring at the time of the given ionization that produces it, is saved up as such until, after fertilization, the chromosomes, now in a different state, have a chance to undergo union at their broken ends.

In plants, at least, more direct evidence has been obtained by McClintock and Rhoades in the finding that, when a ring chromosome becomes broken, by the opposed pulling of spindle fibres, its parts tend to reunite again at their broken ends, and they have observed reunion of fragments of dicentric inverted chromosomes that were broken at meiosis. (Unfortunately for our tests, these causes do not lead to breakage in Drosophila). Moreover, direct observation of X-rayed cells in various organisms has shown that fragments are formed by breakage induced by the radiation; these would furnish material for the process in question.

Provisionally at least, then, we may adopt the "breakage first" conception as at least one mechanism of exchange. Further tests of it can and should be made, however. For instance, if it applies to a part of the rearrangements and not all, the curve of their frequency will more nearly approximate the first power of the dosage at low dosages and the second power at high dosages. Moreover, in that case, multiple-break rearrangements should bear certain characteristic frequency relations to one another and to two-break rearrangements, at different dosages. The latter is a matter which we are now endeavoring to test.

If we admit that some at least of the breakages occur before contact of the threads, there are probably cases in which the broken ends fail ever to find one another before the acentric fragment becomes lost at the ensuing mitosis. In that case the centric portion

TABLE 1

Relation of Frequency of Deletions to Damage of X-rays
(Data of Muller, Koerner and M. Vogt, 1933)
Cross 1: Rayed sc[8] Bw[a] ♂♂ X y w ♀♀ (X's separate)
Cross 2: Rayed sc[8] Bw[a] ♂♂ X y w f ♀♀ (X's attached)

EXP. NO.	CROSS	DOSE IN r (REL. VALUE ACCURATE WITHIN SAME EXPERIMENT)	TOTAL OFFSPRING FROM Y-BEARING SPERM	OFFSPRING FROM X-BEARING SPERM CARRYING			LARGE DELETIONS "EXPECTED" FOR HIGHER DOSES
				NO DETECTABLE ALTERATION	MISC. ABBERATIONS	LARGE DELETIONS FOUND	
1 to 3	1	4000	10,624	10,989½	38½	24	18
		2000	19,109½	18,503½	25	16	
		control	16,469	17,330	2	1	
4	2	4000	2,134	1,529	4	27	17½
		2000	3,642	2,969½	2½	17	
		control	3,257	3,040	0	2	
5 & 6	2	6000	2,629	3,642	9	42	26½
		1500	13,132	15,469	5	33	
		control	6,949	7,408	0	0	
Summary	For higher doses	4000–6000	15,387	16,160½	51½	93*	62*
	For lower doses	1500–2000	35,874½	37,942	32½	66	
	Controls		26,675	29,478	2	1	
(total flies: 161,753)			77,936½	83,580½	86	160	

*Difference = approximately 3½ times its probable error.
(Fractional figures are derived from mosaics.)

("Expectation" for higher dose calculated from results for lower dose on basis of frequency being directly proportional to dose in each experiment.)

399

would have the opportunity to continue as a fragment, formed by simple breakage, and without having received a complementary fragment, by exchange, in substitution for the one it had lost. But, as we have seen, there is no sound evidence for the occurrence of such products of simple breakage among the descendants of irradiated individuals. Hence, if we accept the breakage-first hypothesis, we must infer that fragments, even though provided with a centromere, die if their ends are broken ends, i.e., if their ends do not consist of natural termini, derived from the same or another chromosome.

The conclusion can therefore be drawn, if the breakage-first hypothesis is valid, that the terminal gene must have a special function, that of sealing the end of the chromosome, so to speak, and that for some reason a chromosome cannot persist indefinitely without having its ends thus "sealed." This gene may accordingly be distinguished by a special term, the "telomere" (applied by myself and Darlington, and by Haldane, independently). The telomere is unipolar, being attached to only one other gene—that on the "proximal" side of it, and thus distinguished from all the other, bipolar genes, which are attached to two genes, one on each side. Bipolar genes, then, cannot be made into properly functional unipolar ones by the simple expedient of tearing them loose from their connections on one side. This idea is, it will be seen, merely an extension of the more general one of McClung previously referred to, of the persistence of the individuality, and of the peculiar properties, of the different separable components of the chromatin aggregate, even in the face of extensive rearrangements of these parts.

It may now be asked, why do we still cling to the contact-breakage scheme of rearrangement at all? The answer is, first, because the frequency-dosage relationship for rearrangements, after all, does not follow the typical square rule, and so necessitates some kind of modification of the scheme of merely independent breaks (or reunions). Second, it seems—though this point has not been rigorously proved—as though there were relatively too many rearrangements, such as small deficiencies, which involve pairs of breaks very close together, than can well be accounted for on the idea that all breaks occur independently of one another, even though we supplement this with the very probably postulate that when the breaks have occurred near together they are more likely to undergo an exchanged attachment to one another than when they were far apart. Third, and most important, there is evidence that pairs of breaks very close together obey a rule for the relation of their frequency to dosage which is the same as that of the so-called "gene mutations." That is, their frequency seems to be simply proportional to (the first power of) the dosage. This indicates that the occurrence of each such minute rearrangement, including *both* its breaks, is a result of but *one* effective ionization. For a large proportion of the lethal changes produced by radiation which were formerly regarded

bilities), in reality the effects of the positional changes. Various studies have shown, moreover, that not only the gene immediately contiguous to a breakage point may be thus affected, but also one somewhat further away, although usually the effect fades out at comparatively small distances. Nevertheless, as a result of it, various genes in the neighborhood of a given one are brought into one functional union, and the various groups of functionally related genes no doubt overlap one another throughout the length of the chromosome. Nevertheless, for any one given effect, such as "scute," the chromosome by no means acts as a whole, since only closely neighboring genes take part in the relationship in question.

It will be seen that, on account of this position effect, chromosomal rearrangements in themselves cause phenotypic changes. And so, quite apart from their effect on the recombination of genes in heredity, they will not be completely neutral in respect to natural selection. In perhaps half the cases, however, the changes seem slight, and to these the mechanism termed "drift" by Wright will apply to some extent, in cases like paracentric inversions, in which the productivity of the heterozygote is not reduced. In plants, strange to say, cases of position effect have not yet been discovered, unless a recent finding reported by McClintock be a case in point.

We shall not venture here to discuss the possible causes of the position effect—whether it involves direct chemical influences between genes themselves, that are in this case supposed to be chemically bound together, or local interactions between their products, or influences on their structure coming through the pathway of synaptic forces. As yet, little evidence has been adduced to decide between these very different possibilities.

Before leaving the subject of position effect, it should be pointed out that the chromocentral regions have been found usually to exert an especially marked and far-extending position effect, of peculiar type, resulting in a mosaic expression of the genes that were transplanted to positions in or near to such regions. These so-called "eversporting displacements" do not seem, as various geneticists have thought, usually to involve actual losses, in mosaic patches, of chromosome sections containing the genes concerned. For, as has been argued previously (Muller, 1930), the effect is often only one of degree, and seems capable of reversal, during development, as shown by the arrangement of the spots. Prokofyeva, Belgovsky and I are inclined to attribute the somatic variegation to differences in the type of conformation, or rather the condition, of the chromocentral region involved, and these differences probably persist for a number of cell generations, so as to result in whole groups of cells having a common degree of expression of the position effect. In this case, then, the position effect is probably subject to variation correlated with the type of associations between different chromosomes.

On account of this variable but drastic position effect, transplantations of genes from "active" near to chromocentral regions (or *vice versa*) are likely to result in disfunctionings that tend to prevent the evolutionary establishment of such cases of chromosome rearrangement. Hence, normally, we find the chromocentral region confined to the neighborhood of the centromeres and telomeres, even though, in X-rayed material, a part of it very commonly becomes placed in a more or less medial position within a chromosome arm.

. . . .

It would be impossible to cover, in the given bounds of time and space, all the topics of present interest connected with chromosome rearrangements. We have endeavored here only to touch upon certain of the high spots connected with the problem of the conformation of these rearrangements, their relation to one another, the mechanism of their occurrence, and some of their more immediate effects. We must omit from consideration here the urgent questions of the relation of rearrangements to so-called gene mutations, which I raised some years ago (1932), whether breaks can occur within genes or merely between them, and whether indeed the so-called "gene mutations" are only still minuter variants of the minute rearrangements. The latter question, which both Goldschmidt (1937) and I (1937) have recently raised independently, is now made still more acute by the evidence obtained by Belgovsky, that changes known to be minute rearrangements follow the same law of frequency in relation to dosage of irradiation as gene mutations, and that in this way both alike differ from gross rearrangements. These dosage relations had formed the last distinction positively known to exist between rearrangements and "gene mutations." Together with these questions are bound various others, concerning what the limits of a gene are, the criteria for defining *a* gene, and certain questions concerning the structure and functions of the gene in general. There do, however, seem to be certain possible lines of attack for throwing further light on this series of problems. In fact, this is the genetic field which has been engaging my chief attention for the past five years.

In addition to these, there is a whole series of questions concerning the role played by chromosome rearrangements in evolution. It would be interesting to show how much light has been thrown on these by the facts above reviewed concerning the nature of the rearrangements, taken in connection with the known facts concerning their mode of inheritance. We should see that much that has been found in the studies of the comparative cytology of chromosomes becomes clear in the light of these facts, and also that certain rather widely accepted suppositions about the part taken by chromosome change in speciation turn out to be invalid. These latter topics have been treated in another paper, now in press.

Suffice it, in closing, merely to call attention again to the general consistency of the outlook herein presented upon the nature of structural changes in chromosomes with the earlier views of progressive cytologists regarding the persistence of the individuality of chromosome parts, as well as of chromosomes as a whole. We have seen that this principle now extends even to the matter of the bipolarity versus monopolarity of the parts, and that the telomeres as well as the centromeres, and the genes characteristic of the inert region as well as those more often used in genetic experiments, constitute genetically distinctive structures, having definite properties. This is not to say that, by some sort of peculiar mutation, a unipolar gene might not become bipolar, or *vice versa*, or that it might not even acquire such a composition as would render it potentially either the one or the other, depending on given conditions outside of it, as is the case in Ascaris; similar considerations of course apply to the centromere. But there is no reason to suppose that mere breakage, in itself, ordinarily has such an effect, even though the functions of genes are affected by their positions in the gene chain. And in the light of these conceptions, all at present known cases of structural change, in Drosophila at least, acquire a consistent interpretation. Let us, then, while consolidating this position, move on from it to the attack on the other, more remote questions now appearing before us.

Notes

[1]Until shortly before that, Drosophila geneticists, accepting an early surmise of Stevens which she had later corrected, had usually assumed that Drosophila had the XO type of sex determination and that what we now call the Y was an autosome with the X attached, but Metz's comparative studies of male and female and Bridges' studies of non-disjunction had later (1913) proved that this chromosome was really a Y. In this way the above conclusion was made possible.

[2]But whether their liability to exchange with one another is primarily a cause or effect of this homology, or both, is a question that cannot yet be answered with assurance.

[3]We are omitting from consideration the cases—presumably numerous —in which broken ends that were previously united with one another reunite to reconstitute the original type of chromosome, and also those hypothetical cases—perhaps numerous but, if so, not viable—in which the broken ends fail to undergo reattachment.

[4]No doubt one reason for the loss of dicentric chromosomes is that during mitosis they would sometimes be pulled in both opposite directions at once, and hence would move in neither direction. If this were their only disadvantage, it might be that they could live in cases in which the two centromeres were close together, in which event the normal chromosome should sometimes have two or more neighboring loci that served for fibre attachment. There is as yet no evidence to indicate that this situation may obtain in Drosophila, but we are at present testing the matter out more fully. On the other hand, in plants, multiple juxtaposed centromeres have been described, and McClintock has very recently (1938) presented cyto-

genetic evidence of them, since each of the two sections formed from a breakage in the appropriate region received a functional centromere. If this can happen in Drosophila, however, the occurrence must be vanishingly rare.

GENE REARRANGEMENT IN RELATION TO RADIATION DOSAGE*

by H. J. Muller, A. I. Makki and A. R. Sidky

Institute of Animal Genetics, University of Edinburgh

Recent experiments of the authors confirm the earlier results of the senior author, Belgovsky and other collaborators, to the effect that the frequency of gross rearrangements of genes produced in Drosophila spermatozoa varies approximately as the 3/2 power of the dosage of X-radiation, when the latter is of the order of one to four thousand roentgen units. Thus, 72 translocations combining the two major autosomes occurred among 5901 fertile cultures from fathers treated with a lighter dose (about 1000r), and 67 among 788 fertile cultures from a dose four times as strong. Translocations involving the small autosome and giving the cubitus interruptus phenotype occurred in the numbers 12 in 59,605 F_1 flies examined, for the lighter dose, and 35 in 15,531 for the 4X dose.

If we admit that individual ionizations produce the breakages, these results lead to the conclusion that many or all of these breakages occur independently in the different chromatin regions involved in gross rearrangements, and that union of pieces occurs subsequently. The fact that the power of the dosage (3/2) to which the translocation frequency was found to be proportional is significantly smaller than that (2) expected for the frequency of the coincidence whereby two breaks occur in a given volume may be due entirely to the higher chance of inviable (aneucentric) chromosomes being formed by the more multiple breakages attendant on higher dosages or may be due, in addition, to some breakages in different regions resulting from one and the same ionization, the effect of which spreads. This question is being investigated.

Multiple-break rearrangements are shown, by our data involving the ring chromosome Xc2, to occur oftener, in relation to double-break rearrangements, than a random distribution would allow. This fact seems best explained mainly on the conception that there are usually several breaks at hand, and that when one of the broken ends unites with another end, derived from a second break, instead of reuniting with the piece from which it had originally become detached, the chances are thereby increased for further recombina-

Journal of Genetics, Vol. 37, 1939.

adopts the contact interpretation (assuming the fusion to be made possible by a decharging action of the effective electron).

Because of the above disagreements and doubts, we decided some two years ago (1937) to broaden our attack on the whole problem, and, in conjunction with a considerable group of co-workers at the Institute of Animal Genetics, began the series of studies reported in the present paper.

In the meantime (1938 and 1939), several other series of data on the subject have been reported. The first two of these are by Catcheside (1938 *a*, *b*), and are accompanied by the calculations above-mentioned. Of these, the first (dealing with *Drosophila*) has been regarded by Catcheside as not inconsistent with the linear frequency-dosage relation to be expected on the contact view; the second comprises data on plant material dealing with the frequency relations of rearrangements involving double, triple, quadruple, etc., breaks, and he regards these data also as not being out of harmony with the contact view. Similarly, Buzzati-Traverso (1939), writing in the *Drosophila* Information Service, has recently reported finding a linear frequency-dosage relation for *Drosophila* translocations. And Bauer *et al.* (1938) have presented data which according to them do not depart significantly from linearity except probably at one point (a departure which they think might possibly have resulted from "some uncontrolled experimental factor"). To be sure, they describe their results, despite this circumstance, in terms of the breakage view, but their work concerns itself more with the question of the relative positions of the exchanges than with that of their frequency at different doses, or of a decision between the two alternative mechanisms, and this aspect of the matter is not stressed by them.[4]

On the other hand, Sax (1938), in his recent work on structural changes in *Tradescantia* observed cytologically soon after treatment, has independently arrived at the 3/2 power rule, and interprets his results as furnishing decisive evidence in favour of the application of the breakage-first mechanism in this material. As a matter of fact, his 3/2 power rule represents something different from ours, the mathematical agreement being largely a coincidence. Nevertheless, as we shall see later, his findings, as well as the parallel ones of Fabergé (1939) and ours do lead to the same essential conclusions, although by different routes. Moreover, as we have seen, the same may be said of the recent studies of McClintock (1938 *a*, *b*, 1939).

Ultra-violet Tests: The Problem of the Relation Between Structural Changes and Gene Mutations

(a) The Dubiousness of the Distinction Between "Intra-" and "Extra-genic Mutations"

As was pointed out by Stadler (1932), and as had earlier been fore-shadowed by Serebrovksy (1929) (as mentioned on p. 3), there is at present no certain criterion for distinguishing structural changes, if very minute, from intra-genic mutations, and it is conceivable that all apparent gene mutations produced by irradiation are really "extra-genic" changes, in the sense of changes in the linear ar-rangement and number of genes, including both minute deletions and duplications, and minute rearrangements of other kinds, ac-companied by position effects. This question becomes much more acute now, since our findings (Muller *et al.* 1934, 1935, 1937 *a;* Mul-ler, 1935, Belgovsky, 1938, 1939; Belgovsky & Muller, 1937; Raffel, 1938) that these minute structural changes, with their position ef-fects, do in fact occur and are produced by radiation, that they may be of vanishingly small size, both from the cytological and from the genetic point of view, that they follow the same frequency-dosage curve as the supposed "gene mutations," and that they vary similarly in their incidence with the type of cell treated.

In fact, in *Drosophila*, the question may now be made even broader, to inquire whether the spontaneous gene mutations too— since they seem indistinguishable as a class from the gene muta-tions produced by radiation—may not be extremely minute variants of the structural changes (although in the plant material there has, as Stadler, 1932, has shown, been more reason for supposing that some of the spontaneous "gene mutations," as judged in some cases by their dominance and in others by the inappreciable influence of radiation upon the loci concerned, may belong to a different cate-gory or categories from the radiation mutations). It is not conceiv-able, however, that all spontaneous "gene mutations," forming, as they must, the essential building blocks for an indefinitely great amount of evolution, could consist merely of losses or changes in position of "whole genes," in the sense in which genes have hitherto been conceived, nor would this be consistent with a rational idea of how such a vast number of different genes had come to exist in the first place. It would therefore be necessary, if the linear rearrange-ment view of all spontaneous as well as induced mutations were adopted, to do away, largely, with the distinction between "extra-genic" and "intra-genic mutations." In that case, we could not postulate sharp boundaries between the regions denoted as genes, different from the boundaries between smaller subdivisions within them (such as, perhaps, the amino-acid radicals), and so we should have to admit the possibility of breaks and reunions between these smaller portions, *i.e.* within what had been considered single genes.

This view—which I tentatively proposed some two years ago (1937) only as one possibility, suggested by the state of the evidence then existing, but which Goldschmidt (1937 *a*, *b*, 1938) independently put forward at the same time and urged, in a series of suggestive papers, as the only reasonable interpretation, would seem to make of the "gene" only a rather artificially delimited region of the chromosome, without distinctive boundaries.[5]

(b) Ultra-violet as a Possible Means of Discrimination

It is not feasible here to go into all the ins and outs raised by this question. But although the problem is ultimately a chemical one, it is possible that further genetic results may still throw light upon it. The main results so far which may prove to have a bearing on it are the proof by Stadler (1939) and Stadler & Uber (1938), following earlier indications by Stadler & Sprague (1936), that in maize ultra-violet light causes distinctly fewer structural changes (with the exception of terminal deficiencies) in relation to the frequency of the induced gene mutations, than does high-energy radiation (X- and γ-rays), and, more recently, the proof by Dr Mackenzie and myself (1939), following still earlier indications by Altenburg (1930, 1931, 1936), that in *Drosophila* there is no appreciable production of structural changes at all, by ultra-violet light which induces gene mutations at a fairly high frequency—high enough for them to have been accompanied by a quite appreciable frequency of structural changes if X- or γ-rays had been the agent. As shown by Table XIII, which gives a summary of our tests of this question up to the date of the congress (including data besides those previously published), the evidence for this conclusion is now much more than sufficient. If X-rays of the same gene-mutation producing strength had been used in these experiments instead of ultra-violet, some seventy-five translocations would have been observed, instead of none.

It is apparent, in the *Drosophila* material at any rate, that the ultra-violet light, though producing gene mutations, does so either without producing breaks in the chromosomes at all, or at least without producing thoroughgoing breaks, of the type produced by X-rays and by mechanical means. For, as we have seen previously, real breaks, when produced in *Drosophila* spermatozoa, are later followed by fusions, and consequently by observable structural changes, such as are conspicuously absent after ultra-violet treatment. If we wished to bring the maize results into line with these, we might postulate that the terminal deficiencies (and rarer structural changes?) which are induced by ultra-violet in maize belong to a category more nearly akin to gene mutations, the primary effect being a transformation of an ordinary bipolar interstitial gene into a monopolar one (telomere). In that case the breaks caused in maize by ultra-violet, unlike those caused by X-rays, would only be the secondary products of changes more nearly resembling gene mutations.[6] And "gene mutation" itself might still be considered as arising, not merely by structural change of the linear rearrangement type, involving breakage and reunion of single-file constituents on a minute scale, but also by chemical changes of other kinds. This then would still leave room for the older conception of definitely delimited genes, between which but not within which breakage by X-rays could occur, and within which but not between which changes by ultra-violet could occur. Possible physical reasons for such a difference in effect (such as the ionization of water caused by X-rays and not by ultra-violet, as suggested by Delbrück in a personal communication) would not be far to seek.

TABLE XIII
Effect of ultra-violet light

Series		Tests for lethals			Tests for translocations	
		No. of fertile cultures	No. of lethals in X	% of lethals	No. of fertile cultures	No. of translocations
1		1070	22	2·1	2449	0
2		606	20	3·3	976	0
3		1375	64	4·6	1617	0
	Sum	3051	106	3·7	5042	0

Scheme of matings: In series 1 and 2 y w males were irradiated. For the lethal tests these were mated with ClB females and the Bar daughters bred in individual cultures, while for the translocation tests the y w males (irradiated at the same time as those for the lethal tests) were mated with XX *yellow brown ebony* females, their sons being back-crossed individually to females of the same kind. In series 3, males of composition y sc^4 w sc^8 were irradiated and crossed to females of composition sc dl49 v f dp e. For the lethal tests daughters (F_1) from these matings were bred individually, the F_2 being examined for the presence of y w males. For the translocation tests sons (F_1) derived from the same matings (*i.e.* brothers of the F_1 females that were tested for lethals) were bred individually to dp e females and cases of lack of recombination of the markers, sex dp and e were looked for among the F_2 groups.

Whether such a view, or the alternative previously suggested, emerges as the more plausible one may depend upon whether or not ultra-violet is found to produce demonstrable minute rearrangements. That is a question upon which we are working at present, but extensive data seem to be necessary for answering it. A Notch, possibly a minute deletion, was once obtained in an ultra-violet experiment of Altenburg's in 1931 (reported in a personal communication), but this may have been an accident unrelated to the treatment. If it should be found that minute rearrangements are in fact produced by ultra-violet, then it would be evident that for the production of these minute rearrangements it is not necessary to have thoroughgoing chromosome breakage—like that produced by X-rays —that is, breakage that persists for a considerable time and eventually involves also the chromosome "sheath" and so allows the production of gross rearrangements. Yet even the minute rearrangements would require some sort of breakages. Conceivably these might be followed by fusion more readily, and within the unbroken "sheath." In that case it would be much more likely that apparent "gene mutations" too could be produced in such a manner. And this in turn would raise the presumption that the gene mutations too might be linear rearrangements, but of parts smaller than the putative "genes," the latter thus losing their distinct identities.

If, on the other hand, the ultra-violet were found not to give rise, like X-rays, to demonstrable minute rearrangements, such a restriction of the process of gene mutations to change in the linear order of genetic materials already present would seem as yet uncalled for, and the door would be left wider open to distinguish between gene mutations and gene rearrangements, and so to methods of, as it were, demarking the gene. Ultra-violet mutations might then be considered intra-genic and X-ray breaks intergenic, and it might be that the genic boundaries so established coincided with boundaries established in other ways, as by points where crossing-over was possible and by the limits of certain kinds of functional activities of the genes.

(c) Other Evidence Regarding Chromosome Segmentation

One line of evidence indicating a segmental structure of some sort in the chromonema is provided by my findings of the restricted number of the genetically distinguishable positions of breakage producible by X-rays in the neighbourhood of the loci of scute and yellow in *Drosophila* (Muller & Prokofyeva, 1934). The only plausible escape from the conclusion that there is a rather coarse segmental structure here is to suppose that between these "genes" — or minute chromosome regions whose functions we are observing — there lie longer stretches of genetic material, having so little or so unimportant functions that their total loss would still leave the organism viable and normal-appearing. In that case the visible "genes" would give the appearance of being discontinuous only because they were separated by long interspaces of relatively inert genic material and so the discontinuity would in a sense be of a functional nature only.

In this connection a reason may be mentioned for inferring that the thoroughgoing chromosome breaks at least, those of a kind capable of giving rise to gross structural changes, probably do not break ordinary chemical bonds like the bonds between amino-acid radicals, but only bonds (if any) of indifferent sign, like the bonds between two carbon atoms. This reason lies in the fact that the broken ends cannot be classified into "plus" and "minus," since identical broken· ends of sister chromatids are also capable of uniting with each other. This bespeaks a specialized structure for the places of breakage, that is, again, a segmental structure for the chromonema, constituted of segments larger than the amino-acid radicals.

Another line of evidence in favour of a segmental structure of the chromorema, not finer than would be set by the lengths of protein molecules (if indeed the gene consists of proteins) lies in a consideration of the facts of crossing-over. The principle of interference and the manner of its decrease with distance indicate that crossing-over is caused by a mechanical stress which breaks the chromatids, as has been pointed out by the present author (1916) and as has been more especially supported by further facts and arguments brought forward by Darlington (1932). This conception of crossing-over is now made still more probable by the proof, herein provided, that a part of this supposed mechanism — namely, breakage first, and then union of broken ends — actually does operate when structural change occurs (even though the cause of the breakage itself is not the same here, and cannot lead to breakage at homologous points). Now it seems very unlikely that the mere mechanical tension of the chromonema which breaks the chromosome at crossing-over would reach such a pitch as to be able to break the chemical bond between two amino-acid radicals connected in the ordinary manner within a protein molecule, or to break any similar intramolecular linkage in the chain of a molecule of the type of protein, fat or lipoid. It is much more likely, therefore, that there are special connections, of a looser kind, between larger segments, and that it is at these "internodes" that crossing-over can take place. Moreover, it is difficult to conceive that the breakage would take place by mechanical means with such absolute precision as it does, at quite identical points in the homologous chromatids, if the possible breakage points were so numerous and closely crowded as, say, the links between the members of polypeptide or polysaccharide chains.

At the same time we must be careful not to take it for granted that the chromonemal internodes demarcated by different criteria would necessarily coincide with one another. X-ray breakage, for example, might be possible at more points than crossing-over breakage, or *vice versa*, and the points of crossing-over in turn might be different from the limits set by ultra-violet mutation or from the boundaries pertaining to certain types of gene-functioning, and there might be still different limits prescribed for the smallest amount capable of exerting auto-synthesis or auto-attaction. If then the different criteria gave different results we should have correspondingly different kinds of "genes," according to the definition of gene which we chose to follow. In fact, according to some criteria of their functioning genes are already known to occupy overlapping areas, in that they show the so-called position effect.

Thus we should beware of taking too simplified a view of the problems at issue. There may not merely be "wheels," but "wheels within wheels," in living matter, and if the recent studies of viruses by the X-ray diffraction method, as reported for instance by Astbury (1939) and by Crowfoot (1939) at the Seventh Genetics Congress, may be used as showing what structures might be found in the genetic material, according to the author's (1926) conception of viruses as representing relatively free genes, then it is not unlikely that there are various grades of division and subdivision, each with its special kind of arrangement, between the relatively gross bodies hitherto recognized by the biologist and the very much finer ones hitherto studied by the chemist. We cannot pretend to have answered such problems yet. They are, so far as geneticists are concerned, for the future, while for the present it is a step even to be able to recognize their existence. But that cannot, in my opinion, invalidate the fundamentals thus far established of what has been called "gene theory," even though many geneticists have in the past adopted a too hard and fast if not arbitrary conception of how much constitutes one gene. In this work of the future, it is to be hoped, the techniques of chemistry and physics will increasingly take part, along with those of genetics.

Summary

Data are presented which show that a given number of ionizations produced in *Drosophila* spermatozoa by irradiation result in the same number of gross structural changes regardless of (*a*) wavelength, from 50 kV. X-rays to γ-rays, (*b*) continuous dose or fractionation over a 3-week period, (*c*) fertilization immediately or 1 month after treatment, (d) radiation intensity, from 0.05 to 250r / min., (e) temperature, from 5 to 37° C.. Hence in spermatozoa undergoing irradiation, "primary effects" of individual ionizations accumulate independently until fertilization, and their *final* total number determines the number of structural changes produced.

These primary effects are not the genetically observed rearrangements themselves, but must combine, usually in twos, to produce the rearrangements as secondary effects, although not until after all of the primary changes have been produced (*i.e.* after fertilization). For the frequency of the genetically observed gross rearrangements varies as the 3/2 power of the final (total) dosage, for the range from 1000 to 4000 r. This is (*vide* Stadler & Catcheside) the relation expected at those doses for *surviving* combinations of the primary changes, if the latter consisted of breakages or potential breakages. At lower doses, the observed exponent does not fall towards 1 (linearity), as it would if only a part of the rearrangements represented combinations of independent primary changes, but probably rises nearer to the square, as expected if all of them were formed in this way.

That the "primary changes" in the sperm are really breakages (actual or potential) is further indicated by data on whole chromosome losses, which would be caused by "simple breakages" that had failed to undergo combination (except of sister fragments). For the frequency-dosage relation shown by these cases (which are but a small minority of the total) is found to be an approximately linear one, as expected. It is inferred that XX, XO-type gynandromorphs and other whole-chromosome mosaics resulting from irradiation of spermatozoa represent cases in which union of broken ends was delayed until after chromosome division; restitution then occurred in one. chromatid but not in the other, which consequently was lost. Similarly, chromosome mosaics in which the two first cleavage nuclei must have differed in regard to the structural changes they contained are probably derived not from the chromosomes having already been split in the treated spermatozoon stage, but from union of ends having been delayed until after chromosome division, and having then occurred differently in sister chromatids.

Additional evidence that breakage precedes union is provided by the multiple nature of some of the exchanges, and by data indicating that these multiple-exchange translocations (obtained from ring chromosomes) increase more rapidly than those having ordinary double exchanges, as the dose of radiation is increased. At all doses tested, however, the multiple-exchange cases were found to be more frequent than expected on a random distribution of breaks and unions; this result shows that initial proximity of broken ends favours their union, and that restitutions must therefore be favoured at the expense of all types of new combinations. Sidky's finding of a translocation between a non-radiated maternal and an irradiated paternal chromosome furnishes evidence from another angle that breakage precedes union.

Data are given showing that minute rearrangements of different kinds, unlike gross rearrangements, have a linear frequency-dosage relation. Hence their breaks are interdependent, caused by a spreading of the effects of the same ionization to neighbouring points on the chromonema spiral.

This spreading of effects provides decisive evidence against the assumption that the genetic effects of radiation necessarily result from the ionization of atoms which formed a part of the genetic material affected. For this and other reasons, pointed out in the text, it is fallacious to identify the so-called "sensitive volumes" or "sensitive areas," calculated from the frequency of induced genetic changes, with the actual sizes of the genes or chromonemal material (or viruses) affected.

It is calculated that gross and minute structural changes, together with dominant lethal gene mutations, are, together, of the order of frequency to explain the mortality found for cells (of fertilized eggs and embryos) derived from irradiated spermatozoa. A part of the necrosis produced by irradiation in proliferating tissue in general must be of the same origin, hence studies on the mechanism of structural change and gene mutation should help in the understanding of these effects. But this is not the only way in which irradiation kills such cells, as data (Lamy & Muller) on relative mortalities of irradiated triploid and diploid embryos show their death to be predominantly of non-genetic origin.

The finding that breakage precedes fusion in the process of structural change strengthens, by analogy, the case for the conception of breakage first as opposed to fusion first at the points of exchange of connections in crossing-over, and this in turn favours the theory according to which the chromatids at the time of crossing-over are subject to a stress, which tends to break them mechanically.

The problems are discussed of whether "gene mutations" are only ultra-minute linear rearrangements and of whether the "gene" is not a sharply defined segment of the chromonema. Evidence is presented showing that ultra-violet produces gene mutations without first breaking the chromosomes and this result as well as others is regarded as raising difficulties for such a view. It is held, however, that this matter is as yet far from settled, and the situation may be more complex than is generally realized, as indicated by studies on viruses.

Notes

[1]For diagrams of all types of structural changes capable of surviving indefinitely, derived from two or three breaks, see Muller (1940, Fig. 1).

[2]As Prokofyeva-Belgovskaya & Khvostova (1939) have found, this applies, though in correspondingly lesser degree, to the less extremely heterochromatic regions (perhaps derived from relatively recent duplications) that they have shown to exist in various interstitial locations (Prokofyeva-Belgovskaya, 1937 b, 1938). More recently, Kaufmann (1939) has independently obtained evidence to the same effect.

[3]These results on the frequency-dosage relation, and their possible interpretations, were first presented by the author and Belgovsky at a public meeting at the Institute of Genetics, Moscow, 1935, and were communicated privately to British and American colleagues at the same time. They are restated and discussed in the references to this meeting made in publications of Dubinin & Khvostova (1935), and of Kirssanow (1937). They have also been reported by the author in publications of 1936, 1937, and 1938. The data have been given in the following publications: Belgovsky (1937, on translocations), Muller (1938, on deletions). Similar experiments on inversions, carried out at the author's suggestion by Berg, Panshin and Borisoff in 1935 (unpublished), have given confirmatory results, as stated in some of the papers above cited.

[4]But in an abstract of a paper submitted to the Seventh Congress by Bauer (1939), who left before the time for his address, this author now states that he has obtained evidence that the frequency-dosage relation, as observed in the salivary glands of *Drosophila* larvae derived from treated fathers, is "between a two-hit and a three-hit curve." If this means that the exponent in question is between 2 and 3 it is higher than was to be expected on either the contact or the breakage-first interpretation, although the latter is regarded by Bauer as furnishing the explanation of it.

[5]While it may be seen from our § VI (c) that the present author does not go so far as Goldschmidt in rejecting the conception of genes as corre-

sponding to natural segments of the chromosome, he believes Goldschmidt's insistence upon this possibility, and the bringing forward of the evidence against segmentalism, to constitute a needed step in genetic criticism. A recent summary of Goldschmidt's views on this question, to which the reader may be referred, is the paper "Chromosomes and genes," read at a symposium celebrating the Centenary of the cell theory in Stanford University, 2 July 1939. This paper was distributed in mimeographed form to those attending the gene group conference of the Seventh International Genetics Congress. Our §VI was written before we read this paper.

[6]McClintock's recent (1939) finding that in maize the change from interstitial gene to telomere may follow mere mechanical breakage, in cells of the sporophyte generation, shows that in this material the genes are in fact much more labile in their "polarity" or "genic valency" (*i.e.* in their tendency to unite with one or more other genes—see Kossikov & Muller, 1935) than they are in *Drosophila*. And although this lability is so great, and so subject to regulation, that these changes can perhaps be accounted as "mutations" only by an extension of the term, nevertheless this very lability strengthens our main thesis, according to which the terminal deficiencies produced by ultra-violet in plants were not caused by breakage of the usual kind, but were only secondary consequences of changes primarily induced in the "valency" of an individual gene. The fact that such changes in "valency" occur with so much greater difficulty, if at all, in *Drosophila*—i.e. that the telomere is so much more permanent an organ there—thus fits in with the apparent failure of ultra-violet to produce "simple breakages" in this form. And the basic conclusion would still hold, that ultra-violet, unlike X-rays, cannot cause primary breakage of the chromosomes (breakage that leaves both ends adhesive), either in the plant or animal material.

THE LETHALITY OF DICENTRIC
CHROMOSOMES IN DROSOPHILA*

by G. Pontecorvo and H. J. Muller
University of Edinburgh and Amherst College

The fact that viable translocations formed after X-raying spermatozoa are proportional in frequency only to the 3/2 power of the dose has been shown to signify that union of broken ends of chromosomes occurs without reference to presence or absence of centromere on fragment, the zygote with aneucentric rearrangements, i.e. with chromosomes other than monocentric, dying. If death is due solely to the genic unbalance resulting directly from the loss of the nonmonocentric chromosomes, then, if extra chromosomes homologous to those lost were introduced, in compensation for the losses, the resulting zygote would survive. This can be tested, in *Drosophila melanogaster*, by crossing irradiated males to triploid females; homozygous recessive markers in the triploids allow recognition of

*Genetics, 1941, 26: 165.

the exceptional offspring. Thus, losses of a single paternal autosome, as by simple breakage, will allow one autosomal recessive to show in the F_1 , while losses of two autosomes, as by aneucentric translocations, will "uncover" two recessives simultaneously. Among 8,880 F_1 from crosses of brown ebony triploids by non-brown non-ebony males given 4,000r, 133 showed just one autosomal recessive, and only 3 (one being the approximate expectation for the coincidence of two independent losses) showed both recessives. But the frequency of aneucentric translocations produced must have been such as to have resulted in over 800 zygotes showing both recessives, had these zygotes lived. Hence over 99 per cent of these aneucentric rearrangements are lethal *per se* even though many aneucentrics formed from union of sister chromatid fragments after simple chromosome breakage are not lethal. Investigation of the mechanism involved is proceeding.

THE SURPRISINGLY HIGH FREQUENCY OF SPONTANEOUS AND INDUCED BREAKAGE, AND ITS EXPRESSION THROUGH DOMINANT LETHALS*

by H. J. Muller and G. Pontecorvo
Amherst College and the University of Edinburgh

The unusually low ratio of daughters to sons of irradiated males having ring X-chromosomes is shown to be mainly due to death of zygotes with affected X's. For, at 4000r, only about 3 per cent of females are found to be converted into males by induced loss of an X, whereas the relative number of females is reduced by about 35 per cent. Allowing for deaths from X-translocations (some 10 per cent), most of this dominant lethal effect on the females must be due to "simple breakage," which in rings must often be followed, in cases which would otherwise be restitutional, by formation of dicentrics, occasioned by twisting of the chromomena or chromonema-pair before re-union. The results show over 75 per cent of these sister-dicentrics to be lethal (translocational dicentrics being still oftener lethal). Breaks in non-rings are presumably induced by irradiation as often as in rings, but here the great majority are followed by perfect restitution. Thus at 4000r nearly all offspring contain one or more restituted chromosomes. Nevertheless the lethal losses of non-ring X's are frequent enough (*ca* 5 per cent at 4000r) to show that a considerable part of the dominant lethal effect of sperm ir-

Genetics, 1942, 27: 157-58.

radiation results from "simple breakage" with sister-dicentric formation. The frequency of spontaneous lethal and viable losses of rings (*ca* 13 per cent and 2.5 per cent) is likewise surprisingly high, and may be due to spontaneous breakage. This probably occurs similarly in non-rings but is followed by perfect restitution. Since so few spontaneous structural changes arise, this breakage would usually occur in pre-spermatozoon stages, allowing prompt restitution.

EVIDENCE AGAINST THE HEALING OF X-RAY BREAKAGES IN CHROMOSOMES OF FEMALE DROSOPHILA MELANOGASTER*

I. J. Herskowitz and H. J. Muller
Indiana University, Bloomington, Indiana

Rapoport (1940) reported evidence that when *D. melanogaster* females with attached-X chromosomes were X-rayed single breakages in heterochromatin near the centromere were capable of healing, i.e. forming new "telomeres." This type of experiment was repeated by irradiating nonbar females, having attached-X's marked by recessive genes and no Y-chromosome, with approximately 2000r and crossing them to Bar males. There were 14 nonbar male exceptions among the 17,991 sons and 129 Bar female exceptions among the 15,096 daughters examined. This completely confirmed Rapoport's experimental findings. However, breeding tests of 51 exceptional females (excluding those derived from non-disjunction in the male parents) demonstrated 6 were multi-break cases in which the distal tip of the X-chromosome provided a telomere-bearing piece for the proximal stump. This proportion is not lower than expected on the hypothesis that all the exceptional females were derived from interchanges, for the great majority would have received autosomal distal ends. As another test of whether many of the exceptions represent single breakage followed by healing, females like the above were given 1000r and 4000r and crossed to the Bar males of another, more suitable, stock. The frequencies of exceptional daughters were 0.427 per cent (23/5387) at 1000r and 3.38 per cent (39/1153) at 4000r. These per cents, bearing approximately the ratio 8:1, clearly represent an exponential increase of about the 3/2 power, as expected for interchanges.

Records of the Genetics Society of America, 1953, 22: 79; expanded version in *Genetics*, 38: 653-704.

These data constitute evidence against the occurrence in female *D. melanogaster* of X-ray induced chromosome breakages which are capable of healing to form new telomeres.

EVIDENCE AGAINST A STRAIGHT END-TO-END ALIGNMENT OF CHROMOSOMES IN DROSOPHILA SPERMATOZOA*

Irwin H. Herskowitz and H. J. Muller
Department of Zoology, Indiana University,
Bloomington, Indiana
Received March 17, 1954

Summary

1. The lengths of the chromatin masses were measured in spermatozoa of a normal stock and in those of a stock (Novitski's attached X.Y) in which half of them contained both X and Y and the rest contained neither. The frequency distribution of lengths had a significantly greater dispersion in the latter stock than in the former.

2. It is inferred that this difference in distribution of lengths was caused by the presence in the spermatozoa of heterochromatin blocks, similar to those in mitotic chromosomes, and that these blocks were differently distributed in the two stocks among their two classes of spermatozoa.

3. The relatively small dispersion and the effective unimodality of distribution of chromatin-lengths found in both stocks are facts irreconcilable with the hypothesis of a straight end-to-end arrangement of chromosomes in the sperm head of *Drosophila melanogaster*.

4. When the chromosomes of the spermatozoa are assumed to have the same proportions of parts, including blocks, as those of mitotic and meiotic divisions, and when they are assumed to become squeezed together into masses of substantially the same shape in the sperm head, regardless of the amount of chromatin present, so that the lengths of these masses are proportional to the cube roots of their volumes, the resulting distributions of lengths, calculated for the two stocks, are found to be in excellent statistical agreement with the distributions observed by us.

Genetics, Vol. 39, No. 6, November, 1954, pp. 836-50; summary, only, included; contribution No. 560 of the Department of Zoology, Indiana University.

5. It is to be expected that a method of formation of sperm heads of the type above suggested would entail considerable overlapping of chromosomes and of chromosome parts, along the lengths of the sperm heads. This type of arrangement had been inferred earlier, on the basis of genetic data concerning the relations between neutron dosage and the frequency of induced translocations. If, on the contrary, a straight single-file arrangement of chromosomes had been established for the sperm head, a radical revision of current theories regarding the way in which structural changes of chromosomes are produced would have been required.

GENETIC PROOF FOR HALF-TRANSLOCATIONS DERIVED FROM IRRADIATED OOCYTES OF DROSOPHILA MELANOGASTER*

S. Abrahamson, I. H. Herskowitz and H. J. Muller
Indiana University, Bloomington, Indiana

Strong indirect evidence exists that X-ray-induced "detachments" of attached-X chromosomes in *Drosophila* oocytes containing no Y are usually due to rearrangements between the attached-X and an autosome. In such detachments, the attached-X is broken rather near its centromere, into a centric "J" and an acentric "I," and an autosome ("A") is broken subterminally (anywhere on 4 being subterminal). The stump of the J then becomes "capped" by the telomere-bearing autosomal tip, and/or the I becomes "captured" by attachment to the autosome's remainder in substitution for its tip. An egg receiving a capped J without I must, to survive, receive a complete maternal A, thereby becoming hyperploid for the autosomal tip, while one receiving a captured I without J is hypoploid for the tip. Either condition is genetically demonstrable if the tip includes a known marker. Capturing would also be recognizable by X-autosome linkage.

Thirty-nine detachment cases derived from oocytes irradiated 0-4 days before oviposition have been tested for hyperploidy with regard to markers near the ends of the autosomal linkage maps. Nineteen have so far proved to be half-translocations involving one or more markers. One involved capping by the tip of 2L, including gene al^+; two were cappings by 2R, both including $M33a^+$ and one sp^+ also; while 16 others were either cappings or capturings in-

*Records of the Genetics Society of America, 1954, 23: 28; and *Genetics*, 1954, 39: 955.

volving chromosome 4. This strong tendency toward X-4 translocations (compare independent findings of Lindsley and Novitski, D.I.S. 27) is most simply explained as resulting from the proximity of breakages (often heterochromatic) in appropriate positions in these chromosomes.

GENETIC BASIS OF SOMATIC DAMAGE PRODUCED BY RADIATION*

Wolfram Ostertag and H. J. Muller

That loss of individual chromosomes, caused by their breakage, forms the chief basis of the mortality induced by irradiating *Drosophila* larvae was indicated by results (Oster, 1959) showing that males are more often killed than females, and males with a ring X-chromosome, which restitutes with difficulty, more often than ordinary males. Moreover, Oster's finding that one ring X-chromosome hardly impairs the survival of females indicated chromosome loss, not chromosome bridge formation per se, as the usual cause of mortality. Tests both by Oster (1959) and by us showed further that, as expected for chromosome loss involving breakage, females having attached X-chromosomes considerably exceed ordinary females in mortality (though complications prevent their distinctly exceeding males).

We now find that females heterozygous for either of two known deficiencies in the X-chromosome have as high mortalities as males. Even the loss of a major autosome seldom kills unless its homologue is deficient. These results also bespeak chromosome loss, not bridge formation per se, or mere deletion of a chromosome section.

However, chromosomes which are pulled poleward with high effectiveness (for example, Novitski's "X·Y" and chromosomes of early zygotes) do kill by bridge formation. For mortality caused by irradiating such chromosomes is not conditional on their loss occasioning a deficiency.

Mortality caused by irradiating larvae continues throughout life, thus resembling aging although probably different qualitatively from spontaneous aging. Although these mortality-dosage curves are sigmoid (multi-hit), chromosome losses are induced linearly at low dose-rates; hence "aging" accruing therefrom should depend on total dose accumulated.

Science, 1959, 130: 1422-23; presented before the National Academy of Sciences meeting at Indiana University, Bloomington, November 18, 1959.

7 Heterochromatin

See also in this volume:

"Bearings of the Drosophila Work on Systematics," pp. 482-96

"The Position Effect as Evidence of the Localization of the Immediate Products of Gene Activity," pp. 137-40

Separately published papers having a bearing on the subject of "Heterochromatin" are listed in the bibliography, pp. 593-612, entries 4 and 137.

THE DIFFERENTIATION OF THE SEX CHROMOSOMES OF DROSOPHILA INTO GENETICALLY ACTIVE AND INERT REGIONS*

Genetics by H. J. Muller

Cytology by T. S. Painter

The University of Texas, Austin, Texas

(With 30 Textfigures)

(Received for publication, September 9, 1931)

Table of Contents

*Zeitschrift für induktive Abstammungs -und vererbungslehre, Bd. LXII, Heft 3, 1932; pp. 316—17 (part), and summary, with figures 1 and 30, included.

†Page numbers in the above table of contents are repeated without change from the Zeitschrift für induktive Abstammungs- und vererbungslehre.

In a preliminary note in *Science*, Painter ('31) has recently presented a new map of the X chromosome of *Drosophila melanogaster* obtained by means of a combination of cytological and genetic work carried out at our laboratory by the writers and their collaborators. In the present article the writers have joined in refining upon this map and in showing the cytological and genetic evidence upon which it is based, as well as in pointing out the general bearing which these findings have from the points of view of these two allied fields of research. It has seemed wiser thus to combine rather than to publish independent papers but we wish it understood that each of us has worked independently in our respective fields and that we individually assume responsibility for our respective parts, as indicated in the title.

Figure 1 is a representation of the cytogenetic map, arrived at as a result of our combined work, the evidence for which it will be an object of the following paper to present.

Summary

1. The genetics and cytology of four different translocations, each involving the attachment of a piece of the X chromosome to the fourth, are reviewed. The genetics and cytology of several deletions and other breakages of the X are also reviewed.

2. On the basis of the combined genetic and cytological studies the approximate positions of various loci in the actual X chromosome, as cytologically observed, are deduced (figure 1).

3. This "actual map" is then compared with the linkage map, and with a newly devised map in which the distances are based on mutation frequencies instead of crossover frequencies (figure 30).

4. So far as the rather meagre evidence yet obtained on this point allows us to judge, the relative distances between loci in the left-hand half of the length (the left-hand two thirds of the volume) of the actual chromosome are fairly accurately represented on the mutation-frequency map, and not so well on the crossover-frequency map (the original "linkage map").

5. It is found, however, that the right-hand half of the length (the right-hand one third of the volume) of the actual X chromosome is almost totally unrepresented on either the linkage or the mutation-frequency map.

6. In this right-hand half of the X chromosome (designated as "XI") there is a dearth or absence of detected lethal mutations, and only one "visible" mutation is known to have occurred. This latter is the mutation bobbed, which lies in the third quarter (by length) of the X chromosome, counting from the left end.

7. The relative functional unimportance of the genes normally existing in the "XI" region is indicated by the comparatively slight phaenotypic effect caused by hyperploidy ("overdose") of this region, as compared with other chromatin regions of similar size.

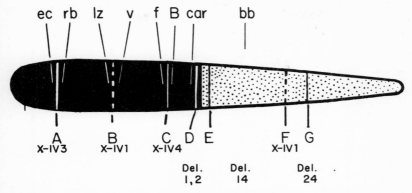

Figure 1. *Cytological Map of the X chromosome of D. melanogaster.*
The black portion of the map indicates the physical part of the chromosome which carries all the known sex-linked genes with the exception of bobbed (bb). The stippled area indicates the inert region of the X chromosome, which carries no known gene except bobbed, and is interpreted as being homologous with the Y chromosome. The capital letters below the map represent the points at which breaks have occurred which have allowed us to determine the physical positions of the gene loci. Below each letter the designation of the translocation or deletion involved is given. The loci of the genes for echinus (ec), ruby (rb), forked (f), and bar (B) have been relatively exactly determined by breaks, within one crossover unit or less. The location of lozenge .(lz), vermilion (v) and carnation (car) is in part inferential, although their approximate positions are probably correct, as explained in the text. Bobbed lies somewhere between the lines E and F, in the stippled area.

8. In this entire right-hand half of the X there is little or no crossing over.

9. Breakage of the X chromosome in this region seems to be induced by X-rays at least as readily as in other regions, in proportion to its visible size. This indicates that the chromonema is probably not shorter (less coiled) in this region, relatively to the visible chromosome size, and that the chromonema itself is therefore more inert genetically in this region.

10. The left-hand half of the X (" XA") fails to exhibit homology with the Y chromosome, as judged by its random segregation with the latter, but the right-hand half exhibits such homology. In a case in which the latter region was broken into two parts, both parts showed homology with the Y.

11. On the basis of the similarity between the Y and the right region of the X chromosome, both (*a*) in their low mutation frequency (*b*), small effect of hyperploidy, (*c*) absence of crossing over, (*d*) possession of an allelomorph of bobbed, and (*e*) pluri-local affinity shown at segregation, it is suggested that they have probably had a common origin much more recent than any common origin of the Y and the left region of the X. If this is true, then the

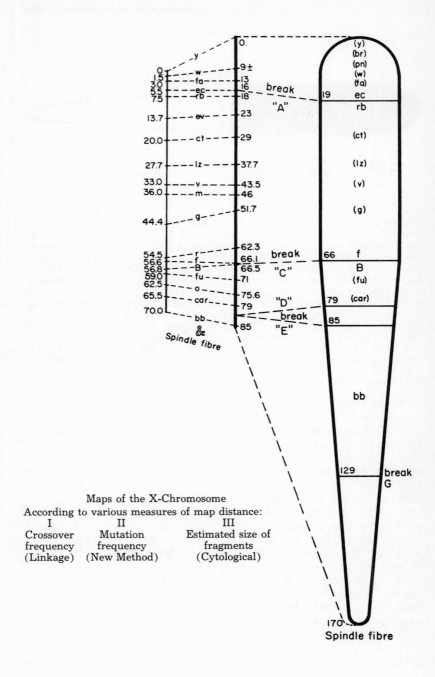

Maps of the X-Chromosome
According to various measures of map distance:

I	II	III
Crossover frequency (Linkage)	Mutation frequency (New Method)	Estimated size of fragments (Cytological)

connection of the active portion of the X with the chromatin ancestral both to the inactive portion of the X and to the present Y probably came about by a translocation. There is already a plausible theory which may account for the inert condition into which the Y had fallen, previously to this translocation.

12. Cytological and genetic bearings of the above findings, and of the interpretation of them above suggested, are discussed. Whatever the interpretation may be, the essential finding herein reported is that *the existence of chromatin which is relatively inert genetically, but which may nevertheless be large in bulk, is not a phenomenon limited to the present Y chromosome,* as has hitherto been tacitly assumed. The possibility of the existence of such inert chromatin in unsuspected locations must be taken into account in chromosome studies, the more so since it cannot as yet be readily detected genetically, nor distinguished from other chromatin cytologically. The causation or mode of origin of such chromatin regions, their distinguishing characteristics and their function, if any, as well as their effects in general, constitute problems for further study.

Figure 30. Value of one unit of map distance (1.0 mm. as printed):
        on map I, equals 1 crossover per 100 eggs;
        on map II, equals 1 mutation per 1000 sperm irradiated with
          2000 r units of X-rays;
        on map III, equals approximately 0.01 microns of chromosome
          length (i. *e.* scale is × 100,000).

For map I the standard linkage map of 1921 has been used as the chief basis (Bridges, 1921; republished 1925 in the "Genetics of *Drosophila*"). Work done since this paper was submitted to the printer, however, indicates that commonly the crossover frequencies between f and bb may be not much more than half or two thirds of those shown on this map. The statements made in the earlier part of this paper, concerning the relative sizes of different sections of the linkage map, should accordingly be slightly modified, so as to be in conformity with the newer linkage results.

The method employed in constructing map II has been explained on pages 321—328; this map is based upon 570 mutations in all.

Map III is based upon the estimated lengths the fragments had as they lay in the normal chromosome before breakage. A map giving distances along a line, proportional to the volumes of the fragments (and therefore to chromonema lengths?), would have the lower (= "right") region, below break C, more contracted, relatively to the upper region, than in the present map.

The positions of the genes represented in larger type on map III have been determined more or less accurately (see text) by means of the cytological observations on the breakages indicated, since they lie the nearest to the latter. These cases have been discussed in the present paper. The genes shown in smaller type, in parenthesis, on map III have in all cases had their *order* definitely determined with reference to one another, by means of one or more cases of chromosome breakage (for the most part cases not discussed in the present paper), but their relative distances from one another, *i.e.* their actual positions, have not yet been determined cytologically.

INERT REGIONS OF CHROMOSOMES AS THE TEMPORARY PRODUCTS OF INDIVIDUAL GENES*

By H. J. Muller and S. M. Gershenson

Institute of Genetics, Academy of Sciences, Moscow

Communicated January 8, 1935

Soon after the phenomenon of no crossing-over in the male was discovered, it was pointed out (Muller 1914, 1918), that this circumstance must lead to the accumulation of recessive mutations, and even losses of some genes and duplications of others, in any chromosome which, like the Y, is constantly carried in heterozygous condition in a sex in which no crossing-over occurs. The lack of active genes in the Y was thus interpreted. It was then taken for granted, however, that the visible material of the Y chromosome was of a nature fundamentally similar to that composing the bulk of other chromosomes, and consisted of more or less inactivated genes together with the usual amount of accessory chromatin and other substances that may normally accompany genes in the chromosome as seen at metaphase. When later it was shown (Muller and Painter, 1932), that the X chromosome had a similarly inert region, homologous to that of a part of the Y, it was concluded that the former had probably been derived from the latter by a kind of translocation, and it was naturally assumed that the inert region of the X, like that of the Y, consisted of inactivated or " degenerated" chromatin.

At this later date, it was, to be sure, realized that the chromosome material of both the Y and XI (the inert region of the X) might really be relatively devoid of genes, rather than full of degenerated genes, and that the actual gene-string in the inert regions might therefore be much smaller, in proportion to the bulk of visible chromatin, than it was in the " active" regions of the chromatin. But it was found by Oliver (1932) that, in the case of inversions, breaks probably occur in the inert region, as compared with the active region of the X, in somewhat the same ratio as that which the bulk of the inert region as seen at metaphase bears to the bulk of the active region (further evidence of this sort will be referred to below), and this was taken by Muller and Oliver as an indication that the inert and active regions were probably constituted in a similar way, an inert region thus containing a chromonema of similar length, degree of coiling and breakability to that in an equal amount of an active region (see Oliver, *Ibid.*). The alternative to this would

Proceedings of the National Academy of Sciences, Vol. 21, No. 2, February, 1935, pp. 69-75.

have been the assumption, which at that time was less plausible, that, length for length of chromonema, breakage occurred more readily in the inactive region, in which the chromonema was shorter (i.e., coiled to a lesser degree).

A review of the evidence now at hand from various sources, however, makes the conclusion now much more probable that the inert regions of the X and Y are fundamentally different in structure from the active regions and do not consist of a row of degenerated genes arranged single file in a coiled chromonema like the functional genes in the active region, but that they consist essentially of non-genic material derived from a very few specific active genes, between which breakage takes place much more readily than between genes in the chromonema of the so-called active region. Whether these chromatin-producing genes of the "inert region" lie in the form of a coiled chromonema in their region of the chromosome at the time of mitosis remains a question that it is still difficult to decide.

Evidence for the above conclusion is to be found in several different directions. Most telling is the fact that in various cases of breakage within the inert region of the X or Y chromosomes, certain large sections of specific size seem to be broken off or carried over *en bloc*. Thus in all of Stern's and of Kaufmann's cases of exchange between the X and the Y, when an arm of the Y was broken off or transferred either the whole of the arm or just half of the long arm was concerned. Again, in the deletions of the X chromosome examined by Painter and Muller (1929; also Muller and Painter, 1929) the size of the piece of the X remaining was sensibly the same in the different cases in which the locus of bobbed was present—amounting to approximately one-third the length of the chromosome, as we would expect if exactly all of the inert regions were present, in addition to a negligible section of active region from the left end. In another case (deletion 24, described by Muller and Painter, 1932) in which the bobbed locus was not present, the fragment was much smaller, being only a few times the size of the fourth chromosome. This fragment must have consisted mostly of inert material, since only that part of the active region to the left of scute was present here, and this inert material must be that which is associated with the fibre attachment locus or other unrecognized loci close to the latter. Conversely, in the case of bobbed-deficiency studied by Dobzhansky (1932, exhibited to the Sixth International Congress of Genetics), the deleted chromosome lacked almost exactly that amount of material which was present in the deleted X chromosomes of Painter and Muller, namely, the inactive material, and it contained the amount of material which was absent in the previously described deletions, namely, the active material. This then constitutes evidence from the reverse direction for the same conclusion, namely, that the inert material is in definite blocks of comparatively large size. The chromosome described by Gershenson (1933), in which by crossing-over between two different inverted chromosomes (scute[4] and scute[8], respectively) a deficiency for the region of bobbed was produced, likewise lacks a region nearly equal to the length of the inert region itself, i.e., Gershenson's crossover chromosome and Dobzhansky's deficient chromosome seem to be of sensibly the same length. All this would lead us to the conclusion that, where the bobbed locus was present, nearly all of the inert region was also present, with the exception of a small section— perhaps one-fourth of the total—which is associated with the spindle fibre locus. In the Y chromosome the bobbed region is apparently of similar length to that in the X, constituting about one-half of the long arm.

Studies of Panshin and Muller (unpublished) on translocations between the Y chromosome and the fourth, furnish another, though less direct, line of evidence in the same direction. They find that in the great majority of translocations of this type—at least 90 per cent—one or more of the genes of the Y chromosome necessary for the fertility of the male have become so affected by their altered position as to be no longer capable of producing the effects necessary for fertility. This indicates that these fertility genes are in all these cases located near the point of breakage. Since, however, the Y chromosome at metaphase appears rather long, and since there are probably not many fertility genes, the result is hard to understand, unless we suppose that in the ordinary " resting" stages of functioning cells, these genes lie close together and are not separated by the great bulk of inert material seen at metaphase.

In view of this interpretation, the observation of Painter (1933, 1934a and b) that the inert regions of the X chromosome are hardly, if at all, to be found in the chromosome structure of the cells in the salivary glands, becomes understandable, and in fact constitutes further evidence for our interpretation itself. We may suppose that in these stages when the genes are functioning in cell metabolism, they do not produce the great local accretions of material to be observed at metaphase in the inert regions, and that the salivary gland chromosomes, therefore, give a truer picture of the chromonema, in so far as the latter represents a string of real genes in which the different genes occupy comparable lengths of the thread. Whether or not the inert material that was present at metaphase still exists somehow in the resting nucleus, and, if so, what its functions may be, is another question. Its functions in segregation and crossing-over likewise remain important subjects for study.

While the above conception disagrees with the idea of the inert region as representing a degenerated gene string, it does not contradict the notion that a process of degeneration and of loss did occur in the past evolution of the Y chromosome, owing to the protection from natural selection afforded by its continually heterozygous condition. The loss, however, has probably, by this time, become complete with regard to all genes that are no longer needed, and the material that is seen, instead of consisting of "degenerated" genes and the material accessory to them, existing in the proportions usual for genes and their accessory material, probably consists almost entirely of the accessory material——i.e., of some sort of especially bulky reaction-product——of the few functional genes that still remain. As for the existence of translocations, to account for the continued similarity between the Y and the inert region of the X, the reality of the occurrence of such translocations (including "crossovers"), even today, is attested to by findings of Stern and of Kaufmann, previously alluded to.

Attention may at this point be recalled to the fact that, on the view here presented, the finding of Oliver of the occurrence of more inversions affecting the right-hand portion of the X than the left-hand portion, is to be interpreted on the basis that there is a much greater likelihood of breakage between two genes which are connected with the inert region than between any two successive genes of the active region. There are several other series of findings which, on our present conception of the inert region, would lead to the same conclusion. One is the fact that x-rays produce translocations of the Y chromosome with approximately the same frequency as those of the X (Muller and Altenburg, 1930), despite the great dearth of active genes in the Y as compared to the X. Secondly, there is the fact (Painter and Muller, 1929, confirmed by later work) that the majority of deleted X chromosomes obtained by crossing irradiated males to yellow females with attached $X's$ have their right-hand break to the right of carnation (and hence probably in the inactive region) despite the fact that there are many more genes to the left of carnation, which are nevertheless so situated that breaks between them would result in deleted $X's$ having a high viability in this cross. Thirdly, of a series of ten gross (i.e., not minute) inversions studied by the present authors, which involved position effects in specific loci near the left end of the X chromosome (yellow, scute, white), six have been found to have their right-hand break in the inert region, and only four to have it in any other part of the chromosome. Fourthly, translocations involving the X have their break in the inert region in a large proportion of cases (Patterson, Stone, Bedichek and Suche, 1934).

The excess of breaks in the inert region is in part due to the fact that breaks are more apt to occur near the ends and near the attachment points of chromosomes, as the latter authors show, but this can be by no means the entire explanation. Thus, in work of Levit and of Muller (unpublished), in which the scute 8 chromosome, which has bobbed and most of the inert region located near but not at the left end (and far from the attachment point), was irradiated, it was found that most of the deleted $X's$ formed had their left-hand breaks in the inert region, rather than in the active region to the left of the latter and still nearer the end, although there are probably many more genes in this left terminal active region than in the inert region. Apparently "simple breaks" of the scute 8 chromosome also occur preferentially in the inert region, as shown by the same authors and also by Patterson (1933). The latter breaks occur about five times as often beyond bobbed as between carnation and bobbed, but among deletions and inversions of $X's$ that were normal before irradiation there seem to be considerably fewer breaks beyond bobbed (between bobbed and the fibre attachment) than between carnation and bobbed, even though the latter interval is further from the end of the chromosome. The breakability, therefore, is in part a specific property of the region concerned, and it is extremely high between genes that lie in the inert region.

On the new conception of the inert region·here proposed, various experimental facts require a different interpretation than they would otherwise receive. One example may suffice here. Four different apparently "simple breaks" were produced by Muller and Koerner (unpublished) in the scute 8 chromosome, in the interval between the gene achaete, in the left-hand active region, and bobbed, the left-hand fragment being lost. On the view that the inert region, like the active region, consists of a large number of small, genetically distinct segments (corresponding to genes), the different "truncated" scute 8 chromosomes thus resulting should be of different lengths, lacking not only the left-hand active region (from the left terminus to achaete, inclusive), but also a part of the inert region lying beyond bobbed. They were accordingly tested with the object of determining whether the latter loss were capable of producing any detectable phaenotypic effect. A really adequate test of this kind had not hitherto been possible, since hitherto only individuals deficient for the region including bobbed had been tested, and these necessarily required a Y chromosome to cover their bobbed-deficiency; this Y then might at the same time have covered the deficiency of other genes of the inert region. In the present case crosses were carried out, the genetic details of which it will not be necessary to describe, to allow the production of zygotes homozygous for the truncated X chromosome, but not containing a Y chromosome, and having their deficiency of the active region at the left end compensated for by the presence of a chromosome fragment (the left part of the X of "mottled 5") containing those genes but not containing any part of the inert region of the X (since this fragment of the X is here attached to the right portion of chromosome IV). The results showed clearly that in all cases such females were viable, and the conclusion seemed to follow that the loss of none of the genes in the inert region that normally lay between bobbed and the fibre attachment caused any detectable phaenotypic effect, even in the absence of Y. Now, however, we see that the result probably means only that in all these cases the break was at, or very nearly at, the same point—between bobbed and achaete—and that there was no part of the inert region absent. That part which may be connected with the bobbed locus is necessary for life, in so far as the bobbed gene itself is necessary for life. Whether the genes of the inert region that affect variegation and fertility and possibly other characters, are at other loci, and also have a part of the inert region connected with them, is as yet not definitely known, although the evidence above would indicate that most of the inert region depends on very few genes. Neither do we know whether the fibre-attachment gene of the X is in any way specific, or may be completely replaced by a fibre-attachment gene from another chromosome.

As most of the evidence for our present interpretation of the inert region depends upon the small series of cases which were observed some time ago without the present question being in view, and as such comparison is subject to considerable error in the estimate of the length of the pieces of chromosome involved, Gershenson is now undertaking a special study and comparison of a more extended series of cases of this sort. This should give a definitive answer to the question of whether or not the inert region is composed of blocks, and of the number and size of such blocks, and the genes with which they are associated.

THE STRUCTURE OF THE CHROMONEMA OF THE INERT REGION OF THE X-CHROMOSOME OF DROSOPHILA*

By H. J. Muller, Corresponding Member of the Academy, and A. A. Prokofjeva

(1) The inert region of the X-chromosome of *Drosophila Melanogaster* is identifiable in especially well prepared specimens of salivary gland material as a very faintly cross-striated region most or all of which is located just to the right of the rightmost band shown in Painter's, standard map; this region is usually obscured by the chromocenter. In Painter's figures it is represented by the two ring-like bodies shown to the right of the rightmost band; this appearance is due to the frequent non-conjugation of the two homologous inert regions in the vicinity of the spindle fibre.

(2) This inert region contains at least five or six rather closely spaced faint cross-striations (more might be demonstrable by a more refined technique), the appearance here being morphologically somewhat similar to that of the fourth chromosome.[1] Comparison

*Comptes Rendus de l'Académie des Sciences de l'URRS, Vol. I, No. 9, March, 1935, pp. 658-60.

of normal material with that containing inversions of genetically known lengths not only makes possible the identification of this region as the inert region, but shows bobbed to lie in the left-hand portion of it, in the region of the first two or three of the demonstrated striations, while the spindle-fibre locus lies in the portion to the right of this. Both of these portions produce an appreciable part of the inert region visible in the metaphase chromosome.

(3) The appearance of this region in salivary gland material indicates that its chromonema has essentially the same structure as that of the active region and contains six or more genes spaced like those in the active region. These genes are no doubt functional, the functions of several being already known in part. All those known are to some degree homologous with genes located in the Y-chromosome, with which they can cross over.

(4) Since the length of this region in the metaphase chromosome is little less than in the salivary gland chromosome, it is evident that—as suggested as one possibility when this region was first discovered (Muller and Painter, 1932), but one not then thought probable—this region simply does not become coiled when the chromosome undergoes the transformations preparatory for mitosis. The chromonema of this region must therefore become laden with much accessory (non-genic) chromatin material, which at the time of mitosis gives it approximately the same thickness as that of the coiled " active" region.

(5) These facts explain both the low frequency of mutation and of crossing-over in the inert region, and the small effect of hyper- and hypoploidy, despite the apparently considerable length of this region at metaphase, on the simple basis that the actual chromonema length and number of genes is relatively very small compared with that of the coiled active region. In accordance with this the conclusion must be drawn that the chromonema of the inert region is much more liable to breakage by X-rays (as well as in making preparations of salivary gland material) than is an equal real length of chromonema of the active region.

(6) The inert region is therefore seen not to be inert in the sense of containing many genes that are relatively functionless, but in the sense of being composed, at metaphase, of an excessively large proportion of material extraneous to the genes themselves. The chromonema is not inert but encrusted, and the genes in it lie normally arranged, except for the lack of coiling of the chromonema, referable perhaps to the presence of this material. It is likely that it is this same extraneous chromatin material which, in the salivary gland and other "resting" cells, forms the basis of the chromocenter.

Institute of Genetics,   Received
Academy of Sciences of the USSR.   14. III. 1935.
Moscow

Note

[1]The article by Bridges (Journ. Hered., Feb. 1935) giving his detailed maps of all the chromosomes has come to hand after the completion of the present article. His map of the X-chromosome shows a region lying to the right of the rightmost conspicuous band, and containing four relatively faint double striations (in such cases the possibility of repetition caused by diffraction must be taken into consideration) and about seven very faint single striations. Although this region has not, in his article, been identified as corresponding to the inert region, it does obviously correspond with this region as identified in the present article, and the more detailed map of it there available should accordingly be indispensable in further cytological investigations of this region. We may say, however, that, short of ultraviolet microphotography, it would be impossible to observe the degree of detail there shown with the optical equipment and equipment for illumination that has been available to us.

A FURTHER ANALYSIS OF LOCI IN THE SO-CALLED "INERT REGION" OF THE X CHROMOSOME OF DROSOPHILA*

H. J. Muller, D. Raffel, S. M. Gershenson and
A. A. Prokofyeva-Belgovskaya
Institute of Genetics, Academy of Sciences of the
USSR, Moscow
Received September 1, 1936

Introduction

The so-called "inert region" of the X chromosome of Drosophila was originally supposed by Muller and Painter (1932) to consist of a line of relatively inactive genes comparable in number per unit of length of the mitotic chromosome to those in the active region. But it was later shown by Muller and Gershenson (1935) that the breaks in this so-called "inert region" took place preferentially in certain discrete positions, and they accordingly proposed the hypothesis that there were relatively few genes in this region, but that these genes, or at any rate certain individual genes amongst them, are represented by a relatively great amount of chromosome material during the mitotic stage of the chromosome. That is, the "inert region" of the mitotic chromosome was compounded of a small number of blocks, each of which resulted from an individual gene (cf the large chromatin nucleoli noted by Wenrich and others at definite points in prophase chromosomes). The latter hypothesis

Genetics, January, 1937, 22: 87-93.

received strong support in the finding of Muller and Prokofyeva (1935) that in the salivary glands the so-called "inert region" of the *X* (*XI*), as well as the whole *Y* chromosome, had a structure fundamentally similar to that of the so-called "active regions," consisting of rows of discs spaced at intervals similar to those in other regions, but that *XI* and *Y* were very short, containing relatively few discs, and therefore presumably relatively few genes. In the salivary chromosome the length of these "inert regions" was in fact not much greater than in the mitotic chromosomes, and so it might be supposed that the chromonema of these regions, or at any rate that part of it representing the genes which caused the blocks, did not become as much coiled as that of other regions during mitosis.

Separability of Bobbed and Block A

In the series of deleted and inverted *X* chromosomes reviewed by Muller and Gershenson which led to their block hypothesis of the "inert regions," the locus of bobbed, whenever present, was found to be associated with a large block of chromosome material in the mitotic chromosome. Whenever the locus of bobbed was present, this block, which in fact constituted the major portion of the "inert region" of mitosis, was present, and when bobbed was absent this block was absent. This block we may call "Block A," and we may provisionally presume it to be likely that it is the product of a single gene. It was accordingly suggested that the gene in question, the gene for Block A, might be identical with the gene of the bobbed locus itself. Having as one object a decision of this question, we have continued with an analysis of further cases of *X* chromosome rearrangements. The results of the work with deleted *X* chromosomes is being reported by Gershenson in another paper. In none of those yet analyzed has a separation between the locus of bobbed and of Block A been found. But in two inversions which we have analyzed, namely the inversions of scute-L8 and mottled-4, we have found that a point of breakage and reattachment of the inversion had come between the locus of bobbed and that of Block A. These loci are therefore separate ones. This accordingly increases the number of loci in the "inert region" that are genetically known to be separate.

The evidence for the above conclusion is derived from the study of chromosomes resulting from single crossing over between the above inversions and other inversions of the *X*. It had been shown by Serebrovsky and Kamshilov (1931) that crossovers having the left-hand portion of the scute-4 inverted chromosome and the right hand portion of the scute-8 inverted chromosome were deficient for the bobbed locus and, as they pointed out, this meant that the right-hand point of breakage of the scute-4 inversion was to the left of bobbed and that of the scute-8 inversion to the right of bobbed.

Gershenson (1933) had found that these crossover chromosomes were considerably shorter than normal; as we would now say, they lacked one or more of the blocks, including certainly Block A. This meant that the right-hand break of scute-4 was to the left of Block A, and that of scute-8 to the right of Block A and possibly of one or more smaller blocks besides. In neither of these cases then had there been a breakage between bobbed and Block A. By the same method of testing of crossovers, applied to combinations of scute-4 and scute-S1 we find that the scute-S1 chromosome, like that of scute-8, is broken to the right of both bobbed and Block A (at least). When, however, we use the scute-L8 inverted chromosome, securing the crossover having the left-hand portion of scute-4 and the right-hand portion of scute-L8, we find that the right-hand break of the scute-L8 chromosome must have occurred between bobbed and Block A. For the crossover chromosome just mentioned is deficient for the bobbed locus but is of normal length showing that the breaks of scute-4 and scute-L8 were on different sides of the bobbed locus (left and right respectively), but on the same side (the left side) of Block A. The complementary crossovers, having the left portion from scute-L8 and the right portion from scute-4 are, as expected, also found to have normal length and they are not deficient for bobbed. These conclusions are checked by the study of crossovers between the scute-S1 and scute-L8 chromosomes. In this case we have the reverse findings since the right-hand breaks of both chromosomes are on the same side of bobbed (to the right of it), and hence neither type of crossover chromosome is deficient for bobbed, but since the breaks of these two chromosomes are on opposite sides of Block A, one crossover class of chromosome is short, like the scute-4 scute-8 combination, being deficient for the block, and the opposite type of crossover is correspondingly more elongated than the normal, having Block A (at least) represented at both ends. The short chromosome is that having the left portion of scute-L8 and the right portion of scute-S1, while the long chromosome is the complementary type of crossover. The scute-8 chromosome, of course, gives the same results in these respects as the scute-S1 chromosome when taken in its crossover combinations with scute-L8.

Similar studies of crossovers between the mottled-4 inversion and the scute-8 inversion give the same results with respect to bobbed and chromosome length as do the studies of scute-L8 and scute-8. That is, mottled-4 also broken between bobbed and Block A. (In order to obtain viable individuals containing the crossover chromosome having the left portion of mottled-4 and the right portion of scute-8, an extra fragment of the left end of the X chromosome derived from the mottled-5 translocation was inserted by crossing, since the crossover chromosome in question lacks the so-called viability gene.)

Properties of Block A

In view of the fact that bobbed is due to a separate locus from that of the large chromatin block, the question of the function of the latter locus becomes more prominent. The short crossover chromosome having the left-hand portion of scute-4 and the right-hand portion of scute-8 was known not to be deficient for any genes necessary for life whose place could not be taken by genes in the Y chromosome, since both males and homozygous females containing this short X and also a Y lived and were apparently normal (except for the expected characters dependent upon the scute genes present). On the other hand such individuals died if they lacked a Y chromosome. But this was to be expected, owing to their deficiency for the locus of bobbed, and so it could not be determined whether they were at the same time deficient in any other locus necessary for life or for a normal appearance. With the use of scute-L8, however, the question could now be attacked whether the locus of Block A or some other locus associated with it and separated from that of bobbed was necessary for life or for a normal phenotype. Accordingly, crosses were made to secure females homozygous for the short crossover chromosome having the left-hand portion of the scute-L8 inversion and the right-hand portion of the scute-8 inversion. It was found that such homozygous females were in fact viable and normal in appearance, except, of course, for the expected scute characteristics. Since, however, there was a possibility that these females might contain a Y chromosome covering their deficiency in the "inert region" of the X, a number of them were tested individually to ascertain whether they contained an extra Y. The test was made by crossing them to males heterozygous for Curly and for a dominant allele of brown eye, that called " A" by Dubinin, which he has shown to give a normal eye color in the presence of an extra Y. It was found by this means that no extra Y had been present in a number of these females. In others, however, it had been present and had given the expected results, thus proving the validity of the test. Hence we may conclude that Block A is neither necessary for life nor fertility, nor for a normal external phenotypic appearance. In fact, as the same tests showed, it does not seem to have a decided effect even on the phenotypic expression of the characters of so-called "eversporting displacements," like the dominant alleles of brown (cf Noujdin's 1935 finding of such an effect by the "inert region" of the X in general). The question of the possible function of the block in the synapsis and segregation of the sex chromosomes has been investigated by Gershenson and is being discussed in a parallel paper.

It is being shown by Prokofyeva and Muller in another paper in which salivary gland chromosome studies are reported of scute-4 and scute-8 chromosomes, that the region including bobbed and

Block A and probably also block B (see below) is represented by only about two of the faint discs of the chromocentral region of the X chromosome, as seen by our optical methods. A considerable portion of the chromocentral region, including of course the spindle fiber locus, lies to the right of this, and another portion lies to the left of it, that is, to the left of bobbed. This narrows down considerably the region of the salivary gland chromosome responsible for the greater bulk of the " inert region" seen in the mitotic chromosome, leaving little or no more than one faint disc, as seen by our methods, for the whole of Block A. Taking only this portion of the salivary gland chromosome, then, we find that it is not even several times longer than the same region in the metaphase chromosome, and we may conclude that in the metaphase chromosome this particular portion has not become coiled or shortened at all as compared with its condition in the salivary gland. This means that most of the rest of the " inert region" has become much shortened, that is, probably coiled, in much the same fashion as the " active" region. The non-coiling then is apparently confined to certain particular loci, those which form the blocks. The functions of the other loci of the " inert region" largely remain to be determined, but there seems little reason to suppose that they are really " inert," even though it was found that Block A itself could be dispensed with.

Other Loci in the "Inert Region"

That " block B," or at any rate two blocks, are contained in the tiny section between the right-hand breaks of scute-4 and scute-8, was shown by another experiment. In this a cytological study of the mitotic chromosomes was made in the case of a mutual translocation between the scute-8 chromosome and the fourth chromosome. A combination chromosome having the left-hand portion of the scute-8 chromosome, not including bobbed or the main block, and right-hand (spindle fiber) portion of the fourth chromosome, which had been broken to the right of bent, was found to be about twice as large as a normal fourth chromosome. This could only mean that it contained a small block of " inert region" that had been present in the left-hand end of the scute-8 chromosome, and that normally must lie to the right of the main block. (This is probably the same as " block B" of the deleted X chromosomes studied by Gershenson). The presence of even this locus, in addition to that of Block A and of bobbed, in the small region between the scute-4 and scute-8 breaks, emphasizes the smallness of the space occupied in the salivary chromosome by Block A itself, that is, by the major portion of the " inert region" of the mitotic chromosome. It thus becomes reduced to approximately a single disc, together perhaps with the internodal region bordering the latter on one or both sides.

The above then illustrates the multi-locus character of the " inert region," and the fact that most of its bulk at mitosis is due to a very few particular genes that form a minority of all the genes within it. The " inertness" seems to be due to these genes only, that is, to the relatively large bulk which they form at mitosis. Most of its other peculiar characteristics depend in large measure at least upon the other genes. For example, the attraction of this region to the chromocenter in the cells of the salivary glands depends upon genes scattered throughout the length of this region. One or more of the latter genes even lie to the left of bobbed and of the right-hand break of the scute-4 chromosome, since Prokofyeva's studies show that the left end of the scute-4 chromosome is attracted to the chromocenter, causing this chromosome to form a loop in the salivary gland. And all the peculiarities of morphological structure that go with this chromocentral position are to be found in this portion of the scute-4 chromosome also. It would perhaps be better then, provisionally, to designate the whole region in question as the " chromocentral region" rather than the " inert region." The chief objection to this term is that in some species, which no doubt contain chromosome regions homologous to this, a real chromocenter is not formed. The same tendencies are probably present however, though to a lesser degree.

The above considerations bring to prominence one of the main questions that remains to be investigated concerning the chromocentral region. That is, why are there so many peculiar properties crowded together in this one region, including: attraction to chromocenter, formation of " blocks," effects on the expression of " eversporting displacements," sensitivity of crossing over proccesses to temperature and other influences, breakability and presence of the fiber locus. Especially noteworthy too is the fact that several of these functions depend upon a number of genes that can exhibit these properties independently of one another, and that in these cases all the genes of this kind are to be found lying close together, within this minute region.

Summary

1. Two cases are reported in which a combination of genetic and cytological analysis shows that breakage and inversion of the X chromosome had occurred between the loci of bobbed and of the main block, " Block A," which forms most of the bulk of the so-called " inert region" seen at the time of mitosis. In itself the locus of bobbed produces little if any of the bulk of the " inert region" at mitosis.

2. " Blocks A" and " B" in the salivary gland chromosome form a relatively small portion (not more than one " disc" each, as seen by our methods) of the whole of the so-called " inert region" seen at that stage, a portion little if any longer than the length of these

regions in the mitotic chromosome. Hence the rest of the "inert region," excepting the loci of these blocks, probably becomes coiled at mitosis, while these loci themselves remain elongated, forming a bulky mass of chromatin.

3. Individuals lacking "Block A" but containing the locus of bobbed are viable, fertile, and normal in their external appearance, even if they do not have a Y chromosome to compensate for the absence of this locus.

4. The problem arises as to why a number of peculiar properties dependent upon different loci occur crowded together in one region of the X chromosome, and probably of other chromosomes, and why, in the case of certain of these properties, there are even several loci of a similar kind in this same region.

5. The most characteristic property of this region seems to lie in the attraction of its loci for other loci so as to result in the tendency to form a chromocenter, rather than in the formation of chromatin blocks, and it is hence suggested that it would be better at present to term these regions "chromocentral regions" rather than "inert regions," recognizing however that most of the chromatin of these regions, as seen at mitosis, is in fact genetically inert, in the sense of containing relatively few genes.

THE ABSENCE OF TRANSMISSIBLE CHROMOSOME FRAGMENTS RESULTING FROM SIMPLE BREAKAGE, AND THEIR SIMULATION AS A RESULT OF COMPOUND BREAKAGE INVOLVING CHROMOCENTRAL REGIONS*

H. J. Muller, A. A. Prokofyeva-Belgovskaya, and D. Raffel
Institute of Genetics, Academy of Sciences of the
USSR, Moscow

Fourteen scute changes produced by irradiation of structurally normal X chromosomes included no losses of entire distal end. Considering the chromosome fragmentation reported by cytologists following irradiation, this indicates inconvertibility of ordinary interstitial into terminal genes by chromosome breakage. However, Levit's irradiation experiments (1931) on scute-8 apparently pro-

Genetics, January, 1938, 23: 161.

duced many distal-end losses by breakage of the interstitial chromocentral region adjoining achaete. The same phenomenon occurs spontaneously comparatively often. Salivary study shows these "broken" scute-8 chromosomes still contain the distal end in situ, though often giving evidence of minute rearrangement near achaete. Thus chromocentral and adjoining regions are especially predisposed not merely to breakage (without restitution) but also to compound breakage with minute rearrangement (deletion, inversion). Similarly, gross deletions and inversions of normal X chromosomes, having two distant breaks including one in proximal chromocentral region, commonly contain an additional chromocentral break nearby, with resultant rearrangement of bobbed with respect to block-A. It seems probable that the few reported single-break deficiencies, inversions, and translocations of normal chromosomes involve second breaks in the terminal chromocentral regions recently found by the second author.

FURTHER EVIDENCE OF THE PREVALENCE OF MINUTE REARRANGEMENT AND ABSENCE OF SIMPLE BREAKAGE IN AND NEAR CHROMOCENTRAL REGIONS, AND ITS BEARING ON THE MECHANISMS OF MOSAICISM AND REARRANGEMENT*

M. L. Belgovsky and H. J. Muller

Institute of Genetics, Academy of Sciences of the
USSR, Moscow

Other X chromosomes constituted like scute-8, for example scute-S_1, give similar results. In Bar-M_2, having an interstitial chromocentral region slightly proximal to forked, absence of simple breaks is phenotypically evident, but irradiation produces comparatively many forked "mutations," often with lethals, mosaicism, etc., illustrating predisposition of chromocentral and any adjoining regions to compound breakage with minute rearrangement.

Supposing the spontaneous tendency to such rearrangement intensified in somatic cells, these results lead to interpretation of

Genetics, January, 1938, 23: 139-40.

"eversporting displacements" essentially like Schultz's recent interpretation based on his salivary finding of minute deletions. (Conceivably, additional chromocentral sections, by conjugating, might, like splints, hinder rearrangement.)

The frequencies and frequency-dosage relations of these rearrangements indicate that the simultaneous neighboring breaks are interdependent, and hence secondary consequences of some primary chemical change occurring outside the parts broken.

THE NON-EQUIVALENCE OF THE BLOCKS AND THE SALIVARY "HETEROCHROMATIN"*

H. J. Muller,
Amherst College, Amherst, Massachusetts

The view that different chromosome regions, whether "euchromatic" or "heterochromatic," have similar breakabilities, approximately proportionate to their mitotic length, was disproved by comparing the results of irradiation of two contrasting X chromosomes. One of these, the crossover scute 8-scute 4, was twice as large as the other, scute 4-scute 8, because of its containing two block-A units, which the latter lacked. These differing chromosomes gave sensibly the same frequency of translocations, and also of rearrangements visibly affecting genes of the left end. These results corroborate the conception of the blocks as being virtually unbreakable units. The fact that "heterochromatic" regions which include blocks ordinarily have a breakability approximately proportionate to the length of these blocks must be only a coincidence, caused by an inordinately high breakability of the "other heterochromatin," that exclusive of the blocks, as compared with euchromatin. That this high breakability is not an indirect effect of the blocks upon the remaining "heterochromatin" (caused for instance by some strain induced by the former, or by a transmission of radiation hits from them) is further shown by the above results, since chromatin lacking blocks has an equally high breakability. For given lengths of "resting" (salivary) chromatin, the breakability must be at least thirty times as high in this remaining "heterochromatin" as in euchromatin. What is called "heterochromatin" in mitotic chromosomes is almost exclusively blocks, whereas "heterochromatin" in salivaries is almost exclusively the remaining portion. It is misleading to identify two types of structure differing so essentially by giving them the same name, "heterochromatin."

*Records of the Genetics Society of America, 1944, 13: 28; and Genetics, 1945, 30: 15.

8 Evolution

See also in this volume:

"The Gene," pp. 205-8

"The Gene as the Basis of Life," pp. 188-204

"The Guidance of Human Evolution," pp. 589-90

"Our Load of Mutations," pp. 560-73

"Variation Due to Change in the Individual Gene," pp. 175-88

WHY POLYPLOIDY IS RARER IN ANIMALS THAN IN PLANTS*

Professor H. J. Muller

University of Texas

A considerable number of cases of tetraploidy and also higher forms of polyploidy have been found amongst plants, some having been observed to arise in cultures that were under observation, others being found already established as varieties or species having twice (thrice, etc.) the amount and number of chromosomes present in related types. Evidence also exists that forms of plants thus established may give rise to larger subdivisions (genera, etc.) inheriting all this chromatin, or even more, since the doubling process may be repeated. On the other hand, amongst animals, cases are very rare where there is critical evidence for the occurrence of this evolutionary process. Apparently this is not because doubling of chromosome number does not occur in cell division—for cases of tetraploid cells in diploid animals have been observed not infrequently. Neither is it likely that polyploid individuals would fail to live. For chromosome conditions in the Hymenoptera show that at least two chromosome numbers are equally viable there—haploid and diploid—and polyploid Drosophilae have been found by Bridges to be very vigorous.

What, then, is the reason for the rare occurrence of polyploidy in animals, as compared with plants? It is, in essence, very simple —animals usually have two sexes which are differentiated by means of a process involving the diploid mechanism of segregation and combination, whereas plants—at least the higher plants—are usually hermaphroditic. Less simple are the details of the working out of this principle, for the diploid sex-determining mechanism and bisexuality act in various ways to hinder the establishment of tetraploid races, as will be shown below.

(1) The triploid individual is a usual intermediate step between diploid and tetraploid individuals in hermaphroditic organisms, the tetraploid in most cases arising by the self-fertilization of a triploid or by the crossing of two triploids. But this will often be impossible in bisexual organisms, for individuals having proportions of the sex-producing genes normal to the heterozygous sex can not exist in triploids and hence triploids of one sex or the other may fail to be fertile. This is due to the fact that the development of sex,

*The American Naturalist, July-August, 1925, LIX: 346-53; Department of Zoology contribution No. 192.

as well as of other characters, depends upon a certain proportion existing between the materials formed by different genes concerned with that character—thus maleness is produced in XX-XY species when that proportion of the genes affecting sex is present which exists in individuals having one X and a pair of all the autosomes, femaleness when two X's and a pair of all the autosomes are present. This "ratio" view of the determination of sex in "XX-XY" and "WZ-ZZ" forms, which conflicts sharply with the hitherto prevalent notion of determination through absolute quantities of the sex chromosomes, had been urged by the present writer, in discussions with Drosophila workers, since 1912; experimental confirmation of it was finally obtained in 1921, in Bridges' findings of triploid Drosophila. In these it is evident that neither the one X- nor the two X-containing triploids are normal sexually, though they have the absolute quantity of X-chromosome material that differentiates males from females among diploids; both these triploid forms are sterile whereas the 3X triploid is a fertile, vigorous female. Thus whenever a fertile triploid is formed in Drosophila it must be a female, and it can have no triploid males with which to breed. Breeding with a diploid male it produces only diploids, triploids and inviable or infertile diploid-triploid mixtures. Thus the numbers of triploids will tend to decrease in each succeeding generation, and no tetraploids will be produced. *Mutatis mutandis*, in WZ-ZZ species, triploid males may be produced, but these will lack fertile triploid females with which to breed, and the occurrence of tetraploidy will be similarly interfered with.

(2) It will occasionally happen, however, that a tetrapolid animal will arise without the interbreeding or selfing of triploids. There are three chief methods whereby such an event may occur: (a) A diploid gamete from a fertile triploid parent may happen to meet an anomalous diploid gamete from a diploid parent in which, owing to a mitotic irregularity, doubling of chromosomes in the germ tract had occurred; (b) a diploid egg formed by mitotic irregularity in a diploid female may happen to be fertilized by a diploid sperm formed by an independent mitotic irregularity in a diploid male (such formation of diploid gametes is more apt to occur in species-hybrids than in "pure" types, and this is especially true in the Lepidoptera, where aberrant maturation divisions, resulting in diploid gametes, are not uncommon in hybrids); (c) a diploid fertilized egg may become tetraploid through mitotic irregularity occurring in early cleavage. The resulting tetraploid should sometimes happen to have two X (or Z) chromosomes; in that case it will be of the type of the heterozygous sex. It may instead happen to have four X's (or Z's), in which case it will be of the type of the homozygous sex.

In any of the above cases, once such a tetraploid has been produced, it will usually have to breed with diploids. Triploids will then result and continued breeding will lead into the genetic *cul de sac* mentioned in section (1). If, however, by a rare coincidence, two or more tetraploids of different sex have been formed and they breed together, or if a tetraploid of the heterozygous sex type breeds with a triploid, tetraploids will be reproduced, and a race of tetraploids could theoretically be established from these. (This would occur more readily in the case of Lepidoptera, after hybridization, for the reason explained above.) Once formed, however, the race of tetraploids could only persist if their genetic isolation were continued in each generation, for interbreeding with diploids would immediately destroy the tetraploid combination, leading to triploids that would usually (again excepting cases like the Lepidopteran species-hybrids) tend to revert to diploids.

(3) If, however, all the above conditions for the establishment of tetraploid lines had been fulfilled the race of tetraploids would still be at a reproductive disadvantage, as compared with the diploids, and so would tend towards extinction under the conditions of a natural struggle for existence. The handicap of the tetraploid forms again lies in their sex-determining mechanism. For, in the tetraploids of the heterozygous sex type, containing, let us say, two X's and two Y's, there is nothing to insure all the gametes getting either both X's or neither.

As the writer pointed out in 1914, in discussing the mechanism of segregation in tetraploids, four homologous chromosomes of two kinds, designated as A, A, a and a, should ordinarily segregate into two pairs at random, giving gametes in the proportions 1 AA : 4 Aa : 1 aa; and Gregory's data gave experimental evidence that this method of segregation occurred. The data of Blakeslee, Belling and Farnham on the Jimson weed have since given abundant proof of its application there. Applied to the X's and Y's this would result in 1 XX : 4 XY : 1 YY gamete. It is likely, however, that, on account of the great genetic difference usually existing between the X and Y, the two X's would tend to synapse with each other more closely than with the Y's, which likewise would tend to form a closer pair with each other than with the X's. There is also some experimental basis for this conclusion, as in non-disjunctional diploid females of Drosophila having two X's and a Y, the X's have been shown genetically to have a greater tendency to synapse with each other than with the single Y there. In the tetraploid, in the cells in which the X's and Y's paired off more closely in this fashion, like with like, they would tend to segregate accordingly at the reduction division, like from like. Such reduction would give rise to XY gametes. Hence we see that there would be a tendency for tetraploids to form an even greater proportion of XY as compared with XX and YY gametes than shown in the above 1 : 4 : 1 ratio, which is based on random synapsis. Certainly the XY gametes of the tetraploids would be in the great majority.

Now whenever one of the XY gametes fertilized an egg (XX) from a tetraploid, a sterile zygote having an inter-proportion of sex-producing genes normal to neither male nor female would result. Only a small fraction of the offspring of a tetraploid, then, would be fertile males and females, and hence "reproductive selection" should soon exterminate the tetraploid lines in competition with the freely reproducing diploids—unless, through some strange chance, the tetraploids were favored by reason of some highly advantageous compensating character not present in the diploids, or were somehow removed from competition with the latter.

(4) The only way in which the tetraploid might be freed from the above reproductive handicap would be through the fusion of like sex chromosomes into single masses of double size and "potency," or through the formation of some temporary attachment or attraction between them, operative at the reduction division in such manner as to carry like chromosomes to the same pole. A fusion of the X's of the kind discovered by L. V. Morgan in Drosophila would meet the requirements. The origination of such changes in the chromosomes is, however, an exceedingly rare event, if we may judge by the rarity with which it has been discovered in genetic work. And, in order to be of advantage in the reproduction of tetraploids, this fusion or peculiar attraction would have to originate practically simultaneously with tetraploidy. It could not originate much later than the tetraploidy, and still be of use, because, without such an arrangement, the tetraploids would soon have died out. On the other hand, if the fusion or attraction had originated much before the tetraploidy it would have become extinct prior to the occurrence of the latter. This is because an attachment between like sex chromosomes in diploids puts the line containing it to a reproductive disadvantage somewhat similar to that caused by non-attachment of sex chromosomes in tetraploids. For, as in the case of L. V. Morgan's Drosophila, half the offspring of such diploids are infertile or inviable—namely, the 2-X eggs fertilized by X-containing sperm and the no-X eggs fertilized by Y-containing sperm.

It is evident from all the foregoing that a most remarkable concatenation of events must obtain before a persistent tetraploid line can actually become established, and capable of surviving in a state of nature, in animals having the prevalent type of sex determination. Amongst most higher plants, however, the above mentioned difficulties do not apply.

If the present theory is correct, it may receive two lines of support from comparative cytology. For amongst groups of plants the sporophytes of which are always dioecious, and have the " XY" or " WZ" type of sex determination, there should be the same lack of evidence of tetraploidy as amongst most animals. And amongst groups of animals like the earthworms and fresh-water snails, which are normally hermaphroditic, tetraploidy or even higher forms of polyploidy might occur as readily as amongst most plants. Other things being equal, of course, the more ancient, abundant and diversified the group, the greater should be the chances of finding species which contained chromosome multiples of other species; hence such a test might only be effective in the case of large animal and plant groups. While in some of these it might be that certain peculiar physiological conditions—*e.g.*, the previous attainment of an optimum surface-volume ratio—might render polyploidy disadvantageous, yet in some groups at least it should occur.

In addition to the hermaphroditic groups of animals some of those bisexual groups in which sex is not determined either by sex-gene ratios or by a haploid-diploid relationship should also show polyploidy. Amongst the latter types may perhaps come such forms as the hymenoptera and the rotifers. For, although the male is commonly "haploid," the female "diploid," in these animals, it is gratuitous to assume (as is generally done) that the difference in chromosome quantities is necessarily the sex-differentiating factor here, any more than that a similar difference determines gametophyte versus sporophyte in the moss. As in the latter organisms it has been shown that the determination of sexual versus asexual habit depends upon some "physiological" reaction-complex, set going early in development, and not upon chromosome number, so too in the bee, wasp, etc., it is possible that sex determination depends upon a physiological event decided by the fertilization or non-fertilization of the egg, but independent of chromatin quantity. If this should prove to be true, then these groups also might give evidence of polyploidy.

One important consequence of the prevention of polyploidy in most animals would be a relatively high fixity in number of genes throughout large groups. Another would be the fact that all regions of the chromatin would, in the course of time, become increasingly differentiated from each other, and incapable of carrying on necessary functions performed by other regions. Hence if only a small section of the chromatin were inactivated or removed from both members of a pair of homologous chromosomes, inviability should result, as in the cases of Bridges' and Mohr's "deficiencies." In plants, on the other hand, where tetraploidy may have occurred in the ancestry fairly recently, from the point of view of evolutionary time, certain pairs of chromosomes would be more apt to be similar to others, and more able to act in substitution for them, than in animals. Here, then, small deficiencies would not so regularly prove lethal, and, in fact, lethal genes as well as "visible mutant genes" should be detectable more rarely (see discussion of tetraploids in paper on balanced lethals). Likewise abnormalities in the numbers of entire chromosomes would have less tendency to produce inviability in plants than in animals, inasmuch as the addition or subtraction of one or more chromosomes from a polyploid-derivative involves a smaller ratio change than a similar addition or substraction from a true diploid. Besides the above, there should be other differences from animals discernible on exhaustive genetic analysis, such as the existence of certain types of duplicate genes, and their arrangement in similar order in different linkage groups.

It is believed that the arguments for the rarity of tetraploidy in animals rest on a firm foundation of fact, but the discussions of the three preceding paragraphs are admittedly more speculative. They are presented, however, because they are testable. Any useful theory should to some extent be able to predict results in fields in which information is not yet at hand, or at least point the way for further lines of investigation.

THE METHOD OF EVOLUTION*

By Professor H. J. Muller
University of Texas

*The Role of Multiplication and of Selection in
Turning Accident into Order*

It does, at first sight, seem incredible that all the marvelous organizations in the living things about us could have been put together by anything partaking of the nature of accident. But we must remember that it did not fall together all at once, and that it was all made possible by that almost magical property which life owes to the gene—the power of multiplication of mutated individuals.

For many millions of years, blind chemical forces must have acted and interacted in early times to build up ever different and more complicated organic compounds and systems of compounds. A turning-point was reached when from these shifting combinations those self-multiplying yet mutable materials which we call genes happened to become formed. From that time on the different genes, or the little systems of organic matter containing an association of genes, would necessarily enter into a destructive competition for multiplication against each other, until, step by step, through mutation, or the alteration of the gene, and heredity, or the multiplication of the gene, the complicated life of the present day became differentiated.

It will be worth our while now to examine more closely just how it is really the peculiar power of multiplication of mutant forms which turns this trick of converting accident into order, by making such very extraordinary combinations of accidents possible as could not

The Scientific Monthly, December, 1929, XXIX: 481-505; sections VIII and IX included.

otherwise occur. For some reason, this fundamental feature of the matter does not seem to have been fully realized.

In examining the process of evolution, let us be content at first to make our case a very simple one, and to proceed for a while in a very elementary fashion, in order to avoid confusion. Let us first see how just a simple combination of advantageous changes, or mutations, may be obtained in an organism. Suppose we start with some extremely simple organism, represented by the straight vertical line at the top of Diagram I. We will now allow it to reproduce, and allow enough time to elapse so that some mutations or other will have appeared in each of its descendants (they need not be regarded as first-generation offspring). In our diagram these descendants are shown as vertical lines placed in a horizontal row just below the vertical line representing the ancestral individual, their derivation from which is indicated by dotted connecting lines. We may suppose that multiplication has brought about the existence of seven of these descendants, each with a different "chance" mutation, indicated by a differently shaped spot, and lettered from a_1 to g_1. g_1 may be taken to represent the "good" mutation—the one of an advantageous nature, which is in the path of progress, that happened to occur amongst all the others of a disadvantageous or neutral kind. Now allow a similar length of time to elapse again, in which multiplication and chance mutations take place much as before. The individual with the "good" mutation, g_1, thus multiplies to form seven again, each carrying g_1 (*i.e., the multiplication has involved the variation itself*), but, in addition to g_1, each of the individuals carrying it now carries a second mutation, lettered from a_2 to g_2. Among these second mutations we may again suppose that only one of the seven, g_2, is "good," in the combination in which it occurs. Thus we get a combination, in one individual, of two good mutations, g_1 and g_2, which supposedly have properties that "fit well together," interacting so as to work out advantageously in combination.

Some or all of the other individuals of the previous generation, bearing mutations a_1 to f_1, may also have multiplied. Whether or not they did would not affect our desired result—the attainment of the g_1 g_2 combination—at all, provided only that the g_1 individual itself had been able to multiply and mutate as indicated. If all the individuals of the previous generation had multiplied to just the same extent as the one having g_1 did, there would obviously have been 7×7, or 7^2, or 49, individuals formed bearing some combination of mutations, and of these forty-nine different combinations just one would be the "good" combination—g_1 g_2. Accordingly, without any "natural selection" or any difference whatever in multiplication rate occurring, there would be one individual in forty-nine having the "good" combination. In still other words, the "chance" of the good combination being present in any particular one of these final individuals, in the absence of natural selection, would have been 1/49. It is to be further observed that, no matter

DIAGRAM I

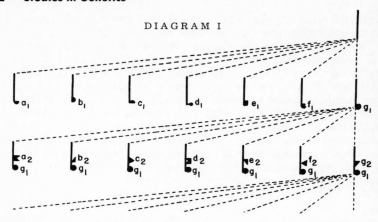

To illustrate the role of multiplication in allowing the origination of a beneficial combination of variations (g_1g_2).

how few or how many of the above forty-nine individuals were actually produced, the ancestors of the g_1 g_2 individual (namely, the g_1-bearing individual and its predecessor, the simple line) had multiplied at the rate required for doing their share in the production of these hypothetical forty-nine individuals.

We may now consider what would happen in the case of some kind of creatures, or objects, which did not have the power of multiplication, but which were otherwise similar to the organisms just discussed, and like them could mutate (or in this case we should simply say, "change"). We may suppose either that these beings produce just one offspring and then themselves die, or that they are potentially immortal and change directly from one form into another. In either case, if their "mutational" possibilities are the same as those of the multiplying organisms previously considered, then we should have to start with seven of them (represented by some of the straight lines at the top of Diagram II) to get one having a change equivalent to g_1. But we should have to be provided with seven already bearing g_1 in order to obtain one having g_2 in addition to g_1. Since in the first place only one in seven come to have g_1 (or its equivalent), we should have to start with 7 × 7, or 7^2, or 49, in order to get the required seven having g_1 (or its equivalent) which would in turn yield the one finally having both g_1 and g_2 (or their equivalents). This is indicated in the diagram. (Here, for convenience in examining the diagram, similar types are grouped together, although chance would scatter them indiscriminately. Also, all forms of "equivalent" type are represented as though identical).

On comparing these non-multiplying objects with the multiplying ones we then see that, to get a given kind of combination by means of a given incidence of "mutation," we have to start with just as many, in the case of the non-multiplying objects, as, in the case of the others, would have been produced in the end by the entire process of multiplication, if all individuals had multiplied at the rate at which the selected individuals did. One out of this total number hence represents the "chance" that our desired combination could have come about purely fortuitously in any particular individual at the end of the given lapse of time, no matter whether the individuals were of the multiplying kind or not. By the laws of chance, if only a few times this total number are given, this combination, or one equivalent to it in "excellence," is practically certain, under the conditions postulated, to be present in one or more individuals.

DIAGRAM II

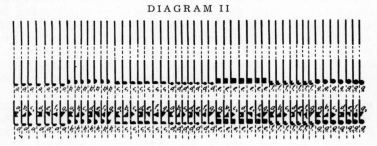

To illustrate the manner in which a beneficial combination of variations (g_1g_2) might arise if there were no multiplication, and the numbers which would then be necessary.

Organisms, however, represent many more than two advantageous features in combination. By the same reasoning as the above, we may find the chance of obtaining a combination of three features— g_1 g_2 g_3. We may assume again that the g_3 change is in itself, at its time of occurrence, about as rare as either g_1 or g_2 alone was: namely, of the frequency of 1 in 7. It will then be seen that the g_1 g_2 individual must be allowed to go through a period (the third period) of mutation and of multiplication times 7, whereupon g_1 g_2 g_3 will arise. Further, it is evident that the rate of multiplication of the individuals in the line of descent that gave rise to the g_1 g_2 g_3-bearing individual was such as to have given rise to $7 \times 7 \times 7$, or 7^3, or 343 individuals, after this lapse of time, if only all descendants of these ancestors had multiplied at the same rate as they themselves had. In the case of non-multiplying objects, it would have been necessary to *start* with 7^3, or 343 individuals, in order to get a corresponding result—an individual with a rare combination of three advantageous mutually adjusted characters, g_1 g_2 g_3. Generalizing, we may say that if the frequency of an advantageous mutation were one in r instead of one in seven, and the number of steps involved was s instead of 3, the corresponding total number of individuals would be r^s. All this is, in fact, only a simple application of a well-known and very elementary mathematical principle applying to the formation of random combinations in general.

It is not, however, until we apply this little formula to the natural conditions pertaining to our immediate problem that its full significance for us becomes clear. What shall we take as our "r" (the *rarity* of advantageous, or "organizational" mutations) and what as our "s" (the number of such advantageous mutational *steps*)?

Undoubtedly r changes its value radically at different stages in the evolutionary sequence, but it would seem quite conservative to represent r, in general, as being as small as 100. In other words, it seems likely that at least 100 mutations must usually occur before one occurs of such a special type that it could take part in the improvement of the life-organization. In flies (*Drosophila*) we find that there are something like ten times as many "lethal" and "semi-lethal" as ordinary visible mutations, and even among the "visibles," the vast majority reduce vitality or lessen the chances of survival in one or more ways. It is certain that not one in 100 detectable mutations is advantageous in flies; in fact, for all we know, the number may be more like one in 100,000.

In the case of s there are almost equally wide limits of uncertainty, but again we may arrive at a safe minimum figure. In flies I have shown that there are at least 1,500 different genes, and probably many times that number. There must then have been at least 1,500 different mutations to produce these genes from their predecessors. This figure, however, seems absurdly small in view of the great complication of a fly's anatomy, physiology and developmental processes. It is very likely, then, that there are many more genes than 1,500 and that each gene has had a history of numerous mutations, which step by step have differentiated it from one original type of gene. Considering too that man is certainly much more complicated than a fly, we might boldly guess that there may have been a million or more advantageous mutational steps in his ancestry (this would allow, say, 50,000 genes, in each of which, on the average, twenty mutational changes had occurred). Let us first, however, take s, for man, at the undoubtedly far too low minimum value of 1,500 and r at 100.

Our total number, r^s, thus becomes $(100)^{1,500}$. That then is the minimum number of individuals we should have to start with in the case of non-multiplying objects, to arrive, by "pure chance," at one having the complication and perfection of organization of a man. We shall examine later what the size of this number implies. It is also the minimum number which the multiplication rate of the ancestors of man would have led to, if all the descendants of these ancestors had continued multiplying at this same rate, *i.e.* without selection.

It might here be inquired whether such a rate of multiplication would have been possible or likely to occur in these ancestors, in the time during which life has existed on the earth. We know that life has been here for a period having an order of magnitude of something like a thousand million years, that is, a million millennia. If there were only 1,500 mutational steps in this time, that would make only one step in each 670,000 years. Our postulate, $r = 100$, requires that an individual in the line of descent of man should multiply at least a hundredfold between each advantageous mutational step that became incorporated in the germ-plasm, and the next one. It is obvious that far more than this much multiplication could easily happen in 670,000 years. For it only takes seven doublings to make a hundredfold multiplication, and the slow-breeding modern European has been able to double his population merely in the space of the last century. The multiplying organisms, then, would have no difficulty in fulfilling these conditions.

Suppose, now, we try the more extreme figures, $r = 10,000$ and $s = 1,000,000$, so that r^s becomes $(10,000)^{1,000,000}$. To go through a million mutational steps in the course of a million millennia would require one mutation to become incorporated in each millennium, or thousand years. It would also be necessary for the selected type of mutant to multiply by 10,000 during this period of time, and meanwhile to undergo another mutation. There can be no reasonable doubt that a millennium is plenty long enough for many another mutation to occur, in all the descendant germ-plasms, but how about the large amount of multiplication here required? Most lower organisms go through a generation in not over a year's time, and are able, when given the opportunity, to multiply many fold in a single generation. If, however, we suppose that the "select" individuals, those with "good" mutations, only increase in numbers, on an average, by 2 per cent in each generation, then, at a year to a generation, each such individual would increase from unity to nearly two hundred million in the course of a thousand years. This is far beyond our requirement of 10,000 times.[1] Thus we see that the multiplying organism could probably do much better than accumulate 1,000,000 mutations during the time that life has already existed here, even though each mutation represented the selection of the best in 10,000.[2] Multiplication hence has probably afforded the opportunity of obtaining an individual that represents a chance of even less than one in $(10,000)^{1,000,000}$.

It should be noticed that, for the evolution of the multiplying organisms, the only two required conditions have been the occurrence of "chance" mutations (which need include only a very minute proportion of "good" ones), and the ability of the individuals carrying the "good" mutations to multiply to an extent which, within the limits of one generation need be only extremely limited, but which, continued over a great lapse of time by something akin to a geometric progression, becomes prodigious indeed. In this process the rôle of "natural selection" consists in just this: that by the elimination of the "unfit" individuals, or the restriction of their numbers, room is made to *allow* the multiplication of the others at the rate required to provide the "chance" for the remarkable 1 in $(100)^{1,500}$ or one in $(10,000)^{1,000,000}$ combination to appear. In other words, selection merely gives opportunity for the multiplication to proceed in the adaptive or better-organized lines at such a rate as would, if uniformly continued throughout, have given the total which automatically contains the "desired" combination.[3]

If we imagine a world in which, through some sort of miraculous intervention, the combinations which we now call the "unfit" are all allowed to persist and reproduce like the others, the evolution of the "fit" would nevertheless proceed much as in our own world, so long as they too were granted the opportunity to multiply as they do here. Thus "natural selection" would not be necessary for their production. But these "fit" or "well-organized" individuals, and lines of individuals, though in absolute numbers as numerous as here, would necessarily form but an infinitesimal fraction of all the unthinkably vast horde of other combinations that had come into existence simultaneously (just as in the hypothetical case of the non-multiplying beings, in which, if we started with this same final number to begin with, we would eventually find included among them by sheer accident creatures as complexly adapted as ourselves). The fact that the fit owed their existence to "chance" would then be obvious, owing to the relative smallness of the minority in which they existed. In our world, the misfits are largely nipped in the bud, and yet, in the sense just explained, we see that we too are really but the vanishingly small, viable, visible fraction of a stupendous ghostly army of potential creatures, involving a total of $(100)^{1,500}$ to $(10,000)^{1,000,000}$, or maybe many more, possible combinations of misfits.

A little consideration may now be given to the size of this theoretical total number, to show that actually it would be quite impossible of physical attainment. Consequently, if there were no selective elimination, multiplication could not possibly have gone on to anything like the required extent in the "good" lines. Likewise, if we had had to do with objects that could not multiply, there could not possibly have been anywhere near enough of them provided in the beginning to allow an organization comparable with that of a higher or even lower organism to be formed in any of them by mere "chance."

Even the admittedly far too low minimum figure, $(100)^{1,500}$, is of staggeringly great dimensions. If there were this many beings actually produced, then, even if each being were as small as an electron, and all the beings were packed tight together, there would not be nearly enough room in the entire Einsteinian universe, packing them in a hundred times beyond the limits of the farthest visible stars and spiral nebulae, for even an insignificant tittle of them. If we allowed each of these packed "creatures" to go through its entire evolution, of 1,500 steps, in the millionth part of a second, and then substituted another "creature" for it and gave the latter a like chance, and so on for a quintillion years, we still should not have begun to make any appreciable impression on the above number. Neither should we if, in addition, each of these packed beings of electron size, present for each instant, were itself expanded into an entire Einsteinian universe, and each of these universes were then crammed with beings of electron size in its turn. In fact, we might continue thus expanding and subdividing worlds time and again without approaching sensibly close to the required figure.

Hence, in beings without the property of multiplication of variations, and its corollary, natural selection, any such incredible combination of accidents as ourselves would have been totally impossible of occurrence within the limits of practically any number of universes. We are thus really justified in feeling that we could not have fallen together by any accident of inanimate nature. But, given the power of multiplication of variations resident in "living" things, due to their genes, and all this is changed, and we are enabled to enjoy the benefits—such as they may be—of being the select of the select, such as it would have taken a surpassingly vast number of worlds to search through, before our match could be found anywhere by the ordinary processes of chance. In that way, I hope, the metaphysician may reach his "philosophical satisfaction" in the contemplation of his own frame and of the processes whereby it came into existence.

The Task Ahead

The biologist is not satisfied to stop there, however. The real problems of the generation of new living things are only commencing to open up. The occurrence of variations, although "accidental" in the sense just explained, nevertheless is subject to a mechanism, our knowledge of which is as yet in its most elementary stage. Moreover, the biologist of broader view is not so well satisfied with his own frame. He knows that there never has been any one objective in the course of evolution, and that every creature, including man, is only on probation, and may give way before another in which a more advantageous succession of mutations happens to come along. The vast majority of species, in fact, have perished along the way, and only a relatively few survive, through change, to form the continuing threads of life that branch out again.

Man, however, is now the first creature in the world to have this advantage—he has reached some understanding of this process of evolution in which he has hitherto been caught and blown about, and with understanding there frequently comes some measure of control. He can now produce mutations for the first time, and I have no doubt he will soon experiment with this knowledge and in time by its means greatly improve and alter the forms and functionings of those domestic animals and plants which he has taken under his care. Look at the motley shapes of flies that have been made in the laboratory, and you may more readily appreciate the possibilities thus presented.

Despite these advantages, we are today almost as far as ever from producing to order the exact mutations which we want. Enough, for the plants and animals, simply to produce a great many mutations and then take our choice, as nature has done in a far slower and more halting fashion. But the research must go on. Man must eventually take his own fate into his own hands, biologically as well as otherwise, and not be content to remain, in his most essential respect, the catspaw of natural forces, to be fashioned, played with and cast aside.

If we have had a billion years of evolution behind us, and have advanced from something like an ameba to something like a man, then, in the many millions of years which are still in store for our world, why may we not be able to make a further great advance, perhaps far greater even than this under our own increasingly intelligent guidance? At least, if we are men as we like to think of men, challenging all things, we must make the attempt, and die fighting if need be, with our eyes open.

Notes

[1]A 1 per cent increase, per generation, would give a multiplication of about 14,000 times in 1,000 years.

[2]Allowance must, however, be made for the fact that accidental elimination wipes out the great majority of mutant genes within a few generations after their origination. That is, the process of "differential multiplication" or "selection" is very haphazard until a sizable number of individuals with the mutant gene happens to become established. This is, of course, very much more true in the case of recessive mutants than of dominants, unless there is very much inbreeding. (One effect of this would be to weight the scales of selection heavily in favor of dominants, leaving the recessives as the "abnormal" forms.)

There is another process which works in the opposite direction to the above, i.e., which hastens the "establishment" of advantageous mutations in the selected lines of descent. This process is the formation of new combinations of genes occurring in sexual reproduction. For the sake of simplicity it has been ignored in the above account. By its means it is made possible that various different advantageous mutant genes which have been multiplying simultaneously in parallel, in as many different (but partially overlapping) sections of a population, can be finally combined into one line of descent. Thus many more mutant genes can be accumulated into one (final) line of descent, in a given length of time, than if all the mutational events and selections had to occur successively in a single line. Owing to this factor, the number of mutational steps may well have been of a considerably higher order of magnitude than 1,000,000.

[3]At the same time, we should not minimize the importance of natural selection in determining which individuals will be allowed to multiply, and, therefore, which of the myriads of possible directions evolution will be allowed to take. The old analogy to the process of pruning a tree is very pertinent in this connection.

SOME GENETIC ASPECTS OF SEX*

Professor H. J. Muller
University of Texas

Sexuality

From the genetic point of view it is advantageous to begin by considering sex in the broader sense of sexuality. It is not generally realized that genetics has finally solved the age-old problem of the reason for the existence (*i.e.*, the function) of sexuality and sex, and that only geneticists can properly answer the question, "Is sex necessary?" There is no basic biological reason why reproduction, variation and evolution can not go on indefinitely without sexuality or sex; therefore, sex is not, in an absolute sense, a necessity, it is a "luxury." It is, however, highly desirable and useful, and so it becomes necessary in a relativistic sense, when our competitor-species also are endowed with sex, for sexless beings, although often at a temporary advantage, can not keep up the pace set by sexual beings in the evolutionary race and, when readjustments are called for, they must eventually lose out. Thus sexual beings form most of the central and the continuing portions of the evolutionary tree from which ever and again new sexless end-twigs sprout off.

Whatever the secondary needs of present-day somatoplasm may be, there is no fundamental protoplasmic need for rejuvenation of the germ plasm through sexual union, no reason to believe that "protoplasmic stimulation" is *per se* produced by mingling of unlike germ plasms, nor any evidence that variation of the hereditary particles is induced by "panmixia." A more reasonable claim might be made out for the new genetic concept of "heterosis" as furnishing the function of sexuality and sex. By heterosis we mean the increased vigor of hybrids, as compared with pure breeds, which is caused by the preponderant dominance of the genes favoring survival and growth furnished by both parents. But a more searching study of this matter shows that, in the main, heterosis affords only a compensatory advantage, in that it makes up for deficiencies that sexual reproduction is itself mostly to blame for. Heterosis arises only when cross breeding is wider than it has been on the average in previous generations. But if this wider crossbreeding is kept up, deleterious recessive genes will accumulate until a new equilibrium is reached, at which stage there is a sufficient abundance of such genes to cause even these more "mixed-blooded" individuals to exhibit as many recessive defects as did their "purer blooded" ancestors. *Vice versa*, if we increase the intensity of inbreeding,

The American Naturalist, Vol. LXVI, March-April, 1932; section I included; paper read at the symposium on "The Biology of Sex" before the American Society of Naturalists, New Orleans, December 31, 1931.

the more rigorous selection ensuing will eventually lead to the inbred line being purged till it has as great vigor as its more crossbred ancestors. The closer the inbreeding, the less does sexual reproduction depart, in its genetic effects, from asexual reproduction, and we may conclude that at the limiting state, that of asexual reproduction, there would not (after the attainment of a state of equilibrium) be less vigor than in sexual organisms. The attainment of equilibrium in regard to the number of harmful mutant genes present may, however, require a very considerable time, and in the meantime sexual reproduction would be of advantage through its induction of heterosis. Heterosis may therefore have been of immediate value, in the first origination of sexuality, and so it may explain how sexuality happened to become established in the beginning, as Altenburg has suggested in an as yet unpublished work. But heterosis can not explain the major function of sexuality and why it has persisted in the long run, and acquired such complicated accessories.

Among the primary and accessory features of sexuality there must be considered not only the differentiation of male from female germ cells, the differentiation of male from female sex organs, the separation of the sexes, with its associated mechanism of sex determination, and the differentiation of secondary sexual and " sex-limited" characters in general, but also the mechanism of Mendelian heredity itself, involving segregation of homologous chromosomes, independent assortment of non-homologous chromosomes and crossing over. Without sexual reproduction, the latter mechanisms are not called for, and would not continue to operate. Which, however, among the attributes mentioned, occupy a more primary and which a more secondary status? It is clear that not only is sexual reproduction necessary for the operation of segregation and recombination of chromosomes and chromosome parts, but, conversely, the latter are necessary in order that sexual reproduction may have any permanent value, while all the other chracteristics of sexuality, though enhancing, are dispensable. Of the two major features, segregation and recombination,[1] only recombination is in itself .f of evolutionary value, but it can not take place without segregation and so we must suppose the two to have sprung into existence at nearly the same time. Mendelian heredity must therefore have arisen almost full fledged, when sexuality arose. This complicated step, which probably required a peculiar concatenation of accidents, along with selection, seems to have been taken in the green algae, and from them to have been inherited by animals and higher plants alike.

The essence of sexuality, then, is Mendelian recombination. Not increased variation in the sense of more change in the hereditary units or genes, now that we know there are these units, but the making and the testing out of all sorts of combinations among these gene mutations which would arise and become evident any way.

Sexuality, through recombination, is a means for making the fullest use of the possibilities of gene mutations; thus it is itself an accessory process, accessory to the primary process of gene mutation.

There are two ways in which recombination of gene mutations is valuable. One, by far the lesser way, is the providing of an opportunity for continual shifting and readjustment of the relative abundance of different types as external conditions vary back and forth, and here and now one, there and then another combination becomes more advantageous for the maintenance of the species. In this process heterozygosity is an asset and the disadvantageous combinations continually produced are an insurance against the day when some of them will be needed.

The other, the major value of recombination, is the production, among many misfits, of some combinations that are of permanent advantage to the species and that eventually become fully established in it as a part of its normal constitution. Without sexual reproduction, the various favorable mutations that occur must simply compete· with each other, and either divide the field among themselves or crowd each other out till but the best adapted for the given conditions remains. In asexual organisms, before the descendants can acquire a combination of beneficial mutations, these must first have occurred in succession, within the same lines of descent. In sexual organisms, however, most of the beneficial mutations that occur simultaneously, or in different original lines of descent, can increase largely independently of one another and diffuse *through* one another, as it were (see Diagram 1). (Our diagram does not accurately represent this spread of genes through one another; it would hold only if the individuals and genes were fixed in geographical position and unable to disseminate freely amongst one another. If their positions were completely random, we should need a new dimension, at right angles to the previous ones, to represent the diffusion of each new mutation. The actual situation lies somewhere between these two extreme alternatives.)

Now it can easily be shown that the ratio which (on the average) the number of individuals in the most favored line of descent, counting from the time of occurrence of one favorable mutation (A) to the time of occurrence, within the same line, of the next favorable mutation (B), bears to the number of individuals in the population as a whole in the same period (in Diagram 1, the ratio of the left-hand mutant shaded area A to the total area, in the region between two horizontal lines drawn through the points of origination of mutant shaded areas A and B) would represent roughly the speed of evolution in an asexual as compared with a sexual organism,[2] provided a correction, making the situation still more favorable to the sexual organism, is made here, namely, multiplication of this ratio by a factor representing the greater speed of increase of the favorable mutations in the sexual than in the asexual organisms, due

EVOLUTIONARY SPREAD OF ADVANTAGEOUS MUTATIONS
In Asexual Reproduction; In Sexual Reproduction

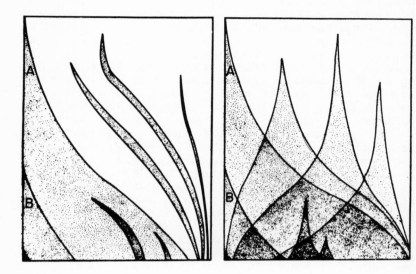

Diagram 1. Showing the method of spreading of advantageous mutations in asexual and sexual organisms, respectively. Time is here the vertical dimension, progressing downwards. In the horizontal dimension a given population stationary in total numbers, is represented. Sections of the population bearing advantageous mutant genes are darkened, proportionally to the number of such genes. In asexual organisms these genes compete and hinder one another's spread; in sexual organisms they spread through one another. See, however, qualifications in text (p. 471), explaining limitations of a diagram in only two dimensions. The diagram is simplified in a number of other ways as well. For example, all mutants represented are shown as spreading at nearly the same rate, if they do spread, and this rate is shown as about the same regardless of the extent to which they have entered into combination with one another.

to the fact that in the former the different favored mutations do not have nearly so much tendency to interfere with one another's increase. When such calculations are made, using any reasonable-seeming premises for mutation rate, selection and population size, within very wide limits, it is found that the advantage of sexual over asexual organisms in the evolutionary race is enormous.

In these calculations, and in the diagram, the assumption has been made, for the sake of simplicity, that the advantage of a mutation is the same regardless of the combination in which it occurs. However, the value of a combination of mutations will sometimes be far greater than the mere sum, or even the product, of the values of each mutant condition taken separately. Therefore, as Wright has recently pointed out, it is sometimes possible, by means of recombination occurring before selection, to get valuable combination-types which would not have come into existence at all, or only with far greater difficulty, if the "complementary" mutations composing them had had to occur and then to become selected in succession, as must happen in asexual reproduction.

While it is true that only the findings of modern genetics could enable our conception of the function of sexuality to take on the definite form above outlined, and only they could furnish real proof of this conception, nevertheless it should be recognized that the core of the idea—the formation of new combinations of "determinants," having a selective value sometimes greater than the original combinations—was conjured up long ago by the genius of Weismann, who herein, as in a number of his other major contentions (non-inheritance of acquired characters, reduction division), to-day stands brilliantly confirmed.[3]

Notes

[1]It is not possible at present to decide definitely whether recombination of whole chromosomes or crossing over was first evolved; either would have been sufficient to give value to sexuality. But it seems more probable that crossing over was a later development.

[2]For while, in the given time, only one new advantageous mutation (B) became available in the favored line (A) of the asexual organism (the mutation rate being such as to give one in this number of individuals), in the sexual organism as many new advantageous mutations would become available, for combination with A, as the area of A goes into the total area.

[3]I am indebted to Professor S. J. Holmes for having redirected my attention to this important historical fact, subsequently to my address at New Orleans.

UNEQUAL CROSSING-OVER IN THE BAR MUTANT AS A RESULT OF DUPLICATION OF A MINUTE CHROMOSOME SECTION*

By H. J. Muller, Corresponding-member of the Academy, A. A. Prokofjeva-Belgovskaja, and K. V. Kossikov

In accordance with a hypothesis long held by the senior author that the mutation "Bar" in *Drosophila melanogaster* involves the duplication *in situ* of a gene or small section of the X-chromosome, salivary gland studies were made by Prokofjeva and revealed the presence of a minute section in the Bar-containing chromosome in addition to the material present in the normal.[1] The extra piece contains at least two very faint visible bands and is somewhat bulged in the transverse direction. In its morphological appearance it seems identical with a section directly adjacent to it, as we had expected on theoretical grounds, and it has no doubt been derived by the duplication of that section. That is, the Bar chromosome has two such sections directly following upon one another (and therefore four bands), and the normal chromosome only one such section (and therefore two bands). They follow in the same order, not mirror-image-wise. This condition obviously arose in the first place by means of breakage and mutual translocation between homologous or sister chromosomes at nearly but not quite the same point. As the complementary recombinational chromosome would have been deficient this also illustrates one method by which small interstitial deficiencies arise.

The Bar phaenotype, then, represents the "position effect" of the extra section of chromatin, interacting with another locus or loci nearby in the chromosome. Unequal crossing-over occurs when the left-hand member of the twin sections in one chromosome happens to conjugate and cross over with the right-hand member in the homologous chromosome, thus giving rise to chromosomes with three and one section—"double-Bar" and normal, respectively. Infra-Bar must have arisen by a mutation in one of the duplicated sections and it can be concluded from Sturtevant's data that in unequal crossing-over the points of breakage must always lie to the right of one infra-Bar locus and to the left of the other one. This probably means that the locus in question lies at or near the point of junction of the two sections. The tendency to asymmetrical synapsis caused by the longitudinal homology of the twin sections expresses itself even among the constituent chromatids of the salivary gland chromosome by a longitudinal displacement of the chromatids in this region, amongst one another, giving an ir-

Comptes Rendus de l'Academie des Sciences de l'URRS, Vol. I, No. 2, January 25, 1936.

regularly zigzag banding effect here. Our present findings also explain the hitherto contradictory-seeming facts that Bar mutation must have involved some sort of change in a locus normally present in this position in the X-chromosome [since Bar has arisen several times in the same region] but that nevertheless, when "the Bar locus" is lost by unequal crossing-over, the resulting individual is viable and normal. For what is lost is not "the Bar locus," but only one of two twin segments. It is also fallacious to consider the "reverse mutation" of Bar to normal as constituting deficiency of an individual gene, as Demerec has done, and his inferences concerning the viability or inviability of single-gene deficiencies in general thus lose validity, since the Bar analogy was used in inferring that only single genes were lost in the other cases.

The senior author has found two other cases of origination of Bar ("moderate-Bar 1" and "moderate-Bar 2") from normal. Both of these were produced in spermatozoa by X-rays and consisted of inversions of a section of chromosome extending from just to the left of the primary Bar locus to the inert region. Salivary gland examinations by Kossikov have confirmed this. In this case, as in Dobzhansky's "baroid" and Stone's "super-Bar," the change is obviously a position effect caused either by the primary Bar locus being separated from some neighbour gene(s) whose coaction normally prevents the Bar effect from being produced, or by the Bar locus coming into the neighbourhood of other genes, which now coact with it to cause the Bar reaction. Presumably the Bar locus also has another, normal function (in the normal fly at least).

Institute of Genetics
Academy of Sciences of the USSR.
Moscow.

Received
15. XII. 1935.

Note

[1] Since the extra section and its peculiar features were first observed by Prokofjeva, her findings have been fully confirmed by observations carried out by the other authors and by other members of the laboratory, and we have also been notified that E. N. Volotov, working at the Institute of Experimental Biology under the direction of Dubinin, has independently noted the presence of an extra section of chromosome in the case of double-Bar, although he believed it to be hardly demonstrable in the case of Bar itself.

BAR DUPLICATION*

by H. J. Muller

In connection with the article "Bar as a Duplication," published in the February 28 issue of *Science*, and signed by C. B. Bridges in Pasadena on February 21, the attention of American readers is called to the fact that essentially the same findings and interpretation as here given by Bridges had already been set forth by the undersigned in co-authorship with Prokofyeva and Kossikov in a preliminary article without figures, entitled "Unequal Crossing over in the Bar Mutant as a Result of Duplication of a Minute Chromosome Section." This article was sent in on December 15, 1935, to the bi-monthly journal, *Comptes Rendus of the Academy of Sciences of the USSR*, and was published in the second number of that journal for 1936, issued on January 25. This issue probably did not reach the United States in February, but our results had been publicly announced at a meeting of geneticists in Moscow on December 26, and privately communicated to a number of American and English colleagues in December and January. We should, of course, in our original article, have called the attention of our readers to Bridges' independent or confirmatory work, had we known of it, but we must here explain that our first information concerning it was contained in the above-mentioned issue of *Science*. On the other hand, we did in our article mention the partially parallel work of Volotoff, of the Institute of Experimental Biology, Moscow (announced at the same meeting but as yet unpublished), in which the presence of an "inserted section," of unidentified origin, had been observed in the case of double Bar.

Our own finding came as the result of a long and deliberate search for the very structure finally found; in this we had long been hampered by technical difficulties. The idea that Bar may represent a duplication in situ had been proposed by the present author some years ago, in consideration of its furnishing an explanation of the phenomenon of unequal crossing over and of certain other peculiarities of the Bar case. It may be noted that Bridges' more refined optical technique has allowed him, in this case as in others, to observe a greater degree of detail in the banding of the chromosomes than has been directly visible to us. The same principles concerning the construction of the duplication were, however, noted in both cases—the immediate juxtaposition of the two identical sections, their identical direction (not mirror-image-wise), the greater degree of transverse expansion of each section when they were duplicated than otherwise and the greater obscurement or zigzagging tendency of the bands when duplicated. The latter two

Science, 1936, 83: 528-30.

phenomena were interpreted by us both as effects of that tendency to synapsis between the anterior and posterior twin sections which when occurring in the germ cells, results in the unequal crossing over.

We would take issue, however, with Bridges' designation of the duplication as an "inserted" piece, the point of "insertion" of which (to right or left of the original single section) is uncertain. Not only the cytological evidence, but, with much more exactitude, the fact that normals derived from Bar by unequal crossing over are never deficient, prove that the two sections follow immediately upon one another, without any intervening section whatever. This in turn shows that if there had been an actual insertion of a piece from one X chromosome into a sister or homologous X chromosome, one of the two points of breakage giving rise to the small fragment of the first chromosome must have been in exactly the same position as the point of breakage of the second chromosome, into which the piece from the first became inserted. Such a coincidence could be plausibly explained only on the hypothesis that a single X chromosome had become broken at the two points in question first, and then, before reattachment occurred, had doubled, forming two parallel chromatids; after that, attachments of the broken ends occurred in such a way as to result in the inclusion of both of the interstitial fragments, one after the other, into the same chromosome, while the other chromosome (if it rejoined at all) was left deficient. On this view both twin pieces would really have been both deleted and inserted. The simpler and more probable explanation for this case, however, is that the two sister or homologous X chromosomes were already separate at the time of breakage, that only the left-hand break occurred in one of them, and only the right-hand break in the other, and that in the subsequent process of attachment, the left-hand piece of the chromosome having the breakage further to the right became attached to the right-hand piece of the chromosome having the breakage further to the left. On this more probable view, then, the duplication did not originate as an insertion at all, and the original mutual breakage point is the point where one twin section now joins the other one. If the remaining pieces also re-united, they must have formed a complementary, deficient chromosome, which was later lost. It is evident that, on this view, the Bar duplication itself has originated by a process which may be termed "unequal crossing over." The unequal crossing over ordinarily observed in Bar is, then, only a kind of secondary unequal crossing over, resulting indirectly from the primary unequal crossing over which established the duplication in the first place.

We would also take issue with Bridges' opinion that the phenotypic effect, Bar eye, may, according to "taste," be considered either as a result of the relative dosage change of genes in the duplicated section, or as a "position effect." For evidence has been found (see discussion by the author, chiefly based on evidence by Offermann), that Bar behaves as a neomorph. That is, the mere addition of extra doses of the general region in question (when these contain genes of normal arrangement and composition) does not increase the Bar effect; only extra doses of the Bar genetic complex itself increase the Bar effect. On the other hand, other rearrangements of genes in the Bar region, which we have no reason to suppose involve duplications, do cause phenotypic effects similar to those of the Bar duplication (the first case known to us being that of Stone's "Super-Bar," 1930, then Dobzhansky's "Baroid," 1931, then two "moderate-Bar" inversions of the author and many rearrangements recently reported by Volotoff). The phenotypic change is therefore solely a result of the "position effect," and this effect must be sharply distinguished from the effect of dosage change, even though in many individual cases in genetics it has not yet been possible to judge with which class of effect we are dealing.

We consider the point of chief interest in the Bar case to be its illustration of the manner of origination of extra genes in evolution. Bar had for a long time offered the best case yet known for the idea that genes could arise *de novo*. Its interpretation as some sort of duplication met with difficulties, in our ignorance of the real existence of a "position effect" of non-allelomorphic genes upon one another. Now these difficulties are resolved and there remains no reason to doubt the application of the dictum "all life from preexisting life" and "every cell from a pre-existing cell" to the gene: "every gene from a pre-existing gene." We need at present make an exception here only of those very special conditions under which life itself, as a naked gene, originates.

That the addition of genes by duplicational processes, such as the insertion of small pieces and primary unequal crossing over, is still a factor in evolution, has previously been urged by us. We have discussed the matter recently in connection with the case of achaete and scute, in which the functional similarity found to exist between these neighbouring genes suggested that a duplication had occurred in the ancestry of the normal form, and we discussed it again in the case of a small insertion (scute 19) produced by X-rays, in which a stock of individuals homozygous for the extra section is viable and fertile. It was pointed out in the latter paper that the twin regions would more commonly lie near to one another, in the same chromosome, rather than far apart, as they did in this case. These papers were independent of the recent paper of Bridges on "Salivary Chromosome Maps." which gives cytological evidence of the repetition of at least two sections in the normal second chromosome, and which, on the basis of these, arrives at the same general conclusions. Another case of this kind (that of the "bulb" in the normal X chromosome) has, independently of the cases of Bridges, been discovered by Offermann, who again draws similar conclusions. And most recently Kossikov has found still another case, as yet unpublished. The Bar case fits in with all this convergent evidence and constitutes the first case actually observed in Drosophila of the spontaneous origination of a minute duplication capable of maintaining itself in the homozygous condition.

BEARINGS OF THE DROSOPHILA WORK ON PROBLEMS OF SYSTEMATICS*

Professor H. J. Muller

Institute of Animal Genetics, University of Edinburgh

The bearings of the *Drosophila* work on systematics have so far lain chiefly in the light this work has thrown on the nature of the processes whereby differentiation between groups of organisms takes place. There is evidence that species of *Drosophila*, as of other animals, very rarely originate at one bound, but originate by the accumulation of what were originally individual genetic differences. It has been found in *Drosophila* that the latter are virtually always Mendelian and chromosomal in nature, and are of two major categories, the first and more important being gene mutations and the second being rearrangements of sections of chromosomes containing groups of genes. Both types arise by sudden steps, mutations, which are occasioned by chemical accidents of ultra-microscopic dimensions.

As this process does not permit a correlation between the kind of condition under which a mutation takes place and the kind of character-change caused by the mutation, most mutations are necessarily detrimental, and the direction of evolution, in so far as it is adaptive at all, must be determined by natural selection, choosing from among many different biological possibilities. In this process the "small mutations," which are more numerous than the large ones, will more often take part, being less likely to be detrimental. In *Drosophila* exact analysis has shown that virtually all genetic individual differences are of this mutational Mendelian and chromosomal nature, even those which are less clear-cut and seem to show continuous variability, there being no genetic residuum due to other causes.

The differences due to gene mutation, and also those due to sectional change, are found not only in the laboratory, but also in nature, in *Drosophila*, any natural population being very heterozygous, especially for "small mutations." The numbers and kinds of mutants present fluctuate in a more or less random way in different regions and at different times, but there are also some adaptive

Proceedings of the Zoological Society, Series C, Vol. 108, 1938 (Meeting of April 26, 1938), pp. 55-57.

local differences which must have resulted from selection. The differences between races and even between species can not only be matched, phaenotypically, by these individual differences, but, in those cases where analysis has been possible, have proved to be of fundamentally the same kind genetically. Most of the racial or specific differences tested, whether in morphological characters or in physiological ones (such as cross-infertility), depend upon numerous gene mutations, individually of small effect.

The non-crossibility of different groups, or the comparative infertility or inviability of their hybrids, receives its explanation in the numerous mutations which cause infertility, sterility, or inviability when in one genetic combination and not another. When geographical or other isolation allows two populations to differentiate genetically, among the mutations differentiating them will be those which, while not reducing fertility in the genetic milieu in which they occur, will reduce it when in combination with the genotype of the other population. Thus a long period of non-mixing of two groups is inevitably attended by the origination of actual immiscibility, *i. e.*, genetic isolation.

Displacements of chromosome sections (gene rearrangements) occur naturally far less frequently than gene mutations, and exactly the same sectional change hardly ever occurs twice. Occasionally, however, a given sectional change may become more or less spread throughout a population. One factor influencing their spread lies in the fact that the rearrangements of the genes influence the functioning of those genes lying near the points of breakage and exchange of the chromosomes ("position effect"), thus giving effects similar to those of gene mutations, which may be selected for or against. Another factor is that the rearranged section may no longer be able to undergo effective interchange (crossing-over) with the original section, and since it will then not accumulate the same recessive mutant genes as the latter it tends to give more vigorous hybrids (heterosis) unless it becomes too greatly multiplied. Being genetically isolated it may serve as a centre within the germ plasm for the building up of a different genetic complex, which may on occasion give opportunity for the origination of a genetically different population. But in early stages its lack of interchangibility will militate against its evolvability.

The kinds of sectional changes that can differentiate species depend in the first place upon the kinds that can occur and survive. Rearrangements able to survive at all always involve a breakage of one or more chromosomes at at least two points, together with a union of the pieces so formed, by their broken ends in a new order, leaving the originally free ends ("telomeres") still free, and leaving one fibre attachment ("centromere") on each chromosome. But of the different types of translocations, inversions, etc. thus formed only those can easily become spread in a population which, when in heterozygous combination with the normal type, do not lead to a reduction of fertility by the formation of inviable combinations. In *Drosophila* this condition is only met by inversions confined to a given chromosome arm, and to a lesser extent by exchanges between virtually whole arms. Hence the former chiefly, and to a much lesser extent the latter, form the great bulk of the sectional differentiations between races and species of *Drosophila*. That other types occasionally occur also shows that on rare occasions, the whole population may arise from a very few individuals. For the smaller the population the more chance would a rearrangement suffering from the temporary disadvantage in question have to become multiplied, accidentally, despite this disadvantage, so as to become the predominant type in the group.

While the sectional differences between races and species are more easily studied than the differences caused by gene mutations, they are far less numerous than the latter, and evolution and differentiation between groups could go on without them. However, they can afford a useful means for the tracing of phylogeny. The relative frequencies of the different kinds of sectional changes which will predominate in the evolution of different groups, and the relative frequencies of sectional rearrangements as a whole as compared with gene mutations will depend on various factors. Among these are those which influence the frequencies of mutations of different kinds, the amount of crossing-over, and whether it occurs in male, female, or both, the length of generation, degree of inbreeding, amount of migration, amount of accidental differential multiplication of the individuals of the population, the intensity and character of the position effects, etc. The principles governing the operation of these factors are to some extent already known, so that deductions can be made regarding the types of differentiation occurring in different groups, in so far as these factors have been determined. However, there remains a wide field for study here, and much may be learned from investigations of "population genetics" and from genetic analyses of racial and specific differences.

Although all the work agrees in showing that speciation represents no absolute stage in evolution, but is gradually arrived at, and intergrades imperceptibly into racial differentiation beneath it and generic differentiation above, nevertheless the concept represents a real stage, corresponding to something of significance in nature, in so far as we may identify it with the stage at which effective intercrossing stops. For divergence goes on very differently, and much more freely, between groups that cannot cross than it does between those which can and do cross, and it is therefore justifiable and useful, even though difficult, to make the species distinction. At the same time it must be recognized that the species are in flux, and that an adequate understanding of their relationships can be arrived at only on the basis of an understanding of the relationships between the minor groups and even between the individuals, supplemented by the study of the differences found through observations on the systematics of the larger groups.

BEARINGS OF THE DROSOPHILA WORK ON SYSTEMATICS*

H. J. Muller

Received for Publication 28 August, 1938

The Genesis of Interspecific Incompatibility through Gene-mutations

In the light of the above examples, it will be clear that whenever two populations, originally of one type, are long prevented from interbreeding, by whatever means, the divergent processes of spread of rare accidentally arising mutations must tend to result in such disharmonious systems being formed as those cited above. Within any one population, of course, only such mutations can become established as leave the system harmonious. This is true no matter whether they become established by accidental spreading or by direct aid of natural selection, but in either case the harmoniousness of the result may be regarded as an aspect of natural selection, taken in a larger sense. But since there are so many genes, not only in the whole germ-plasm, but so many affecting any one given complex character, like fertility, or, to say the same thing in a different way, since so many mutations are possible that produce similar end-results though by different chemical mechanisms of development and physiology, some of the mutations which become established in the two isolated groups will be different from one another even when selection is tending in the same direction, or even when it is tending to maintain the *status quo* with regard to the character-effects in relation to which it is operating. For these character-effects are in a sense end-results, and it is these end-results, rather than the mechanism whereby they are produced, that determine whether or not a given mutation that accidentally arises and spreads to the point where it may be tested shall be allowed to persist. The nature of the mechanism only becomes important later, if two different mechanisms are mixed!

As those newly established mutations which differ in the two

The New Systematics (J. S. Huxley, ed.), Oxford: Clarendon Press, 1940, pp. 185—268; section 5, last part of section 8, and all of section 9 (with figure 2) included.

groups have not been selected for their compatability with one another, some must eventually arise which are more or less incompatible. Thus, if these two systems of mutations are later brought together by crossing, abnormalities will be engendered in the development or functioning of the character under consideration. In our present case, the character considered is fertility, but the same applies to viability, "crossability," and, in general, to physiological as well as morphological characters. As a morphological effect of this kind we may cite the irregular development of the bristles noted by Sturtevant in F_1 hybrids of *D. melanogaster* and *simulans*, each of which in the original species has a regular set of bristles, of the same pattern in the two. Which kind of character becomes affected earliest, and to what degree, in the course of the evolutionary divergence, will depend in part upon its general complexity (which is correlated with the number of genes affecting it), in part on the nicety or instability of the equilibria of processes necessary for its proper functioning, and in part on the accidental circumstances that determined just which incompatible mutations happened to become established first. The large role of accident here is proved by the frequency and extent to which, in Drosophila, interspecific hybrid males (or, in general, hybrids of the heterozygous sex) from reciprocal crosses differ in the disturbance of their viability and of their germ-cell development.

In addition to this mutual incompatibility of the two genetically metamorphosing groups (groups which perhaps are changing little or not at all in their morphology and in the general features of their embryology and physiology), there will eventually arise incompatibilities between each of them and the original system from which both sprang, and the same general mechanism will also make them incompatible with other branches of the original species. For, once some mutations become established in an evolving group under consideration, even though these in themselves may still be harmonious in their action in connexion with the original system, they now provide a different genetic background for further mutations. That is, some of the latter can and will become established now which, though functioning innocuously or favourably in connexion with these genes which mutated earlier, act in a deleterious way when these are not present, or when (as in F_1 hybrids) they are less completely expressed. These earlier mutations thereby have their role changed from that of superfluous or merely advantageous deviations to necessary parts of the system.[1] Now, even where no single mutations produced marked effects of the kinds in question (like those called the "earlier" or the "later" ones), nevertheless mutations having slight effects of this sort, on accumulating, will eventually bring about the same result, and so cause a complete sterility of the first-generation hybrids—although in some cases inviability of the F_1, or an inability to cross, or to cross-fertilize, on the part of the P_1, may arise first, by an essentially similar process (or in the case of non-crossability more directly, as explained in the third paragraph below).

Although no such cases have been observed in *Drosophila*, it is conceivable that, rarely, a single mutant gene might arise having the peculiarity of giving individuals that were viable and fertile *inter se*, but that were productive of infertile or inviable hybrids with those of the original stock (differing only in their non-possession of this gene). But unless this gene made its appearance in a selfable hermaphrodite, or in several individuals at once, and unless it at the same time (!) fulfilled the very unusual condition of giving a strong tendency to individuals possessing it to undergo selfing, or assortative mating with the others like themselves, it would soon be wiped out through its unsuccessful crossings with the normal type. Moreover, as such a gene could hardly arise in homozygous condition to begin with, it would seldom be able to survive its preliminary period of heterozygosity (before it had "made its appearance"), since the heterozygotes are in this case the infertile or inviable individuals. (Exceptionally, however, "delayed inheritance", i.e. the influence of the parental genotype, in the determination of the viability or sterility of the individuals, might afford a means of saving those heterozygotes derived from parents that were alike.) Hence hybrid sterility should very seldom be brought about by such individually acting mutations. Its origination through the establishment of a series of two or more "complementary" mutations differentiating the two groups, in the manner above described, would ordinarily have as a prerequisite some form of isolation which kept these groups from recombining in the first place (at times, this isolation might begin as an intragenomic one, with the complementary mutations closely linked.

The same argument as above given applies against hybrid sterility being brought about directly in one step by a sectional rearrangement.[2] The special case of polyploidy, however, is on a somewhat different footing in this respect, since the stage corresponding to the heterozygote may be skipped, or may be incompletely sterile.

The above considerations, applying to the genesis of hybrid sterility and hybrid inviability, do not, however, apply in equal measure to non-crossability. By this we mean a tendency on the part of a given, "variant" type to *breed* with its own rather than with the alternative, "normal" type, either by virtue of assortative mating (of which various kinds exist),[3] or by some block to successful cross-impregnation or cross-fertilization. That is, non-crossability could arise more readily than hybrid sterility or inviability without *previous* isolation, by the intermediation of a single decisive differentiating mutation. This point is in no wise invalidated by the fact that this "chief" mutation would not usually operate to cause effective genetic isolation until a number of specific "intensifiers" became established along with it, which had been selected to increase its differential effect in a suitable manner—as no doubt happens also in other cases of pronounced di- and polymorphism (such as sexual dimorphism) having a selective value (see Ford, 1937). (However, in the commoner case, in which two or more sections of a population existing in the same region were differentiated, not by some "chief factor", but merely by cumulatively acting "multiple factors," that were kept partially sorted out by means of assortative mating, there would be far greater difficulty in arriving at a discontinuity sharp enough so to limit the exchange of genes between the sub-groups as finally to allow of the establishment of hybrid sterility or inviability.) Thus, even in the absence of any previously existing isolation imposed from without (as by geographical barriers), a genetic isolation may be engendered as a result of mutations giving a tendency to non-interbreeding of the individuals in different sub-groups of a population, and this isolation may finally become pronounced enough to allow the differential accumulation, in these sub-groups, of those other, "complementary" mutations (or "suppressor" combinations) that give hybrid sterility and inviability.

In such cases, then, as Hogben especially has urged, physiological (including psychological and ecological) isolation, of genetic origin, instead of that of geographical type, could lay the primary basis for the splitting of the group. Here the genetic non-crossing tendency would necessarily arise before the hybrid sterility or inviability. It is also conceivable that a species might sometimes be first split into non-interbreeding parts by some barrier of habit and/or ecology which, while in a general sense "physiological", was not genetic in its basis and also not geographical (*sensu strictu*). Between the parts thus isolated, too, if the isolation became marked enough, a genetic differentiation in respect to fertility, viability, and "crossability" would tend to evolve later. In all the above cases, however, the hybrid sterility and inviability would still follow on the isolation (here "physiological" rather than geographical) in the manner previously outlined. It is at present difficult to assess the relative frequency of splitting caused by different kinds of "physiological", as opposed to geographical, isolation, although there is no doubt that organisms of different kinds must differ greatly in this respect.

In the production of hybrid sterility and inviability the operation of Haldane's rule, stating that the heterozygous sex tends to be more affected than the homozygous one, is evident in *Drosophila*, as in other forms. Haldane in 1922 (but not in 1932) rightly gave as the explanation of it that the hybrid of the heterozygous sex, although having the distinctive genes of both systems represented in its autosomes, had those of only one system in its major sex-chromosome ("X" or "Z"), and hence entirely failed to provide some sex-linked genes that might be necessary complements for those in the autosomes of one of the systems.

It may here be added that many of the distinctive genes in the one sex-chromosome that is present are especially strongly developed, as compared with those in the autosomes, because of the fact that some mutations (probably many) are more or less recessive. In the hybrid of heterozygous sex, then, those distinctive recessives and incomplete dominants that were (since the divergence of the two groups from their common ancestor) established in the sex-chromosome (X or Z) of one of the species, will, unlike the autosomal recessives and incomplete dominants, be as strongly expressed as in that parent species itself. Hence in the hybrids these sex-linked genes will find the expression of their autosomal complements especially inadequate, in relation to the strength of their own expression. Or, to put the matter conversely, they will be especially apt to meet with disharmonies of functioning, in reaction with the autosomal genes of the other system. But in the hybrid of homozygous sex, where the distinctive sex-linked genes of neither system have a tendency to be more strongly expressed than the autosomal ones, this additional cause of disharmony does not operate. The above causes of disharmony in the hybrid of heterozygous sex are further intensified by the fact, discovered by Berg in *D. melanogaster*, that the X-chromosome has, length for length, a far higher frequency of mutations affecting fertility, and probably also a greater number of loci affecting fertility, than do the autosomes. This is, as she points out, no doubt a consequency of the special role of the X in sex-determination. Hence a disagreement between the complement of genes in the X and that in the autosomes would tend to be especially detrimental to fertility, much more so than would a disagreement between the complement of genes in any one of the autosomes and in the remainder of the chromosomes.

Although Dobzhansky in his important recent work *Genetics and the Origin of Species* (1937) does not offer any of these interpretations of Haldane's rule,[4] his own experiments with *D. pseudoobscura* A and B, above cited, clearly show the preponderant effect of the X-chromosome in relation to the others in producing the sterility of the F_1 and backcross individuals.

In cases where it is possible for the F_1 hybrids to breed, a special mechanism similar to that underlying Haldane's rule must operate in later generations with respect to the autosomes as well, so as to cause, in many of the individuals of succeeding generations, infertility, inviability, and various physiological and morphological disturbances, different in some of their genetic bases and developmental mechanisms from the infertility, &c. of the F_1. For, by recombination of chromosomes and of genes of the two species or subspecies, occurring in one or both parents of a given F_2 individual, the latter may come to receive certain of the genes of one system in homozygous condition, together with other genes of the other system. This will cause a malfunctioning of those recessive (or partly recessive) genes, now homozygous, that require complements (here missing, or relatively unexpressed) of the same system, or, to put the same thing conversely, certain dominants of the other system, necessary as complements for other genes of that system that are present, will be lacking. Where such genes are numerous, the offspring from crosses of F_1 by F_1, or from other similar crosses, would necessarily include many individuals containing some such disharmony, and the resulting abnormalities in reproduction and other processes might in consequence be considerably greater, on the average, than in the F_1 hybrid itself.

Such situations are well known in plants (where fertile F_1 hybrids in which regular segregation occurs may give progeny consisting of a majority of inviable and sterile types), but—even until after the foregoing sentences were written!—they had not been described in crosses of natural populations of *Drosophila*, since the special crosses and tests necessary for their detection had seldom been made. Even the above experiments on *D. pseudo-obscura* A and B, for example, were not the best adapted for the detection of such effects, since they are so closely related and since the use of backcrosses alone provides no opportunity for the combination of any homozygous genes from one race with others from the other race. But I am informed by W. P. Spencer that tests of the requisite kind have now been made in the cross of *D. virilis* and *D. (virilis?) americana*, by means of the breeding of the F_1 hybrid females and males with one another. Here it is found in F_2 that some sterile recombinational individuals are formed, the eggs of which are obviously more abnormal than those of the F_1. It is suggestive in this connexion that Hughes has obtained some provisional cytological evidence which seems to indicate that more of the viable F_2 larvae of this cross have a salivary chromosome composition like that of F_1, or of the pure species, than would be expected on the basis of equal viability of the different expected classes; larger numbers are being obtained to determine whether this result is more than accidental. It seems probable, because of the prevalence of recessive mutations, that if a search were made, much sterility as well as inviability and other abnormality due to the above cause might be found among the heterogeneous descendants of crosses that had given little or no noticeable infertility in F_1. In fact, we might expect such effects usually to precede those of disturbances in the F_1, of homozygous sex, at least, in the incipient stages of species splitting.

*　　*　　*　　*　　*

In fact, if a given rearranged chromosome, not crossing-over effectively with the normal one, persists long, and attains considerable abundance, there must tend to develop within it a whole system of mutant genes, viable homozygously and also in heterozygous combination with the "normal", a system harmonious if kept together but detrimental if somehow broken up. Thus something must eventually result that resembles speciation but is confined to a section of the germ-plasm, and that passes freely about, as a block, within the larger genotype of the species proper. It is conceivable that this might some time, in conjunction with some sort of isolation, even serve as the centre for the organization of a new departure in real speciation.[5]

On the other hand, as would follow from previous considerations, such a process is by no means a necessary condition for genetic isolation or speciation, and the state of affairs in which it forms the occasion for speciation is probably unusual. And certainly those cytologists and geneticists who thought of sectional rearrangements as leading immediately to an effective genetic isolation and so to speciation (or vice versa) had a vastly oversimplified view of the situation, as shown by the fact that those rearrangements which most commonly differentiate related species also exist commonly as variations within freely interbreeding populations. They do not, in themselves, prevent interbreeding, or cause infertility. In fact, it is a foregone conclusion that they must be able to persist fairly well as heterozygotes; otherwise they could not pass through that prolonged phase of heterozygosis which must usually precede their becoming established as the type of their own population.

An aid, of more or less temporary and limited character, in the process of spread or maintenance of numbers of a given rearranged chromosome is to be found in the fact that it may happen to carry the normal alleles of various detrimental genes which are, collectively, more or less widespread in the non-rearranged (or otherwise arranged) chromosomes of the population. Being unable to exchange mutants with the latter, it will, in the process of accidental multiplication and decline of mutant genes (Muller, 1918), termed "drift" by Wright, accumulate a divergent set of recessive detrimental mutant genes from that in the otherwise arranged homologous chromosomes of the population, thus being conducive to heterosis so long as it does not spread too much.[6]

But in addition, quite apart from any selective advantages or disadvantages attendant upon the phenotypic effects associated with them, rearrangements (that is, those which do not lead to inviable zygotes through recombination, as explained below) must be subject to the same processes of "drift" as are gene-mutations themselves. In these ways, it is possible even for rearrangements of indifferent survival value to gain foothold in large populations. It is not conceivable, however, in the case of a population like that of the whole of *D. melanogaster*, which always remains large in numbers when the combined extent of all its local portions is considered, and in which these local portions remain so incompletely isolated from one another, that a given rearrangement which had gained some foothold through "drift" should finally become established throughout the population simply by the same process. For the rearrangement could scarcely be, and remain, so extremely devoid of selective advantages, or disadvantages, primary and secondary, that these would not eventually overcome the effect of drift before the latter had a chance to go so far. On the other hand, in populations which over a protracted length of time remain small in total numbers, or pass repeatedly through periods of small numbers, no matter whether they be geographically diffuse or much localized, a rearrangement of comparatively indifferent survival value or, in exceptional cases, an actually detrimental one may, by drift, finally become established as the predominant, "normal" form. The smaller the numbers, of course, the more readily will this occur, just as in the case of indifferent gene-mutations, including such as lead to genetic isolation.

Factors Hindering the Spread of Sectional Rearrangements

Despite the factors above mentioned, which facilitate the spread and even establishment of sectional rearrangements, there are other factors, that tend to make their occurrence or establishment much rarer than that of gene-mutations.

One of these is the important circumstance, already referred to, that sectional rearrangements are far less frequent in spontaneous origination than gene-mutations.

Secondly, while allelic gene-mutations of virtually the same type (able to replace one another) recur with frequencies that appear to be approximately of the order of, or even higher than, one in a million gametes, each rearrangement constitutes a practically unique case. This is because of the fact that two rearrangements, to be mutally interchangeable, must have *both* of their points of breakage in sensibly identical positions—a circumstance which, instead of merely doubling the rarity of a given type of two-break rearrangement, as compared with that of a change affecting one locus, raises it as the square. (We leave out of account here the abundant but qualitatively limited class of rearrangements in which one or more of the breaks has occurred in a chromocentral region; other factors militate against the establishment of these.) If just one of the two points of breakage is sensibly different in two rearrangements, then not only will their phenotypic effects, if any, tend to be very different, but, on undergoing crossing-over or other recombination with one another, they will give rise to abnormal, usually inviable zygotes. This means that in any population all apparently identical gene-rearrangements (that is, those which are capable of giving normal recombinants with one another) which do not involve breakage of chromocentral or other duplicated regions are descended from a single original chromosome in which that rearrangement took place, no matter how widely scattered their representatives may now be. Given types of gene-mutations, on the other hand, can be polyphyletic, and this factor of recurrence has been shown by calculation to be of great help in their final establishment.

A third factor which acts to hinder the establishment, in a large population, of a chromosome with a rearrangement that interferes much with the production of crossovers is the disadvantage attendant upon its having so many genes not interchangeable with those of the general population. This handicaps the rearranged chromosome both in the minor, more temporary, processes of genetic adjustment and readjustment and in those longer-trend or large-scale processes that are more commonly thought of when the term "evolution" is used. The rearranged chromosome has a much smaller stock of mutants to draw upon, corresponding with its lesser abundance, and this stock is in fact far less than correspondingly available for the furnishing of recombinants (by crossing-over). For the recombinational forms of it can only arise from individuals homozygous for the rearrangement, and the relative frequency of such individuals is only the square of that of the rearranged chromosome itself. On the other hand, the more abundant the chromosome becomes in any given locality, the less will this factor operate against it there, and if it manages to exceed 50 per cent, the tide will even turn in its favour.[7] Considering a large population as a whole, this difficulty would seem to be one very rarely to be overcome, unless by the heterosis effect of the rearrangement, so long as the population remains large and thus subject to a steadier and more discriminating action of selection. For any advantageous trait attributable to a rearrangement should also arise occasionally by gene-mutation, before the rearrangement can become established, and since the mutant gene would not suffer from the recombinational disadvantage of the rearrangement it should eventually prevail over the latter, except in the very rare cases where the rearrangement happens to be associated with a very advantageous combination of traits, not easily paralleled.

As Koller in 1932 pointed out, and Sturtevant and Beadle in 1936 developed further, there is a fourth, far more serious hindrance to establishment which applies to all the commoner types of sectional rearrangements, except inversions that are confined to one arm of a chromosome. This consists in the fact that individuals heterozygous for them give rise, as a result of crossing-over or of reassortment of whole chromosomes, to a certain proportion of "aneuploid" germ-cells (not having just one complete set of genes), and the latter in turn result in offspring that are lethal or abnormal. In *Drosophila* the types of rearrangements having the largest reduction of productivity of this sort are the translocations, both those of the insertional and the mutual type (among these, mutual translocations that involve the exchange of practically whole arms give the best productivity). Inversions that include the centromere (i.e. *pericentric* inversions) have their productivity reduced approximately in proportion to their length, and in the case of shifts, whether within the same or to a different arm, a similar relation holds.

However, in the case of inversions that lie to one side of the centromere (intra-arm or *paracentric* inversions), it has long been known both that aneuploid (crossover) imagos are not produced, and also that there is no high death-rate of the zygotes in earlier stages. It was thought that this was because the inversion had prevented crossing-over and so prevented aneuploidy, but it has recently been found by Sturtevant and Beadle that the explanation lies mainly in another mechanism. In forms like *Drosophila*, where the three polar bodies are formed in a straight line directed radially outwards from the egg-nucleus, one of the non-crossover chromatids is shunted into the egg-nucleus at the maturation divisions whenever (as in such a case) the crossover chromatids are acentric or dicentric. For the latter chromatids, left lying in the middle of the spindle, repel the two movable chromatids—that is, the monocentric non-crossover ones—towards the two poles, i.e. into the egg and outer polar body nuclei, respectively. Thus the paracentric (intra-arm) inversions remain as the one type of more commonly occurring rearrangement not handicapped from the start by a definitely reduced productivity.[8]

It should be noted that a small pericentric inversion, as well as a shift of a short section for a fairly short distance, can give rise to very few crossovers of the aneuploid type. For this reason the selection militating against its survival will be less intense, and correspondingly more such cases should become established. Moreover, in the case of any shift or translocation transferring only a short section, the resulting aneuploidy may be too slight to reduce the viability much (at least, when heterozygous), and here, too, there will be less selection acting against the survival of the rearrangement.

Aneuploids that entail duplications only, and not deficiencies, often have a fairly high viability even in homozygous condition, when the duplicated section is a small one. They will therefore become established at times, and as a result the germ-plasm will come to contain "repeats", such as were demonstrated by Bridges (1935) to form a part of the normal constitution of the salivary chromosomes. Except for the method of polyploidy, which is far less important even when it is of common occurrence, as in many higher plants, the establishment of these "repeats" constitutes the only effective means of gene increase in evolution. Thus the whole of the chromosome complement must really represent an accumulation of such repeats, most of which, however, are of such ancient origin that they have become changed beyond recognition. Small viable repeats may arise in various ways. Among these are: crossing-over between similar but non-identical inversions or translocations (Muller 1930 *et seq.*); recombination following the occurrence of a small translocation, usually one of the insertional type (as in the case of scute-19; Muller, 1935); crossing-over involving a small shift; and —especially—unequal exchange or insertion between homologous chromosomes (as in *Bar*; Muller, Prokofyeva, and Kossikov, 1936, Bridges, 1936).

In the establishment of these repeats, however, as well as in the establishment of rearrangements of the type mentioned in the last paragraph but one, there will usually be a certain amount of selection, even though a small amount, acting against the new type. In the case of the repeats this is caused by the " gene unbalance," while in the case of the rearrangements previously discussed it is caused by the production of a certain small proportion of inviable aneuploid crossovers. The greater the amount of this unfavourable selection, the more incapable of establishment would the change in question be, without the aid of that process of accidental reproduction which must attend the diminution of an isolated population to a number bordering on extinction. Each translocation, then, each shift, and each large " repeat" which has become established in a species denotes the occurrence of such a "bottle-neck" in its past history, when drift would outweigh selection. The same limitation in the mechanism of establishment applies with correspondingly more force to translocations and pericentric inversions of larger size; their establishment implies some former reduction to a few individuals, on the part of the population from which the group arose in which they were found to be established.

We may next consider a more complicated, though simple enough appearing, type of rearrangement, which is very little subject to the disadvantage occasioned by the production of aneuploids. This is the apparent division of a V-shaped chromosome to form two " rods" or the reverse process—the apparent union of two " rods" to form a V. It is easy to see that individuals heterozygous for such a change should be little subject to aneuploid formation. But for a change to occur from V to " rods" according to the principles already set forth requires a very special concatenation, or succession, of breaks and reattachments, not a mere breakage of the V as formerly imagined. Hence this type of change could be expected to arise only on very rare occasions.

The difficulty of formation of two " rods" from one V arises from the fact that, whereas the one V has but one centromere and two telomeres, the two " rods," considered together, have two centromeres and four telomeres—no " rods" being quite terminal in attachment. These extra parts must be acquired by the duplication of sections including them, sections of the chromocentral regions too small for such duplication to be seriously detrimental. On any of the various possible configurations leading to such duplications, a considerable number of rather precisely placed breaks (in most cases, followed by a special type of chromosome assortment) must have occurred. The most readily occurring V-to-rod change is a mutual or insertional translocation between the V and some other chromosome such as the Y-, the fourth or the X-chromosome of *D. melanogaster*. This would have to be followed at some later time (if not accompanied) by deletions of the extra part or parts derived from this other chromosome. (See Fig. 2) In the case of the X and fourth, there would be a tendency to the formation of some aneuploids until the deletion had occurred. If the V had undergone such a translocation with another large V, many aneuploids would be produced until the two necessary deletions had occurred. Another possibility, involving, however, four breaks at once, two sub-centric and two sub-terminal, is simultaneous deletion of the active region of different arms of homologous or sister V's, followed by nondisjunction of the deleted rod-like chromosomes. Other permutations of reattachment, following four simultaneous breakages in similar positions, would lead to the same result. It will be seen from the above that the Y-chromosome is the one best fitted to subserve the type of change in question, both because of its high breakage frequency (even higher than previously realized, according to results of Neuhaus, 1938) and because of the fact that, consisting so largely of " inert" chromatin, its aneuploids (formed before the deletions mentioned had occurred) would be relatively normal. Hence it should be the Y which usually furnishes the " anchorage" (centromere and adjacent chromocentral material) for newly formed " rods" derived from V's, as suggested by Muller and Painter (1932). And so, after a succession of V-to-rod and rod-to-V changes had occurred in the evolutionary history, the chromocentral regions of all the chromosomes would tend to be of common origin, i.e. derived from the Y, and thus to be more or less homologous, as they in fact do seem to be.

The rods-to-V change should occur more readily than the reverse one, in cases where the " rudimentary arms" of the rods consist only of dispensable chromocentral regions. For here only a mutual translocation, involving a subcentric break in the long arm of one " rod" and in the rudimentary arm of the other, is required. But where there were genes necessary for life in either of the rudimentary arms such a simple exchange would not work. We have a simultaneous rod-to-V and V-to-rod change in the case of an exchange of one rod with an arm of a V. This would in fact occur with greater ease than either the pure rods-to-V or V-to-rods change, although the proportion of aneuploids from the resultant heterozygote is doubtful. It may also be noted that the transference (by mutual or insertional translocation) of a rod or arm of a V on to, or into, either arm of a small chromosome like the fourth of *D. melanogaster*, with resultant disappearance of the latter as a free chromosome, can occur with comparatively little disturbance of productivity through aneuploidy; so, too, can the insertion of the bulk of the latter into the former.

The establishment of rearrangements in which only one of the

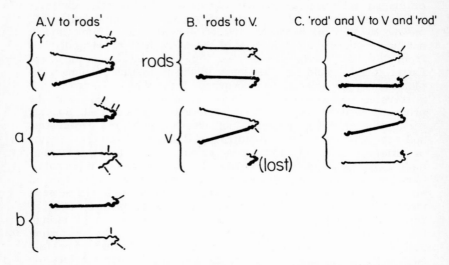

Fig. 2. Preferential Types of Changes in the Attachment of Whole Arms.

Wavy line denotes "inert" region, near centromere, position of which is here indicated by bend. Stroke vertical to chromosome indicates point where first break will or has occurred; where a later set of breaks occurs these are represented by an exclamation point. The original configuration is in each case shown above. Transformation A, of V-to-"rods," takes place by (a) mutual translocation between the V and Y, followed (b) by two deletions of the arms derived from the Y. Transformation B, of "rods"-to-V, takes place by mutual translocation occurring within the subcentric "inert" regions; the small chromosome thus formed may be superfluous and so may be lost. In each case the small "inert" arm of the "rod" is taken as being too small to be visible in the mitotic chromosome.

breakage points at which an exchange of connexions occurs lies in the chromocentral region with the consequent removal of a part of this region from its position near the centromere or telomere to some interstitial position within a chromosome arm, is hindered by the special position-effect whereby a chromocentral region tends to cause a mosaic expression of genes in an originally "active" region that has, by gene rearrangement, become transferred into the neighbourhood of a chromocentral region. This factor and others seem to have been fairly effective in keeping the more typical chromocentral ("inert") regions in positions near the centromeres and free ends.

Notes

[1]"Most present-day animals are the result of a long process of evolution, in which at least thousands of mutations must have taken place. Each

new mutant in turn must have derived its survival value from the effect which it produced upon the ' reaction system' that had been brought into being by the many previously formed factors in co-operation; thus a complicated machine was gradually built up whose effective working was dependent upon the interlocking action of very numerous different elementary parts or factors, and many of *the characters and factors which, when new, were originally merely an asset finally became necessary* because other necessary characters and factors had subsequently become changed so as to be dependent on the former. It must result, in consequence, that a dropping out of, or even a slight change in any one of these parts is very likely to disturb fatally the whole machinery; for this reason we should expect very many, if not most, mutations to result in lethal factors, and of the rest, the majority should be 'semi-lethal' or at least disadvantageous in the struggle for life, and likely to set wrong any delicately balanced system, such as the reproductive system" (Cited from paper by the author, 1918, in *Genetics*, 3, 463-4; italics in original.)

²See note 8, on p.496 for discussion of how the result may be attained by more than one step of rearrangement. Note also that *partial* hybrid sterility may occasionally arise by one such step (e.g. translocation) becoming established in times of great reduction of numbers.

³Assortative mating might in some cases, for example, be the result, not of sexual preference, but of a differentiation of the individuals of a population in respect to the preferential times, places, or conditions under which they mated (or lived and mated). Any assortative mating could entail a more or less effective tendency to split the population into non-crossable parts only on the condition that the offspring tended to share the same preferences as their parents, either through inheritance, conditioning, or force of other circumstances.

⁴An explanation of it based on translocations (his pp. 252-3) can be shown to be inapplicable to some of the known instances of the rule in *Drosophila*. On the other hand, an explanation of hybrid sterility based on gene mutations (his p. 256) which does not take into account the special properties of the sex-chromosomes is also inadequate to account for Haldane's rule.

⁵Darlington (1934) has independently put forward substantially the same conception, but it did not come to the present writer's attention until after the above had been sent to press.

⁶See also Sturtevant and Mather (1938), who have independently made similar suggestions concerning the relation between inversions and heterosis, as well as concerning the limitation of the abundance of inversions caused by the relatively detrimental effect of their restriction of recombination (as explained in the next section). Our own suggestions were made in ignorance of those by the latter authors, whose paper appeared two months after the above text had been submitted. In evaluating the heterosis effect quantitatively, the latter authors give the formula $\frac{p}{q} = \frac{b}{a}$, where p and q are the relative frequencies, at equilibrium, of two alternative non-recombining gene-rearrangements, A and B, in a population, and a and b are the respective depressions of the survival value of homozygous A and B as compared with the heterozygous individuals (in which the heterosis occurs). More important and more difficult is the question as to how a and b themselves may vary in the course of time, in response to needs for gene-recombination, and in correlation with mutation pressure, degree of inbreeding, population size, amount of migration, &c. Since some of these factors themselves vary with p and q it can be seen that the determination

of the equilibrium, or, alternatively, of the manner of flux, of the latter, presents a complicated problem.

[7]Sturtevant and Mather (1938, op. cit.) point out that when one inversion has already attained, in some way, a high frequency (approaching 50%) in a population, as compared with the alternative, older arrangement, further inversions in the same type of chromosome suffer progressively less from that hindrance to their establishment occasioned by the detriment involved in their reduction of gene-recombination, since the *relative* reduction of recombination which they cause is less under these circumstances. In this way these authors seek to explain the fact that inversions are so much more abundant in the third than in the other chromosomes of wild populations of *Drosophila pseudo-obscura*.

[8]Sturtevant has pointed out—in a paper, 1938 b, that appeared after the above text was submitted—that chromosomes differing by two overlapping (paracentric) inversions will give heterozygotes that are partially "sterile," unlike individuals heterozygous for one inversion. For the heterozygotes for two inversions in the same chromosome pair are structurally like individuals heterozygous for shifts, and, unlike single-inversion heterozygotes, produce some inviable aneuploids by crossing-over. The same result is brought about no matter whether the two inversions have originated successively in the same chromosome, or separately in the different, homologous ones. Thus we must class paracentric inversions as being among those mutational changes which, like the complementary gene-mutations or "suppressor" combinations do not lower fertility, either heterozygously or homozygously, so long as they occur as individual steps, and so are able gradually to become established and accumulate, but do lower it in those heterozygotes the homologous chromosomes of which differ by more than one step, and hence finally contribute to hybrid infertility.

Sturtevant emphasizes further the point that the existence of such partial hybrid infertility, where the two groups having the double or multiple differences come into contact, occasions a natural selection for changes that further increase the genetic isolation. It should be noted, however, that, as in the case of the complementary gene-differences for sterility, the very fact that the forms differing in respect to both changes at once (whether gene-mutations or inversions) would give partially sterile hybrids, would tend to have prevented the later of these two changes from gaining a foothold or becoming established, so long as the types having the double difference were liable to come into contact and cross with one another. If, on the other hand, they remained isolated from each other, not only could they become established but a succession of other, similarly acting changes could become established likewise, and so non-crossability would finally result even in the absence of any selective influence that directly favoured it. The selective mechanism proposed would therefore have the effect only of hastening the acquisition of immiscibility in the case of groups which had first been isolated and later brought into contact.

RECOMBINANTS BETWEEN DROSOPHILA SPECIES THE F_1 HYBRIDS OF WHICH ARE STERILE*

The genetic analysis of species differences is of especial interest in precisely those cases where the sterility or inviability of the hybrids between the species stands in the way of such analysis. A notable case of this kind is that of *Drosophila melanogaster* and *simulans*, species which otherwise would present most favourable conditions for detailed analysis, on account of the already existing knowledge of the genetics of each species and the existence of abundant stocks providing suitable genetic tools ("markers"). We have found a means of circumventing the sterility of the F_1 hybrids between these species and thus obtaining types of the same kind as would be produced in a backcross of the F_1 hybrid, were it fertile, to *melanogaster;* it is at the same time possible to recognize, by means of the markers used, what combination of chromosomes is present in the pseudo-backcross progeny and thus to determine the effects of the different chromosome combinations.

The means used is to take triploid *melanogaster* females carrying recessive mutant genes in all their major chromosomes and to cross them with heavily irradiated *simulans* males bearing the dominant normal alleles of these genes. The triploid females produce eggs most of which have one or more of their chromosomes in diploid number. On the other hand the X-ray treatment, as we had found in earlier work with *melanogaster* alone, causes the loss of individual chromosomes, presumably by breakage, in some 5 per cent or more of the spermatozoa capable of giving viable offspring, although sperm in which two chromosomes have been simultaneously affected by a mutual translocation resulting in acentric and dicentric combination-chromosomes are incapable of giving viable offspring. When an egg with an extra chromosome or chromosomes happens to be fertilized by a sperm in which the homologous chromosome or chromosomes have been incapacitated, a viable diploid results, in which the chromosomes in question are of homozygous *melanogaster* type and the others are heterozygous as in the species hybrid. The kind of recessive character shown by the individual indicates which chromosomes are of homozygous *melanogaster* type. The resemblance to a backcross fails only in that the chromosomes are inherited as units; that is, there has been no opportunity for crossing-over.

Some 450 progeny have been obtained from this pseudo-backcross. The majority of the types of recombinants prove to be viable, although most have a viability considerably below normal. The in-

*Nature, August 10, 1940, 146: 199.

viability of hybrids bearing no *simulans X*, reported by Sturtevant in 1920, proves to be due to interactions of genes in the *X* with those in both the second and third chromosomes, but more especially with the latter. Thus it has been possible to obtain viable adult hybrids without a *simulans X* but with a *simulans* II, and also (but not so readily) those without a *simulans X* but with a *simulans* III, when the other pair of major autosomes (III or II, respectively) is purely of *melanogaster* type. Study of the frequencies indicates the existence of several inter-chromosomal viability interactions. Similarly, it can be concluded that there are several interacting genes affecting fertility, as all viable recombinants of the major autosomes show sterility, although the degree of reduction of the gonad is (as shown by histological studies, carried out by Koller) different for the different chromosome combinations. The chief morphological abnormality of the hybrids—the bristle reduction and associated abnormality of the abdominal banding—proves to be due to interaction between a gene or genes in the *X* of *simulans* with an autosomal gene or genes of *melanogaster*, located at least in part in the second chromosome.

That the sterility and inviability effects are wholly chromosomal (and therefore Mendelian) in origin was shown by the obtaining of a single individual which happened to have all its major chromosomes from *melanogaster* and which alone, of all the progeny, proved to be fertile. The breeding of this individual to *melanogaster* has made it possible to transfer the fourth and the *Y* chromosomes into an otherwise purely *melanogaster* genotype. Here their *simulans* origin has been verified by cytological observations, carried out by Slizynski. Both chromosomes when in the *melanogaster* genotype show important genetic differences from their *melanogaster* homologues; a detailed analysis of these differences is in progress.

A full account of the above experiments and of the bearing of the results on problems of speciation is being prepared by us, and accounts of the histological and cytological observations will be published by Koller and by Slizynski, respectively.

Institute of Animal Genetics,   H. J. Muller.
University of Edinburgh.   G. Pontecorvo.
           July 18.

THE ARTIFICIAL MIXING OF
INCOMPATIBLE GERM PLASMS
IN DROSOPHILA*

by H. J. Muller and G. Pontecorvo
Institute of Animal Genetics, University of Edinburgh

It has often been asserted that the differences between "good species" of animals, such as those which give sterile "mules" when crossed, are probably not Mendelian or chromosomal, and that the findings of geneticists therefore do not concern the more fundamental features of living things. As genetic analysis of such differences would require the obtaining of mixtures of various kinds —"recombinants"—that would only arise in the later generations of crosses between the two contrasted types, the impossibility of breeding the first generation hybrids has hitherto hindered a direct attack on the above problem.

Drosophila melanogaster and D. simulans are examples of two such "good species," which in nature yield only sterile hybrids. We have found it possible to circumvent the difficulty inherent in this sterility, and to obtain and distinguish, in the first generation of this species cross, the types that would be characteristic of the second generation, derived from a back-cross between the sterile hybrids and pure melanogaster. The method involves the crossing of triploid melanogaster females, which produce eggs with some extra chromosomes, by X-rayed simulans males, which produce sperms with some incapacitated chromosomes. This situation provides opportunity for some of the offspring to receive two chromosomes of a given kind from one species and none of that kind from the other species, while at the same time, in the case of other kinds of chromosomes, they receive one chromosome from each species.

Study of the different types thus produced gives evidence that those differences between these species which cause their hybrids to be sterile, morphologically abnormal or inviable are dependent upon the properties of their chromosomes. The abnormalities can be analyzed into a series of effects each of which results (as in Dobzhansky's crosses between different "races" of Drosophila pseudo-obscura) from the inharmonious interaction of a factor or factors in a given chromosome derived from one species with another ("complementary") factor or factors in chromosomes from the other species.

A "recombinant" female having all its major chromosomes from melanogaster and only minor chromosomes (the Y and one fourth) from simulans was normal and fertile—the only fertile hybrid—a

*Science, 1940, 92: 418.

result that verified the whole interpretation. By breeding this female the minor chromosomes were established in stocks which otherwise were purely *melanogaster*. It was found that in this *melanogaster* setting various genes of these minor chromosomes fail to act in precisely a normal manner. This supports our inference that the number of cryptic genetic differences between species far outrun those causing obvious differences between them or those working in a "complementary" way to cause abnormalties of their first-generation hybrids.

RECESSIVE GENES CAUSING INTERSPECIFIC STERILITY AND OTHER DISHARMONIES BETWEEN DROSOPHILA MELANOGASTER AND SIMULANS*

By H. J. Muller and G. Pontecorvo
Amherst College and University of Edinburgh

The effects were studied of the minor chromosomes of *Drosophila simulans* after their transfer (by a method previously reported) into an otherwise *melanogaster* genotype. Males with *simulans* Y were sterile, like XO males. Y-sim. suppresses variegation somewhat, but less than Y-mel. It undergoes some nondisjunction with attached *melanogaster* X's.

Homozygous IV-sim., in *melanogaster*, allows fair viability. But it results in a complex of slight, variable phenotypic peculiarities, e.g., flattened form, heavier trident, eye reduction, semi-*simulans* male genitalia. Homozygous IV-sim. males, unlike females, are sterile; their testes are fairly developed but, as Ephrussi observed, their vasa contain few or no spermatozoa. This sterility depends upon a narrowly localized chromatin region, almost certainly one gene, since it appears in compounds of IV-sim. with IV-mel. containing a "Minute-IV" deficiency. This result is not due to nonallelic interaction between the "Minute" and the sterility process, since normal-appearing triplo-IV's having two IV-sim.'s and one Minute-deficient IV-mel. are likewise sterile.

Evidence for peculiarities of other genes in IV-sim. is found in IV-sim./IV-mel. heterozygotes in which the IV-mel. carries a known mutant gene. Thus the recessive "cubitus" becomes partially dominant under these conditions while the dominant "Cataract"

Genetics, 1942, 27: 157.

becomes nearly recessive. Nevertheless, segregation of IV-sim. from IV-mel. seems fairly regular.

The fact that even these minor chromosomes exhibit so many gene differences indicates that the reaction systems producing the similar phenotypes of apparently closely related species may be highly divergent. Hybrid sterility is but one expression of this cryptic divergence, which need not in itself have had a selective value.

LIFE*

H. J. Muller
Department of Zoology, Indiana University, Bloomington

To many an unsophisticated human being, the universe of stars seems only a fancy backdrop, provided for embellishing his own and his fellow-creatures' performances. On the other hand, from the converse position, that of the universe of stars, not only all human beings but the totality of life is merely a fancy kind of rust, afflicting the surfaces of certain lukewarm minor planets. However, even when we admit our own littleness and the egotistical complexion of our interest in this rust, we remain confronted with the question: What is it that causes the rust to be so very fancy?

In the childhood of our species, the answer to this question seemed obvious: Life is a spirit. This spirit, inhabiting the matter we call *living* works its will upon it, enduing it with wondrous forms and with purposeful activities. Sometimes the idea of spirit was clothed in more pretentious terms, such as perfecting principle, entelechy, vital force, or mneme, yet all these still implied some sort of conscious or semi-conscious entity, striving to dominate matter. The verbal subtlety of the terms veiled a naive animism.

Life as Result of the Mode of Organization of Matter

The animistic view has been increasingly called into question. For instance, with the invention of machinery it was found that entirely lifeless matter can be fashioned into complex forms, capable of engaging in remarkable activities, some of them reminiscent of those of living things. Further, it was found that even in a state of nature some lifeless matter attains considerable complexity, and that in some cases it can give extraordinary reactions, which, al-

Science, Vol. 121, No. 3132, January 7, 1955, pp. 1-9; prepared for the Columbia University Bicentennial Lecture Series and read in abbreviated form as the third lecture in Series B, Part I, *The Nature of Things*, broadcast on 17 October, 1954 by CBS.

though based on the regular principles of operation of lifeless material, simulate one or another supposedly "vital" phenomenon.

These doubts concerning the animistic interpretation were strengthened by the studies on living matter itself. All of its activities were found to conform strictly to the law of conservation of energy. That is, no energy was involved in any of its operations except what had been supplied to it from measurable physicochemical sources, nor was any of this energy done away with by it. Its atoms were found to be the same as atoms elsewhere. They were bound by the same rules into molecules. These molecules could in many cases be constructed artificially, and even the reactions that they underwent within living things could often be repeated in a test tube. Moreover, for some important operations, such as chromosome movements, for which physicochemical formulas were still lacking, regular rules of procedure were nevertheless discovered which elucidated age-old mysteries in terms of orderly material processes.

At the same time, however, such studies have revealed in living things greater and greater complications, which in this respect remove them ever further both from natural nonliving things and from artificial devices. For, as we examine the interior of a living thing and then magnify it more and more, we find at each successive level of magnification a new and different set of complications: first, on naked-eye inspection, that of organs, then that of tissues, then of cells, then of cell parts and of parts within these, until immense molecules are reached, some containing hundreds of thousands of atoms, precisely and intricately arranged into groupings composed of subgroupings of several grades. Such molecules are present in even the simplest microbes known.

Yet this prodigious complication, even in its many still unexplained features, encourages not vitalism but the common-sense interpretation that it is this organization itself on which life's remarkable properties depend. If, on the contrary, an imponderable spirit were the source of life's capabilities, these complications would be superfluous. Daily this inference becomes reenforced as more and more of the operations of living things are traced to the orderly workings of given parts of the complex. Moreover, each living thing as a whole is ever more clearly seen to be one great integrated system, the operations of which are all coordinated in such a way that, collectively, they tend to result in one ultimate outcome: the maximal extension of the given type.

Genesis of the Organization

Granting all this, the question is thereby rendered especially acute: How did these marvelous organizations, constituted in such a way as to achieve so peculiar an effect, come into being? The process of their origination, surely, appears at first thought to require some sort of conscious designing. To begin with, it was believed that all species had been designed and created separately in their present forms; but in the 19th century the evidence for their gradual interconnected development out of one or a few primitive forms that were the common ancestors of all became convincing. It was then speculated by certain schools that the ancestral organisms had been endowed with built-in, long-range designs that forced them to evolve as they did. Another view, which has been revived by the so-called "Michurinists" of Iron Curtain countries, where it has (until recently at any rate) been obligatory, postulated a generalized adaptive ability in living things. By its means they altered themselves in advantageous ways when they were subjected to changed conditions and, along with this, they somehow implanted into their reproductive cells specifications for these same alterations. Such an ability to select and to install just the kind of alteration that is going to work out advantageously, *before it has been tried out*, clearly implies some sort of foresight, despite the disclaiming of this implication by some of the advocates of this view. In this case, then, the designing is merely done in bits, instead of in the grand manner.

Darwin's and Wallace's greatest contribution was to show that, even without planning, complex adaptations necessarily evolve. Since members of any population show manifold variations which their offspring tend to inherit, some of these variations—those that happen to be conducive to survival and multiplication—will find themselves more abundantly represented in the next generation. Thus the population will gradually accumulate more characteristics of an "adaptive" kind, that is, of a kind advantageous for the species' preservation and increase, even though there has been no tendency for helpful rather than harmful variations to arise in the first place.

In confirmation of this principle, modern studies in genetics, the science of heredity and variation, have shown that the great majority of newly arisen variations of an inheritable sort are indeed detrimental, as must be true of unplanned alterations that occur in a complex organization of any kind. Moreover, when outer conditions are changed, the few variations that happen to be useful in coping with these outer changes are found not to arise in greater relative abundance than they did before. Yet of course they do succeed better: that is, they are *naturally selected* afterward, in the actual tests of living.

From Gene to Protoplasm

The major actor in this great drama of evolution by natural selection has proved to be the *gene*, a particle too tiny to be seen under the microscope but immense by inorganic standards. There are thousands of different genes in a cell of a plant or animal, each gene with its distinctive pattern and, in consequence, its special type of chemical influence. For the most part, at any rate, the genes are strung together to make up the threadlike bodies called *chromosomes*, which are visible under the microscope in the inner compartment or nucleus of the cell. Although the genes form only a small part of the cell's bulk, they control through their diverse products, primary, secondary, and more remote, the composition and the arrangement of most or all of the other materials in the cell and, therefore, in the entire body. Their control is a conditional one, however, since the nature of the setting in which the genes' products find themselves has much to do with which of their potentialities are allowed to come to fruition.

Recent evidence indicates that the gene consists of the substance known as *nucleic acid*, in the form of a much coiled chain, or double chain, composed of a great number (thousands) of links. The links, called *nucleotides*, are of only four kinds. Yet there are so many links in each chain that, through their different arrangements in line, they would make possible a practically unlimited number of kinds of genes. How such differing arrangements would result in the very different functional effects that different genes are known to exert is a question now being widely asked, but the attack on it is only beginning.

The most remarkable thing about the gene is that each hugh chain-molecule has the faculty of capturing, by some specialized sort or affinity peculiar to its links, chemical groups in its vicinity which in some way correspond to these links. The captured groups thereby become matched up alongside the gene's links in an arrangement similar to that in the gene itself, and they are enabled to become bound together, just as the gene's own links are. As a result, they finally constitute another gene essentially like the original one. Thus the gene reproduces itself.

The details of gene reproduction have long eluded investigation. The most direct interpretation was to suppose that each subunit of the gene tended to attract and fasten next to itself a free subunit of the same type that happened to come into its neighborhood. Although the seeming attraction between like groups of genes (chromosomes) has lent support to this view, it has met with difficulties on physical grounds. Recently, however, my suggestion that the attraction may derive from electric oscillations has been developed by Jehle. Calculations of his group along these lines are now giving promising results.

On the other hand, a number of investigators have proposed that gene reproduction, instead of involving the direct capturing or molding of like by like subunits, is a two-step process in which each subunit of the gene captures or molds one of an opposite or "complementary" kind, and that when the complementary structure in turn captures or molds its own complement a formation like the original one becomes reconstructed. An analogy would be the use of a positive print to make a negative one, from which in turn another positive is derived. On the most recent and best supported variant of this idea, Watson and Crick, in a series of brilliant papers, have proposed that each nucleotide has as its complement a nucleotide of a given one of the three other types. By capturing their complements from materials in the medium about the gene, the chained nucleotides in a gene are thought to construct alongside themselves a complementary chain of nucleotides. This at its own next act of reproduction, by constructing a chain complementary to itself, gives rise to a formation identical in type with the original gene. Moreover, since on the view of these investigators the original chain is really a double one, with one member of the doublet the complement of the other to begin with, the construction by each of these two parallel chains of another chain complementary to itself would even at the first step result in a new pair of chains which, considered as a whole, would be identical with the original pair. Further complications have been proposed, involving interchanges of subunits between the original chains and those in process of formation, but as yet these serve to point up difficulties of the hypothesis rather than to answer them.

With the present activity in this field, it may well be that a relatively few years will suffice to establish definitely the solution of the problem of gene reproduction and, thus, to elucidate the most essential phenomenon in the operation of living matter. At this point, however, the important thing to note is the fact that, whatever the means by which it does so, each gene succeeds in constructing a physicochemical duplicate of itself. Later, when the cell containing the genes divides to form two daughter cells, the two identical genes that are present as a result of the duplication of every gene originally existing in the cell become drawn apart into different daughter cells. The fact that the genes are strung together in line to form the chromosomes provides a means for the orderly carrying out of this separation. Thereby the descendant cells come to contain identical genes.

Despite this identity of gene content, however, the groups of cells in different parts of a many-celled body are differentiated from one another. This is because the structure of the cells in each group results from a limited set of reactions, representing only a part of the numerous potentialities of the contained constellation of genes. These limits have been fixed by the special conditions prevailing within the given groups of cells. On the other hand, in a reproductive cell the same outfit of genes is sufficient, when multiplied, to organize the development of the entire body. In this way the genes serve as the basis of heredity.

On rare occasions a gene meets with an ultramicroscopic collision or other accident, which jolts its parts (or those of the duplicate that it has under construction) into a new arrangement, having a different chemical influence from before. We call this event a *mutation.* The mutant gene, in reproducing itself thereafter, tends to copy its new pattern as faithfully as the original gene had copied its old pattern. Thus, if the mutation has occurred in a reproductive cell, it may become evident as a variation inherited by a line of descendants. In this way, the mutations of the genes provide the inherited variations on which the process of evolution by natural selection is based. The reason why this role is reserved for the genes alone is that only they have the strange property of making copies of themselves in just such a way as to incorporate within the daughter particles even those features that have been newly introduced into their own structure. In other words, their most important peculiarity is their ability to reproduce, not merely themselves as they originally were, but also their variations.

The material that forms the bulk of most cells, although often designated by the single word *protoplasm*, is really a most elaborate composite of numerous constituents. The production of many of these constituents, including fundamentally important ones, has been shown to depend upon groups of special genes. Remove one of these genes and a given protoplasmic substance disappears or is replaced by something different; restore the gene and that protoplasmic substance reappears. In contrast to this, the production of any distinctive type of gene is not ordinarily a process initiated by the presence of certain distinctive protoplasmic substances. For, when a new type of gene arises by the mutation of some pre-existing gene, this mutant gene proceeds to reproduce itself, along with the growth and division of the cell, even though the protoplasmic substances present were, to start with, no different from those in other cells not containing the given mutant gene. On the basis of this, as well as other considerations (including that of economy of assumptions), it is reasonable to infer that in the origination of life the gene arose first, and that protoplasm came into existence later, very gradually, in the form of a series of products of the chemical action of aggregates of genes that had mutated in such ways as to be able to give rise to these products. Protoplasm would thus consist of substances accessory to and produced by the genes. Its existence would be due to the fact that those mutant genes had been naturally selected whose products happened to afford chemical tools, such as enzymes, that are useful for the survival and multiplication of these genes themselves.

It may be concluded that the essence of life is not protoplasm or its operations, collectively termed *metabolism*, as has often been asserted, but that these are themselves results of biological evolution. Life's essence lies in the capability of undergoing such evolution, and this capability is inherent in the gene, by virtue of its property of duplicating its variations. At the present time, protoplasm is so highly evolved and complex, even in the most primitive cells known, that we should probably be justified in estimating the amount of advance in complexity between the stage of the simplest gene and that of a single cell, such as a bacterium, to be at least as great as that from the bacterium to the highest many-celled organism.

It is not surprising that, in the remote past, the gene itself should have come into existence. For conditions were such, in the envelopes of the primitive earth, that the accidental encounters of substances, together with the absorption of energetic radiation, continued during many millions of years, must have provided a tremendous accumulation of ever more complicated organic compounds, including many of those occurring today within cells. And if, among the myriad types of molecules thereby produced, genes were included (only one successful gene being required!), then the component parts also would already have been formed, out of which these genes could manufacture duplicates of themselves. Moreover, there would also be numerous other ready-made constituents present, which were capable of being utilized as accessory substances after mutations implementing such utilization had occurred in the descendant genes.

Advances in Protoplasmic Organization

The chemical nature of the pathways whereby the genes control the composition and workings of the protoplasm have not yet been made clear. In any case, these pathways today involve so many steps and are so intricately branched and conjoined that much of the control is very indirect. With regard to the primary step in gene functioning, the long-neglected view is now gaining ground that this consists in the construction by the genes in the chromosomes of modified likenesses of themselves which enter the general protoplasm and there act as the genes' working delegates. Now that there is reason to regard the genes as being composed of nucleic acid, it is natural to suppose that the modified kind of nucleic acid, ribonucleic acid, found in high concentration in special protoplasmic granules, represents these gene delegates. Rich and Watson, who advocate this view, present evidence that this kind of nucleic acid, like that of the genes themselves, consists of coiled chains, possibly double, of nucleotides—in this case, however, of the four corresponding "ribonucleotide" types. Since the synthesis of protein and possibly of other substances occurs in association with these granules, it seems likely that it is the ribonucleotide chains in them that conduct this synthesis. Perhaps they also, to a limited extent, carry out some duplication of their own substance. The proteins and other materials, in their turn, engage in the multitudinous other reactions that occur in the cell.

In addition to those ribonucleotide links that are united in long chains, to form the ribonucleic acids, there are more or less separated units of them, and these have been found to be indispensable in many protoplasmic reactions. In these reactions they act as conveyors of large amounts of energy (carried on detachable phosphate groups) from one type of molecule to another, under the guidance of proteins and other companion substances. It may be that this special ability to transfer energy is also possessed by chained nucleotides and comes into play when they carry out their synthetic activities, both in gene duplication and in the building of other materials.

Aside from the nucleic acids themselves, the proteins are the most highly organized and diversified of the protoplasmic substances. In connection with most of the chemical steps taken by organic materials in protoplasm, there is some distinctive protein that acts as an enzyme for just that reaction—that is, a substance that induces the given change in other molecules without itself being used up. One or a few molecules of enzyme, because they can continue to do the same job repeatedly, are able to change a relatively large amount of other material. In consequence, an outfit of numerous different enzymes, sufficient for a multitude of different operations, can be contained within a minute bulk of protoplasm.

The molecules of proteins, like those of nucleic acids, are made up of chains, often coiled, composed of a great number of links. Important in determining the physical and chemical potentialities of any given protein molecule is (for one thing) the exact arrangement in line of its diverse types of links, called *amino-acid groups*. Nucleic-acid molecules, both those of the genes and those elsewhere (ribonucleic acids), commonly exist in close association with protein molecules. These and other considerations have lent plausibility to the idea that the building of protein molecules involves an activity of the nucleic acids of the genes somewhat resembling that by which they duplicate themselves. Even more likely is the possibility that the ribonucleic acids work in this way.

If, however, the construction of a protein molecule is pictured as a capturing, by the links of a nucleotide chain-molecule, of amino acids corresponding to these nucleotides, with the resultant formation of a parallel amino-acid chain-molecule, the difficulty arises that, whereas there are only four types of nucleotides, there are some two dozen types of amino acids. How then can a given nucleotide specify which amino acid is to be selected at a given point? Gamow has suggested what appears to be a likely solution: namely, it takes a group of four neighboring nucleotides to capture one amino acid, and the type of amino acid selected depends upon how these four nucleotides (of their four possible types) are arranged with respect to one another, somewhat as the arrangement of letters determines the meaning of a word. He points out that, at any point in a coiled double chain of nucleotides, the number of effectively different arrangements of four neighboring nucleotides would just about correspond with the number of different types of amino acids in proteins. Whether or not the details of his hypothesis are correct, it would seem that some such relationship must exist if, as seems likely, the nucleic acids synthesize the proteins directly.

Even if the protein molecules are produced in this way in the first place, however, they would still be subject to considerable and diverse alterations afterward, since proteins are among the most modifiable substances known. It would therefore be unwarranted to suppose that any given enzyme or other protein of functional importance is the product of some one special gene alone and that other genes have played no part in the determination of its nature. In fact, there is, in particular cases, direct genetic evidence against this oversimplified view.

Whatever the means by which proteins and other organic substances were synthesized, there must, soon after the earliest stages of their association with genes, have been great advantage in the ability to utilize, as raw materials for them, other materials than those constituent groups out of which they were immediately put together in the process of capture and arrangement by nucleotide chains. These hitherto alien materials would become available for use if they could be subjected to reactions that converted them into such constituents, and these reactions could be brought about by appropriate enzymes and other accessory substances, resulting from given mutations of genes. Moreover, in the construction of some substances methods of their manufacture would be worked out which did not require any direct reshaping of their constituents by the nucleotides themselves. In consequence, as the operations of gene aggregates, gradually aided by more numerous accessory substances, became more complicated through the natural selection of advantageous mutations in the genes, means must have been evolved for transforming into the materials of living things substances that required an ever more extended series of steps for the conversion process. At the same time, increasingly elaborate and effective methods were also developed for obtaining energy, storing it, and transferring it. Thus ultimately some organisms, the typical plants, became able to live entirely on certain inorganic substances and to derive their energy directly from the prime source, sunlight.

Other organisms meanwhile evolved mechanisms for utilizing other substances, some inorganic, some organic, for material, or for energy, or for both, until at last there was one vast interconnected system of living things on earth, diversely specialized chemically. This system kept in circulation the materials for life and also, until it had become dissipated, the captured energy, instead of letting them accumulate in the form of unusable wastes, as many of them must have done before. Life was thereby able to attain far greater abundance, faster turnover, increased diversity, and speedier, richer evolution.

Another circumstance that accelerated evolution, probably even at a prebacterial stage, was the establishment of sexual reproduction, in its more general sense of the coming together of two sets of genes from different sources. Before this process could be biologically effective, the series of maneuvers known as *meiosis* had to be developed. In meiosis some of the genes of each of the two sets that meet become recombined so as to form a single complete set. By the repetition of this process in successive generations, an entire population comes to constitute one great pool of genes, out of the innumerable shifting combinations of which the choicest (from the standpoint of self-perpetuation) tend to prevail. The accumulation of advantageous mutant genes is thereby caused to take place much more rapidly than in organisms that reproduce only asexually, which have their genes confined within mutually isolated lines of descent. Undoubtedly sexual reproduction owes its survival to the other advantages that, secondarily, accrued in its possessors by virtue of their faster evolution. Its function, therefore, is to make more effective the gene's ability to evolve.

Still another innovation the main significance of which lies in its hastening of evolution, or, to be more accurate, in its hindering of the retardation of evolution, is the natural death of the body. Of course this phenomenon arises, in its more typical manifestations, only in the later stages of evolution, in which organisms have become many-celled and have had their reproductive cells differentiated from the cells of their body proper. Natural death is not the expression of an inherent principle of protoplasm, but in each species natural selection has tended to develop a length of life that is optimal, in relation to the other characteristics of that species and to its conditions of living. In other words death is an advantage to life. Its advantage lies chiefly in its giving ampler opportunities for the genes of the newer generation to have their merits tested out. That is, by clearing the way for fresh starts, it prevents the clogging of genetic progress by the older individuals. Secondarily, in higher organisms which as a result of the existence of natural death have allowed defects to develop during senescence, death has become doubly advantageous, in that it now serves also to sweep away these defects for which it is indirectly responsible.

Even before the attainment of the many-celled stage, with its complicated embryonic development, passing into adulthood, senescence, and death, many organisms had evolved regular sequences of transformations, constituting developmental cycles. They had also evolved numerous regulatory mechanisms that adapted them to environmental changes of those types that had been repeatedly encountered. Some of these mechanisms stabilized the organism internally, in reaction to outside disturbances; others set on foot operations that counteracted harmful circumstances or that took advantage of potentially helpful circumstances. Among the mechanisms were those that endowed the organism with the properties known loosely as *irritability*, *conductivity*, and *contractility*, all of which were so interadjusted as to result in adaptive (that is, advantageous) movements.

These diverse adaptive reactions all have their bases in specific structures, caused by genes, accidentally arisen by mutation, which had won out in the struggle for survival when the given conditions were met with many times in the past. They are not, however, expressions of any generalized adaptive ability, and they do not control the course of variation in the genes themselves. Thus the pre-Darwinian evolutionists and their Michurinist descendants have put the cart before the horse in assuming that living matter, by virtue of its inherent nature, makes an effort to adapt itself directly to new circumstances, and that evolution has consisted in the accumulation, by inheritance, of the adaptations thereby evoked.

Plant and Animal Ways

In some lines of one-celled organisms, which had probably been typical plants, adjustments of the structures subserving movement enabled the organism to add to its income by capturing and assimilating bits of already formed organic material and finally even other organisms. It then proved profitable for them to concentrate entirely on the predatory mode of life, with resultant loss of most synthetic abilities and ever-increasing development of the motor ones. Thus animals arose.

Although animals and plants thereafter diverged, there were some parallelisms in their evolution. In both groups increased size proved advantageous for some ways of living and was accomplished by the integration of many cells into a larger organism. This in turn allowed the development of far greater specialization of parts. However, in plants the fact that the supplies needed could usually be had best by simply "staying put" and reaching steadily out for them caused this specialization to take the form of relatively motionless branched structures, with (for land plants) roots in the ground for securing minerals and water, leaves above for sunlight and carbon dioxide, and a strong conducting structure between. Movements were still necessary to bring the male reproductive cells to the eggs and to disseminate the products of fertilization, but these were in the main accomplished passively, by mechanisms that utilized motions of water, air, or animals.

On the animal side, the nature of the food put a premium on the development of means of capturing it and of avoiding being captured. It is true that many small bits of food which floated or swam through water could be caught even by sedentary animals, provided that these sifted the food out from the water that was swept by them or sucked into them. Hence such animals are often plantlike in appearance. But more of a challenge was presented by food that was large, well protected, difficult of access, elusive, or possessed of counter-activity. The more the food used had such characteristics, the more advantageous was it for the animal to develop adroitness and strength of movement, including locomotion. The same capabilities also became valuable in protecting it against predators equipped with them. In varied lines of animals, therefore, natural selection favored the accumulation of those mutations that resulted in more effective sensory, coordinating, motor, and supporting systems. At the same time, since the exercise of strength requires a comparatively massive body, in the interior of which materials are not introduced or removed at a fast enough rate by diffusion alone to service a high level of activity, it became important to elaborate systems for ingesting and processing food materials and oxygen, for supplying them effectively to the cells, and for extracting and eliminating the wastes.

The strikingly divergent forms taken by many of these advances in different groups were, of course, evolved in adaptation to their great differences in circumstances and ways of living. Often these differences were in considerable measure dependent upon one or a few major peculiarities of their construction, such as a gliding membrane or tube-feet, which furnished a key to the mode of construction of many other parts. It is evident that some of the features, including even some of those in the key positions, were originally adopted, at least in the particular form taken by them, as a result of some unusual combination of minor, temporary circumstances, which would be unlikely to recur. Having once arisen, however, they proved their usefulness, which sometimes extended to some very different function, and they thereby became a solid, important part of the pattern of the organism. In this position, they might help to determine the natural selection of a long series of further steps, proceeding in a given direction. Because the method of evolution was thus opportunistic instead of farsighted, it is found that organisms, despite the marvelous interworking of their parts, conceal many imperfections and indirections of structure and functioning. In fact, evolution presents such a curious combination of arbitrariness and consequentialness as to lead us to infer that on another world physically like ours only remotely analogous forms of life would have evolved.

Learning and Consciousness

Among the more regularly occurring of the higher developments in active animals is the elaboration of the coordinating system and the inclusion within it of mechanisms for modifying its operations in adjustment with the individual's experiences. The basic feature in this process, which from the objective standpoint is called *conditioning* and from the subjective standpoint *learning* or *association,* is the formation of connections among different groups of neuronic (nerve cell) reactions that have been aroused at or nearly at the same time, so that subsequently the arousal of either tends to invoke the other as well. These connections form an ever more intricate web, since if reaction-group *A* becomes connected with *B* at one time and *B* becomes connected with *C* at another time, it follows that *A* thereby becomes connected with *C*, in the arrangement *ABC*.

Also essential in learning is the procedure called *analysis*, whereby particular components or relationships existing within a neuronic reaction-complex become dissected out, as it were, so that when they occur in different settings they can serve to cross-connect these other features with one another, somewhat as *B* connected *A* and *C* in the foregoing illustration. Doubtless there are as yet unguessed but far-reaching inherited neural mechanisms that effect the isolation of certain characteristic relationships, such as (on a sensory-motor level) possession of the same color or motion of a given kind across the field of view. However, much of the analysis at deeper levels depends also upon associational procedures in which the neuronic reaction-complex is subjected to various learned operations. These, in modifying it, bring out features implicit in it which it shares with some other complex.

All these processes become useful to the organism only by virtue of their modification of its behavior. This modification is made possible by the fact that the neuronic activities for movements become strengthened or inhibited according to whether these movements have been followed by experiences (neuronic reactions and reaction-complexes) of the types subjectively designated as desirable or undesirable. Which experiences are originally felt to be desirable or undesirable, and which emotional and behavioral ("instinctive") responses are concomitantly aroused by them, are matters determined by inherited neuronic structures. These have been shaped by evolution in such wise that the creature, in working for its own goals, unwittingly furthers the multiplication of its kind. However, through association it learns to achieve its primary desires by more effective means, better adjusted to the circumstances surrounding it, and learns to coordinate and subordinate its different desires to one another so as to attain greater total gratification.

Despite our present ignorance of the nature of the physicochemical bases of all these phenomena, their physicochemical *existence* is attested by numerous facts of observation and experiment.

As, through association and analysis, an increasingly coherent and serviceable formulation or representation of the world outside becomes built up out of the neuronic reaction-complexes, we become justified in speaking of intelligence. Only here, at last, does foresight make its debut in the operations of living things. Moreover, within this same neuronic reaction-system, a representation of the individual himself, including his own associations, gradually takes its place. A speaking individual, in referring to this phenomenon, then uses the expression *consciousness* or some equivalent.

Although this term denotes what may be called the inner or subjective view of oneself, it is only by a confusion of ideas that it is thought of as implying the existence of two "parallel sides," conscious and material, to neuronic or other processes: that is, two systems of phenomena that coexist and completely correspond but do not interact. If this view were correct the existence of consciousness, being only "parallel," could in no way affect our behavior. Hence we could not speak of it. Nor could we, for that matter, even think of it (for the conscious could no more than parallel the material side, and the latter could not be affected by the former). It follows that the conscious phenomena *are* the physicochemical phenomena or, at least, are some integrated portion of them. In other words, matter and mind present no real antithesis. Moreover, in the case of mind, as in the case of life, its difference from matter and energy in their more ordinary forms lies in the peculiarities of its mode of organization and resultant operation.

Pooling of Learning

Turning to a consideration of the native intelligence of our own species, we find that it is not so very much greater than that of some other existing animals. However, this relatively moderate difference, taken in conjunction with man's social disposition and with his queer proclivities for vocalizing and symbolizing, enables him far more effectively than other animals to communicate with others of his kind. This has resulted in his social evolution, by the accumulation of tradition, a process wherein each individual becomes provided with the distilled experience of a vast, ever-increasing body of his ancestors and associates. Through this knowledge and the cooperative activities and resultant material equipment based upon it, man has become incomparably more potent than any other form of life on earth, even without any perceptible improvement having taken place in his genes since before civilization began.

It is true that ancient tradition is often faulty and tends to over-elaborate itself by an inner inertia in arbitrary and injurious ways. Moreover, the strange human propensity for symbolization, although invaluable not only for communication but for thought itself, has often led men astray, running away with them, causing them to misinterpret and glorify their own symbols and to confuse them with the things denoted. But with the increase of useful knowledge men have come to realize that tradition, even when ancient, is manmade, and that only the systematic testing, unhampered criticism, and rational judgment denoted as *science* can give them a more correct understanding of things. By the conscious, organized use of this method life today, in the form of man, is ever more rapidly reaching out to new spheres and to new modes of existence. At the same time, transcending its role of animal, it is making its position firmer by learning to promote, and in part even to supersede, the synthetic functions of the plant kingdom.

It must be recognized that at this point man's social development has lagged far behind his "material" development, and that the resultant insufficiency of cooperation among his own members may bring about the annihilation of his hard-won achievements, if not of man himself. Alternatively, he may begin to advance to hitherto unimagined outer and inner conquests. Such advance, however, will require a wisdom that can be gained only by genuinely free inquiry, based solidly upon our advancing knowledge of the nature of things and backed by the broadest, most unbiased good will.

If our dangerous drifting from one short-range goal to another is to be replaced by really long-range foresight, we shall have to overhaul courageously all our ancient standards of value, for value judgments, far from being immune to scientific investigation as is sometimes asserted, should be a main object of such study. In accordance with the conclusions thereby reached, we shall then have the task of modifying our systems of inner motivation and the relationships of individual with individual and group with group. Recognizing that our conscious objectives, which we subsume under the expression the *pursuit of happiness*, are the complex and modifiable resultants of more primitive urges chosen by natural selection in compliance with the pressure of the gene to preserve itself and to extend its domain, we must seek more *functional* ways of pursuing happiness. These should more successfully harmonize the gene's trend to increase and evolve with the deepest fulfillment of our conscious natures, so that the serving of either of these ends will by that very act promote the other. In fact, any other policy is ultimately self-defeating, in this world of interpenetrating competition and cooperation.

Crisis in Gene Increase

It is, however, a mistake to assume that the gene's tendency to increase gives biological victory to the organisms with the highest gross fertility. In general, the "higher" the organism, the greater the security of individual life that it achieves and the lower its production of offspring. Natural selection has decreased the fertility because, with too high a pressure toward population increase, the well-being and efficiency of the organisms are so reduced as actually to lower the potential of the species to undergo biological expansion. In fact, civilized man, through his advanced techniques, has attained such security of life (except for war!) that an even lower fertility now becomes appropriate for him, both biologically and for his individual happiness, than that which was established for him by natural selection in adjustment to primitive conditions.

Civilized man is now going part of the way toward meeting this requirement artificially, by means of birth control, but it will be necessary for him to make much more widespread and adequate use of such technique, in order that he may attain and maintain a world-wide optimum per-capita supply of energy and of food and other materials. Otherwise he would be forced back into a misery and disorganization that would not only rob him of most of the benefits of his previous progress but would find him deprived, perhaps permanently, of the resources needed to raise himself again and at last to expand into new and more commodious realms of living. Thus it is preeminently true of civilized man that his success in pursuing happiness is a necessary basis for the success of his genes in their job of multiplication. Conversely, however, the pursuit of happiness must also be so directed as ultimately to lead to biological expansion, if man is to utilize his opportunities for bringing "the greatest good to the greatest number," and if he is to minimize the risks of disaster and of being left behind in the universal struggle for existence.

But even if we grant that man will achieve adequate control over his numbers and will advance to untold reaches in his social evolution, all this progress must still rest on a crumbling biological basis, unless not merely the quantity but also the quality of that basis is vigilantly taken care of. For the artificial saving of lives under modern civilization will allow the increasing accumulation of detrimental mutant genes, unless this accumulation is deliberately compensated by an enlightened control over the types of genes to be reproduced. This course of action, to be both sound in its direction and effective in its execution, must be entered upon not under compulsion but in the spirit of freely given cooperation, founded not upon illusions but upon the idealism that is natural to men who engage in a great mutual endeavor.

Man a Transitional Phase

The spirit thus aroused would inevitably tend to proceed further, to the realization that the mere prevention of deterioration is an inadequate, uninspiring biological ideal and that instead, by extension and supplementation of the methods followed for maintaining our genetic foundation as it is, it can actually be raised to ever higher levels. Acceptance of this course will be facilitated by the rapid growth of human understanding and technical proficiency that we see under way about us now. This present progress is, as we have seen, not based on any changes in the hereditary endowment but only on the extreme responsiveness of the human organism, even with its present endowment, to educational and other environmental influences. But great as are the advances possible in this way, men cannot remain satisfied with them alone when they become aware of the vastly greater enhancement of life that could result from the combination of this kind of progress with that in their underlying genetic constitution. This would include the genetic remodeling of our primitive urges, the improvement of our intellectual ability, and even of our bodily construction.

There is no limit in sight to the possible extent of such advances, provided that we *will* them to take place. However, the possibility of their coming about automatically, by the type of unconscious natural selection that has operated in past ages, has been done away with, as explained earlier, by the conditions resulting from social evolution. For these conditions rightly lead to the increasing protection, by society at large, of those who are weak and ailing by heredity, as well as of those handicapped by misfortunes caused by outer circumstances. Yet at the same time this very social evolution has provided and will provide increasingly effective knowledge and techniques for the voluntary, artificial guidance of biological evolution. These make available, in compensation for the deficiency of natural selection under civilization, novel means of directing many of the processes involved in reproduction and heredity.

Among the methods of this kind that are being, and will be further, developed are those for managing the generation and the storage of the reproductive cells, both within the body and outside of it, those for artificially controlling insemination and fertilization, for instigating parthenogenesis and twinning or polyembryony, and for instituting foster pregnancy. It should be possible eventually to find ways of influencing the behavior and distribution of the chromosomes themselves. Means of substituting, for the original nuclei of eggs, other cell nuclei, of chosen types, are even now being worked out, and such operations may in time be made fine enough to deal with individual chromosomes or their parts. Far more remote and unlikely than these possibilities, however, is that of regulating the direction taken by the mutations of genes.

However that may be, the rate at which biological progress could be made even by the means available today is already incomparably greater than that to which it was limited by the slow unconscious processes of nature. Only fear of the dead hand of ancient superstition today holds most men back from a recognition of these opportunities for greater life. But, with the progress of enlightenment, this fear must wither away. Thus, man as we know him is to be regarded as only a transitional operative in the progression of life, but one who commands a critical turning of the road. For at this point the method of evolution may change from the unconscious to the conscious, from that of trial and error to that of long-range foresight.

Man in the shackles of authoritarianism is incapable of such advances. Should he attempt them, his efforts would be misdirected and corrupting. But, with the amplified opportunity to create that is his when he is free to see things as they are, he will find his greatest inspiration in the realization that he is by no means the final acme and end of existence, but that, through his own efforts, he may become the favored vehicle of life today. That is, he can be the means whereby life is conducted onward and outward, to forms in ever better harmony within themselves, with one another, and with outer nature, endowed with ever keener sentience, deeper wisdom, and further reaching powers.

Who can say how far this seed of self-awareness and self-transfiguration that is within us may in ages to come extend itself down the corridors of the cosmos, challenging in its progression those insenate forces and masses in relation to which it has seemed to be but a trivial infestation or rust? For the law of the gene is ever to increase, and to evolve to such forms as will more effectively manipulate and control materials outside itself so as to safeguard and promote its own increase. And if the mindless gene has thereby generated mind and foresight and then advanced this product from the individual to the social mind, to what reaches may not we and our heirs, the incarnations of that social mind, be able, if we will, to carry consciously the conquests of life?

9 Human and General Genetics

MENTAL TRAITS AND HEREDITY

The Extent to Which Mental Traits are Independent of Heredity
As Tested in a Case of Identical Twins Reared Apart

H. J. Muller*
University of Texas

I. The Problem

There can be no doubt that the characters whose inheritance is of paramount importance to us are human psychological traits. What makes the world today, as well as what directly makes ourselves what we are, is man's psychology. To attain an understanding of, and finally the guidance of the heredity of man's own psychological nature, must for a long time to come be the hoped-for ultimate goal of applied genetics, far overshadowing any of its other possible attainments.

Our direct efforts at reaching an understanding of the heredity of mental characters have so far been largely confined to the recording of pedigrees, in which traits of the individuals, such as mental capacity, or immorality, or patience, are indicated simply as present or absent, according to some subjective estimate often received at second hand—then, assuming that these assigned differences are mainly genetic in origin, the attempt is made to work out from the pedigree the method of their inheritance. But inasmuch as man's brain is his chief mechanism of adaptation to diverse outer environments, his brain being, primarily, an organ expressly constructed in such a way that it confers upon its possessor the maximum *plasticity* of adjustment known anywhere in the universe, it should be evident that many psychic traits, especially as judged by casual estimate, will be extremely reflective of the environment that the individual has had. And as the human individual tends largely to hand down both his physical and his specific psychic environments, such as amount of schooling, habits of ill-temper, alcoholism, etc., *ad infinitum*, there will thereby be created in the pedigrees a false appearance of inheritance which may be inextricable from the effects of heredity itself. It should accordingly be one of the first concerns of workers in this field to determine how much the traits involved, as estimated by them, are subject to alteration by environmental differences commonly met with, and, secondly, they should seek to find what traits, and what methods of estimating

Journal of Heredity, 1925, 16: 433-48; Department of Zoology contribution No. 191.

traits, give data least affected by environmental differences and therefore most reliable for genetic study.

In most laboratory animals, the above objects can be attained by inbreeding brothers to sisters for a large number of generations and thus obtaining pure (homozygous) lines, and then studying the amount of variation of different traits, as estimated by different means, within these lines, as compared with the amount of variation between individuals of different lines. In man, this is scarcely feasible "in this day and generation," but fortunately we are presented with material of the type sought for, namely, genetically identical individuals, in the cases of identical twins. Although only two individuals here belong to each pure line, observations on enough pairs should tell us the amount of effect of certain kinds of environmental differences, such as accidents of embryonic history, or incidental daily occurrences, or adult experiences, on all sorts of traits. This was first pointed out by Francis Galton, who, after reviewing the histories of thirty-five pairs of probably "identical" twins, came to the conclusion that none of the environmental conditions, except disease, which had differentiated the members of the pairs of twins, had exerted a pronounced effect upon their psychic traits.

Unfortunately for the purposes of the present problem, however, cases of identical twins are usually the very ones in which most kinds of environmental differences, especially those of more protracted action during the earlier more plastic years, are reduced to a minimum, and so these cases can supply us with only very limited data on "genetic indetermination." This criticism holds against the cases of Galton above referred to. Cases are required in which the identical twins are *reared apart* under environments differing as much as those commonly met with do, in order that we may gain an idea of the amount of effect of such environmental differences as distinguish separate families in a community. Not one such case has heretofore been systematically investigated by modern methods, as such cases are very rare. Each such case is extremely valuable, however, since in any *one* such case, if a mental trait is found which shows marked similarity in the two members of the pair, and wide diversity in other individuals, in spite of the fact that the environments of the two members differed considerably in such features as would be most likely to influence the trait, it may be pretty safely concluded that the trait in question, when measured by the method used, is genetically narrowly determined, and is reliable as a genetic indicator; where on the other hand, great differences appear, it is highly probable that the latitude of genetic indetermination is great, that the character differences so indicated are largely non-genetic, and that some other method of observation or of testing must be used for estimating the genes which may be concerned in such characters. The results, then, may indicate not only the amount of variation caused by environment in the trait measured, but also the reliability of the method of measurement used, for indicating genetic facts.

Psychological tests of all kinds are much in vogue at present, and have multiplied rapidly. Doubtless their objectiveness and the comparative lack of personal equation in determining the scores make them superior, for most scientific purposes, to the old scheme of using untrained personal opinion as to traits, but until they have been tried out by work of the kind just outlined, the *genetic* significance of these tests; as well as of the earlier methods of estimating psychological characteristics, must remain most dubious. In the present work on a case of identical twins reared apart, then, mental tests of various kinds were used, not because they were highly trusted as indicators of "innate" tendencies or capabilities, but because they were the only kind of objective measures yet available, and because the use of them in this connection might furnish a test of the tests themselves.

The idea of applying mental tests of various kinds to twins had been conceived and already put into operation by Dr. Helen Koch, psychologist at the University of Texas. The pair of twins reared apart, that are dealt with in the present paper, had been brought to the writer's attention through the note by Popenoe, in the *Journal of Heredity* in 1922, which had given a picture of them and a brief description of their characters and histories, based on a statement sent in by one of the twins (J.). If, then, these twins were identical, all that was necessary for the present writer to do, in order to obtain evidence on the problems indicated above, was to apply the same series of tests and general technique as was being used by Dr. Koch to the twins reported by Popenoe. This was made possible by the generous collaboration of Dr. Koch, who furnished the present writer with tests of the kind she was using and acquainted him with their technique, and in addition planned a series of questions calculated to give pertinent data in the life history investigation. At her suggestion, funds which helped to defray the expenses of the trip were placed at the disposal of the writer by the Department of Education of the University of Texas. The writer wishes here to acknowledge this assistance and also the efficient and invaluable cooperation rendered by both of the twins, and by the writer's wife, Dr. Jessie Jacobs-Muller.

There was an important reason for giving the twins exactly the same tests as Dr. Koch was using, aside from the greater convenience of such a procedure for the present investigator. If any wide differences should be found between the responses of the two identical (?) twins in the present case, the question would arise whether these differences had really been caused by the conspicuous differences in the rearing and manners of life of the twins, or by other causes—such as temporary moods, or the lasting influence of fortuitous but critical events in the pre- or post-natal life, that might conceivably have caused just as pronounced divergencies between individuals that had been reared together. Although Galton's data above referred to does indicate the slightness of effect of such influences on psychological characters, the latter were not actually measured by mental tests in his work and it might be that the tests would have shown greater differences. Some evidence on the point in question might, however, be gained by noting whether the differences in the results of the tests in the present case were or were not of the sort that might be expected to follow from the ascertainable differences in the life histories of the twins. But the most dependable evidence would be derived from a study of the results of the same tests when applied to twins reared together. When the results of the study undertaken by Dr. Koch appear, therefore, they should have an important bearing on the present case, in indicating how much any differences here found are really attributable to the differences in "upbringing" of the twins, rather than to the other environmental factors above alluded to.

II. The Determination of Genetic Identity

The problem next arose, of how the genetic identity or non-identity of the twins could be established. For this a new method had to be devised. A list of largely non-correlated physical traits was drawn up *a priori* such as stature, coloration, prominence of chin, curling of hair, etc. In doing this the attempt was made to choose traits (1) in respect to which marked differences, readily noted, are commonly to be found within families, (2) which there would be as little *a priori* reason as possible to suspect would be connected in development, or influenced by the same genetic difference, (3) which general observation indicates often to be inherited separately from each other within families, and (4) which are probably influenced as little as possible by environic differences. What, now, will be the chance, *a priori* that the twins should agree in some one of these traits in which one or more of the sibs differ from the others, if the twins are not "identicals"? Or what will be the chance that they should resemble each other more closely than they do the other twins? These chances can be calculated with considerable accuracy.

Let us suppose, first, that in respect to a given trait—say body build—certain "classes" may be distinguished among the sibs—e.g., heavier and lighter build—into which the sibs may be classified in such a manner that all the individuals found to be in the same class clearly differ less from each other than any of those in different classes do. In the present case there were two "heavier" and three "lighter" (including the twins). Now, accepting the given numerical division of the sibs into these classes—e.g., two in one and three in the other in our case,—what were the *a priori* chances that both of the twins should have fallen into the same class? The chances are in our case two in five that one of them should have fallen into the heavier class, and, this being so, one in four that the other should have fallen into this class, or $2/5 \times 1/4$, $= 1/10$, that both should be in the heavier class. Similarly, the chances are $3/5 \times 2/4$, or $3/10$, that both should be in the lighter class, and the total chances that both should be in the same class, either heavier or lighter, are $1/10 + 3/10$, or $4/10$. In general, if there are n sibs altogether (including the twins), a of them falling into class a with respect to a given trait, b into class b, c into class c, etc., the chance that the twins should have been found in the same class is:

$$\frac{a}{n}\frac{a-1}{n-1} + \frac{b}{n}\frac{b-1}{n-1} + \frac{c}{n}\frac{c-1}{n-1} + \text{etc.}$$

If, now, the traits are inherited independently, as they usually will be to a large extent, the chance that two sibs should be in the same class in respect to all the traits considered is the product of all these chances found in the case of each separate trait. By this means it was shown that, if the twins in the present case were non-identical, the chance that they should have been in the same class, as they were, in respect to all the six traits thus investigated was only 1 in 386 (see table A). The latter number would probably have been even higher, were it not for the fact that in a number of cases (marked "?") the class of a sib in regard to a given trait had not been definitely determined and in these cases the sib had been reckoned as belonging in the same class as the twins, in order that any mistake in the final number should be on the side of caution.

If actual measurements could be made of the traits in each sib, instead of a mere division into "classes," a much more exact estimate of the probabilities could be made. For $2(n-2)$ resemblances exist between each of the two twins and each of the $(n-2)$ sibs other than the twins, in any given trait, the resemblance between the twins themselves therefore being only 1 in a total of $2(n-2) + 1$, or $2n-3$, resemblances; the chance, then, that the resemblance between non-identical twins is closer than the resemblance of either to any of the other sibs, in a given trait, is $\frac{1}{2n-3}$. For this relation to hold for all of m traits. the chance would be $\left(\frac{1}{2n-3}\right)^m$. If the relation failed to hold in the case of any traits the chance could also be calculated of the resemblance being as close as it was found to be. It is important that the investigation be made of traits chosen *a priori* or at least before their extent of development in *two* of the sibs (including at least one of the twins) is known, else the investigator may be more apt to choose for investigation traits in which the twins differ from other sibs, and agree with each other.

After we have established the chance $\frac{1}{P}$ —e.g. $\frac{1}{386}$ in our case— that non-identical twins would agree so closely, we may then legitimately turn this statement around, to say that the chance, in such case, that the twins are identical, is approximately $\frac{P}{P+1}$ i.e. $\frac{386}{387}$.

The latter calculation assumes that identical twins would always fall into the same "classes," or agree more closely than ordinary sibs, in the traits studied. Then, since approximately half the cases of twins of the same sex are "identicals" (as shown by the fact that twins are of the same sex twice as often as of opposite sex), we should find, in a collection of 2P pairs of twins (772), P (or 386) identicals, all agreeing closely, and P (or 386) non-identicals, of which only one pair agreed as closely as in the case observed. Hence, amongst each P + 1 (387) that resembled each other by the required amount, only one pair would be non-identical, and the chance that the observed pair was one of the identicals would be $\frac{P}{P+1}$, i.e., $\frac{386}{387}$.

The above methods can be used in all cases where a pair of twins have another sib concerning whom information can be obtained, and they should prove useful, as the crucial question of whether or not a given pair of twins is identical could heretofore be answered only very vaguely. These methods are themselves still capable of considerable refinement, however, and as yet yield results only approximately correct, inasmuch as they do not take into account discrepancies caused by possible association of the traits considered in a family, due either to linkage or to their dependence on identical factors, or possible evironic effects that might occasionally cause identical twins to differ more than ordinary sibs in a given trait, or cause non-identical twins to be more alike than ordinary sibs. The method of *a priori* selection of the traits minimizes these discrepancies, and if the classification instead of the measurement method is used there is little chance that traits like eye color will be caused by environment to overstep their "class" boundaries. However, the precise amount of allowance to be made for each of these sources of inexactness can be definitely determined by statistics involving actual measurements or classifications of the traits in question in ordinary sibs and in twins. These statistics will disclose (1) the amount of correlation of the traits amongst sibs within families, (2) the frequency with which identicals show greater differences than ordinary sibs and (3) the amount to which non-identical twins show a greater resemblance than ordinary sibs. In making this determination the genetic identity or non-identity of twins could be established sufficiently well for the first approximation by the methods as given above. When these three values have been found their use in connection with the above methods would render the probabilities yielded by the latter very narrowly accurate, and independent of any assumptions such as those made in the present case.

In this case, in addition to the traits in the *a priori* list, there were striking resemblances between the twins in special points that had not been considered before examination. For example, they both had double ankle prominences on the mesial side of each tibia. Further examinations of the twins were conducted, on various physical characteristics, and when corresponding data can be obtained from the other sibs a considerably higher probability for identity than 386:1 will doubtless be adduced.

It may be of interest to note some of the results of the examinations (see Table F). The twins were of the same height, to the half inch, and the same weight, to the pound, when examined, though J had a very slightly larger head, and cephalic index, than B. Both belonged in group II with respect to blood agglutinins. Their strength of grip was nearly the same. In their iris color and iris pattern, hair color, distribution, and curliness no difference could be detected. Both had teeth similarly defective. There was a slight asymmetry of incisors, of iris patterns, and of lower lip in both, and, in both, these asymmetries were in the same direction. Both twins, moreover, had early shown lefthandedness, though B had been broken of it. Such asymmetry, in the same direction, appears to indicate earlier separation of the two cell masses of the embryo that were to form the two individuals than does asymmetry in opposite directions (the "mirror image" condition), but it is probably even better evidence of identical twins than the mirror-image condition is when the asymmetry of both is of the more unusual type (like lefthandedness). Finger prints showed themselves, in this case, to be no more definite identifying marks than general cast of features, for there was considerable difference between the two hands of each twin, which was probably due in the main to fortuitous embryological events, since where corresponding fingers of opposite hands of one twin differed in type from each other both these fingers of the other twin were of the same type as one of those of the first twin. In this respect, then, the asymmetries of the twins did not correspond, neither were they mirror-images, yet if the right hand of J had been interchanged with the right hand of B the twins would have had hands which matched each other—right with left of the same twin—about as well as before the exchange. The finger nails of the pair were very much alike. The features were very similar in the more easily definable aspects of contour and also of expression, and the twins have often been mistaken for each other; nevertheless there seemed to be distinct differences in the impression created on the observer. These differences were partly, but by no means entirely, due to the effect of differences of dress and of dressing the hair, and to the effect of a nasal operation on J.

III. The Histories of the Twins

A detailed study of the past history of the twins was made when they were visited and given the tests in the summer of 1923. B was then living in Wyoming, and J in Arizona. They were thirty years old at that time. They had been separated when two weeks old, did not see each other until they were eighteen years of age, and since then have lived in different places over nine-tenths of the time. Although they were brought up in a rather similar social and material environment, in the northwestern mining and ranch country, there were important differences in their upbringings, as will be seen from the following brief sketch.

B was brought up by foster parents who did mining, logging, and hauling, and often changed their locality. B as a child was out with the teams all day and had only four years formal schooling altogether, including nine months in business college. At fifteen B obtained clerical work, and she has had a strenuous but successful business career, varied by clerical, administrative, and secretarial work in many places—in Montana, Wyoming, New York, Washington, D. C., California, and in France during and after the war.

As for J, her foster parents owned a ranch and roadhouse, where things were very lively and she saw much of people when a child. She, too, was outdoors much of the time, and, like B, was a "tomboy," but being better off (tho not better educated), J's folks sent her right through school and through high school, and she has since had some summer university work. J has stayed west (mainly in South Dakota), and taught school there until her marriage nine years ago. (At this time B had a broken engagement.) J has had a child and is now teaching again, her especial interest being in education.

Both twins read voraciously when children, and have always been intellectually active, so that their class room work by no means measures the extent of their real education. Both have been extremely energetic, capable, and popular, and they have been prominent in all sorts of club work in their respective communities. On casual observation they appear very similar in character.

It appears that J was far the healthier baby, probably because of better treatment, B, the "runt," being badly fed and given much laudanum; B has had stomach trouble ever since. Both have had two or three attacks of tuberculosis, almost simultaneously. B had, and J nearly had, a nervous breakdown in her late teens.

IV. Results of the Psychological Tests

The twins were given two so-called "intelligence tests" which are well known in America: firstly, the "Army Alpha Test" (Form 8, July 9, 1918) which is doubtless familiar to most of the readers of this article at first or second hand, and secondly, the "Otis Advanced Intelligence Test" (Form A, 1922), which is very similar in character. The total scores (see Table B) were almost identical—B obtaining 156 and J 153 on the former, B 64 and J 62 on the latter. Scores so high are taken as indicating "very superior intelligence"; they are not common amongst persons attending school or college, except amongst students in universities of high standing, and they occur very seldom amongst persons of the social class in which the twins were raised.

The very extensive tests of the army draft showed that scores above 135 (called " A") on the Army Alpha occur in only about one in twenty-five men drawn at random from the general white population, and, as the results from persons of different occupations show, such scores can certainly be no more frequent than this amongst men whose parents belong to the social class to which the foster parents of the twins belonged. Further data on various groups shows that amongst persons of grade A (i.e., above 135), nearly half have scores below those of the twins (even in groups in which relatively high intelligence is expected); hence the *a priori* chance of a man with the social origin of the twins attaining as high a score as they did on the Army Alpha test is about one in fifty; data show that the chances are not higher for women than for men. But the chance for an individual of such origin not only attaining approximately as high a score as either of the twins, but also a score differing from one of these by no more than these differed from each other, is very much smaller yet, for much less than a fourth of individuals having scores as high as either of the twins fall within the range between them,—accordingly one in two hundred would be an ultra-conservative estimate. When in addition we take into consideration the consistently very high Otis scores, and their close parity, the chance becomes even more reduced. If the tests have no genetic significance, then, the chances were decidedly over two hundred to one against obtaining such a coincidence in scores as was observed. In fact, unless the correlation between genetic composition and test scores were very high (for individuals of a given region and status) the chances of getting a result like the above would still have been exceedingly small.

It should, however, be noted that the twins' responses were not equally alike throughout all sections of the tests. For in one section of the Army Alpha in particular—that known as "analogies," where a fourth suitable term has to be found for series like "sky: blue:: grass: (table, green, warm, or big?),"—"green" here being the correct answer—the scores seemed significantly different, B obtaining fourteen and J twenty-five out of forty. This difference is three times its "probable error," representing a chance of not more than one in twenty (even if all questions had been equally hard for a given twin). Yet on the face of it this would appear to be a test most indicative of innate analytical ability—if any such general ability exists. B answered seven and J eight out of ten correctly, however, on the similar section of the Otis test. A possibly significant difference in the other direction was found in the arithmetic scores: 15 for the clerical but less schooled B, 11 for J, out of a total of 20, in the Army Alpha; 10 for B and 6 for J, out of 10, in the Otis. Yet arithmetical problems also are sometimes considered particularly good tests of "reasoning ability," if any such general ability exists. The only other difference of any account at all was in the results of the "synonym-antonym" tests of the Army Alpha (section 4), where

B scored thirty-nine, J thirty-two out of forty, but in the rather similar section of the Otis test both scored eleven out of eleven. The similarity in scores of all other sections was extremely close, especially when the scores in corresponding sections of both tests were added together.

On the whole, then, we return to the conclusion, for most individual sections of these tests, that, when applied to persons of a given social class and territory, they provide a fairly reliable index of genetic or inherent capability for work of this nature; or, one may say, the expressions of intelligence measured by most sections of these tests are little affected by environmental differences, such as kind of schooling, occurring within the limits of such a class. (Note that the twin with less regular schooling scored slightly higher, if anything, in "intelligence.") We must, however, be careful not to draw the more sweeping conclusion from these results that environmental influences in general would have little effect upon scores attained, because the twins were after all raised in the same kind of community, and in families of a similar status; what the effect might have been of changing the social class, the country, or the color (were that possible) of one of them, it would be impossible to predict from present data.

Let us now compare with the above the results of other psychological tests, not of intelligence, but of volitional traits, of effort, emotional trends, social attitudes, etc. A glance at Tables C, D and E reveals the utterly different character of the findings. In Table C, for example, we see that J, the more schooled, responds about twice as rapidly to the stimulus-words in the Kent Rosanoff Association Test—tho her responses involve correspondingly more superficial associations. Such a difference is commonly found between the more and the less drilled in class-rooms. But B, the typist, "naturally" can make much faster taps, and she likewise makes faster dash marks within the squares of cross-section paper, tho here she is correspondingly less accurate.

In the Pressey X-O Tests for emotions and social attitudes (Table D) the subjects are given various selected lists of words, with instructions to cross out those representing things that they like, dislike, worry about, or have other specified attitudes towards (according to the section of the test). The results of these tests show that B—who has been so much knocked about—is much less perturbable in every way: she is less unpleasantly aroused either by things that might excite disgust, fear, sexual associations, or suspicions, having far fewer dislikes in all than J, and far fewer than the "norms," whereas J has more than the average number. B also has a smaller list of worries, and a smaller list of things she regards as wrong. In both these latter respects J is considerably above the average and B is approximately average. Part of the differences in fears, wrongs, and worries may also be explained by the fact that J had a much more fearsome, worrisome foster mother than B, and that she now has a family herself. On the other hand J, having more school training, exhibits more associations. She also had developed more likes.

The differences in results in the Pressey Tests are on the whole of the same order as for two unrelated persons taken at random from the group on which the norms of the test were based. In fact, the differences in results in Form A of these tests averaged just 1.0 times the average (or rather, median) difference between two individuals taken at random from this original group. (For the differences in Form A scores between B and J average exactly $\sqrt{2}$ times the quartile deviation of the whole group.) Certain sections of the Pressey tests (Form B) are taken a day or two after the rest, and the first two sections of the latter involve a repetition of some of the kinds of work previously done; this gives us a check on the previous results. In such cases (indicated in the rows marked "Form B") each twin gave answers fully consistent with those given by her before, and entirely different from those of the other twin. The difference between the responses of the twins in Form B is about one and one quarter times the average (median) difference between two individuals selected randomly from the group that was originally studied by Pressey.

In the Downey "Will-Temperament Test" (Table E) the twins made scores that were at least as different from each other as were those of the Pressey tests. In the Downey test the examinee is assigned various tasks, such as writing as fast as possible, and as slowly, and, again, under various circumstances that may try his patience, his temper, his perseverance, etc. He is also given certain decisions to make—and later to unmake, if he so chooses. In these acts he is taken off his guard, however, as the real object of the test is generally hidden under the cloak of some other ostensible purpose; so there is little chance for the tell-tale reaction to be purposely strengthened, weakened, or disguised by the subject.

The scores of these tests, marked off as points on a scale, and connected by lines, as in the table, are called the "Will-Profile." It will be seen that in nine of the twelve cases, where one twin's score was above the median (5.5), the other scored below, so that in this sense the scores were almost opposites of each other. The scores differed from each other, on the average, by four points, whereas the average (or rather, median) difference in scores of individuals chosen at random from the group on which the original data concerning the test were secured by Downey was 3.5 (as calculated from the quartile range, 2.5). Examining some of the individual records, we see that B—who has long been the director of clerical underlings and who in childhood was systematically tormented by her foster brother—reacted much more strenuously to contradiction (No. 6), and to opposition (No. 7), than J, the married. She also showed (so far as her responses to the tests could be taken as indicative) greater power of speedy movement (No. 1), went more nearly at her top speed habitually (No. 2), and had greater ability to do several things at once (No. 11), than J, but she was far less patient (No. 9), less really interested in detail on its own account (No. 10), less "flexible" (No. 3), and less likely to change previous decisions (No. 8), and not quite so desirous of continuing the work on her own initiative (No. 12).

The responses of the twins to all these tests—except the intelligence tests—are so decisively different almost throughout, that this one case is enough to show that the scores obtained in such tests indicate little or nothing of the genetic basis of the psychic make-up. And yet the results of such tests have, it is claimed, been shown to be correlated distinctly with characteristics of importance in the conduct of life, and in the successful holding of various types of positions. If, then, traits apparently so important, and so objectively defined as these, are not fixed by heredity, it is still more probable that many of the psychological differences commonly shown in human pedigree charts likewise have no genetic basis, and it is necessary to institute an intensive search for ways of identifying more truly genetic psychic characters.

Such an investigation can be conducted, firstly, by more thoroughly studying the effects of differing environments on identical twins, as well as (with certain checks and precautions difficult to realize in practice) on the same individual; secondly, by noting the differences and likenesses in response of individuals of different ancestry raised in the same general environment (as in orphanages or by foster-parents), and correlating these responses with those of their relatives and of their educators; thirdly, by studies of linkage or other genetic association between definite physical or physiological traits, that may be used as "identifying characters," and psychic reactions. The first two kinds of studies involve further developments in psychology. The third (as pointed out by Altenburg and the present writer in their study of truncate wing inheritance in the fruit fly, where such methods were first used in analyzing a modifiable character), requires also a much higher development of the study of human heredity. For this purpose knowledge is needed of the inheritance of numerous human character differences commonly met with that may seem unimportant in themselves; a fuller elucidation of this matter has been given in the paper above referred to.

V. Results of General Observations on Traits of the Twins

In the present case of identical twins reared apart, indications are not lacking, despite the diverse reactions to almost all the non-intellectual tests used, that there are really many other mental characteristics in which the twins would agree closely could we but find appropriate means of measuring them. Thus, as previously noted, the twins both seem possessed of similar energy and even tension, in their daily activity, with a tendency to "overdo" to the point of breakdown; both have similar mental alertness and interest in the practical problems about them, but not in remote or more purely intellectual abstractions and puzzles; both are personally very agreeable (as indicated by their popularity); both displayed similar attitudes throughout in taking the tests, even to such details as lack of squeamishness in blackening the fingers for the finger-prints, and in being pricked for the blood test—but turning away before the needle struck. The tastes of both in books and in people appear very similar. It would seem, then, that the operations of the human mind have many aspects not yet reached by psychological testing, and that some of these are more closely dependent upon the genetic composition than those now being studied.

The twins themselves both believed their likenesses far to out-weigh their differences. Whether or not these opinions were mainly due to unconscious bias favoring the finding of similarities (they were very fond of each other), or to inadequacy of the psychological tests in disclosing many important traits, it is difficult to decide. However that be, the results of Galton—which were based upon just such personal estimates—are thereby thrown open to a similar question: i.e., psychological tests upon his twins too might have given very different scores despite the alleged likeness in char-acter of the twins. The divergence between his results and those of the present paper may be explained either in this way or on the ground that differences in rearing during the earlier years, such as occurred in the present case, are far more effective in modifying mental characters than differences in adult life, which operated in Galton's cases.

The conclusion that there were really marked psychological differences between the twins in the present case does not rest solely upon the results of the tests, however, for we have also found apparent differences between the twins in various important partic-ulars that were not subjected to measurement. Such differences are at once evident on comparing the brisk, correct, and businesslike style of a letter written by B, with the more "homey" and sym-pathetic tone of a letter by J, who, despite her formal schooling, has much less perfect command of English than B. A similar impression is produced on the observer interviewing them. Turning to their more general attitudes, it is claimed that B has always been much less fond of children than J, who was brought up with so many more children about her (but B now seems to be changing in this respect). Again, J, brought up in such a lively home, seems to have been much more "vivacious," in the sense of caring for social affairs, "dates" with men, etc.—but the meetings between B and J and their months of life together since eighteen years of age are said to have exerted a marked effect upon B in these matters, as well as in other respects, making her much more like J. B had a period of great religious fervor in her teens, before her nervous breakdown, with leanings towards Catholicism; she has since been very liberal in religious matters. J had no such great religious outburst during youth, but since her last illness, which was more severe than B's, has turned to Christian Science. There are also some sharp differences in their attitudes towards minor conventions, partly traceable to experiences during the war.

Such differences as those just noted, then, supplement those shown in the volitional and emotional tests, in indicating the great latitude of genetic indetermination to which many psychic characters of man must be subject. The whole problem is thus seen to be an extremely complicated one, and it will in the future require the efforts of an army of psychologists and geneticists to help untangle the skein of psychic determination. In so doing, they must attempt to ascertain in quantitative fashion how much, and how commonly, various "traits" are affected by environic as compared with genetic differences, just what causal agents are involved in each trait, and what methods of measurement are the best for a given purpose. On the other hand, the demonstration that the determination of mind in civilized communities is by no means purely and simply a matter of the hereditary elements, or genes, should not be a source of discouragement or despair, for in the characters the genetic indetermination of which is found to be great lies the hopeful field for the educator, and for the agent of social reconstruction.

Summary

1. A new method is presented for determining the degree of probability that twins are genetically identical, when information concerning one or more of their other sibs can be obtained. Applied to the present case, the method yields a probability of approximately 386 to 1 that the twins here studied are identical genetically.

2. "Intelligence tests" applied to these twins yielded scores very significantly alike, despite great differences in the amounts and kinds of the formal schooling they have had, and other environmental differences dating from two weeks of age onward. J (the more schooled), however, had a considerably higher score in the section of the Army Alpha test dealing with more abstract word relations, while B scored slightly higher in arithmetic and in the section of the Army Alpha test involving rapid distinction between synonyms and antonyms. Only the difference in arithmetic was borne out in the Otis tests. In general, it may be concluded as probable that most sections of the Army Alpha Test and the Otis Advanced Intelligence Test yield results highly correlated with the genetic basis of intelligence (or at least, of those aspects of intelligence therein dealt with), *when they are applied to individuals brought up in the same general territory and social class*. Were there no such genetic basis for the scores of the twins, the chance for them to have been as much alike as they were would have been less than 1 in 200.

3. The non-intellectual tests—of motor reaction time, association time, "will-temperament," emotions and social attitudes—gave results in striking contrast with those of the intelligence tests, in that the twins made markedly different scores on all these tests. The differences were, on the average, slightly greater than the median differences between the scores of two individuals chosen *at random* from the groups in which the "norms" of the tests had been established. Many of the differences in responses of the twins seemed, moreover, to be correlated with salient differences in their past experiences and habits of life. Scores made on such tests, therefore, would seem to be of little value in indicating psychological differences determined by heredity, however usful such tests may be in enabling us to predict an individual's behavior.

4. If the above is true of traits as measured by tried psychological tests, the results of which seem to be correlated with success or failure in various walks of life, it is probably also true that many of the psychological traits assigned to individuals in the familiar human pedigree charts, on the basis of the personal opinions of varying casual observers, are even less trustworthy genetically. But in so far as such unmeasured traits may be determined by specific familial environments that can be handed down through habit, training, material and social circumstances, they may present in the charts a semblance of hereditary transmission, which is really spurious.

5. It is important, therefore, that research be carried further for the finding of better means of ascertaining such truly genetic differences as undoubtedly do underlie much human psychological variation. Three chief lines are pointed out which such research may follow, including further intensive work on human identical twins.

TABLE A—CLASSIFICATION OF THE TWINS AND THEIR SIBS, FOR DETER-
MINATION REGARDING GENETIC IDENTITY

	Height	Build	Color	Hair	Chin Prominence	Nose Form
Twin B	Med.	Light	Med.	Wavy	Decided	Straight
Twin J	Med.	Light	Med.	Wavy	Decided	Straight
Elder Brother	V. tall	Light?	V. dark	?	Moderate	Roman
Younger Brother	Med.	Heavy	V. light hair; eyes brown	?	Decided	?
Younger Sister	V. short	Heavy	V. light hair and eyes	V. curly	Decided	?
Chance of any two being in the same class	.3	.4	.1	.6	.6	.6

Product of chances = .002592 = $\frac{1}{386}$

(Where character was undetermined (marked '?'), sib was regarded as in same class
as twin for the calculation.)

TABLE B—INTELLIGENCE TESTS

I. Group Examination Alpha. Form 8, 1918 (U. S. Army)

Designation of Sections	Scores of: B	Scores of: J	*Maximum Possible*
1. Hard directions..................................	8	10	12
2. "Arithmetical problems".........................	15	11	20
3. "Practical Judgment" (as shown by selection of best answers in multiple choice).....................	12	11	16
4. "Synonym-Antonym Test" (involving rapid decision as to whether words are same or opposite)........	39	32	40
5. "Disarranged Sentences" (involving facility in recombining words into proper order and deciding truth of statement).......................................	21	21	24
6. "Number Series Completion" (involving ready comprehension of numerical series)..................	12	9	20
7. "Analogies" (involving ability to grasp and apply abstract relations between words)..................	14	25	40
8. "Information Test"..............................	35	34	40
Totals	156	153	212

II. Otis Self-Administering Test of Mental Ability; Higher Examination: Form A, 1922.

Classification of Questions. (Adapted by Present Writer for Comparison with I.)	Scores of:		Maximum Possible
	B	J	
1. Hard directions (involving ability to manipulate elements and positions)	5	6	8
2. "Arithmetical Problems" (as in I)	10	6	10
3. Logical relations, as shown in rational completion of sentences	17	16	17
4. Opposites test (involving rapid selection of words of different meaning, in multiple choice)	11	11	11
5. "Disarranged sentences" (involving facility in recombining words into proper order)	2	2	2
6. "Number series completion" (as in I)	0	2	3
7. "Analogies" (as in I)	7	8	10
8. "Proverbs" (involving ability to analyze precisely the meaning of statements)	6	6	6
9. Syllogisms (a test of logical reasoning)	3	2	4
10. "Geometrical Test"	3	3	4
Totals	64	62	75

(Scores consist of number of questions answered correctly, except in sections 4 and 5 of Army Alpha Test, in which chance of obtaining correct answer is one-half; in these sections score consists of total number of questions minus twice the number answered incorrectly.)

TABLE C—TESTS OF SPEED OF REACTION

	B	J
I. Kent Rosanoff Association Test. Average time of association per word	2.48 sec.	1.27 sec.
II. Tapping Test. Number of taps in given time	207	164
III. Crossing Test. Number of crosses in given time	63	55
Number of errors in crossing	10	4

TABLE D—TESTS OF EMOTIONAL AND SOCIAL ATTITUDES

PRESSEY X-O TESTS

Subject Investigated:	Section of Test	Number of Words Crossed by					Ratio of Twin to Random Difference
		B	J	Median of Group	Upper and Lower Quartiles of Group	Upper and Lower Deciles of Group	
Number of things judged wrong	Form A, III.	72	81	73	60–86		0.5
	Form B, I.	63	88	68		40–97	1.2
Number of causes of worry	Form A, IV.	46	61	46	33–55		1.0
	Form B, II.	38	67	34		15–65	1.6
Number of words with unpleasant meaning:							
a. connected with disgust	Form A, I.	2	16	14.2			
b. connected with fear	Form A, I.	1	11	8.6			
c. connected with sex	Form A, I.	4	10	13.0			
d. connected with suspicion	Form A, I.	0	14	10.1			
e. total dislikes	Form A, I.	7	51	42	27–56		0.8
Number of likes	Form B, III.	56	76	64		36–90	1.0
Number of associations	Form A, II.	35	56	55	41–70		1.0
Total number of words designated	Form A.	160	249	230	200–260		1.6
	Form B.	157	231	168			
Total number of deviations from averages in responses	Form A.	64	45	49			
	Form B.	48	45	41			

("Random differences" are taken as $\sqrt{2}$ times average difference between median and quartiles of the group. The last column gives the ratio of the twin difference to the corresponding random difference.)

TABLE E—DOWNEY INDIVIDUAL WILL-TEMPERAMENT TEST

"Will-Profile" of B shown by solid line that of J by dotted line.

Designation of Trait	Section of Test	1	2	3	4	5	6	7	8	9	10
1 Speed of Movement	VI-1		×						×		
2 Freedom from load	II-1, 2; VI-1, 2		×						×		
3 Flexibility	VIII				×				×		
4 Speed of Decision	I					×					
5 Motor Impulsion	X			×							
6 Reaction to Contradiction	XI			×				×			
7 Resistance to Opposition	XII				×				×		
8 Finality of Judgement	XIII					×				×	
9 Motor Inhibition	VII	×						×			
10 Interest in Detail	IX			×				×			
11 Coordination of Impulses	V		×				×				
12 Volitional Perseverance	VIII-2							×			×

	B	J
Height...............	62½ inches	62½ inches
Weight a. when tested.... b. maximum ...... c. adult minimum..	110–111 lb. 123½ lb. 104 lb.	110–111 lb. 138½ lb. (before childbirth) 99 lb. (after childbirth)
Head length .... Head width............	17.9 cm. 15.2 cm.	18.1 cm. 15.4 cm.
Iris color and pattern	(1) Innermost zone of light brown fibers. (2) Adjacent zone of whitish radiating branched filaments, with some light brown "spokes" interspersed. (3) Imbedded in zone (2), particularly in left eye, some dark brown patches. (4) Outer zone of light brown fibers. (5) Dark homogeneous outer border.	Same 5 characteristics as noted in case of B. (Resultant effect "hazel" in both twins.)
Mouth.................	Droops slightly towards left.	Droops slightly towards left.
Teeth.................	(1) All molars filled several times. (2) Have tendency to be too strongly implanted. (3) Only corners of wisdom teeth came through. (4) Upper right incisor overlaps left.	Same 4 characteristics as noted in case of B.
Finger nails	(1) Flat. (2) Somewhat large, but (3) little finger nail proportionally smaller. (4) Middle finger nail triangular.	Same 4 characteristics as noted in case of B.
Glove size	6⅛	6⅛
Strength of grip (maximum dynamometer readings): Right hand .... Left hand	39 35	36 36
Structure of tibia........	Presence of additional ankle prominence on mesial aspect of tibia, below the normal prominence.	Additional ankle prominence as in B.
Blood group	II	II

HUMAN HEREDITY*

by Erwin Baur, Eugen Fischer and Fritz Lenz,
Translated from the German by Eden and Cedar Paul.
Macmillan, New York. 1931. $8.00
*Reviewed by H. J. Muller**

The fact that this is the best work on the subject of human heredity which has yet appeared emphasizes only the more strongly the
need for more extensive and intensive research and for more scientific methods of reasoning in this vitally important field.

The book begins with an exposition of the general principles of
heredity by Professor Erwin Baur, the leading geneticist of Europe
engaged in active work at the present time. Despite the points of
disagreement noted below, we would commend this section of the
book highly, along with everything else that has issued from Baur's
pen. We must, however, take exception to Baur's acceptance of the
unproved conjecture that part of the inheritance in man and animals
is probably non-Mendelian, and still more do we object to the
claims, unsupported by critical work, that alcohol and other chemical influences have already been shown to cause injurious mutations
in the hereditary material, and that both inbreeding and cross-
breeding may also cause such mutations. These opinions regarding
mutations, mentioned more or less casually by Baur, are later considerably elaborated and emphasized by Lenz, who gives an impres-
sive list of substances—alcohol, nicotine, lead, iodine, mercury,
etc.—which he dignifies with the formidable appellation "idiokinetic
influences." It must be repeated (and the great majority of American geneticists will agree with me in this) that there is no sound
evidence for the belief that any of these substances cause heritable
changes. The most thorough experiments—those of Hanson and Heys
on the genetic effects of lead on guinea pigs—have given entirely
negative results. The claim that such agents probably injure the
germ plasm is likely to result in unwarranted fears and misapplied
birth control on the part of the many who have been exposed to the
various chemical influences mentioned.

More specifically valuable for the student of human heredity are
Lenz's excellent section on "Methodology," and the two hundred and
forty page chapter in which he performs the important service of
gathering together a great store of data relative to the inheritance
of various human defects. It is not his fault that the data are very
unequal in trustworthiness and genetic significance, but the critical
geneticist, reading these pages, will realize more than ever what a
stupendous task still confronts the investigator in this field.

Only by utilizing an army of genetically trained physicians and

*Birth Control Review, January, 1933, 17: 19-21.

psychologists (something as yet non-existent in this country), and by having, at the same time, the active cooperation of various public institutions (such as hospitals, schools, orphanages, etc.) on a large scale, as Levit has begun to do in Russia, can we make important progress in this study. This is (1) because individual human families are so small that we have to compensate by studying numerous families, and extensive pedigrees, (2) because so many different genes cause superficially similar characteristics that expert physical or psychological diagnosis and refined genetic analysis, working hand in hand, become essential, and (3) because the effects of environmental and of hereditary agents overlap so much, and are commonly so alike, that very special and cumbersome methods are often required to differentiate between them, when this can be done at all. The more unusual the characteristic, the less applicable do these objections become, and the more convincingly does the mode of recurrence of the trait in a family indicate the true course of its heredity. Hence much of Lenz's material deals with rare abnormalities, and here he is on his safest ground. Unfortunately, such traits are usually the least important for humanity in general.

It is regrettable that the remainder of the book is not on the same level of scientific accuracy as the portions noted above. As they stray further and further from the fields in which rigorous genetic investigations have been conducted, and venture into psychology, anthropology, history and sociology, Fischer and Lenz rapidly become less and less scientific, and we soon find them acting as mouthpieces for the crassest kind of popular prejudice. Throwing overboard their previously admitted principle that environment as well as heredity is of immense importance in the development of human characteristics, particularly those of a mental nature, they readily accept all the superficially apparent differences between human groups as indicative of corresponding genetic distinctions. Intelligence quotients, which are now known to be strongly influenced by training, serve as their courts of highest appeal. In addition, they twist the records of history and anthropology so as to favor the preconceptions born of their own egotism.

Some quotations from Lenz may be appropriate here:

"Great women" endowed with "greatness" in the sense of outstanding creative faculty are practically unknown.... A person whose mental hereditary equipment is a good one can be recognized with great probability when his forehead, his nose, etc., are of a particular shape.... Criminals very often exhibit characters which remind us of Neanderthal man or of other primitive races...Average specimens of the Monogoloid races greatly excel the average Negro in mental equipment.... [But] brilliant thinkers, inventors, and investigators—men of genius as we know genius in Europe —can hardly be said to have existed among the Mongols.... It is indisputable that the population of southern Europe is less well equipped mentally than that of northern Europe, and the population of eastern Europe than that of western Europe... both by temperament and character, and also in respect to rational endowment, the Mediterranean occupies an intermediate position between the Nordic and the Negro.... The near Eastern race has been selected to excel, not so much in the control and the exploitation of nature, as in the control and the exploitation of man... On the whole... it is indisputable that in the domain of mental life, too, they [the Jews] are more prominent as intermediaries and interpreters than in the primary work of production.... I do not think it would be an exaggeration to say that in respect of mental gifts the Nordic race marches in the van of mankind.

What a curious coincidence, that Lenz and Fischer should both be Nordics: Fischer, for his illustrations of racial types, chooses in the main prepossessing looking Nordics and disreputable specimens of other races. He writes of races in exactly the same vein as Lenz, and asserts that racial differences in mental endowment "are among the most influential [factors] in determining the course of a nation's history." According to these authors, nearly all the great advances of mankind, whether among Greeks, Romans, or even Hindus, were due to Nordic blood (though recent findings show that Hindu civilization long antedated the time of the Aryan conquest, and it is obvious that in Europe civilization in general advanced from the Southeast, in fact from southern Asia, towards the North and West). As to the crossing of human races, it may sometimes be harmless, especially if the races are closely allied, but "injury to the constitution" may also result from hybridization" (Fischer), and "the crossing of Teutons and Jews is likely, as a rule, to have an unfavorable effect" (Lenz).

The mere statement of views like those quoted above should be, for intelligent and fairminded general readers of the present day, sufficient condemnation of them. Suffice it to say that there is not one iota of evidence from genetics for any such conclusions, and it is too bad to have them issued with the apparent stamp of genetic authority. They form just the sort of ground which reactionaries desire, on which to raise a pseudo-scientific edifice for the defense of their system of sex, class and race exploitation. Indeed, Hitler is said to have studied the Baur-Fischer-Lenz book very seriously, and to have been won over to it, while Lenz has recently written an article favoring Hitlerism.

Captivated by the above fallacies, Fischer and Lenz lose sight of what are really the most important possibilities opened up by the study of human heredity. Hence, Lenz settles down into the position that "degeneration is the central problem of racial hygiene, and the prevention and the overcoming of degeneration are its main objects." The prevention of degeneration is laudable enough in itself, but how weak-kneed, negative, and uninspiring as the major ideal for eugenics! What a concession to the champions of mediocrity and the *status quo*. Quite in line with this is his fallacious contention, which has so often been disproved, that the geniuses of the past have been in large measure of psychopathic heredity and that "a population consisting exclusively of geniuses would certainly be little fitted to survive." No doubt the geniuses sometimes make it uncomfortable for the Hitlers. But in that direction lies biological progress.

ON THE VARIABILITY OF MIXED RACES*

H. J. Muller
Consultant, Medico-Genetical Research Institute

Summary

Anthropological data indicating that mixed races formed by hybridization between the major known races have on the whole little or no more variability, and perhaps in some cases even less, than the original races, are in no wise out of accord with the principles of modern genetics based on Mendelism. On any Mendelian interpretation, however, the unincreased variability cannot (as sometimes stated) be related to the number of generations of breeding of the mixed race, but must be as evident in F_2 as later.

Several Mendelian interpretations are possible. The most plausible involves the postulate that most of the intra-racial variation of the original races is caused by relatively recessive genes that individually (at each given locus) are rather rare, but, taken together, are very numerous, and the further postulate that the loci causing most of the variance are different in the different major races, even though a variance of a similar phaenotypic kind is produced. On this interpretation a part of the intra-racial variance of the original races would be suppressed in the mixed race (see mathematical example in section 2), its place being taken by the segregation of inter-racial differences. Since these two causes of change in the variance would rarely completely compensate each other, the mixed race may show either some increase or decrease of variance, as compared with the original races. The fact that the increase or decrease was small would then indicate that the inter-individual differences within a race are of comparable magnitude or greater than the inter-racial differences between the original major races.

An alternative Mendelian interpretation would postulate that the intra-racial differences within the two major races were due mainly to genes in the same loci having very similar but not quite identical frequencies in the two races. The difference between the means of the two races would then depend either on the cumulative effect of these differences, present in numerous loci and tending to act in the same phaenotypic direction, or else upon other genes, individually very small in their effect, but collectively very numerous, in regard

Proceedings of the Medico-Genetical Institute, 1936, 4: 213-16; summary, in English, of Russian article.

to which the two races were relatively homozygous for opposite allelomorphs. Either of these later postulates, however, meets with serious difficulties.

Tables are given showing quantitatively the effects on the variability of a race which would be produced by the presence of alternative allelomorphs having different frequencies and degrees of dominance. These tables show further how much (for any given locus) the variability of the mixed race would be decreased or increased relatively to that of the original races, under various possible conditions of gene frequency and dominance in each of the two races crossed. The effect of the assumed conditions on the difference between the means of the races is also given. These tables are of use in judging the genetic meaning of a given body of data on race and hybrid variability.

The requirements are stated which should be met by any future body of data dealing with the problem at issue, in order that a decision may be reached between the various possible Mendelian interpretations stated. It is shown that separate data concerning F_1 and F_2 are needed, and data on intra-familial correlation in F_1, F_2 and F_{2+n} as compared with that in the original races.

THE "GENETICISTS' MANIFESTO"*

The question "how could the world's population be improved most effectively genetically" raises far broader problems than the purely biological ones, problems which the biologist unavoidably encounters as soon as he tries to get the principles of his own special field put into practice. For the effective genetic improvement of mankind is dependent upon major changes in social conditions, and correlative changes in human attitudes. In the first place there can be no valid basis for estimating and comparing the intrinsic worth of different individuals without economic and social conditions which provide approximately equal opportunities for all members of society instead of stratifying them from birth into classes with widely different privileges.

The second major hindrance to genetic improvement lies in the economic and political conditions which foster antagonism between different peoples, nations and "races." The removal of race prejudices and of the unscientific doctrine that good or bad genes are the monopoly of particular peoples or of persons with features of a given kind will not be possible, however, before the conditions which make for war and economic exploitation have been eliminated. This

*Journal of Heredity, 1939, 30: 371-73.

requires some effective sort of federation of the whole world, based on the common interests of all its peoples.

Thirdly, it cannot be expected that the raising of children will be influenced actively by considerations of the worth of future generations unless parents in general have a very considerable economic security and unless they are extended such adequate economic, medical, educational and other aids in the bearing and rearing of each additional child that the having of more children does not overburden either of them. As the woman is more especially affected by child bearing and rearing she must be given special protection to ensure that her reproductive duties do not interfere too greatly with her opportunities to participate in the life and work of the community at large. These objects cannot be achieved unless there is an organization of production primarily for the benefit of consumer and worker, unless the conditions of employment are adapted to the needs of parents and especially of mothers, and unless dwellings, towns and community services generally are reshaped with the good of children as one of their main objectives.

A fourth prerequisite for effective genetic improvement is the legalization, the universal dissemination, and the further development through scientific investigation, of ever more efficacious means of birth control, both negative and positive, that can be put into effect at all stages of the reproductive process—as by voluntary temporary or permanent sterilization, contraception, abortion (as a third line of defense), control of fertility and of the sexual cycle, artificial insemination, etc. Along with all this the development of social consciousness and responsibility in regard to the production of children is required, and this cannot be expected to be operative unless the above-mentioned economic and social conditions for its fulfilment are present and unless the superstitious attitude towards sex and reproduction now prevalent has been replaced by a scientific and social attitude. This will result in its being regarded as an honour and a privilege, if not a duty, for a mother, married or unmarried, or for a couple, to have the best children possible, both in respect of their upbringing and of their genetic endowment, even where the latter would mean an artificial—though always voluntary—control over the processes of parentage.

Before people in general, or the state which is supposed to represent them, can be relied upon to adopt rational policies for the guidance of their reproduction, there will have to be, fifthly, a far wider spread of knowledge of biological principles and of recognition of the truth that both environment and heredity constitute dominating and inescapable complementary factors in human well-being, but factors both of which are under the potential control of man and admit of unlimited but interdependent progress. Betterment of environmental conditions enhances the opportunities for genetic betterment in the ways above indicated. But it must also be understood that the effect of the bettered environment is not a direct one on the germ cells and that the Lamarckian doctrine is fallacious, according to which the children of parents who have had better opportunities for physical and mental development inherit these improvements, biologically, and according to which in consequence, the dominant classes and peoples would have become genetically superior to the underprivileged ones. The intrinsic (genetic) characteristics of any generation can be better than those of the preceding generation only as a result of some kind of *selection*, i.e., by those persons of the preceding generation who had a better genetic equipment having produced more offspring, on the whole, than the rest, either through conscious choice, or as an automatic result of the way in which they lived. Under modern civilized conditions such selection is far less likely to be automatic than under primitive conditions, hence some kind of conscious guidance of selection is called for. To make this possible, however, the population must first appreciate the force of the above principles, and the social value which a wisely guided selection would have.

Sixthly, conscious selection requires, in addition, an agreed direction or directions for selection to take, and these directions cannot be social ones, that is, for the good of mankind at large, unless social motives predominate in society. This in turn implies its socialized organization. The most important genetic objectives, from a social point of view, are the improvement of those genetic characteristics which make (a) for health, (b) for the complex called intelligence and (c) for those temperamental qualities which favour fellow-feeling and social behaviour rather than those (today most esteemed by many) which make for personal "success," as success is usually understood at present.

A more widespread understanding of biological principles will bring with it the realization that much more than the prevention of genetic deterioration is to be sought for and that the raising of the level of the average of the population nearly to that of the highest now existing in isolated individuals, in regard to physical well-being, intelligence and temperamental qualities, is an achievement that would—so far as purely genetic considerations are concerned—be physically possible within a comparatively small number of generations. Thus everyone might look upon "genius," combined of course with stability, as his birthright. And, as the course of evolution shows, this would represent no final stage at all, but only an earnest of still further progress in the future.

The effectiveness of such progress, however, would demand increasingly extensive and intensive research in human genetics and in the numerous fields of investigations correlated therewith. This would involve the coöperation of specialists in various branches of medicine, psychology, chemistry and, not the least, the social sciences, with the improvement of the inner constitution of man himself as their central theme. The organization of the human body is marvellously intricate and the study of its genetics is beset with special difficulties which require the prosecution of research in this field to be on a much vaster scale, as well as more exact and analytical, than hitherto contemplated. This can, however, come about when men's minds are turned from war and hate and the struggle for the elementary means of subsistence to larger aims, pursued in common.

The day when economic reconstruction will reach the stage where such human forces will be released is not yet, but it is the task of this generation to prepare for it, and all steps along the way will represent a gain, not only for the possibilities of the ultimate genetic improvement of man, to a degree seldom dreamed of hitherto, but at the same time, more directly, for human mastery over those more immediate evils which are so threatening our modern civilization.

(original signers)

F. A. E. Crew	J. S. Huxley
J. B. S. Haldane	H. J. Muller
S. C. Harland	J. Needham
L. T. Hogben	

(additional signers)

G. P. Child	C. L. Huskins
P. R. David	W. Landauer
G. Dahlberg	H. H. Plough
Th. Dobzhansky	E. Price
R. A. Emerson	J. Schultz
C. Gordon	A. G. Steinberg
John Hammond	C. H. Waddington

Note

The Seventh International Congress of Genetics adjourned at Edinburgh only three days before World War II got under way. It is interesting to recall that just before the shooting started a group of geneticists at that Congress informally formulated what we might call an Edinburgh Charter of the genetic rights of man. (At the time it was called by some who signed it the "Geneticists' Manifesto.") Now that we are setting forth on a sea of words toward the New Horizon and the Four Freedoms it may not be amiss to recall this statement of fundamentals, drawn up and subscribed to at a very solemn time, by some of the leaders of genetic thought.

THE ROLE PLAYED BY RADIATION MUTATIONS IN MANKIND*

By H. J. Muller, University of Edinburgh and Amherst College

Calculations are presented of the average number of generations to be expected between the production of a recessive gene-mutation in man and its manifestation in a homozygous individual. The chance of the mutated gene meeting another like it that originated by an independent mutation depends on the frequency of such mutations, on the survival value of the abnormal type, and on the randomness of breeding. Taking the maximal values for these factors (the values favoring the highest frequencies of recessive abnormalities), it turns out that at least 30 or, more likely, over 100 generations would on the average occur—i.e., 750 to 3000 years or more—before a seriously harmful recessive abnormality (one having less than 90 per cent of normal survival) would manifest itself by this process.

Another mechanism of manifestation involves the meeting of two genes each descended from the same original mutated gene. The frequency of this depends upon the total degree of inbreeding. A new method for gauging this is presented, involving the principle that the frequency of homozygosis from this cause is one fourth the frequency of marriages between two related individuals having the same name. From statistics on this point and on cousin marriages it is found that, even in the most closely inbred groups in modern civilized society, the chance of a mutated gene manifesting itself by this process is not over 0.5 per cent. This represents a "latent period" of some 5000 years. Both processes together would give over 600 and probably thousands of years of latency.

The large number of mutated genes accidentally dying out while thus "under cover" are compensated for by those accidentally multiplying. Thus the inherited damage from irradiation, though so long postponed, is in no wise prevented. Judging by results in mice (P. Hertwig), we may provisionally take the order of frequency of seriously harmful recessive mutations induced by 300 r as one to several per cent (perhaps doubling the natural frequency). This chance of damage would seldom overweigh the direct benefits of diagnostic or therapeutic irradiations, excepting those designed to stimulate or temporarily inhibit reproduction. However, in irradiation intended for other parts, the gonads should be shielded.

Natural radioactivity, while of no consequence in flies, may appreciably influence human mutation frequency. For the long duration of the human generation sometimes allows the reception of ten or

*Science, 1941, 93: 438; abridged abstract of paper presented before the National Academy of Sciences, April 29, 1941.

more r. Thus, under special conditions, the amount might conceivably be enough to be significant in evolution.

SCIENCE IN BONDAGE*

by H. J. Muller, Indiana University

Unlike the other major cultural activities of mankind, science is a relative newcomer, almost an intruder on the human scene. Many so-called primitive peoples have for ages had highly advanced arts of both visual, sonic, kinesthetic and verbal types, and have been masters of elaborate techniques for arousing human emotions of all kinds, for creating individual and mass anger, fear, awe or ecstasy, and for instilling given attitudes of mind, and given systems of beliefs. This is not true of science. In our present-day sense of the systematic search for truth in all directions, based on the pooled observations, experiments, reasonings, and counter-criticisms of numberless persons who have made an effort to free their judgment of any but objective criteria—in this sense science has been almost non-existent throughout the long history of *Homo sapiens* until we come to Greece and her outposts. Even there it flickered rather spottily. It is only since the rekindling of this small flame by medieval Arabs, Persians, Moors, Jews and then Italians, followed by its gradual fanning into a full flare with the rise and dissemination of Western civilization in the last five centuries, that science has acquired a widespread and secure existence—or at least one that has *appeared* to be secure.

Nevertheless there is ample evidence that the *ability* to think scientifically has long been widely diffused among the peoples of the earth. This is clearly shown by the mathematical and astronomical achievements of various ancient peoples, especially the Babylonians, Mayas, Hindus, Chinese and Egyptians. It is also illustrated by the engineering, the metalworking and other material techniques developed by, for instance, some Central Africans and Peruvians, and by the various agricultural methods that arose independently in all of the seven great centers of origin of cultivated plants delineated by Vavilov—Ethiopia, China, India, Iraq-Iran, Peru, Mexico, and the Southeastern Mediterranean-Caucasus area. And today, individuals of all "races" have shown themselves capable of making major contributions to science as we know it. This obvious possession by peoples in general of the potentiality for successfully pursuing science, coupled with the marked restriction of science as such in human history, shows what an extremely delicate cultural plant

*Address delivered at the panel on "Science and Totalitarianism" of the Congress for Cultural Freedom, in Berlin, Germany, June 27, 1950.

science is. Let us then inquire into the nature of the highly special soil and climate which its continued growth demands.

It should be recognized first that the growth of science (and without growth it withers) does not depend only on a few great discoveries. It depends equally on that slow accretion of multitudinous small steps which furnish the bases for and the necessary extensions of those discoveries, and also on the correction of the even more numerous missteps that are continually being made. Now, for the carrying out of all this painstaking work it is evident that a very considerable body of scientific workers is necessary. This means not only a large educated public but a large economic surplus. However, in most societies of the past in which a large surplus has existed, it has come almost exclusively into the possession of people who wherever possible made leisure a profession and whose ideal was "conspicuous consumption," as Veblen has termed it. The development of science, on the contrary, requires that much of the economic surplus become available for those groups who do the actual work of the world and who have an ideal of constructive achievement.

The attainment of such a distribution of the products of labor, and the existence of such an ideal, implies that, in the society in which science develops, a large proportion of the so-called "common people" has a high standard of living, highly developed techniques and considerable education. This means too that they have an effective voice in the management of their own affairs, and participate in decisions affecting the whole community. Along with this comes a sense of their own dignity, and a basis for believing that they can still further improve their situation, both materially and culturally. All these factors together form a part of the groundwork that is necessary before the "common" man and woman can produce individuals with that controlled initiative and creativeness which characterizes scientific activity. Such conditions cannot exist long or securely in any community founded upon slavery, nor in one resting upon the work of oppressed and poverty stricken masses who live on a bare subsistence level. In other words, a rather high level of democracy is necessary—one that until recent times has rarely been found in communities above a very primitive level.

But the community that nourishes science must not only be free from the physical oppression of nature and of other men, and have grounds for hope in its own prospects. It must also be relatively free from the despotism of imposed ideas. Its history must have entailed processes of intellectual disequilibration which led men in great numbers to doubt the dogmas of their forefathers. Rarest of all—into the breach thus made there must have entered, in considerable strength, not merely a new and equally rigid set of dogmas, but a spirit of inquiry and objectivity, a wide tolerance for objectively reached but conflicting conclusions of others, a custom of candid criticism, a distrust of all argument by authority and of all wishful thinking.

Western civilization has approached these conditions only by dint of centuries of struggle towards higher material techniques, towards ever wider and more potent democratic procedures, and better popular education. At the same time, following contact with other cultures, including those represented in the rediscovered literature of the ancients, men were led to question further and further the voice of ancient tradition, as well as that of contemporary authorities. Moreover, travel brought men new knowledge and new problems, as well as fresh opportunities for gain and for adventure. In all these ways, then, the stage has been set for the rise of science, but this rise has only been at the cost of constant effort, and contention with both man-made and natural obstacles.

Even yet, however, the very findings of science which are of the greatest significance for a deeper understanding of ourselves and of the universe are the most apt to arouse concerted opposition from powerfully organized groups who represent established ideologies and institutions that the new knowledge would upset. Hence even in Western civilization persistent vigilance and endeavor are necessary in the defense of the honest search for truth and of the teaching of it. Yet it is one of the greatest strengths of this civilization that, viewed over the course of the centuries, it has after all made very much progress in this respect, and that it is so constructed that the efforts of enlightened men to push this progress still further *can* have a considerable measure of success.

However, in the profound discouragement and paralysis following the wreckage of war, some of the people even of Western countries have been misled by the lure of a reversion to complete despotism, masquerading under the name of "national socialism" or "international communism." Where one of these movements has gained control, it has become clear only too late that modern technology, both material and social, affords the tyrant a far more inescapable, efficient and personalized grip over his unhappy subjects than in any ancient or oriental tyranny. Under such conditions science and indeed all culture becomes a trained bear with a ring through his nose. At the tweak of his master's hand he must try to dance, but his virility is gone, he languishes away his life in desperation, and his days are numbered.

An audience in Berlin knows only too well the disillusionment with regard to the progress of science and of cultural life in general which eventually followed the accession of Hitler, with its disastrous purges on grounds of race and of politics, and its deadening regimentation of ideas. My own branch of science, genetics, was the most perverted and outraged of all, since in its place a tissue of lies was fabricated in support of the dictator's racist psychosis. This would have been used to justify a state of world slavery in which, had it continued, all fundamental science must at last have perished.

To many an outsider it seems amazing that any persons who have suffered such disillusionment and loss as those who experienced Nazism should be ready to turn again to a dictatorship. But the Soviet dictatorship claims to be the very antithesis of Hitler's, and presents a very different façade, reflecting the great differences in its earlier aims. It pretends to be a movement of liberation, as indeed it was originally intended to be. In the first flushes of release that followed the demolition of the semi-feudalistic Tsarist system it did in fact afford the people, not more food, fuel or clothing, but more voice over their conditions of work, more education, more right to live and think as they wished to, and more hope. With this went a great upsurge of culture, including science.

But gradually, secretly, by hook and by crook, as well as openly at the point of guns, the Communist Party, claiming to represent the common man, took more and more power out of his hands, ostensibly for his own good, until there was no check left on the power the Party had. In each place of work, whether economic or cultural, an inner Party cell is planted which directs and redirects activities. Moreover, by its false accusations, its condemnations and dismissals of individuals, usually based on jealousy, and its glorifications of others, who play its game, it holds workers and intellectuals alike in fear and subjection. At the same time, within the Party itself, all vestiges of democracy have sedulously been rooted out.

Thus the entire Soviet system has become like a gigantic spider-web. All of its radii—political, military, economic, social, cultural, educational and scientific—have been brought under the absolute control of the one center, and of the one many-armed omnipotent being who sits grasping all these strands at their very junction. In this structure, all directives proceed outwards, and peripheral criticism of more central decisions is never allowed. Neither the central group nor its innermost member, however, are characterized by high cultural development, nor by an appreciation of the methods or spirit of objective science. Yet their pronouncements on matters of science and culture are hailed as revelations, even as were those of Nero in ancient Rome.

For the security of a tyranny so unparalled in its thoroughness it it was important for all expression of thought to be brought under the complete domination of the Party. For this purpose Party organs were established for the control of all instruments of propaganda, education and communication—the schools, press, film, radio, organizations of scientific, professional, trade union and social character, sports, celebrations and public assemblages. As a second check, a vast secret intelligence system was set up in parallel to all this, and espionage was inordinately expanded and intensified. To render the spying still more effective, a new concept of morality was inculcated. This makes it a man's first duty, above all personal ties, to report any signs of dissatisfaction with the

Party or with its leader which might be shown even by the closest friend or relative. On top of all this were superimposed the great mass arrests and "trials," which gained such momentum in the 'thirties. These not only provided a mobile labor force of ten to twenty million out-and-out slaves, but reduced the remaining population to abject submission in all intellectual as well as physical spheres of life. Thereafter, conformity must be complete, in deeds, in words, and even in facial expressions. Could any setting be less propitious for the encouragement of that adventurous thinking in new directions which must characterize fundamental science?

As an official apologetics for all Soviet policies and doctrines, whether in science or elsewhere, recourse was had to the heterogeneous collection of notions on matters of science and philosophy, largely borrowed from Hegel, which Marx and Engels had long ago put together under the title of "dialectical materialism." Although it had embodied some important advances over earlier views, nevertheless its artificial schemes do not correspond with the operations of nature as we have now come to know them. Moreover, so far as natural science is concerned, this view is especially at fault in maintaining that all reactions in nature are at bottom a struggle between "opposites." This is a transparent attempt to make natural processes resemble that antiquated concept of social processes according to which the class struggle is always the prime mover in human progress. In this way, conflict and hate are made to lie at the bottom of all good.

But today dialectical materialism is no longer even an earnest attempt to interpret natural and social changes. It has been frozen into medieval scholasticism. On the one hand it is reduced to mystical and unintelligible slogans which are taught by rote to hundreds of millions in place of the credos of the church. On the other hand, since the mode of application of these doctrines for the reaching of specific conclusions is seldom clear, and may lead to the most divergent results, official interpreters have been trained to twist the doctrines so as to provide "philosophical" justifications, as wanted, for any opinions, policies or programs that happen to be favored by the central power. Thus dialectical materialism has become a club, wherewith dissident opinions are condemned as undialectical or unmaterialistic and therefore anti-communistic, and persons holding such views become branded as traitors and enemies of the people.

And if it still remains too obvious that the condemned views are directly founded on facts and logic, as has been the case with genetics, then there is another club in reserve. The views are labelled objective, in quotation marks, instead of partisan, class views, and it is proclaimed that the "most important principle in any science is the party principle."[1]

Whereas in some branches of science all these conditions have simply worked to undermine the spirit of the scientists, and to retard and deflect them in their work by the action of numerous individually minor restrictions and disturbances, in other branches there have been systematically organized frontal attacks, controlled by the center, upon the main scientific principles and the main personnel engaged in it. In the case of genetics, I happen to know much of the story of these attacks at first hand, and will use them to illustrate the fate to which science in bondage is likely to fall victim.

Genetics, the science of heredity, variation and evolution, had attracted a considerable body of able young Russian scientific workers shortly after the Russian revolution. For this new science had itself been revolutionary in its discoveries, by establishing the existence of units of living matter, called the genes, far smaller and more fundamental than the cell itself. These genes serve to carry the biological heritage from one generation to another, according to an amazingly precise and fertile set of principles. And these same genes, when they undergo changes, called mutations, give rise to that possibility of biological evolution which Darwin had seen at a distance, as it were. It was found, quite definitely, that the changes in the genes are usually caused by accidental molecular events, like those occurring on application of heat or of X-rays. The genes do not become altered in correspondence with the alterations which exercise, nutrition or other environmental conditions induce in the body that carries the genes. In other words, Lamarck's old doctrine of the inheritance of acquired characters, that antedated Darwin's theory of evolution by the natural selection of accidental changes, was proved erroneous.

Realizing the significance of this fundamental subject for an understanding of the nature and history of living things, and of the future possibilities of mankind, as well as for that improvement of agriculture so needed by the U.S.S.R., the Russian scientists soon forged their way into the front rank in this field. They became conspicuous among those who helped to make it the most exact and well documented of all the biological sciences, the field most nearly comparable both in the precision of its methods and in the reliability of its conclusions with the sciences of physics and chemistry.

However, beginning in 1936, a series of attacks upon genetics was instituted. These ranged from deliberate misrepresentations and vilifications in the press to forced " confessions" of error and guilt from some of the leading geneticists, followed by their disappearance and the closing of their laboratories. These men, as some of them whom I knew well explained to me, made their false " confessions" out of loyalty to the Party which had ordered them to do so. However, that did not save them.

At about the same time, since no real scientist could be found to attack genetics this assignment was delegated to a half-educated and paranoic young demagogue, named Lysenko, who had done some work in raising plants but who was in fact ignorant of scientific principles and incapable of understanding them. Lysenko's reputation was systematically inflated before the public eye. And he was provided with a very sophisticated interpreter of dialectical materialism, a cynical weaver of words, named Present, so that Lysenko's crudities might be disguised and served up to the public as profundities. After Lysenko and Present had been given some preliminary practice in decrying genetics and in influencing farmers, and had been furnished with a kind of band of mercenaries from the farms who posed as scientists also but were still more ignorant, a kind of public gladiatorial combat between Lysenkoists and geneticists, taking place in a great auditorium, was arranged by the Party in December, 1936. Although it was apparent to the hundreds of scientists in the audience that the contest was one between science and bigotry, and they showed this by the distribution of their applause, nevertheless the administrators sitting in the chair made speeches critical of the geneticists, in the summing up. And in the public press it was made to appear as if the geneticists had come out poor seconds.

Having been thus castigated and weakened, the geneticists were thereafter subjected to a continuous sniping process, and to two more staged tournaments, one in 1939 and the last in August, 1948. By the latter date all the noted names of Russian genetics had disappeared, the great Vavilov had perished at a labor camp in Siberia and many others whose memory I hold dear had lost their lives in unexplained ways. Thus only a feeble remnant of comparative weaklings in the science were left to defend or compromise it. The show of 1948 was settled however when, after the last word for genetics had been said, Lysenko made the smug announcement that the Communist Party had in fact approved his position in advance, and had declared the geneticists wrong. According to *Pravda*'s accusation they had been " objective," they had forgotten "the party principle" in science. But of course the Party, in its greater wisdom concerning matters of science, was able to override them.

Following this exhibition of barbarism, there were of course recantations and apologies, and the Academies of Sciences, of Medicine and of Agriculture all sent thanks to Stalin for the personal guidance on his part whereby this great reform had come about. At the same time, the laboratories of genetics were closed, their remaining workers were somehow disposed of, courses on genetics were abolished, and all books on the subject were banned. But, since all science is connected, this was only the beginning. The principles of genetics are essential to all modern biology, and so it was necessary to extirpate them from all curricula and publications dealing with biological subjects. Texts had to be rewritten, and staffs of colleges and of scientific publishing houses had to be purged. In various other lines of biology, medicine and agriculture, world famous scientists were dismissed or disgraced merely because, although not specialists in genetics themselves, they had refused to renounce its principles.[2]

The same campaign was soon after carried into the satellite countries, where geneticists have been terrorized wholesale or forced into other lines. The death of my old friend Kostov, well known geneticist and Minister of Agriculture in Bulgaria, occurring during a genetics purge, was announced last autumn (1949). Throughout China the same sweeping out of scientists in this field has taken place. As for the Soviet zone of Germany, the situation will surely be understood by those in Berlin who have followed the controversy on the subject in the local press.

It has for a long time been evident that genetics has been distasteful to the very center, that is, to Stalin himself. We might speculate at length on the causes for this, and still we could not be sure, for the interpretation would turn chiefly on matters of personality. (What a reflection on the doctrine of the economic determination of history, under a totalitarian system!) But, whatever its causes, we can be sure of the consequences of this destruction of a basic field of science. It must inevitably, as all science is becoming more closely interdependent, have vitiating effects in many other theoretical fields. At the same time, practical progress in agriculture and animal husbandry will be greatly held back. In fact many previous achievements—such as Vavilov's invaluable world collections of cultivated plants, the basis for the construction of improved combinations—have already been lost.

It is especially to be noted that, in the sphere of the bearing of biology on theories of the nature and possibilities of man, the Communists have lost the scientific basis for answering the pernicious racist doctrines of the Nazi's. For they have thrown overboard the geneticists' findings that the great changes wrought by differences in environment on living things are not inherited. Thus the Communists, if they are logical from this point on, are driven to believe that those peoples whose environments have given them too little opportunity for mental and physical development must also, by reason of the inheritance of these effects through many past generations, have become stunted and inferior in their inborn capacities. Some of the Communists have admitted holding to this brand of the doctrine of the inferiority of the economically less developed peoples. Their dilemma concerning this point explains why, from the time the open attack on genetics was started in the U.S.S.R. in 1936, the efforts which geneticists there had been making to refute the Nazi racial dogmas were all called off, and awkward but effective steps were taken to avoid being drawn into controversy on this crucial subject.

Since that time, however, after I had called their hand concerning this matter[3], other Soviet apologists, including the Soviet Academy of Sciences itself, have tried to dismiss the matter by resorting to the curious doctrine, not unknown elsewhere, that the laws of biological science stop short with man. Man, they proclaim, is a being of a so much higher order that only social laws apply to him. They do not attempt to reconcile this doctrine with such slogans as "Work and Bread," but it is not clear why, if man's alimentary system requires food, his reproductive system also does not work according to biological principles. This is a good illustration of the depth to which so-called scientific thinking has sunk when it is caught in the great spider-web.

Genetics is by no means the only branch of science which has been directly attacked by the Soviet totalitarianism, quite obviously on Stalin's orders. For example, even the germ theory of disease and the work of Koch have been derided by the Party-sponsored theory of disease of Speransky, which attributes most ailments to malnutrition of the nervous system. Important sectors of psychology, of astronomy, of quantum physics and of statistical theory are among the other fields which have been openly assaulted. But it is evident that even the branches of science not subjected to a frontal attack must lose their vitality, their spirit of spontaneity and adventure, of free criticism, of objectivity, and of profiting by the advances; made in the rest of the world, in the face of the restrictions, the interference, the insecurity, the terrorism engendered in scientific workers by the all pervading despotism of Stalin. The conditions basic for continued scientific growth, which we reviewed in the beginning, are gone. And while it will doubtless be possible to continue to milk the cow for awhile, that milk will get thinner and more meagre, and will at last become positively poisonous.

If civilization does not have sound fundamental science to guide it, it is doomed eventually to decline, through the action of numerous slow-moving insidious processes that are not evident to the superficial view. Illustrations of this can be drawn from mutation theory, from geo-chemistry, and from various other fields. But the question must also be asked, of what value, in any acceptable sense of the word value, would a civilization be in which men's minds were closed, so that they lived in an artificial, unreal world of dogma and illusion, from which they were not allowed to break out? Would it not be better to start afresh again, as pioneers or even as savages, contending with the rigors of nature, yes, even with hunger, privation and sudden death from wild beasts, until men could again rise by their own efforts, rather than to be plunged into the hopeless slavery and delusion of a totalitarian despotism? It would be shortsighted and selfish in the extreme if we should try to buy our own lives at the cost of the intellectual and cultural slavery of our children and descendants.

Let us hope, however, that we shall be confronted with no such decision. It may be that, instead, our long oppressed brothers east of the Iron Curtain will manage to achieve a loosening of their bonds. We have no quarrel with them, but only the deepest sympathy with them. In the meantime, it is one of our obligations to exert ourselves to extend and make more effective our own intellectual, cultural and material freedoms, thereby enriching and making more secure the heritage of our children, and increasing the moral and physical strength of all the people of this rapidly shrinking world. But remember that we should be very thankful that we have the right thus to declare that we ourselves do not yet have as much liberty, democracy and opportunity, physical or intellectual, as our ideals demand. For this right to think differently, to question, and to express our disagreements, this is the primary moral basis for the development of science, and indeed of all that is valuable in the intellectual life of man.

Notes

[1]Quoted from an editorial in *Pravda*, August 27, 1948.

[2]For details of the Communist Party's attack on the science of genetics, the reader may be referred to the following books: P. S. Hudson and R. H. Richens' *The New Genetics in the Soviet Union* (1946), Julian Huxley's *Heredity East and West* (1949), J. Langdon-Davies' *Russia Puts the Clock Back* (1949), Conway Zirkle's *The Death of a Science in Russia* (1949), and finally *The Situation in Biological Science* a verbatim report of the sessions of the Lenin Academy of Agricultural Sciences, July 31-August 7, 1948, published separately in German and in English by the Foreign Languages Publishing House, Moscow (1949). In the last named book the Russian administrators stand self-condemned. Their temerity in themselves publishing these otherwise incredible proceedings shows how far they now are from a realization of what is meant by science or, indeed, by rational thought itself. Among articles dealing with the subject, see Robert C. Cook's "Lysenko's Marxist Genetics" (*Journal of Heredity*, July, 1949), C. D. Darlington's "A Revolution in Soviet Science" (*Journal of Heredity*, May, 1947) and "Science Rejects Dictation" (*New Leader*, November 26, 1949), T. Dobzhansky's "Lysenko's Genetics" (*Journal of Heredity*, January, 1946), J. Huxley's "Soviet Genetics: the Real Issue" (*Nature*, June 18 and 25, 1949), S. Kaftanov's "In Support of Michurin's Biological Theory in Higher Institutions of Learning" (*Science*, January 28, 1949), J. Langdon-Davies' "The Russian Attack on Reason" (*Fortnightly Review*, May, 1949), H. J. Muller's "The Destruction of Science in the U.S.S.R.", Pts. I and II (*Saturday Review of Literature*, December 4 and 11, 1948), H. H. Plough's "Bourgeois Genetics and Party-Line Darwinism" (*American Scholar*, Summer, 1949), and the May and August-September, 1949 issues of *The Bulletin of Atomic Scientists*.

[3]In an open letter to the Academy of Sciences of the U.S.S.R., published in *Science*, October 22, 1948.

OUR LOAD OF MUTATIONS*

H. J. Muller

Indiana University, Bloomington, Indiana

Received June 6, 1950

The Effective Dominance of "Recessives" in Drosophila

We have seen that the rate of genetic elimination of individuals in a population is a function not only of μ_t but also of a factor d, which depends upon the degree of dominance of mutant genes and varies between the limits 2 (for the more dominant) and 1 (for complete recessives). We may now inquire into the probable value of this factor, considering first the evidence from *Drosophila*.

At first sight, the answer to our present problem seems easy, since it has been known for over thirty years (cf. Muller, 1918, pp. 466-7; and 1923) that in *Drosophila*, and probably in organisms in general, the great majority of mutant genes are recessive, in the sense of having much less dominance than the normal genes from which they arise. However, as has been pointed out by various persons (e.g. Muller, 1940, p. 252; Dobzhansky & Wright, 1941; Berg, 1942), this knowledge is not precise enough. For a little consideration shows that even a very slight degree of dominance of the mutants will be of preponderant importance, by leading to the elimination of the genes in heterozygotes before they have a chance to become homozygous. And a number of reasons were already given in the *Mechanism of Mendelian Heredity* in 1915, indicating that the recessivity of the so-called recessives is not really complete.

Since the early studies of several mutants of *Drosophila* (vestigial, miniature, white eye, black body, etc.) giving this result, a significant series of facts pointing clearly in the same direction has emerged. One is the finding that in *Drosophila* the heterozygous deficiency of even a comparatively short section of a chromosome, probably containing only some tens of genes, is somewhat detrimental, while that of a somewhat longer section is quite lethal. Moreover, even duplications of chromosome sections have effects of this sort, although, as expected, in somewhat lesser degree.

Another clear line of evidence in the same direction lies in the phenomenon called "dosage compensation." This refers to the fact that most sex-linked genes tested have been found to be provided with a series of modifying genes called compensators, located elsewhere in the X-chromosome. For, when we study mutant alleles of these sex-linked genes, it is found that the naturally existing sex

American Journal of Human Genetics, Vol. 2, No. 2, June, 1950; sections 8, 9, and résumé, included; based on a presidential address entitled "Our Mutations," presented before the second annual meeting of the American Society of Human Genetics, New York City, December.

difference in dosage of these other parts of the X-chromosome renders the effectiveness of the single dose of the given mutant gene which the male has almost exactly as great as that of the two doses which the female has. Nevertheless, it is usually impossible to detect, by superficial observation, any difference between the effects of one and two doses of the normal allele, even when the compensators are held constant. That is, outwardly, the "dominance" of the normal gene over its absence or over its recessive mutant allele appears complete. Yet, despite this, the effect of a single dose of the normal gene, uncompensated, must be sufficiently different from that of the homozygous normal to have influenced the organism's survival adversely to a significant degree, for otherwise the system of compensators would not have been evolved. Now since the individual heterozygous for a hypomorphic mutant is often much like one having but one dose of the normal gene, uncompensated, we must conclude that the dominance of the normal gene, though sufficient to give a superficially normal phenotype, is often incomplete enough to be effective in lowering the expectation of life or reproduction of the heterozygote. A more extended treatment of this matter (Muller, 1950a) has brought forward various further facts in support of this interpretation.

Finally, direct tests of the possible dominance of lethal or nearly lethal mutants have been made or published during the past two years, which clinch the matter for *Drosophila*. There are two sets of data. In the first place, Stern and Novitski (1948) showed that a series of thirty-three sex-linked lethals, most of them (twenty-six) produced by X-raying *Drosophila* spermatozoa, caused when heterozygous an undoubtedly significant lowering of viability. One may reckon from their data that the average disadvantage of the heterozygote in their material is some 10 per cent (a result which would imply, for lethals, a 10 per cent grade of dominance).

Independently of the above work, and before it was published, the present writer, in collaboration with Mr. S. L. Campbell, had started some very similar work, utilizing however autosomal lethals and near-lethals that had been induced in our laboratory by Meyer and Edmondson (see Meyer, Edmondson, L. Altenburg & Muller, 1949) by means of ultraviolet acting upon primordial germ cells in an interphase (polar cap) stage. Thirteen lethals and sublethals were studied, as well as thirteen cases of untreated non-lethal chromosomes, to serve as controls. Lethals induced by X-rays in spermatozoa were purposely avoided because of the fact that some 30 per cent of these are deficiencies, involving the more or less cumulative action of an indeterminate number of genes. The ultraviolet lethals, on the other hand, particularly when induced in the extended chromosomes of interphase, would in great majority be one-locus gene mutations, like spontaneous ones. Moreover, tests of some not quite lethal genes also were desired, since in the case of complete lethals one can never know just how drastic the homozygous effect really is and so one cannot adequately assess the significance of a certain degree of heterozygous effect in its relation to the homozygous effect. Finally, autosomal mutants were preferred to sex-linked ones because of the fact that the degree of detriment shown by females heterozygous for sex-linked genes would depend very largely upon the exactitude of the dosage compensation which the given loci had attained and upon related selective factors, difficult to assess, whereas this complication does not exist with the atuosomal mutants. The genetic methods used were also very different from those of Stern and Novitski.

Our results, obtained in 1948-49 but only now ready for publication, show a distinct departure from complete recessiveness on the part of both the complete and the partial lethals. In our experiments the grade of dominance of both these classes of mutants averages about 4.5 per cent. However, it is only safe to say that the dominance probably lies between 3 and 6 per cent and *very* probably between 2 and 7 per cent. Stupendous counts would be needed to attain greater exactitude than this.

We have calculated that the difference in average dominance values between the two sets of experiments (Stern and Novitski's and our own) is statistically significant and is of the magnitude to be expected in view of the probable difference in frequency of deficiencies. However, it can also be shown that Stern and Novitski's practice of not including, in their total count of heterozygous lethals versus homozygous normals, individuals which when tested gave cultures below a certain size, was another factor that may have lowered the apparent frequency of the heterozygotes and thus raised the apparent degree of dominance appreciably. For the lethal-bearing individuals (the heterozygotes) must have given smaller average counts in the given type of test and must therefore have been excluded in greater abundance. To what extent lethals in the X may be taken as representative in regard to dominance is, as above remarked, another very problematical question. In view of all these considerations then, as well as considerations of the sizes of the purely statistical errors in the two series of observations, we feel that the earlier data, although based on more genes, should not be regarded as throwing doubt on the quantitative aspects of our own conclusions. That is, it may be regarded as very unlikely that the average degree of dominance of autosomal lethal and near-lethal gene mutations in *Drosophila* lies outside the range 2 to 7 per cent.

Let us next assess what this degree of dominance would mean in terms of our factor d, used in determining the equilibrium rate of elimination of individuals from the population. It can very readily be made clear by means of approximation methods that, in a population breeding with the degree of randomness of a human one, an apparently recessive lethal with a dominance of only 2 per cent, even if it had a mutation frequency as high as one in 50,000, would produce most of its genetically killing and damaging action on heterozygotes. For the selective disadvantage of 2 per cent in the heterozygote, or one in fifty, would on the average allow the gene to pass down only through fifty generations of heterozygous individuals, supposing that it remained heterozygous all that time, as it usually would. Moreover, the very rare occasions when it did become homozygous would cause its average persistence, p, to be somewhat less even than fifty. Thus the equilibrium frequency of the gene in the germ cells of the population would be somewhat less than fifty times its mutation rate, and, if we take its μ as being one in 50,000, its equilibrium frequency would be somewhat below one in 1,000. With purely random breeding a given mutant gene of this type would therefore have a chance, in any one generation, of somewhat less than one in 1,000 of meeting another gene like itself in fertilization and so becoming eliminated in a homozygote. This chance is so much lower than the chance of one in 50, for it to become eliminated in any generation in which it is heterozygous, that it is evident that even the 2 per cent degree of dominance here assumed leads to an amount of elimination and damage of heterozygotes far out-weighing that of homozygotes.

We have in the above ignored the effect of inbreeding. In man there would usually be another chance, approaching one in 1,000 fertilizations in urban districts or one in some hundreds in small, long-isolated rural or primitive communities, for a mutant gene of the given kind to become homozygous through inbreeding of a near or remote nature. Yet, since the chance of elimination in any heterozygote would always remain one in fifty for such a gene, we may nevertheless conclude that its chief action in causing elimination of individuals must be exerted through the slight manifestation which it attains in heterozygotes.

The mutant gene of 2 per cent dominance would also wreak much the greater part of its damage short of death in heterozygotes, because the number of deaths serves as a kind of index to the total damage or risk. The individual heterozygote would, to be sure, be far less affected, on the whole, than the individual homozygote, but there would be so many more of the heterozygotes as to much more than compensate, in the production of the total damage, for their individually lesser degree of impairment.

Dominance in Man

There are a number of considerations and lines of evidence leading towards the conclusion that the degree of dominance of mutant genes in man is, on the whole, at least as high as in *Drosophila*. These may now be examined.

In the first place, there are good grounds for inferring that the dominance of mutant genes has arisen through a selective process. Whether this selection has mainly occurred, as inferred by Fisher

(1928*a*, *b*, 1930), by virtue of the advantage that the dominance of the normal gene confers on the heterozygotes themselves or, as both the present writer (1932, 1935, 1950*a*, *c*) and Plunkett (1932, 1933) later argued, by reason of its stabilization of the phenotype of the homozygous normal in the presence of disturbing environmental and genetic influences in general, the process must be one which only approaches but does not actually attain completion. Thus it would leave a certain degree of dominance to the mutant gene. The incompleteness of the process must be caused, among other things, by the physico-chemical improbability of reaching an absolute maximum of gene effectiveness, and by biological impairments entailed by interference with other processes as such a maximum is approached. It must be caused, further, by mutation pressure tending towards lower levels of gene effectiveness. Another factor must be the occurrence of evolutionary changes in the optimum. And finally, the attainment of perfect precision of dominance would be obstructed by the particulateness or what might be called the "graininess," the ultimately quantized nature, of the processes of mutation, selection and evolution in general.

Now there is no evident reason why the effectiveness of any of the above factors should be less in man or mammals than in *Drosophila*. In fact, as Levit (1936) has pointed out, the far greater ability of the higher forms, and more especially man, to adapt themselves by behavioral means to new and unfavorable conditions and thus better to compensate for ailments even when they are of genetic origin, should tend, on any selectionist conception of dominance, to make the dominance of normals less complete in man than in *Drosophila*. We may add to this argument that the factors of mutation pressure, recency of change in optima, and graininess, should all be more potent in man than in *Drosophila*, in view (1) of man's higher mutation rate, (2) his greater amount of evolution and consequent destabilization in recent times, and (3) the relatively small number of human individuals that exist either in space (due to their size) or in time (due to their length of generation).

Evidence was presented by Levit in 1934 to 1936, in several memorable papers summarizing the results of a series of investigations by himself and his co-workers, and critically surveying the literature, that recessive abnormalities in man are much rarer, in comparison with dominant ones, than had till then been believed. In these papers, which appeared on the eve of the abolition of his institute and his own "liquidation," he showed that a series of eight different hereditary diseases studied intensively by his group, some of which, such as a prevalent form of diabetes mellitus, had previously been taken for recessives, were all of them in reality dominants. What had been deceptive about them was that they appeared to skip generations but this was shown to be because of their "incomplete penetrance" (usually below 20 per cent). It would be better to say that they commonly remained at such a low level of expression that they could not readily be detected, for in some cases they could be revealed by more refined means (e.g. by blood sugar determinations in the case of diabetes mellitus).

However, as Levit further pointed out, these dominants should only be called " conditional dominants." For the rare homozygous mutant, when known, might be much more extreme than the heterozygous one, as had been proved for a number of genes. In fact, if they had occurred in *Drosophila*, many of these cases would not have been noticed as being abnormal at all when heterozygous, and yet, by reason of the inbreeding so often used in laboratory work with this organism, they would have been picked up in the extreme form, as homozygotes, and hence would have been called recessive visible mutations or recessive lethals, as the case might be. Thus there is no reason to believe that these conditional dominants in man usually depart from the principle that the normal gene has the greater dominance, but they do indicate that despite this the mutant often has a significant amount of dominance.

The evidence that the above relations hold for most mutant genes in man was greatly strengthened by Levit's systematic analysis of the literature on inherited diseases of the skin, eye and nervous system. He showed that of fifty-five different cases as many as forty-one, that is, approximately three-quarters, had some demonstrable degree of dominance, and that the great majority of obviously affected individuals in these forty-one cases were heterozygotes. The evidence for dominant inheritance was derived from studies (1) of the frequency with which the affected individuals were the products of inbreeding and (2) of the relative frequencies with which different types of relatives of the affected individuals were themselves affected.

Proceeding to a study of the literature on sex-linked mutant genes, which had been considered to furnish particularly good evidence of the prevalence of complete recessiveness, Levit was able to show that in only a very small proportion of cases had this conclusion been well founded. In twenty-four of the thirty-six cases reviewed the evidence was found to be insufficient even to classify these genes as sex-linked rather than, for instance, sex-influenced autosomal dominants, while among the twelve cases which could be safely accepted as sex-linked, there were three for which the evidence was insufficient to allow conclusions concerning dominance to be drawn. In the residuum of nine cases, only two turned out to be recessive (as judged by the tests then in use), the other seven all having some detectable degree of expression in the heterozygous female.

Despite the above momentous findings, which have received insufficient attention, there are, all told, not a few apparently recessive abnormalities now established in man, i.e. abnormalities caused by homozygosity of a gene whose effect in the heterozygote has so far failed of detection. Moreover, the ratio of such " recessives" to the "dominants" found would undoubtedly have been a good deal higher, and more nearly like that observed in *Drosophila*, if the circumstances of finding them had, as in *Drosophila*, involved more inbreeding, and less detailed phenotypic observation. Yet, even conceding this, the very fact that these circumstances of breeding and of observation have resulted in a much lower apparent ratio of recessives to dominants in man appears to lead to the conclusion that the apparent recessives in man, if not actually less frequent than in *Drosophila*, have, on the whole, enough dominance to affect their chances of survival significantly in the heterozygous condition (and/or to produce an observable effect on the phenotype of the heterozygous individual). For a permanently low degree of inbreeding cannot result in a lower equilibrium frequency of appearance of homozygous "recessives" in any population unless the frequency of these "recessive" genes has been kept at a low level by means of a selection that was effective against them even when they were heterozygous. This would imply that they were "effectively dominant," in the sense previously explained.

The above argument must be qualified by the consideration (Haldane, 1939*b*) that in recent generations the amount of inbreeding in man has been reduced to a level even lower than in earlier times. This change in the system of breeding (not the low degree of inbreeding in itself) must reduce the frequency of homozygous recessives in the present population below the equilibrium value. However, this influence turns out, on calculation, to be far from sufficient, by itself, to explain the shortage of recessives found in man as compared with *Drosophila.* This is the more true in consideration of the circumstance that some of the best studied groups in man in which dominants have been found have been long settled peasant populations. Moreover, the studies of Bell (1940) on the consanguinity of parents of hospitalized patients did not yield as much evidence of the importance of this factor in morbidity as was to be expected on the view that homozygosity plays a major role in the causation of genetic damage. Similarly, the studies of Bedichek and Haldane (1938), so far as they went, gave no ground for assuming that recessive lethals occur as frequently as might be expected if their origination by mutation were only as high, per generation, as in *Drosophila*, and if they were eliminated only as homozygous recessives.

In further evidence of the conclusions that the great majority of mutant genes in man have a significant degree of dominance, attention should be drawn to the important series of facts brought together by Neel in his address to the American Society of Human Genetics in September, 1948 and published in the first number of this journal (1949). In this paper it was shown that, as those abnormalities of man which are actually known in homozygous state and which appear to be recessive have become subjected to intensive study by the more delicate modern methods, more and more of them, such as thalassemia, sickle cell anemia, epilepsy, etc., have been demonstrated to leave distinct traces of their effect on the heterozygote.

In this connection, however, a difficulty arises for the supposition that the effect in the heterozygote is sufficiently detrimental to cause a selection against the gene. For a few of these superficially recessive conditions, of undoubtedly detrimental nature when homozygous, have proved to have so high a frequency in certain populations as to appear to require either an inordinately high mutation frequency or a slightly advantageous action when heterozygous, as compared with homozygous normals. Among these are thalassemia major in Mediterranean countries, sickle anemia in Africa and amaurotic idiocy in Sweden. As the interpretation of positive selection of heterozygotes seems more probable, the question arises as to how common this type of effect, sometimes referred to as "overdominance," may be. For, if abundant, it would work in direct opposition to the effects of ordinary dominance which have been considered above, and would seriously disturb our main calcuations.

In regard to this question, it may in the first place be remarked that such cases of the phenomenon as do exist would, in consequence of the effect on frequency which they involve, become unduly conspicuous, and would thereby tend to give the impression of having originated more frequently than was actually the case. Secondly, it should be recalled that the above mentioned tests of recessive lethal and deleterious genes, both by Stern and Novitski and by the author and Campbell, gave definite evidence that, in *Drosophila* at any rate, the great majority of genes harmful to the homozygote, when picked up as mutants soon after their origination, are in fact disadvantageous to the heterozygote also. The same conclusion is to be drawn from the gene dosage and dosage compensation studies. There are, to be sure, contrary claims in *Drosophila* (Masing, 1938, 1939; Dubinin, 1946), as well as in some plant material, but careful scrutiny of the published reports indicates that in these cases adequate precautions were not taken to avoid complications due to ordinary heterosis. That is, the homozygous "normals" studied are likely to have been homozygous at the same time for more invisible detrimental genes than were those individuals which were heterozygous for the primary gene in question.

Looking at the matter from a more theoretical standpoint, it is to be expected that, despite occasional cases of mutant genes which happen, under certain conditions at any rate, to give the heterozygote a net advantage over both the normal and the homozygous mutant, the general run of mutant genes would give a detrimental effect in the heterozygote, similar to but lesser than that shown in the homozygote. That is, the heterozygote would tend to deviate from normal in the same direction as the homozygote, and the grade of detriment would tend to be proportional to the amount of this deviation. To suppose otherwise would involve the postulate that a deviant of minor degree is very often better adapted than the normal type. This is improbable except in the case of characters that are still becoming adapted to a condition which is new for the species, in terms of evolutionary time, or, what is much the same thing to a condition that is local in its incidence on the species. For, except in special cases of balanced polymorphic types, any given character tends to become stabilized at a normal value that is optimal for the long-term conditions, so that only the very rare mutant, even if small in its homozygous effect, will succeed in being advantageous at all. And where, along the evolutionary track, some mutant gene did arise which was advantageous in its heterozygous degree of expression but deleterious homozygously, that gene, though temporarily multiplied as a make-shift arrangement, would usually have become replaced, after a while, by mutant genes of less deviant expression, occupying the same or other loci, which gave an equivalent advantage when they were present homozygously. For such genes would make possible a more uniform, and therefore (when all individuals were averaged) a closer approach to the adaptational optimum.

The reservation must of course be admitted that in civilized mankind the conditions of living have become so consistently transformed as to make many old optima out-of-date, thus opening the way for relatively many deviations formerly damaging to be advantageous. This makes it more likely now than in times past for some mutant genes of man which are still so extreme as to be detrimental when homozygous to be somewhat beneficial in their heterozygous expression. Nevertheless, even now such mutations must be far less frequent in origination than are those which are detrimental both to the homozygote and (roughly in proportion to their degree of expression in him) to the heterozygote. For there must always be many more disadvantageous kinds of change than advantageous ones, especially in a very highly organized system. And even when the system has become somewhat maladjusted in relation to its surroundings its complicated internal inter-adjustments would still cause the great majority of its individually taken blind steps of alteration, even those of slight degree, to result in its less harmonious operation. We may therefore, in view of all the above considerations, regard the great majority of mutant genes, even in man of today, as having a detrimental effect not only homozygously but also heterozygously, insofar as they manifest themselves at all in heterozygotes. Moreover, there are, as we have seen, cogent reasons for concluding that they do usually have a significant degree of heterozygous manifestation in man, probably at least as much as in *Drosophila*.

General Résumé

1. It is shown that, contrary to the view alleged to have been prevailing in medical circles, according to which mutation is virtually negligible as a cause of disease in man, it must in human populations that live in a state of approximate genetic equilibrium be the differential cause of the death or failure to reproduce of between one-fifth and two-thirds of the persons who escape being killed before reproduction, or being prevented from reproducing, by other, purely extrinsic causes.

2. The above conclusion is arrived at by the use of Danforth's (1921) fundamental theorem of genetic equilibrium. According to this, the frequency with which a given mutant characteristic is present in a population is equal to the frequency with which it arises by mutation, multiplied by the average number of generations during which a gene for the given characteristic has been able to manifest itself before being eliminated by reason of the disability it confers. Examples and extensions of the theorem are discussed. In applying it for the purpose of deriving the conclusion stated in the preceding paragraph, it was necessary to have estimates of the total mutation rate and of the usual amount of dominance.

3. On the basis of existing data in man, supported by evidence from *Drosophila*, the total human mutation rate is judged to be probably not less than one newly arisen mutant gene in ten germ cells, on the average, and not more than one in two germ cells.

4. Evidence is presented in support of the finding of Levit (1935, 1936) that the great majority of mutant genes in man have some degree of dominance. It is shown that, both in *Drosophila* and in man, although most mutant genes are recessive in the sense of producing less than half as much aberration when heterozygous as when homozygous, nevertheless they are "effectively dominant," in the sense that most of their total damaging effect on the population is exerted through their action while in heterozygous condition.

5. The probable distribution of mutant genes with regard to the amount of detrimental effect which they produce when homozygous and when heterozygous is considered. It is estimated that, although "effectively dominant," the mutant genes of a given locus usually produce, in any single individual, but a very small effect when heterozygous, but accumulate until they reach a reciprocally high frequency in the population, and so do as much total damage as if they were completely lethal. It is calculated that the average individual is probably heterozygous for at least eight genes, and possibly for scores, each of which produces a significant but usually slight detrimental effect on him. (The number thus arrived at would vary greatly according to the exact grade of detriment at which the line was drawn between genes designated as significantly detrimental and those designated as practically indifferent for survival, in view of the high degree of accumulation of genes of the borderline kinds.) All the detrimental genes together tend to give each individual his

own characteristic, more or less familial pattern of weaknesses, most of which however are not to be distinguished sharply from disabilities of environmental origin and which are intimately combined with the latter.

6. The number of mutant genes in different individuals forms approximately a Poisson series. Those individuals who undergo genetic elimination, constituting some 20 per cent or more of populations living in a state of genetic equilibrium, do not on the average have much more than one gene in excess of the survivors and are therefore not, as a group, markedly inferior to them. In correspondence with this, the great majority of individuals suffer from a genetically occasioned depression of viability approximately great enough to result in a risk of extinction that is equal to the frequency of individuals who do become genetically eliminated in each generation.

7. The above estimates of the frequency of extinction due to genetic causes and of the amount of depression of viability of the average individual apply only to a population living under the same conditions as those which existed while approximately the present gene frequency was being established (i.e. under the conditions for which it represents an equilibrium). The improvements in living conditions, medicine, etc. under our modern civilization must result in a saving for reproduction, at present, of a large proportion of those who under the earlier conditions would have been genetically proscribed, and in a corresponding mitigation of the effects of the genetic disabilities of the great majority of the population.

8. If, as at present happens, the individuals saved for reproduction by these procedures actually do reproduce, the mutant gene frequency will gradually rise in the direction of a new equilibrium level (probably not half attained a thousand years from now even if conditions remained constant in the interim). At the new level, despite the ameliorative measures, as large a proportion would again suffer genetic elimination as under primitive conditions, while those not eliminated would again be as much afflicted as originally. A much greater proportion of their time and effort than at present would then be expended in the attempt to counteract their accumulated internal disabilities (which would amount to lethality for the great majority of them if they again had to live under primitive conditions), rather than difficulties of external origin. It is unrealistic to suppose that technique could continue to advance indefinitely to such an extent as to avoid this denouement.

9. It is shown that the only means by which the effects of the genetic load can be lightened permanently and securely is by the coupling of ameliorative techniques, such as medicine, with a rationally directed guidance of reproduction. In other words, the latter procedure is a necessary complement to medicine, and to the other practices of civilization, if they are not to defeat their own purposes, and it is in the end equally as important for our health and

well-being as all of them together. Under this procedure, if it is to be successful in attaining its objectives by means consistent with its aims, the equilibrium quota of detrimental genes must become eliminated as a result of voluntary decisions and not as a result of failure in a struggle for existence.

10. It is also shown, with the aid of a numerical illustration, that highly developed knowledge of human genetics would, theoretically at least, make possible the elimination of the necessary quota of mutant genes by means of the abstention from reproduction of a much smaller proportion of individuals than that proportion (equal to nearly twice the mutation rate) whose elimination is required for equilibrium under ordinary natural selection. This would be made possible by the systematic choosing, for such abstention, of individuals having an especially high excess of mutant genes, beyond the average number.

11. A long-term increase in the mutation rate, if of moderate degree, would eventually result in a proportionate increase in the genetic load (e.g., a doubled rate would double the load), if the load were expressed in terms of either the proportion of the population suffering genetic elimination or the amount of disability suffered by the average individual.

12. If the long-term increase were of more than moderate degree, however, the mutation rate might have exceeded the " critical value," beyond which equilibrium was impossible and extinction of the population was (if the conditions continued) inevitable. For the usual mutation rate of man must be not far below the level which would have been critical under primitive conditions of reproduction. But in the presence of the low rate of reproduction prevailing among most of the technically advanced peoples, the present mutation rate must be very nearly at or is perhaps even beyond the value which is critical in this situation. Under these circumstances even a moderate increase in mutation rate, such as one of 25 per cent, might be more than could be tolerated indefinitely.

13. The use of ionizing radiation and of radioactive materials is increasing and promises to continue increasing to such an extent, both in medical treatment and diagnosis, and in commerce and industry, even without considering military affairs in this connection, that unless more caution is exercised than at present the majority of the population may in each successive generation have its gonads exposed to enough radiation to raise the mutation rate by a significant amount, such as 25 per cent or 50 per cent.

14. How much a given exposure increases the mutation rate is a matter that cannot readily be determined by observations on human or other indiscriminately breeding populations. Even a quadrupling of the mutation rate, occurring throughout a whole population for just one or a few generations, would probably affect the viability of the descendants in too scattered a manner (see paragraph below) for these effects to be distinguished from those of uncontrolled circum-

stances. Moreover, vast numbers would be necessary for the finding of statistically significant differences in the frequency of clear-cut mutational abnormalities.

15. Yet despite the fact that the evidence of a short-term rise in mutation rate is so hidden, the total amount of damage caused to all later generations by even a moderate rise, confined to one parental generation, would if gathered together be seen to be enormous. Thus only a 25 per cent rise in mutation rate for one generation would, in a population of 100,000,000 per generation whose usual spontaneous rate was only one mutant gene in ten germ cells, cause the eventual "genetic death" of 5,000,000 individuals, scattered throughout scores of generations. It would probably cause, in addition, hundreds of millions to be slightly more afflicted than they would otherwise have been, i.e. to have their viability lowered by an average of some 2 or 3 per cent. These effects are hidden only because distributed over so many generations and because so intermingled with those of other factors. Moreover, once the mutations have been produced, they will take their eventual toll despite all counteracting measures that may hereafter be instituted, short of a consciously directed selection.

16. The total effect eventually exerted, over the course of an unlimited number of generations, by a given one-generation rise in mutation rate, although hidden from view, is quantitatively the same as the effect which would be observable in any single generation if an increased mutation rate of the same magnitude were indefinitely continued and equilibrium for it had been reached. Similarly, the total average magnitude or risk of effect in subsequent generations when only a small part of the population or even one individual has had his mutation rate raised is proportional to the above mentioned effect which would be observable in one generation in an entire population that had reached equilibrium for the given rate, and may be expressed in terms of the probable number of descendants meeting genetic extinction or of the corresponding total amount of genetically occasioned affliction. These values for a given number of r units applied to human material remain to be determined, however, and until they are we cannot well judge of the value or disadvantage of procedures which, in helping the immediate generation, cause an unknown amount of damage to subsequent ones.

17. Attention is called to social obstacles which tend to prevent the medical and lay public, educators, and administrators from recognizing the above principles and from taking steps to modify current attitudes and practices in accordance with them. In this connection fundamental educational reforms—the institution of which, unfortunately, is subject to the same hindrances—are needed.

18. It is pointed out that mental traits are subject to the same principles regarding mutational load, selection, equilibrium, etc., as

have been reviewed above for physical traits but that, being more important for man, they should be given first priority.

19. A number of important changes in our point of view regarding genetic processes in man are called for by consideration of the fact that most mutant genes have a certain degree of dominance, usually enough to be "effective," and probably greater in the case of the less detrimental mutant genes than of the more detrimental ones. It is seen, for example, that equilibria, though still very slow of attainment, are not nearly as long delayed as on the older view; that selection, both negative and positive, is more effective and rapid in its action than had been thought; and that the amount of inbreeding practiced becomes a matter of somewhat lesser consequence. In general, previous discussions and calculations will require major revision, in order to be brought into line with this altered genetic outlook concerning dominance.

FURTHER STUDIES BEARING ON THE LOAD OF MUTATIONS IN MAN*

By H. J. Muller
Department of Zoology, Indiana University,
Bloomington, Indiana, U.S.A.

The Load as Disclosed by Inbreeding

A different approach to the problem of how much mutational load has been accumulated in human populations is through studies of the effects of inbreeding. One application of this method has recently been used by *Slatis* [1954] in deriving a tentative figure (8) for the frequency of recessive genes causing definitely distinguishable rare abnormalities. We are here interested, however, in a more general view, that will bring us closer to an estimation of the total mutational load.

The present writer made a start at such an approach some fifteen years ago, on coming across a study published in 1908 by *G. B. L. Arner,* entitled "Consanguineous Marriages in the American Population." In this monograph data were obtained from genealogies that dealt, among other things, with the survival up to twenty years of age of 672 children resulting from first-cousin marriages and that of 3184 children, of the same genealogies, resulting from marriages between non-relatives. The former group showed 83.2 per cent sur-

*Acta Genetica et Statistica Medica, 1956, 6: 157-68; sections 3 and 4 included; Zoology Department contribution No. 630.

vival and the latter 88.4 per cent, the difference being highly significant. Dividing the former figure by the latter, it turns out that only 94.1 per cent of those who should have survived if the parents had not been inbred were able to survive if their parents were first cousins. That is, the inbreeding resulted in the death, before twenty years of age, of about 6 per cent of those who would otherwise have lived. Since, however, first-cousin inbreeding gives only a 1/16 probability of homozygosis of genes that would otherwise have been heterozygous, we may multiply this 6 per cent mortality by 16. This gives us 96 per cent as the sum of the excess risks of genetic death (as compared with non-inbred individuals) that would on the average be undergone between birth and twenty years by hypothetical individuals that were homozygous for all the genes contained in just one of the gametes that produced them.

It was this calculation that led the present writer to say, at a symposium on genetics and public health held in 1947 (published 1948): "a calculation... from results of inbreeding in man... leads to the conclusion that every person on the average contains heterozygously at least one lethal gene or group of genes which (homozygously would)... kill an individual between birth and maturity." Actually, the above data indicate the possession by each individual of two such groups of genes, heterozygously, since he is derived from two gametes, each containing one such group. That the lower value given in the statement, which was intended to be a minimum estimate, probably made much more allowance than necessary for statistical and other errors has been indicated by estimates recently made, in part independently, by *Morton* and *Crow*, on the basis of other data (see *Morton*, *Crow* and *Muller* [1956]). Moreover, judging by the frequency of deaths at other periods of life than that here considered—deaths that nevertheless play a role in genetic survival,—and judging also by the frequency of genetically influenced infecundity, the effects noted in *Arner*'s study probably represent not more than half of the total number of "lethal equivalents" (to use *Morton* and *Crow*'s term). Thus the indicated number of these lethal equivalents per diploid individual is probably at least four. It should be emphasized that this does not mean four actual lethals, but a collection of slightly detrimental genes and of some lethals, all of which would, if dispersed among different individuals in homozygous condition, tend to give a total of four genetic eliminations.

The Derivation of Mutation Rate From Total Load

Crow (*Morton*, *Crow* and *Muller*, *ibid.*) has found a relatively simple way of translating this accumulated load into terms of mutation frequency, provided that the assumption is accepted that the great majority of mutant genes have a certain low degree of dominance. Direct evidence that most mutant genes in man have some dominance was long ago given in studies of *Levit* [1936] that have recently received support in work of others. Grounds for inferring that the same principle applies in Drosophila and other organisms have been adduced by the present writer [1950 a, b, c] on consideration of the mode of expression of deficiencies and duplications, the facts of dosage compensation, and special studies of the expression of "visible" mutants when heterozygous. Further both *Stern et al.* [1948, 1952] and the present writer in collaboration with *Campbell (Muller, ibid.)*, in independent work, have found that lethal and near-lethal genes in Drosophila have, on the average, some 4 to 5 per cent of dominance.

Some indirect evidence that detrimental mutant genes in man have an amount of dominance of this same order is to be found in the similarity in the frequency of specific genes for detrimental recessive abnormalities in Japanese and European-derived populations (as found by *Komai* [1947, 1956], and by *Neel et al.* [1949]). For, as compared with modern Europe and America, the amount of in-breeding in Japan is exceedingly high and probably has been so for millenia, resulting, we may calculate, in at least 1/2 per cent of homozygosity due to this cause in Japan and very likely 1 per cent (i.e. the coefficient of inbreeding is .005 to .01). In consequence of this very high degree of inbreeding, mutant genes in the Japanese population would have been eliminated much faster than in Europe and would have attained distinctly lower frequencies than in Europe, unless one of the following conditions had held. (1) If the dominance of the so-called recessive mutants were usually distinctly more than 1 per cent, so as to constitute the overriding cause of their elimination; or (2) if the amount of inbreeding in medieval and ancient Europe was (as some indications suggest[1]) about as high as in Japan.

There is to be sure a third possibility, namely, that there is a much lower mutation rate in Europe, which compensates for the supposed lesser rate of elimination via homozygotes. This, however, would be a purely *ad hoc* assumption of very questionable character, and we shall ignore it here. If the first possibility and not the second is correct (although it should be noted that they are not mutually exclusive) it would follow that the usual dominance in man should be taken as at least 2 per cent, to mask the difference in inbreeding, and it might well be a good deal higher. We should postpone until later a consideration of the consequences of the second possibility.

Now the method of conversion of our figure for lethal equivalents —four or more—into one for mutation rate, when the amount of dominance is given and when it overrides the effects of homozygosity, may be explained as follows. We have seen that any given mutant gene tends to persist in the population until it causes one elimination (if we neglect the overlapping of eliminations). This elimination, if the dominance is as great as we have inferred, usually takes place in the heterozygote. Thus the frequency of eliminations, and the associated "damage" or "loss of fitness" in the population, caused by detrimental mutations arising at any given locus or chromosome region, is about equal to the frequency of mutations at that locus or region that arise in germ cells of both sexes; that is, it is about twice the mutation rate. And the *total* frequency of eliminations or or total amount of genetic damage, either in the population as a whole or in the average individual is, roughly, twice the total rate at which detrimental mutant genes are arising. In other words, the four or more lethal equivalents contained by the average person, that would be sufficient to kill four times over if they were made homozygous, actually exert in their usual heterozygous condition a tendency to genetic death equal to 2μ (where μ is the mutation rate). Assuming, as an approximation sufficiently close at this stage, that they are all heterozygous and that, to be conservative, their dominance (that is, their degree of expression in heterozygous as compared with homozygous condition) is only 2 per cent, it is evident that in the ordinary individual this load is bringing about an amount of damage or risk of elimination of $4\times.02$, or 8 per cent. Moreover, since as we have just seen this is approximately twice the mutation rate per gamete, μ would be .04. If, however, dominance should be taken as 5 per cent μ would be .1. In either case the result is in satisfactory agreement, considering the uncertainties involved, with the figure of .1 for μ arrived at by our first, entirely different method.

The details of the calculations, together with various qualifications, subsidiary considerations, and mathematical relations, are being set forth elsehwere *(Morton, Crow* and *Muller, ibid.).* It may be noted here that, as *Crow* has pointed out, the value for dominance to be used in this calculation should be the harmonic mean value, since the persistence of a gene is reciprocally related to its dominance, and that the harmonic mean value indicated by certain not too extensive Drosophila data suitable for a study of this question (*Muller* and *Campbell,* unpublished) has turned out to be about 2 per cent, although with a relatively large error, whereas the arithmetic mean was 4.4 per cent. There are, however, reasons for suspecting that the value may be higher for the more numerous less detrimental genes, and that it may be higher for man than for Drosophila. This would tend to make our estimate of mutation rate based on this method, like that on the other one, a conservative estimate. On the other hand, the true value could not be inordinately higher than on this estimate. For if it were the rate of elimination would have to be higher than could be tolerated by an ordinary human population, with its relatively low rate of reproduction.

* * * * *

Conclusions and Prospectives

We may conclude that modern studies, through two independent routes, support the conclusion that the frequency of detrimental mutations in man is of the order of one in ten gametes, with a present factor of uncertainty of about three in either direction. That is, the rate is of the order of magnitude centering, geometrically, about one tenth. The elimination rate and the loss of fitness, under equilibrium conditions, would probably be somewhat less than twice as great as the mutation rate.

It is to be expected that further studies along these lines will provide qualitative detail and greater exactitude. Among questions on which light will be thrown by application of the second method, based on consanguinity differences, are the following. (1) The extent to which detrimental mutations are eliminated as heterozygotes, as shown by a comparison of their frequencies, individually or *en masse* (e.g. through mortality studies), in populations that have long been subjected to very different degrees of inbreeding. (2) The frequency of so-called " over-dominant" mutants (those which although detrimental when homozygous are superior to normal when heterozygous). (3) The extent of synergism between non-allelic mutants in the causation of damage and elimination, as judged by the degree of upward curvature, rather than linearity, of the graph relating mortality and other damage to the closeness of inbreeding, when results from unusually close inbreeding are included. (4) The extent to which differences in mortality, infecundity, etc., are in general genetic, i.e. selectable, as found by comparison of the mortality, infecundity, etc., of the offspring of non-relatives with the value for the genetic contingent of these quantities as deduced from the results for homozygotes taken in connection with determinations of dominance. (5) The extent to which our modern civilization is decreasing genetic elimination below the equilibrium level. This would be evidenced by the differences in mortality, infecundity, etc., resulting from inbreeding, between populations subjected to different present standards of living and medical care. Further evidence would be obtained by a study of the differences between the calculated genetically occasioned contingent of the mortality, infecundity etc., among the offspring of non-relatives in the compared populations. For this purpose it is imperative that data of these kinds be obtained from populations still living under primitive conditions of selection, before it is too late. (6) The amount of increase in mutation rate that a population under given conditions of living can tolerate without serious or continued genetic deterioration or, alternatively, the rapidity, duration, and quality of deterioration that a given increase in mutation rate would cause. In this connection it may be noted that knowledge of the total spontaneous mutation rate and load, whether obtained by this or any other method, is an invaluable means of assessing the total effect that would be produced by a given amount of radiation or other mutagenic agent, if an index of the mutagen's effectiveness had been obtained by data on mutations at specific loci or of some otherwise specified category.

Note

[1] I am indebted to Dr. W. Lenz for having called my attention to the likelihood of this possibility.

GENETIC DAMAGE PRODUCED BY RADIATION*

H. J. Muller
Zoology Department, Indiana University, Bloomington

Genetics seems to be the field of "natural" science that is most abused by persons with political and other special interests in their attempts to fabricate theoretical bases for their practices, as in the cases of Hitler's racist obsessions and Stalin's Michurinism. Although these two perversions are now gradually weakening their hold, they served in their day as tools in the wreaking of untold harm. In these two situations, those of us scientists who were in or near the field concerned felt it incumbent upon ourselves to speak up in the defense of science as we knew it, even though it was certainly not the force of our own words that finally turned the tide.

And now today, even in our own country, we see certain versions —or is it perversions?—of genetics raising their heads, not primarily among geneticists, but among groups who wish to create a semblance of scientific support for some preconceived policy. The matter at issue now is that of the genetic effects of radiation.[1] This is a subject on which I have given my only previous talks before the National Academy of Sciences, one of twenty-seven years ago and one of fourteen years ago. At the present time, in view of the grave danger to which the growing distortions of this subject may lead, it would seem to be in the spirit of the Kimber Genetics Award for this occasion to be used, not for another purely academic treatment, but for a frank discussion of the matter in relation to current affairs.

Wide circulation has recently been given to statements by certain prominent publicists, including physicians and others working on government projects, alleging that the bombings of Hiroshima and Nagasaki have left the descendant populations unharmed or, possibly, even improved. Opposed to these are other voices, calling loudly,

Science, Vol. 121, No. 3155, June 17, 1955, pp. 837-40.

and in some cases in a suspiciously vitriolic tone, for an end to all nuclear test explosions, on the ground that even the tests are already seriously undermining the genetic basis of all mankind. To geneticists, both of these contrary claims appear so far from the truth that they can be interpreted only as special pleadings, dictated by ulterior motives.

It is no longer a matter of doubt among scientists working in this field that radiation, of the types derived from radioactive substances or x-ray machines, does produce permanent changes, mutations, in the hereditary constitution of living things of all kinds. The most numerous and important of these changes, occurring in the individual hereditary particles, or genes, and therefore called gene mutations, arise with a frequency depending proportionately on the total dose of radiation. For instance, one-tenth of a given dose produces one-tenth of the number of gene mutations, no matter in how long or how short a time that total dose was received. Thus, no exposure is so tiny that it does not carry its corresponding mutational risk.

Inconclusiveness of Hiroshima and Nagasaki data. It is well established that the overwhelming majority of mutations (more than 99 percent) are harmful, causing some functional impairment. However, any given harmful effect is usually too small to be recognized by ordinary means, especially when it is inherited from only one parent, as is almost always the case, and when, as in any human population, it occurs in the midst of a motley throng of variant characteristics, differing from person to person, which arose as natural mutations among many generations of ancestors. For these reasons, statistics on human populations, such as those obtained at Hiroshima and Nagasaki, are ill suited for finding out whether mutations have been produced by a given exposure. This is why the group of responsible scientists who signed the official report on these investigations in Japan stated that it had "always been doubtful whether significant findings" could be obtained by the methods there used and pointed out that the inconclusive results, although not definitely positive, were at the same time "entirely consistent with what is known of the radiation genetics of a wide variety of [other] material." In other words, there could well have been as many harmful mutations produced in these human populations, but lying undetected, as experiments with other animals have shown to be produced in them by such exposure.

Each detrimental mutation, even though small in effect and lost to view in the jumble of a heterogeneous population, tends to continue from generation to generation and to hamper successive descendants, until at last it happens to tip the scales against one of its possessors, and that line of descent then dies out in consequence of the inherited disability. This involves either the premature death of the affected individual or his failure to reproduce.

A significant attack on the problem of how many mutations are produced by a given dose has required refined genetic tests, utilizing reasonably uniform biological material in precisely controlled crosses. This has meant experimenting on animals and plants. The notable recent work of W. L. Russell at Oak Ridge shows that at least ten times as many gene mutations are produced in mice by a given dose of radiation as my coworkers and I had found to be produced at a corresponding stage in fruit flies, which had previously been the best studied material. Since human beings are so much closer to mice than to flies in all important respects, we must take Russell's figure as a closer approximation to that for human beings than the one obtained for flies.

Working on this premise, we find that, on a conservative estimate, a dose of 200 reps, such as many Hiroshima survivors must have received, would probably have caused each of their offspring to inherit, on the average, at least one mutation produced by the exposure, in addition to the several or many natural mutations, mostly derived from long past generations. It is only wishful thinking to regard the inconclusive statistics gathered on the Hiroshima population as casting any doubt on this conclusion.

Since the numerous disabilities and deaths occasioned by the induced mutations will be spread out very thinly over a large number of generations, the over-all cost, although great, will be much too scattered and insidious to affect the population as a whole noticeably. And the individual sufferers will be unable to trace their troubles to the source. At long last, the damaged heredity must become eliminated from the race by the painful process of extinction of lines. But modern high standards of living and of medical practice tend greatly to delay this elimination.

Among fruit flies, the elimination can be much faster, because it is the usual thing for more than 100 young to die for every one that survives. Thus even after massive irradiations, repeated for generations, as in the experiments carried out by Bruce Wallace at Cold Spring Harbor, the population may recover relatively soon. In fact, it may even be benefited, by the rapid multiplication, at the expense of both the weaklings and the original type, of the extremely rare beneficial mutations that the radiation had produced. But such treatment would be ruinous to a modern human population, with its already extreme variability, its very low rate of multiplication, and its artificial hindrances to selection.

Genetic effects of test explosions. To calculate the genetic damage caused in this country by all the nuclear tests to date (including both those in the U.S.A. and those in the Pacific and the Soviet Union), we will provisionally take the U.S. Atomic Energy Commission's published estimate of 0.1 r as the average for each American. In the statement that this amount is about equal to that of a chest x-ray, it is doubtless meant that the total dose reaching the reproductive organs from all the tests is about as much as reaches the interior of the chest from one chest x-ray. This amount seems minute, but we must multiply it by 160 million, representing the population. It is curious that the product that we then obtain, 16 million "man r's," is the same as that obtained when we take 100 r, assuming this to be not far from the average dose received by all Hiroshima survivors, and multiply it by 160,000, the approximate number of those survivors. Hence, the number of harmful mutations that will be inherited by our own descendants as a result of all test explosions turns out to be not far from the number among the Japanese as a result of the Hiroshima explosion.

This number of mutations is certainly in the tens of thousands at least (our reckoning gives about 80,000 as the number present in our successor population), and it will mean, in the end, several times this number of hampered lives. Yet, far more than at Hiroshima, the effects will be so scattered, in this case not only in time but also in space and separated by many more individuals who have mutations of natural origin only, that, as a group, the effects will be completely lost to sight. That is, their connection with the radiation will not be traceable. It is, nevertheless, true that each individual casualty, although concealed, must be regarded as a significant evil, which we have no right to dismiss lightly.

On the other hand, when the effects here in question are taken in relation to the total American population (numbered in billions) of the scores of generations in which they find expression, and to the total number, much larger still, of natural mutations contained in that population, it is evident that *relatively* to these totals the damage is in this case minute. It cannot be said to involve a significant undermining of the hereditary constitution of the population as a whole, for it results in an increase of much less than 1 per cent (possibly less than one one-hundredth of 1 per cent) in the number of mutations contained in that population.

It is true that the AEC's figure of 0.1 r received by each of us from the tests seems to represent only the gamma radiation penetrating us from the outside. Until we are given more information on how much "soft" radiation we may be getting from fallout substances that have entered our bodies, and on its persistence, all estimates of the genetic damage must remain subject to much revision upward. Yet, unless the amount of radioactive material that we take into ourselves in this way turns out to be far greater than we have been led to suppose, our general conclusion could not be altered that, relatively to the natural mutations already present, those produced by the test explosions would form only a minute contingent.

In order to decide whether a continuance of the tests is justified, it is necessary first to admit the damage and then to weigh our estimate of it against the potential benefits to be derived from the tests or, rather, against the probable damage that would follow from the alternative policy. It is only by this kind of criterion that we can justify the use of so lethal a device as the automobile, for example. In fact, automobiles kill and maim tens of thousands of us, not over a period of hundreds of years as the test explosions will, but every single year. On the other hand, automobiles in many indirect and direct ways help to save lives as well as to bring many other benefits that outweigh the accidents.

The same kind of reasoning is necessary to justify the use of carefully controlled x-rays and radioactivity in medicine. A recent U. S. Public Health Service survey indicates that our people are annually receiving much more radiation in these ways than they do as a result of nuclear test explosions. A significant fraction of this radiation reaches the reproductive organs. Unfortunately, however, the majority of physicians have for twenty eight years closed their eyes to the genetic damage. Hence, they neglect, as a rule, to provide shields over the reproductive organs of their patients and to take other elementary precautions for limiting the exposures and keeping track of the total exposure of each patient throughout his life. These practices result in the committing of entirely unnecessary and indefensible genetic damage, far greater in its totality to date, and probably per year, than that caused by all test explosions. It is largely this reckless attitude on the part of physicians that has encouraged extremists to claim that nuclear explosions are genetically harmless or beneficial.

Weighing of alternatives. So many of the public are already aware of the genetic damage produced by radiation that their morale is weakened and their apprehensions are increased when they see that the damage is denied by prominent sponsors of our national defense. Thus the door is opened for their acceptance of the defeatist propaganda which alleges that even the tests are seriously undermining the biological integrity of mankind. In this situation, the only defensible or effective course for our democratic society is to recognize the truth, to admit the damage, and to base our case for continuance of the tests on a weighing of the alternative consequences.

I submit that we do not need to fear the results of this appeal to our better judgment. Have we no right to expect individual sacrifices when the stakes are democracy and intellectual freedom themselves? Surely there is good evidence that ruthless antagonists would long since have imposed totalitarianism on all the world if we had not pushed the development of our nuclear arms, and that in fact the development of our more conventional arms, as well as of measures for reducing our vulnerability to nuclear attack, are today no less important? Is not this procedure, even though it is fraught with direst peril and requires monumental self-control, nevertheless indispensable at this stage, before we can pass to the further stage at which both sides alike will recognize the long-term futility of this unstable equilibrium and will at last agree to the globally controlled disarmament, necessarily embracing not only nuclear, biological, and chemical arms, but also conventional arms, short of which humanity will never be safe?

It is natural that those in opposition to us should be making every effort to have nuclear arms prohibited *selectively*, for that would change the military balance greatly in their favor, in view of the fact that at present we are ahead in nuclear arms and they in conventional arms and armies. Some of the critics who demand a ban on test explosions are so silent on this point that one wonders whether they are not actually aiming at this very result. But for many of us who abhor totalitarianism this form of slavery appears to be a condition as miserable and as hopeless, if grown worldwide, as the barbarism that total war might bring. Another reason why those who sincerely desire a reduction of human suffering should not limit their demand for disarmament to the more radical mass-destruction techniques is that, today, weapons of the more traditional types have been so developed that they also, in the full-scale use occasioned by a world war, would bring about wholesale catastrophe. Our own tactics, therefore, should be to continue the development of both nuclear and other arms, as well as means of protection, while at the same time earnestly offering to join in a really balanced and controlled reduction of all kinds of armaments. If we steadfastly insist on this proposition, it is unlikely that any group will be in a position to refuse it indefinitely.

Need for perspective. If we may look forward to a time when our present international tensions have become less acute, we may anticipate that in that situation the public will be in a better mind-set for viewing the whole question of the genetic damage from radiation in a still wider perspective, based upon a fuller realization of genetic processes in general. They may then come to see that even the considerable toll of genetic deterioration that a nuclear war might bring is probably not as great as that resulting from a couple of centuries of our modern peacetime civilization.

It is probably an undervaluation to suppose that in each generation we today succeed, by means of our advanced medical, industrial, and social techniques, in saving for reproduction only half of the people who in past times would have had their lines of descent extinguished as a result of their genetic shortcomings. On the basis of this conservative premise, our population would, in the course of some eight generations (not much more than 200 years), have added to its habitual "load of mutations" about as many more as would have arisen naturally in $1/2 \times 8$, that is, in four generations. On a provisional estimate, this would be about the same as the number of mutations that would have been produced by the irradiation of every member of one generation with 320r. This is a dose much greater than that received by the average Hiroshima survivor. It is not, however, as great as what would have been received by a person occupationally exposed for twenty-five years to radiation given at the rate that conforms to what has been officially termed the "permissible dose" (0.3 r/wk).

A mutation is bad, no matter whether its presence results from the action of a previous generation in having perpetuated one that was already in existence in consequence of natural causes, or whether it had been artificially produced by application of radiation or of mustard gas. The first of these two means of getting it represents the boomerang effect, whereby our highly developed techniques result in the visiting of more of our own biological plagues upon our descendants. The only way in which such an aftermath can be avoided is by the development of more understanding and a more socially directed motivation among the public at large in regard to matters of genetics and reproduction.

Here again the way out requires us frankly to admit and to face the problem, in the hope that the public will not wish indefinitely to continue favoring practices that lead to its genetic deterioration. Of course, this does not mean that we should abandon modern technology—far from it. It means that, in order to enable our descendants to retain the benefits of our technology, we must match it with a higher conception of our duties to subsequent generations. According to this more advanced morality, the saving of a life does not automatically justify its production of offspring, for the chief criterion on which to base decisions in the planning of parenthood would be the welfare of the descendants themselves.

Such a revision of outlook involves the development of a new and more intelligent type of idealism in regard to genetics: one that consciously strives to bequeath to each succeeding generation as good an outfit of genes as it can manage to. It is true that we might here dispute at length the meaning of the word *good*, as it is used in this connection. However, this question also is one that must be tackled eventually. There are indications that it will be found to be by no means a hopeless question, still less a meaningless one, as some critics contend, and that even genetics, through evolution science, will have some contribution to make in regard to it. If all this comes to pass, then finally in the field of human genetics, even as in that of nuclear war, the old words of Edwin Markham may prove to have been prophetic:

> The world is a vapor,
> And only the vision is real;
> Yea, nothing can hold against Hell
> But the wingèd ideal!

Note

[1]This article is based on an address given before the National Academy of Sciences in Washington, D.C., 25 Apr. 1955, in acceptance of the Kimber Genetics award on the first occasion of its being granted. I wish to express again my deep appreciation to the sponsors of the Kimber Genetics award, for having provided this potent means of strengthening the morale of geneticists, and this opportunity for them publicly to air the problems and the prospects of their science. This article is contribution 590 from the Zoology Department of Indiana University. It is being published simultaneously in the *Bulletin of the Atomic Scientists*.

COMMENTS ON THE GENETIC EFFECTS
OF RADIATION
ON HUMAN POPULATIONS*

H. J. Muller
Indiana University

According to newspaper reports, the United States Atomic Energy Commission has recently called attention to the fact that it has long been known, first, that the great majority of mutations are harmful and second, that ionizing radiation produces mutations of genes with a frequency proportional to the dose. At the present moment, when protection policies and installations are being established, it cannot be emphasized too strongly that these two principles are solidly based.

Moreover, the long known fact that the expressions of genes vary, so that, rarely, a harmful gene may in some special combination or environment prove advantageous, is quite irrelevant to the point that under any given circumstances the vast majority of mutant genes *are* harmful. They are also harmful, though usually to a much lesser degree, even when heterozygous, despite the rare exceptions like sickle cell anemia in malarial regions, that natural selection tends to make abundant.

Geneticists are in general agreed that it is the exceedingly rare advantageous mutations that make evolution possible, by their multiplication under the influence of either natural or artificial selection. Hence radiation, by supplying more mutations, may result in a considerable speeding of evolution, *provided* selection is sufficiently rigorous and the rate of multiplication of the advantageous mutants is correspondingly high. This is possible in fruit flies or crop plants, where one pair of parents can produce hundreds of offspring. On the contrary, in human populations, especially in modern civilized communities, with their very successful saving of their genetically weaker members and their very low rate of reproduction on the part of the genetically better endowed, any increase in the number of mutations can only add to human suffering. Thus even though we grant that a gene for greater ability of some particular kind

Journal of Heredity, Vol. XLVI, No. 5, September-October, 1955, pp. 199-200.

Proposed five-minute discussion, prepared at the request of Dr. Tage Kemp, chairman of the session on "Genetic Effects of Radiation: Human Implications," of the International Conference on the Peaceful Uses of Atomic Energy, Geneva, Aug. 15, 1955. Permission to present this discussion had been granted by the Secretary General of the Conference but was revoked as the session in question began, on the ground that the author had not been made a technical adviser by the U.S.A.E.C.

could, very rarely, be produced, nevertheless so many more genes for reduced ability, or disability, would at the same time be produced as to prevent the development of high ability in many of those who otherwise would have had it, the net effect being a loss in the number of abler individuals.

A fourth fact requiring emphasis is that, paradoxically, even a slightly harmful mutation does an amount of harm comparable in the end to that done by an extremely harmful one. This is because the number of descendants to which any given mutant gene is transmitted before it causes extinction of its line of descent tends to vary inversely with the amount of harm it does. That is, it makes up for doing less harm to each individual by afflicting more individuals and thereby harms the population about as much in the end. We all suffer from an accumulation of several or many so-called small mutations.

To know the total genetic harm done by mutations we must therefore know the total frequency of occurrence of mutations, including the small ones. A direct approach to a solution of this problem has been made only in fruit flies, where it is found that there are some 10,000 times as many mutations altogether, including small ones, as the number that occur, on the average, as "alleles" (or "pseudoalleles") of any one given mutant. Since it is highly unlikely that mammals are genetically less complicated than fruit flies we are therefore probably obtaining minimum estimates of total mutation frequency in mice when we multiply by only 10,000 the mutation frequencies found by Russell for alleles of any given mutant. This reckoning, *which in no sense depends on the problematical question of the total number of genes*, shows that, in mice, at least one individual in five has a new spontaneous mutation and that exposure to about 40r produces as many mutations as arise spontaneously. The details of the arguments and calculations are given in the paper which I prepared for this Conference.

If humans react like mice, then exposure of one parent to the so-called permissible dose of .3r per week for some 15 years before his reproduction would result in half his children carrying an induced mutation. This would usually be small in effect and not identifiable, yet it would tend to hamper successive descendants until it led to the extinction of its line, frustrating a life. It is therefore necessary to reconsider our protection policies and our standard of permissible dose now, before it becomes too hard to change them.

As a matter of fact, at such American installations as Oak Ridge, workers are in practice not allowed to receive an average of more than about a tenth of the so-called permissible dose. Moreover, the International Commission on Radiation Protection has recommended that this lower ceiling be adopted in cases of wide-spread exposure. It is to be hoped that industrial, military, medical and research establishments everywhere will be influenced thereby to revise their protection standards, so as to bring them into conformity with the facts of genetic damage.

APPROXIMATION TO A GRAVITY-FREE SITUATION FORTHE HUMAN ORGANISM ACHIEVABLE AT MODERATE EXPENSE*

So far as their effects on the human organism are concerned, the chief peculiarities of weightlessness consist in (i) the cessation of unidirectional stimulation of the vestibular system, together with the sequelae accruing therefrom through reactions of the autonomic and central nervous systems, and (ii) the letting up of the hydrostatic drag on the circulatory system, especially that associated with the erect posture of man. Both of these peculiarities can be approximated to a considerable degree by a combination of relatively simple devices. The use of these would enable data on the effects of this pseudo-weightlessness, maintained for several hours at least, to be obtained long before the still exceedingly costly direct tests of subjecting human beings to prolonged free fall can be carried out by Western scientists.

By far the greater portion of the hydrostatic drag is absent in human beings whose body axis is in a horizontal position, as it is when they are recumbent. Most of the remainder can be evened out and in effect nullified by subjecting them to a moderate spinning motion about their horizontal axis, through the automatic rotation of a cylinder within which they are held. At the same time, little sense of the pressure caused by their body weight would remain if the body, including the limbs, were encased in a skin-tight envelope, and held immersed in a brine having the same specific gravity as the average for the body itself.

Considerable freedom of movement can be allowed for the limbs. The head can be encased in a transparent helmet that is serviced for respiration and oral communication. It is to be held with its axis in alignment with the body axis. That is, the head is not permitted tilting movements that would set its axis at an angle to that of the body; however, it is left free to carry out any desired voluntary movements of rotation on its axis. A field of view, imitative of furnishings and, for example, of a window showing a skyscape, would be arranged that remained in a fixed position with reference

Science, Vol. 128, No. 3327, 1958, p. 772; this report is based upon a paper read at Symposium on Possible Uses of Earth Satellites for Life-Sciences Experiments, Washington, D.C., 17 May 1958; Contribution No. 659 of Zoology Department, Indiana University.

to the subject. Thus the field of view would spin together with the subject himself, and the subject would lack the visual stimuli associated with an imposed rotary movement.

The subject, after having been fastened within the cylinder, would at first be at rest but by insensible degrees would be subjected to a rotary movement about his horizontal axis, at a speed that increased until it attained the psycho-physiological optimum for disengaging his vestibular apparatus from an effective pull by gravity in any given direction. Thereafter the motion is to be kept smooth and steady. Preliminary experiments have shown that under such circumstances, so long as the subject's head remains with its original relation to the body axis, he soon becomes quite unaware of the rotary movement as such. This is because the fluid in his semicircular canals has come to rest, in relation to their walls (except for any voluntary axial turning movements, which then give rise only to the effects usual for them), and because he has no notification of the imposed rotation through vision and very little through skin or internal bodily pressures.

It is likely that a suitable speed of rotation could be found which was too fast, in relation to the sensitivity of that part of the vestibular apparatus which detects translational (linear) acceleration or gravity in any one direction, to allow such stimuli to accumulate to an appreciable degree. That is, not so rapid a periodicity should be required to transcend "flicker" in the case of the sensation of linear acceleration here in question as in the case of optical flashes. For psychological and physiological purposes, a condition approximating that of weightlessness or free fall would thereby have been achieved. Essentially the same mechanism has long been used for nullifying gravity in studies on plants, but the speed of rotation for this apparatus, called a clinostat, can be much slower because of the much slower reactivity of plant tissues.

Among other questions that would thereby be opened for investigation are those concerned with the effects, on free-fall tolerance, of individual differences (as between persons of differing tendencies to become giddy or motion-sick) and of the effects of differing physiological conditions and of diverse drugs (such as those used against motion sickness). The relatively small cost of the apparatus required for such experiments, and the relatively short time required for its construction, recommend it for pilot studies on the effects of fairly prolonged weightlessness.

H. J. Muller

Department of Zoology,
Indiana University, Bloomington

THE GUIDANCE OF HUMAN EVOLUTION*

by Hermann J. Muller
Zoology Department, Indiana University, Bloomington

The past cultural evolution of man, by changing his ways and conditions of living, has altered the types and intensities of genetic selection so as better to adapt the hereditary basis of his physical, mental and affective constitution to his cultural circumstances. These biological changes have in turn facilitated the development of culture. At the present time, however, the erasal of barriers among groups and subgroups of men is tending to do away with intergroup selection, while the increasingly effective transfer to society in general of the burden of individual genetic defects and of the benefit of individual genetic gifts is tending to reduce intra-group selection also. Any relaxation of genetic selection results in some genetic deterioration, by allowing detrimental mutant genes to accumulate to a higher equilibrium frequency. In this way modern culture is giving rein to biological decadence of types inimical to culture itself. In fact, it is probable that the selection now operating is in some respects even the reverse of what would ultimately be useful and, from a considered human viewpoint, desirable.

The only method consistent with cultural progress whereby this situation can be met is not a reduction of socially directed activity but the opposite: the extension of social awareness and motivation to matters of reproduction, i.e. the increasing recognition by individuals of their responsibility not only for the education and living conditions but also of the genetic endowment of the generation succeeding them. Factors working to increase this awareness, and to instigate behavior based upon it, are the increasingly acute pressure of overpopulation, and the origination of practicable techniques whereby individuals may limit births. As a realization of the importance of genes grows (in part in response to the challenges arising from modern uses of radiation), it will also become more evident that not only the quantity but also the genetic quality of the population presents an issue of paramount concern, that could be under human control if the attitude toward reproduction were more rational and more socially directed.

The main values to be striven for genetically are the same as those generally recognized already as the chief aims in the bringing up and education of individual children: namely, on the physical side, more robust health; on the intellectual side, keener, deeper and more creative intelligence; on the moral side, more genuine warmth of fellow feeling and cooperative disposition; on the ap-

*Expanded version in *Perspectives in Biology and Medicine*, 1959, 3: 1-43; and *Evolution after Darwin* (Sol Tax, ed.), Chicago: University of Chicago Press, 1959. Copyright 1959 by the University of Chicago.

perceptive side, richer appreciation and its more adequate expression. A conscience that is socially oriented in regard to reproduction will lead many of the persons who are loaded with more than the average share of defects in the genetic bases of these faculties to refrain voluntarily from engaging in reproduction to the average extent, while vice versa it will be considered a social service for those more fortunately endowed to reproduce to more than the average extent.

This trend will be greatly promoted as techniques and facilities are improved and accepted that allow the transfer of germ cells or potential germ cells, their accumulation and maintenance in frozen or multiplying condition, and their rational testing, selection and manipulation. Thus children can be adopted not merely after birth but even (as it were) before fertilization. These children may come to attain the status and enjoy the affection and other advantages of those naturally conceived.

By these means the way can be opened up for unlimited progress in the genetic constitution of man, to match and re-enforce his cultural progress and, reciprocally, to be re-enforced by it, in a perhaps never-ending succession.

WORKS BY H. J. MULLER

Titles are arranged chronologically according to the date when each was read or published for the first time.

1. 1911-12. Erroneous assumptions regarding genes. MS unpublished except for excerpt on sex formulae published as appendix to "Some genetic aspects of sex," *Amer. Nat.*, 1932, 66: 118-38.
2. 1914. A new mode of segregation in Gregory's tetraploid primulas. *Ibid.*, 48: 508-12.
3. 1914. The bearing of the selection experiments of Castle and Phillips on the variability of genes. *Ibid.*, pp. 567-76.
4. 1914. A factor for the fourth chromosome of *Drosophila. Science,* 39: 906.
5. 1914. A gene for the fourth chromosome of Drosophila. *Exp. Zool.,* 17: 325-36.
6. Morgan, T. H., Sturtevant, A. H., Muller, H. J., and Bridges, C. B. 1915. *The mechanism of Mendelian heredity.* New York: Henry Holt & Co., xiii + 262 pp.; Revised edition, 1923, 357 pp.
7. 1916. The mechanism of crossing over. I-IV. *Amer. Nat.*, 50: 193-221, 284-305, 350-66, 421-34. (Revised version appears in this volume.)
8. Marshall, W. W., and Muller, H. J. 1917. The effect of long-continued heterozygosis on a variable character in *Drosophila. J. Exp. Zool.*, 22: 457-70.
9. 1917. An Oenothera-like case in Drosophila. *Proc. Nat. Acad. Sci.,* 3: 619-26.
10. 1918. Genetic variability, twin hybrids and constant hybrids, in a case of balanced lethal factors. *Genetics*, 3: 422-99.
11. 1919. A series of allelomorphs in *Drosophila* with non-quantitative relationships. Read before Amer. Soc. Nat., Princeton, December 31. Title in *Science*, 1920, 51: 171; and *Rec. Amer. Soc. Nat.*, 1921, 3: 66.
12. Muller, H. J., and Altenburg, E. 1919. The rate of change of hereditary factors in *Drosophila. Proc. Soc. Exp. Biol. Med.*, 17: 10-14.
13. Altenburg, E., and Muller, H. J. 1920. The genetic basis of truncate wing—an inconstant and modifiable character in *Drosophila. Genetics*, 5: 1-59.
14. 1920. Are the factors of heredity arranged in a line? *Amer. Nat.,* 54: 97-121.
15. 1920. Further changes in the white-eye series of *Drosophila* and their bearing on the manner of occurrence of mutation. *J. Exp. Zool.,* 31: 443-73.
16. 1920. A quantitative study of mutation in the second chromosome of

Drosophila. Read before Amer. Soc. Nat., Chicago, December 31. Title in *Science*, 1921, 53: 97; and *Rec. Amer. Soc. Nat.*, 1921, 3: 69.

17. Muller, H. J., and Altenburg, E. 1921. A study of the character and mode of origin of eighteen mutations in the X-chromosome of *Drosophila.* (Abstract) *Anat. Rec.*, 20: 213.

18. 1921. A lethal gene which changes the order of the loci in the chromosome map. Read before Genet. Sec., Amer. Ass. Adv. Sci., Toronto, December, 1921. Title in *Ibid.*, 1922, 23: 83 (Proc. Amer. Soc. Zool.).

19. 1921. A decade of *Drosophila.* Read at Carnegie Inst., Cold Spr. Harb., August, 1921, and deposited in the archives of the Institute. Published in Russian, 1922, under the title "Results of a decade of research on *Drosophila.*" *Prog. Exp. Biol.*, 1: 292-322.

20. 1921. Mutation. Read before 3rd Int. Eug. Congr., New York. Published without change, in 1923, in *Eugenics, Genetics, and the Family*, Baltimore: Williams and Wilkins, Inc., 1: 106-12; re-published, in 1925, in Newman's *Readings in Evolution, Genetics, and Eugenics*, pp. 495-502.

21. 1921. Variation due to change in the individual gene. Read before Amer. Soc. Nat., Toronto, December, 1921. Published in *Amer. Nat.*, 1922, 56: 32-50. Title in *Science*, 55: 106.

22. 1921. Micromanipulation by light waves. Read and demonstrated before Amer. Soc. Zool., Toronto.

23. 1922. The measurement of mutation frequency made practicable. Read before Genet. Sec., December, 1922. (Abstract) *Anat. Rec.*, 1923, 24: 419.

24. 1923. A simple formula giving the number of individuals required for obtaining one of a given frequency. *Amer. Nat.*, 57: 66-73.

25. 1923. Recurrent mutations of normal genes of *Drosophila* not caused by crossing over. Read before Genet. Sec., December, 1923. (Abstract) *Anat. Rec.*, 1924, 26: 397-98.

26. 1923. Observations of biological science in Russia. *Sci. Mon.*, 16: 539-52.

27. 1923. Partial list of biological institutes and biologists doing experimental work in Russia at the present time. *Science*, 57: 472-73.

28. 1924. Chromosome breakage by X-rays and the production of eggs from genetically male tissue in *Drosophila.* (Abstract) *Anat. Rec.*, 1925, 29: 150. Full article: Muller, H. J., and Dipple, A. L. 1926. *Brit. J. Exp. Biol.*, 3: 85-122.

29. 1924. The latitude of genetic indetermination of psychic characters in man, as indicated in a case of identical twins reared apart. Read before Genet. Sec., December, 1924. (Abstract) *Anat. Rec.*, 29: 144-45.

30. 1924. A moving model of mitosis and segregation, for use in the teaching of genetics. Exhibit before Amer. Soc. Zool. Title in *Anat. Rec.*, 29: 86.

31. 1925. The regionally differential effect of X-rays on crossing over in autosomes of *Drosophila. Genetics*, 10: 470-507.

32. Muller, H. J., and Jacobs-Muller, J. M. 1925. The standard errors of chromosome distances and coincidence. *Ibid.*, pp. 509-24.

33. 1925. Why polyploidy is rarer in animals than in plants. *Amer. Nat.*, 59: 346-53.

34. 1925. Mental traits and heredity as studied in a case of identical twins reared apart. *J. Hered.*, 16: 433-48.

35. Muller, H. J., and Settles, F. 1925. The non-functioning of the genes in spermatozoa. Read before Genet. Sec., December, 1925. (Abstract) *Anat. Rec.*, 31: 347; full paper in *Zeit. f. ind. Abst. u. Vererb.*, 1927, 43: 285-312.

36. 1925. Life histories of identical twins, B. and J. Mimeographed notes distributed privately to geneticists.

37. 1926. Determining identity of twins. *J. Hered.*, 17: 195-206.

38. 1926. Inbreeding versus "accumulation of blood." *Ibid.*, pp. 240-42.

39. 1926. The gene as the basis of life. Read before Int. Congr. Plant Sci., Ithaca, August, 1926. Published in *Proc. Int. Congr. Plant Sci.*, 1929, 1: 897-921. Revised edition in Russian in *Collected Works on Genetics* (H. J. Muller). *"Sel' khozgiz" Mosc.-Leningr.*, 1937, pp. 148-77.

40. 1926. Induced crossing over variation in the X-chromosome of *Drosophila. Amer. Nat.*, 60: 192-95.

41. 1926. Quantitative methods in genetic research. Read before the American Society of Naturalists, Philadelphia, December, 1926. Published in *Ibid.*, 1927, 61: 407-19.

42. 1927. Artificial transmutation of the gene. *Science*, 66: 84-87.

43. 1927. The problem of genic modification. Read before Fifth Int. Genet. Congr., Berlin, September, 1927. Published in *Verh. d. v. Kongr. f. Vererb.*: *Suppl. Bd. I des Zeit. f. ind. Abst. u. Vererb.*, 1928, pp. 234-60.

44. 1927. Effects of X-radiation on genes and chromosomes. Read before Genet. Sec., Nashville, December, 1927. Awarded the annual prize of the A. A. A. S. (Abstract) *Anat. Rec.*, 1927, 37: 174. (More detailed Abstract) *Science*, 1928, 67: 82-85.

45. 1928. The production of mutations by X-rays. Read before Nat. Acad. Sci., Washington, D. C., April, 1928. Published in *Proc. Nat. Acad. Sci.*, 14: 714-26.

46. 1928. Genetics humanized. Review of Altenburg's *How We Inherit*. *J. Hered.*, 19: 345-47.

47. 1928. The measurement of gene mutation rate in Drosophila, its high variability, and its dependence upon temperature. *Genetics*, 13: 279-357.

48. Muller, H. J., and Altenburg, E. 1928. Chromosome translocations produced by X-rays in *Drosophila*. Read before Genet. Sec., New York, December, 1928. (Abstract) *Anat. Rec.*, 41: 100.

49. 1929. The method of evolution. Research professorship lecture read at the University of Texas, May, 1928. Published in *Sci. Mon.*, 1929, 29: 481-505. Reprinted in revised form under the title "Heritable variations, their production by X-rays and their relation to evolution." *Annual Rept. Smithsonian Inst.* for 1929 (1930), pp. 345-62.

50. Muller, H. J., and Painter, T. S. 1929. The cytological expression of changes in gene alignment produced by X-rays in *Drosophila. Amer. Nat.*, 63: 193-200.

51. Painter, T. S., and Muller, H. J. 1929. Parallel cytology and

genetics of induced translocations and deletions in *Drosophila. J. Hered.*, 20: 287-98.

52. 1929. Variation (experimental). *Encyclopedia Britannica* (14th ed.), pp. 987-89.

53. 1929. The first cytological demonstration of a translocation in *Drosophila. Amer. Nat.*, 63: 481-86.

54. 1930. Radiation and genetics. Read before Amer. Soc. Nat., January, 1930. Published in *Amer. Nat.*, 64: 220-51.

55. Muller, H. J., and Altenburg, E. 1930. The frequency of translocations produced by X-rays in *Drosophila. Genetics*, 15: 283-311.

56. Muller, H. J., and Mott-Smith, L. M. 1930. Evidence that natural radioactivity is inadequate to explain the frequency of "natural" mutations. *Proc. Nat. Acad. Sci.*, 16: 277-85.

57. 1930. Oneothera-like linkage of chromosomes in *Drosophila. J. Genet.*, 22: 335-57.

58. 1930. Types of visible variations induced by X-rays in *Drosophila. Ibid.*, pp. 299-334.

59. Patterson, J. T., and Muller, H. J. 1930. Are "progressive" mutations produced by X-rays? *Genetics*, 15: 495-578.

60. Muller, H. J., and Stone, W. S. 1930. Analysis of several induced gene-rearrangements involving the X-chromosome of *Drosophila.* Read before Genet. Sec., December, 1930. (Abstract) *Anat. Rec.*, 47: 393-94.

61. Muller, H. J., League, B. B., and Offermann, C. A. 1931. Effect of dosage changes of sex-linked genes, and the compensatory effect of other gene-differences between male and female. Read before Genet. Sec., New Orleans, December 31. 1931. (Abstract) *Ibid.* 51 (Suppl.): 110.

62. Offermann, C. A., Stone, W. S., and Muller, H. J. 1931. Causes of interregional differences in crossover frequency, studied in individuals homozygous for gene arrangements. Read before Genet. Sec., New Orleans, December, 1931. (Abstract) *Ibid.*, p. 109.

63. 1931. Some genetic aspects of sex. Read before Amer. Soc. Nat., New Orleans, December, 1931. Published in *Amer. Nat.*, 1932, 64: 118-38.

64. Offermann, C. A., and Muller, H. J. 1932. Regional differences in crossing over as a function of the chromosome structure. *Proc. 6th Int. Congr. Genet.*, 1933, 2: 143-45.

65. Muller, H. J., and Painter, T. S. 1932. The differentiation of the sex chromosomes of *Drosophila* into genetically active and inert regions. *Zeit. f. ind. Abst. u. Vererb.*, 62: 316-65.

66. Painter, T. S., and Muller, H. J. 1932. A cytological map of the X-chromosome of *Drosophila. Proc. 6th Int. Congr. Genet.*, 1933, 2: 147-48.

67. 1932. Heribert Nilsson's evidence against the artificial production of mutations. *Hereditas*, 16: 160-68.

68. 1932. Where angels fear to tread? Review of Gaskell's *What is Life?* and Kraft's *Can Science Explain Life? J. Hered.*, 23: 80-86.

69. 1932. Further studies on the nature and causes of gene mutations. *Proc. 6th Int. Congr. Genet.*, 1933, 1: 213-55.

70. 1932. The dominance of economics over eugenics. Read before 6th Int. Congr. Eug., New York, August, 1932. Published in *Sci. Mon.*,

1933, 37: 40-47. Also printed in *Proc. 3rd Int. Congr. Eug.*, 1934; and in part in *Evolution*, 1933, and in the *Birth Cont. Rev.*, 1932, Vol. 16. (Russian translation in 1933 under the title "Eugenics under the conditions of capitalistic society" in *Prog. Mod. Biol.*, 2: 3-11; in *Priroda*, 1934, 1: 100-106, under the title "Eugenics in the service of the National-Socialists." Also Norwegian and Spanish translations.) Revised version in *Fact* (London), 1939, 24: 58-75.

71. Muller, H. J., and Weinstein, A. 1932. Evidence against the occurrence of crossing-over between sister chromatids. (Abstract) *Rec. Genet. Soc. Amer.*, 1933, 1: 7-8; published in *Amer. Nat.*, 1933, 67: 64-65.

72. 1933. The effects of Roentgen rays upon the hereditary material. In *The Science of Radiology*, Springfield, Ill.: A. Thomas, 1933, Chap. 17, pp. 305-18. (Book also published in Great Britain; London: Balliere, Tindall and Cox, 1934.) Spanish translation in *Revista de Radiol. Fisioter.*, 1934, 1: 9-12, and 1935, Vol. 2. German translation in *Strahlentherapie*, 1936, 55: 207-24.

73. 1933. Haldane on evolution. Review of Haldane's *Causes of Evolution*. *Prog. Mod. Biol.* (Russian), Vol. 2, No. 3, pp. 90-92.

74. 1933. Human heredity. A review of Bauer, Fischer and Lenz' *Human Heredity*. *Birth Cont. Rev.*, 17: 19-21.

75. 1933. Report on 6th Int. Genet. Congr. *Prog. Mod. Biol.* (Russian), 2: 135-46.

76. 1934. Radiation genetics. Read before Int. Congr. Radiol., Zürich, July, 1934. (Abstract) *Proc. 4th Int. Radiologen Kongr.*, 2: 100-102.

77. Muller, H. J., Prokofyeva, A. A., and Raffel, D. 1934. Apparent gene mutations due to the position-effect of minute gene rearrangements. (Abstract) *Rec. Genet. Soc. Amer.*, 3: 48-49; and *Amer. Nat.*, 1935, 69: 72-73.

78. 1934. The views of Haeckel in the light of genetics. Read at Haeckel centenary, Leningrad. Published in *Philos. of Sci.*, 1934, 3: 313-22. Published in Russian in *Priroda*, 1936, Vol. 10, No. 1, pp. 128-33, under the title "Haeckel and genetics."

79. 1934. Inversions; attached X's: rearrangement in general; deficiency; balancing of deleted X-chromosomes; triploids; extension of third chromosome; etherizing bottles; stock lists. *D. I. S.*, 2: 57-60, 62-63, 66.

80. 1934. Some fundamental lines of development of theoretical genetics and their significance from the standpoint of medicine. Read before the Medico-Genet. Conf., Moscow, May 1, 1934. Published in Russian in *Sovietskaya Clinica*, 20: 17-28.

81. 1934. Lenin's doctrines in relation to genetics. *Pamyati Lenina*. Moscow: Acad. Sci. U.S.S.R., pp. 565-79.

82. 1934. Genetics as opposed to the concept of "pure races." (Russian) *Prog. Mod. Biol.*, 3: 525-41.

83. 1934. The problem of the stratostat in connection with problems of interest for genetics, *Acad. Sci. U.S.S.R.*, pp. 569-73.

84. Muller, H. J., and Prokofyeva, A. A. 1934. Continuity and discontinuity of the hereditary material. *Dokl. Akad. Nauk S.S.S.R.*, N.S., 4: 74-83 (Russian and English). Reprinted in enlarged and re-

vised form under the title "The individual gene in relation to the chromomere and the chromosome," in *Proc. Nat. Acad. Sci.*, 1935, 21: 16-26.

85. Muller, H. J., Prokofyeva, A. A., and Raffel, D. 1935. Minute intergenic rearrangements as a cause of apparent "gene mutation." *Nat.*, 135: 253-55.

86. Ellenhorn, J., Prokofyeva, A. A., and Muller, H. J. 1935. The optical dissociation of *Drosophila* chromomeres by means of ultraviolet light. *C. R. (Dokl.) Acad. Sci. U.R.S.S., N.S.*, 1: 234-41.

87. 1935. On the incomplete dominance of the normal allelomorphs of white in Drosophila. *J. Genet.*, 30: 407-14.

88. 1935. The origination of chromatin deficiencies as minute deletions subject to insertion elsewhere. *Genetica*, 17: 237-52.

89. 1935. A viable two-gene deficiency phaenotypically resembling the corresponding hypomorphic mutations. *J. Hered.*, 26: 469-78.

90. 1935. On the dimensions of chromosomes and genes in Dipteran salivary glands. *Amer. Nat.*, 69: 405-11.

91. Kossikov, K. V., and Muller, H. J. 1935. Invalidation of the genetic evidence for branched chromonemas in the case of the pale translocation in *Drosophila*. *J. Hered.*, 26: 305-12.

92. Muller, H. J., and Gershenson, S. M. 1935. Inert regions of chromosomes as the temporary products of individual genes. *Proc. Nat. Acad. Sci.*, 21: 69-75.

93. 1935. (Genetics) *Cumul. Rep. Comm. Effects Radiat.*, 1928-1934. Washington, D. C.: Nat. Res. Counc., pp. 16-19.

94. 1935. Introductory chapter in book *Factors of Evolution*, by J. B. S. Haldane. (Russian translation) *Biol. Med. Pub.*, pp. 7-27.

95. 1935. Human genetics in Russia. *Journal of Heredity*, 26: 193-96.

96. 1935. The position effect as evidence of the localization of the immediate products of gene activity. In *Summaries of Communications of 15th Int. Physiol. Congr., Leningrad*, pp. 286-89; and (1938) in *Proc. 15th Int. Physiol. Congr., U.S.S.R.* Vol. 21, Nos. 5-6, pp. 587-89.

97. 1935. Nomenclature of alleles; balancing chromosome-1 with scute [sl]; labeling of stock cultures; fly morgue; seeding with yeast, supplying vials with paper. *D. I. S.*, 3: 48, 50, 52.

98. Muller, H. J., and Prokofyeva, A. A. 1935. The structure of the chromonema of the inert region of the X-chromosome of *Drosophila*. *C. R. (Dokl.) Acad. Sci. U.R.S.S., N.S.* (Russian and English), 1: 658-60.

99. 1935. *Out of the Night: a Biologist's View of the Future.* New York: Vanguard Press, 1935, 127 pp.; British edition, London: Gollancz, 1936; French translation, Paris: Gallimard, 1938.

100. 1935. The present status of the mutation theory. Read at De Vries Memorial Meeting, Leningrad, November, 1935. Published in Russian in *Priroda*, 1936, 6: 40-50; and in English in *Curr. Sci.* (Bangalore, India), Special No., March, 1938, pp. 4-15.

101. 1936. Bar duplication. *Science*, 83: 528-30.

102. 1936. Construction of homozygous stocks; insertion of foreign chromosome into homozygous host stock; insertion of desired genes into attached X's; combination of invisible genes; to balance sex-linked genes; labor-saving method of starting homozygous or

balanced stocks of ♂-fertile sex-linked genes; balancing of duplications by deficiencies or lethals and vice versa; detection of mutations; accumulation of mutations (negativing of natural selection); accumulation of mutations in given sex. *D. I. S.*, 6: 7-9, 10-11, 12-13, 14-17.

103. 1936. Muller, H. J., and Bridges, C. B. Balanced stocks. *Ibid.*, pp. 9-10.

104. 1936. Physics in the attack on the fundamental problems of genetics. *Sci. Mon.*, 44: 210-14; and in Russian in *Izv. Akad. Nauk. U.S.S.R.*, 1937, pp. 51-58. (Russian Summary).

105. Muller, H. J., Prokoyeva-Belgovskaya, A. A., and Kossikov, K. V. 1936. Unequal crossing over in the Bar mutant as a result of duplication of a minute chromosome section. *C. R. (Dokl.) Acad. Sci., U.R.S.S., N.S.*, 1 (10): 83-84, 87-88 (Russian and English, respectively).

106. 1936. The determination of the relation between the dosage of irradiation and the frequency of induced mutations. (In German) *Strahlentherapie*, 55: 72-76.

107. 1936. On the variability of mixed races. *Proc. Med. Genet. Inst.*, 4: 213-36 (Russian with English summary); and in English in *Amer. Nat.*, 70: 409-42.

108. 1936. The present status of the experimental evidence concerning the nature of the gene. (Russian translation) Address at symposium on "Production of New Sorts of Cultivated Plants and Domestic Animals," Lenin Acad. of Agric. Sci., December 23, 1936. Abstract published December, 1936, in *Summaries of Proceedings*. Article published in 1937 in Russian in *Controversial Questions of Genetics and Selection*, Press of Acad. Agric. Sci. of U.S.S.R., pp. 114-49.

109. Muller, H. J., Raffel, D., Gershenson, S. M., and Prokofyeva-Belgovskaya, A. A. 1937. A further analysis of loci in the so-called "inert region" of the X-chromosome of *Drosophila*. *Genetics* 22: 87-93.

110. Lus, J. J., Liepin, T. K., Sapehin, A. A., Kostoff, D., and Muller, H. J. 1937. (Main results of investigations made in the Institute of Genetics of the Academy of Sciences of the USSR). *Izv. Akad. Nauk. S.S.S.R. (Otd. mat.-est., Ser. biol.)*, pp. 1469-92 (Russian with English summary).

111. 1937. Reversibility in evolution considered from the standpoint of genetics. Read before Soc. Exp. Biol., London, December, 21, 1937. Published in *Biol. Rev.*, 1939, 14: 261-80.

112. 1937. The biological effects of radiation, with especial reference to mutation. Read before Réunion Inter. de Physique, Chimie et Biologie, VIII, Paris, October, 1937; published in *Act. Sci. et Industr.*, Vol. XI, No. 725, pp. 477-94.

113. 1937. Evolution as viewed by Morgan. Review of T. H. Morgan's *Scientific Basis of Evolution. Book and Proleterian Revol.* (Russian), 8: 128-34.

114. Muller, H. J., Prokofyeva-Belgovskaya, A. A., and Raffel, D. 1937. The absence of transmissible chromosome fragments resulting from simple breakage, and their simulation as a result of com-

pound breakage involving chromocentral regions. (Abstract) *Rec. Genet. Soc. Amer.*, 6; and *Genetics*, 1938, 23: 161.

115. Belgovsky, M. L., and Muller, H. J. 1937. Further evidence of the prevalence of minute rearrangement and absence of simple breakage in and near chromocentral regions, and its bearing on the mechanisms of mosaicism and rearrangement. (Abstract) *Rec. Genet. Soc. Amer.*, 6; and *Genetics*, 1938, 23: 139-40.

116. 1938. The remaking of chromosomes. *Collect. Net* (Woods Hole), 13: 181, 183-95, 198; title in *Rec. Genet. Soc. Amer.* 7: 15.

117. 1938. Bearings of the *Drosophila* work on problems of systematics. (Abstract) *Proc. Zool. Soc.*, Series C, 108: 55-57.

118. Muller, H. J., Makki, A. I., and Sidky, A. R. 1938. Gene rearrangement in relation to radiation dosage. Read before the Genet. Soc. London, December 1, 1938; (Abstract), *J. Genet.*, Vol. 37, No. 3, 1939 (Proc. Genet. Soc.).

119. 1939. Dr. Calvin B. Bridges. *Nature*, 143: 191-92.

120. 1939. New mutants; additions and corrections to symbol list in D. I. S. 9. *D. I. S.*, 12: 39-43.

121. 1939. *Bibliography on the genetics of Drosophila.* Edinburgh: Oliver and Boyd, 132 pp.

122. Muller, H. J., and Mackenzie, K. 1939. Discriminatory effect of ultraviolet rays on mutation in *Drosophila*. *Nature*, 143: 83-84.

123. 1939. The Seventh International Congress of Genetics. Gene and chromosome theory. *Ibid.*, 144: 813-16.

124. 1939. How heredity works. *The Listener* (London), 21: 845-47.

125. 1939. (Report of investigations with radium) *Medical Research Council Special Report Series*, No. 236, pp. 14-15.

126. 1939. (Report of Dr. H. J. Muller and collaborators, working at the Institute of Animal Genetics, University of Edinburgh) *Sixteenth Annual Report, British Empire Cancer Campaign*, pp. 226-31.

127. 1939. Genetics and society. *Fact* (London), 27: 92-98.

128. 1939. How genetic systems come about. Review of Darlington's *The Evolution of Genetic Systems*. *Nature*, 144: 648-49.

129. 1939. The mechanism of structural change in chromosomes of *Drosophila*. Read before the 7th Int. Congr. Genet., Edinburgh, September, 1939. Abstract published in *Proc. 7th Int. Congr. Genet.*; *J. Genet.*, suppl. vol., 1941, pp. 221-22.

130. 1939. The "Geneticists' Manifesto." (With twenty-one signatures) *J. Hered.*, 30: 371-73; and under title "Social Biology and Population Improvement" (with twenty-three signatures) in *Nature*, 144: 521-22.

131. Lamy, R., and Muller, H. J. 1939. Evidence of the nongenetic nature of the lethal effect of radiation on *Drosophila* embryos. Read before 7th Int. Genet. Congr., Edinburgh, September, 1939. Abstract published in *Proc. 7th Int. Congr. Genet.*; *J. Genet.*, suppl. vol., 1941, pp. 180-81.

132. 1940. Bearings of the *Drosophila* work on systematics. *The New Systematics*, J. Huxley (ed.). Oxford: Clarendon Press, pp. 185-268.

133. 1940. An analysis of the process of structural change in chromosomes of *Drosophila*. *J. Genet.*, 40: 1-66.

134. 1940. New mutants. *D. I. S.,* 13: 52.
135. 1941. (Report on experiments with gamma radiation) In "Medical Uses of Radium. Summary of Reports from Experimental Research Centers for 1939." *Brit. J. Radiol.,* 14: 157-58.
136. Muller, H. J., and Pontecorvo, G. 1940. Recombinants between *Drosophila* species the F_1 hybrids of which are sterile. *Nature,* 145: 199-200.
137. Raffel, D., and Muller, H. J. 1940. Position effect and gene divisibility considered in connection with three strikingly similar scute mutations. *Genetics,* 25: 541-83.
138. Muller, H. J., and Pontecorvo, G. 1940. The artificial mixing of incompatible germ plasms in *Drosophila.* Read before Nat. Acad. Sci., October 29, 1940. (Abstract) *Science,* 92: 418, 476.
139. Mackenzie, K., and Muller, H. J. 1940. Mutation effects of ultraviolet light in *Drosophila, Proc. Roy. Soc. London, B,* Vol. 129, No. 857, pp. 491-517.
140. Pontecorvo, G., and Muller, H. J. 1940. The lethality of dicentric chromosomes in *Drosophila.* (Abstract) *Rec. Genet. Soc. Amer.,* 9: 165; and *Genetics,* 1941, 26: 165.
141. 1941. On judging the significance of a difference obtained by averaging essentially different series. *Amer. Nat.,* 75: 264-71.
142. 1941. The threads that weave evolution. *Trans. N. Y. Acad. Sci.,* Ser. II, 3: 117-25.
143. 1941. The role played by radiation mutations in mankind. Abstract of address mimeographed by Nat. Acad. Sci., April, 1941. Shorter abstract in *Science,* 93: 438.
144. 1941. (Report on ultraviolet induced chromosome changes and other investigations.) *Ann. Rep. Biol. Lab.* (Long Is. Biol. Ass., Cold Spr. Harb.), 52: 42-43.
145. Muller, H. J., and Pontecorvo, G. 1941. Recessive genes causing interspecific sterility and other disharmonies between *Drosophila melanogaster* and *Drosophila simulans.* (Abstract) *Rec. Genet. Soc. Amer.,* 10: 157; and *Genetics,* 1942, 27: 157.
146. Muller, H. J., and Pontecorvo, G. 1941. The surprisingly high frequency of spontaneous and induced breakage and its expression through dominant lethals. (Abstract) *Rec. Genet. Soc. Amer.,* 10: 157-58; and *Genetics,* 1942, 27: 157-58.
147. 1941. Induced mutations in *Drosophila. Cold Spr. Harb. Sympos. Quant. Biol.,* 9: 151-65.
148. 1941. Résumé and perspectives of the Symposium on Genes and Chromosomes. *Ibid.,* pp. 290-308.
149. 1941. Isolating mechanisms, evolution and temperature. Read before Amer. Soc. Nat., December, 1941. Published in *Biol. Sympos.,* 1942, 6: 71-125.
150. 1942. Locus of pale lethal; insertional translocation involved in "In (dp)," viable non-crossover X-chromosome; stock with marked inversions of all major chromosomes. *D. I. S.,* 16: 64-65.
151. 1942. Mutation rate dependent on the size of the X-chromosome. (Abstract) *Rec. Genet. Soc. Amer.,* 1942, Vol. 11; and *Genetics,* 1943, 28: 83.
152. 1943. Edmund B. Wilson—and appreciation. *Amer. Nat.,* 77: 5-37, 142-72.

153. 1943. A stable double X-chromosome. *D. I. S.*, 17: 61-62.

154. 1943. The mechanism of chromosome breakage by irradiation. (Abstract) *Yrbk. Amer. Philos. Soc. for 1943* (published 1944), pp. 162-65.

155. 1944. The non-equivalence of the blocks and the salivary "heterochromatin." (Abstract) *Rec. Genet. Soc. Amer.*, 13: 28; and *Genetics*, 1945, 30: 15.

156. 1944. Failure of desemination by nitrogen; high primary non-disjunction of the insertional double-X; reddish—a new near-normal allele of white; tandem attached X's producing ring chromosomes; use of males with defective Y's to promote the laying of unfertilized eggs. *D. I. S.*, 18: 56-58.

157. 1945. Age in relation to the frequency of spontaneous mutations in *Drosophila. Yrbk. Amer. Philos. Soc. for 1945* (published 1946), pp. 150-53.

158. 1945. Genetic fundamentals. I. The work of the genes. II. the dance of the genes. Messenger lectures at Cornell University, November, 1945. Published in *Genetics, Medicine and Man*, by H. J. Muller, C. C. Littie, and L. H. Snyder. Ithaca, N. Y.: Cornell University Press, 1947, pp. 1-65.

159. 1945. The gene. Pilgrim Trust Lecture, read before Roy. Soc., London, November 1, 1945. Published in *Proc. Roy. Soc. B*, 1947, 134: 1-37.

160. 1946. Physiological effects on "spontaneous" mutation rate in *Drosophila*. (Abstract) *Rec. Genet. Soc. Amer.*, 14: 55; and *Genetics*, 31: 225.

161. 1946. New mutants; two mutants of mosaic expression not caused by gross rearrangement of heterochromatin; stock list: changes in manner of classification; nomenclature changes adopted in stock list. *D. I. S.*, 20: 66-68, 88-89, 93-96.

162. Lieb, M., Valencia, J., and Muller, H. J. 1946. New translocations between the X and 4th chromosomes. *Ibid.*, p. 87.

163. 1946. A physicist stands amazed at genetics. (Review of Schrödinger's *What Is Life? The Physical Aspect of the Living Cell. J. Hered.*, 37: 90-92.

164. 1946. The production of mutations. Nobel prize lecture read before the Caroline Institute, Stockholm December 10, 1946. Published in *Ibid.*, 1947, 38: 259-70; and in *Les Prix Nobel en 1946*, Stockholm, 1948, pp. 257-74.

165. 1946. Twin needs of science. Read at Crown Prince's banquet, Stockholm Town Hall, December 10, 1946. Published in the *Ibid.*, p. 258; and in *Les Prix Nobel en 1946*, Stockholm, 1948, pp. 60-62.

166. 1946. A comparison of the potentialities of individual loci for different types of visible mutations. (Abstract) *Rec. Genet. Soc. Amer.*, 15: 61-62; and *Genetics*, 1947, 32: 98-99.

167. 1946. Thomas Hunt Morgan. *Science* 103: 550-51.

168. 1947. Redintegration of the symposium on Genetics, Paleontology and Evolution. Read at Princeton, January, 1947. *Genetics, Paleontology and Evolution.* Princeton, N. J.: Princeton University Press, 1949, pp. 421-45.

169. 1947. Mutational prophylaxis. Read April 1, 1947, before N. Y. Acad.

Med. Conf. on Problems of Public Health. Published in *Bull. N. Y. Acad. Med.*, 1948, 24: 447-69.

170. Muller, H. J., and Valencia, J. I. 1947. New Mutants. *D. I. S.*, 21: 69-71.
171. 1947. Changing genes: their effects on evolution. *Bull. Atom. Sci.*, 3: 267-72, 274. Published with changes, in German, in *Universitas*, 5: 569-76, under title "Genmutation und Evolution."
172. 1947. Gene. *Encyclopaedia Britannica*, 1950, X: 100-101.
173. 1947. (Excerpts from Honor Day Address) Indiana Univ. Sch. Dentistry, *Alumni Bull.*, Indiana Univ. Sch. Dentistry, 3rd Quarter, pp. 5, 13.
174. 1948. The destruction of science in the U.S.S.R. Published in abridged form in *Sat. Rev. Lit.*: Part I, 31 (December 4, 1948: 13-15, 65-66); Part II, 31 (December 11, 1948): 8-10; under editor's title "Back to barbarism—scientifically." First sect. of Part I published in unabridged form, under title "The crushing of genetics in the U.S.S.R.," in *Bull. Atom. Sci.*, 12: 369-71.
175. 1948. Genetics in the scheme of things. Presidential address, read before the 8th Int. Congr. Genet., Stockholm, July 7, 1948. *Proc. 8th Int. Congr. Genet.*, Stockholm; *Hereditas*, suppl. vol., 1949, 96-127.
176. 1948. (Letter of resignation from the Academy of Sciences of the U.S.S.R.) *Science*, 108: 436.
177. 1948. (Autobiographical note.) *Les Prix Nobel en 1946*. Stockholm, pp. 109-11.
178. 1948. The construction of several new types of Y chromosomes. *D. I. S.*, 22: 73.
179. 1948. Time bombing our descendants. *Amer. Wkly*, January 3.
180. 1948. Gene. *Amer. Peoples Encyc.* Chicago: Spencer Publishing Co., 9: 349-51.
181. 1949. The Darwinian and modern conceptions of natural selection. *Proc. Amer. Philos. Soc.*, 93 (6): 459-70.
182. 1949. Is radiation a menace to posterity? *Sci. News Let.*, 55 (June 11): 374, 379-80, under editor's title "The menace of radiation."
183. 1949. Progress and prospects in human genetics. (Preface) *J. Human Genet.*, 1: 1-18.
184. Valencia, J. I., and Muller, H. J. 1949. The mutational potentialities of some individual loci in *Drosophila*. (Abstract) *Proc. 8th Int. Congr. Genet.*, Stockholm, 1948; *Hereditas*, suppl. vol., 681-83.
185. Luria, Z., Valencia, J. I., and Muller, H. J. 1949. Simultaneous induction of chromatid and chromosome rearrangements of the same chromosome. *D. I. S.*, 23: 93.
186. Valencia, R. M., Muller, H. J., and Valencia, J. I. 1949. Formation of attached X's by reverse crossing over in the heterochromatic region. *D. I. S.*, 23: 99-102.
187. 1949. Shaw on Lysenko. *Sat. Rev. Lit.*, 32 (April 16): 11-12, 61; under editor's title "It still isn't a science."
188. 1949. E. B. Wilson. *Genetics*, 34: 1-9.
189. Altenburg, L., Altenburg, E., Meyer, H. U., and Muller, H. J. 1949. The lack of proportionality of mutations recovered to dosage of ultra-violet administered to the polar cap of *Drosophila*. (Ab-

stract) *Rec. Genet. Soc. Amer.*, 18: 75; and *Genetics*, 1950, 35: 95.

190. Meyer, H. U., Edmondson, M., Altenburg, L., and Muller, H. J. 1949. Studies on mutations induced by ultra-violet in the polar cap of *Drosophila*. (Abstract) *Rec. Genet. Soc. Amer.*, 18: 103-4; and *Genetics*, 1950, 35: 123-24.

191. Muller, H. J., Valencia, J. I., and Valencia, R. M. 1949. The frequency of spontaneous mutations at individual loci in Drosophila. (Abstract) *Rec. Genet. Soc. Amer.*, 18: 105-6; and *Genetics*, 1950, 35: 125-26.

192. Muller, H. J., Valencia, R. M., and Valencia, J. I. 1949. The production of mutations at individual loci in *Drosophila* by irradiation of oocytes and oogonia. (Abstract) *Rec. Genet. Soc. Amer.*, 18: 106; and *Genetics*, 1950, 35: 126.

193. 1949. The use of rearranged X's and Y's in facilitating class work with *Drosophila*. *D. I. S.*, 23: 110-11.

194. 1949. Russia's counter-revolution against biological science. Review of *Death of a Science in Russia*, by C. Zirkle. *N. Y. Herald-Tribune*, December 11, 1949.

195. 1950. Evidence of the precision of genetic adaptation. *The Harvey Lectures*, Series XLIII, 1947-1948 (Lecture delivered before the N. Y. Acad. Med., February 19, 1948). Springfield, Ill: Charles C. Thomas, pp. 165-229.

196. 1950. Radiation damage to the genetic material. Sigma Xi Lecture, first read November 4, 1948. (Part I), *Amer. Sci.*, Vol. 38, No. 1, pp. 35-59, 126; (Part II), *Ibid.*, Vol. 38, No. 3, pp. 399-425. Reprinted in German in *Strahlentherapie*, 85: 362-90, 509-36. Revised edition: *Science in Progress*, New Haven: Yale University Press, 1951, Chap. IV, pp. 93-165, 481-93. Abstract under title "Radiation damage of genetic origin," *J. Hered.*, 1948, 39: 357-58.

197. 1950. Some present problems in the genetic effects of radiation. Oak Ridge Symposium on Radiation Genetics, March 26-27, 1948. *J. Cell. Comp. Physiol.*, 35 (Suppl. 1): 9-70.

198. 1950. Partial dominance in relation to the need for studying induced mutations individually. (A discussion following the paper by Sewall Wright.) Oak Ridge Symposium on Radiation Genetics, March 26-27, 1948. *Ibid.*, pp. 205-10.

199. 1950. Science in bondage. Address delivered at the panel on "Science and Totalitarianism" of the Congress for Cultural Freedom, in Berlin, Germany, June 27, 1950. Published in German in *Der Monat*, Vol. 2, Nos. 22 and 23, pp. 356-61 (under editor's title "Die Grundlage freier Forschungsarbeit"). Published in English in *Science*, 1951, 113: 25-29; and in *Thought* (Delhi, India), 1952, Vol. 4, No. 3, pp. 7-8, 16.

200. 1950. Our load of mutations. (Presidential address, read before American Society of Human Genetics, New York, December 28, 1949.) *Amer. J. Human Genet.*, 2: 111-76. Excerpts published by editor under title "The growing backlog of genetic defect," *J. Hered.* 1951, 41: 230,240.

201. 1950. The development of the gene theory. Presented at Columbus,

Ohio, September 12, 1950, at the Golden Jubilee of Genetics. Published in *Genetics in the 20th Century*. New York: Macmillan Co., 1951, Chap. V, pp. 77-99.

202. 1951. (Message to university students studying science.) *Kagaku Asahi* (Tokyo), Vol. 11, No. 6, pp. 28-29. (In Japanese and English.)

203. 1951. (Science and freedom.) *Indian Congress for Cultural Freedom*, pp. 20-26. Bombay: Kanada Press.

204. 1951. Detection of mutations in the second chromosome by use of the "sifter" stock; homosexual copulation in the male of *Drosophila*, and the problem of the fate of sperm of males isolated from females; localization of $Y: bw^+$ insertion and cr-u sterile (crs.). *D. I. S.*, 25: 117-18, 118-19, 119.

205. Muller, H. J., and associates. 1951. Ultra-violet induction of mutants at loci at which spontaneous mutants are known. *Ibid.*, pp. 119-20.

206. Muller, H. J., and Valencia, J. I. 1951. The localization of the mutagenic action of neutron-induced ionizations in *Drosophila*. (Abstract) *Rec. Genet. Soc. Amer.*, 20: 115-16; and *Genetics*, 36: 567-68.

207. 1952. Gene mutations caused by radiation. *Symposium on Radiobiology*, June 14-18, 1950. New York: John Wiley & Sons, Chap. 17, pp. 296-332.

208. 1952. Genetic effects of cosmic radiation. *Proceedings of Symposium on Physics and Medicine of the Upper Atmosphere*, San Antonio, Texas, November 6-9, 1951. Albuquerque: The University of New Mexico Press, Chap. 17, pp. 316-30.

209. 1952. Genetics and its relations with other fields of knowledge. *The Indiana Teacher*, Vol. 96, No. 8 (April), pp. 248-49.

210. 1952. Sterility of Soviet Science (editor's title). United States Information Service (USIS) Feature, 3 pp., IIA-IPS CFVII-4-1152.

211. 1949-51. A comparative study of mutations arising under different conditions in *Drosophila*. (Abstract) *4th Ann. Rep. to Amer. Cancer Soc.*, 1949, pp. 123-24; *5th Ann. Rep. to Amer. Cancer Soc.*, 1950, p. 153; *6th Ann. Rep. to Amer. Cancer Soc.*, 1951, p. 119. Washington, D. C.: Div. Med. Sci. Nat Res. Coun.

212. 1952. The standard error of the frequency of mutants some of which are of common origin. (Abstract) *Rec. Genet. Soc. Amer.* 21: 52; and *Genetics*, 37: 608.

213. Meyer, Helen U., and Muller, H. J. 1952. Influence of oxygen and of temperature on the rate of autosomal recessive lethals induced by ultra-violet in the polar cap of *Drosophila melanogaster*. (Abstract) *Rec. Genet. Soc. Amer.*, 21: 48; and *Genetics*, 37: 604.

214. Byers, Helen L., and Muller, H. J. 1952. Influence of ageing at two different temperatures on the spontaneous mutation rate in mature spermatozoa of *Drosophila melanogaster*. (Abstract) *Rec. Genet. Soc. Amer.*, 21: 14; and *Genetics*, 37: 570-71.

215. 1952. Will science continue? *Bull. Atom. Sci.*, Vol. 8, No. 9, pp. 301-7. Address first delivered for the annual Talent Search, Junior Scientists' Assembly, Indianapolis, Indiana, April 5, 1952, under title "Science—mankind's greatest adventure."

216. 1952. Breeding systems for detection of sex-linked lethals in successive generations. *D. I. S.*, 26: 113-14.

217. 1953. Review of Charles Galton Darwin's *The Next Million Years.* Published in Book Review of the *N. Y. Herald-Tribune*, January 11, 1953, p. 3, under the editor's title "Back to Malthus: A Dubious Document of Doom for the Human Race." (Author's title: "Can Man Shape His Own Future?")

218. 1953. Autosomal mutation studies by means of crisscrossed lethals and balanced male-steriles. *D. I. S.*, 27: 104-5.

219. 1953. Autosomal nondisjunction associated with the rotund translocation. *Ibid.*, pp. 106-7.

220. 1953. Further evidence of abnormal types of copulation by the male *D. melanogaster. Ibid.*, pp. 107-8.

221. 1953. The call of biology. *A.I.B.S. Bull.*, 3: 4.

222. 1953. Preface. *Bibliography on the genetics of Drosophila*, Part II, by I. H. Herskowitz. Oxford: Alden Press, v + 212 pp.

223. 1953. Russia's shackled science. *New Leader*, October 26, pp. 15-16.

224. Herskowitz, I. H., and Muller, H. J. 1953. Evidence against the healing of X-ray breakages in chromosomes of female *Drosophila melanogaster.* (Abstract) *Rec. Genet. Soc. Amer.*, 22: 79; and *Genetics*, 38: 669.

225. 1954. The nature of the genetic effects produced by radiation. *Radiation Biology*, A. Hollaender (ed.). New York: McGraw-Hill, Vol. 1, Chap. 7, pp. 351-473.

226. 1954. The manner of production of mutations by radiation. *Ibid.*, Chap. 8, pp. 475-626.

227. 1954. Damage to posterity caused by the irradiation of the gonads. *Amer. J. Obstet. and Gynec.*, 67: 467-83.

228. 1954. The manner of dependence of the "permissible dose" of radiation on the amount of genetic damage. *Acta Radiol.*, 41: 5-19.

229. 1954. Science under Soviet totalitarianism. *Totalitarianism*, C. Friedrich (ed.). Cambridge, Mass.: Harvard University Press, x + 386 pp; Chap 12, pp. 233-44.

230. Muller, H. J., Altenburg, L. S., Meyer, H. U., Edmondson, M., and Altenburg, E. 1954. The lack of proportionality between mutation rate and ultra-violet dose in Drosophila. *Heredity*, 8: 153-85.

231. Muller, H. J., and Herskowitz, I. H. 1954. Concerning the healing of chromosome ends produced by breakage in *Drosophila melanogaster. Amer. Nat.*, 88: 177-208.

232. Muller, H. J., Herskowitz, I. H., Abrahamson, S., and Oster, I. I. 1954. A nonlinear relation between X-ray dose and recovered lethal mutations in *Drosophila. Genetics*, 39: 741-49.

233. Muller, H. J. 1954. The relation of neutron dose to chromosome changes and point mutations in *Drosophila.* I. Translocations. *Amer. Nat.*, 88: 437-59.

234. 1954. A semi-automatic breeding system ("Maxy") for finding sex-linked mutations at specific "visible" loci. *D. I. S.*, 28: 140-41.

235. 1954. A stably breeding attached-X stock ("snoc") designed for discriminating between deletional and other "detachments." *Ibid.*, pp. 141-43.

236. 1954. A stock for automatic accumulation of lethals arising in the female. *Ibid.*, pp. 143-44.

237. 1954. Multipurpose stocks for studies of mutagenesis. *Ibid.*, pp. 144-46.

238. 1954. Origination of a viable achaete deficiency by nearly homologous nonreciprocal exchange. *Ibid.*, pp. 146-47.

239. Herskowitz, I. H., and Muller, H. J. 1954. Evidence against a straight end-to-end alignment of chromosomes in Drosophila spermatozoa. *Genetics*, 39: 836-50.

240. Abrahamson, S., Herskowitz, I. H., and Muller, H. J. 1954. Genetic proof for half-translocations derived from irradiated oocytes of *Drosophila melanogaster*. (Abstract) *Rec. Genet. Soc. Amer.*, 23: 28; and *Genetics*, 39: 955.

241. Verderosa, F., and Muller, H. J. 1954. Another case of dissimilar characters in Drosophila apparently representing changes of the same locus. (Abstract) *Rec. Genet. Soc. Amer.* 23: 72; and *Genetics*, 39: 999.

242. 1954. Characteristics of the far stronger but "spottier" mutagenicity of fast neutrons as compared with X-rays in Drosophila spermatozoa. (Abstract) *Rec. Genet. Soc. Amer.* 23: 58; and *Genetics*, 39: 985.

243. 1955. Life. *Science*, 121: 1-9. (Shorter version in *Man's Right to Knowledge*, 2nd Series. New York: Columbia University Press, pp. 19-33.)

244. 1951-54. A comparative study of mutations arising under different conditions in *Drosophila*. (Abstract) 7th, 8th and 9th *Ann. Rep. Amer. Cancer Soc.*, 1951, 1952 and 1953. Washington, D. C.: Div. Med. Sci. Nat. Res. Counc., pp. 120-21, 130-39, 113-14, respectively.

245. 1955. The Soviet change of attitude in genetics. *Christian Science Monitor*, February 4, 1955. (Mimeographed without deletions, as in original MS.)

246. Muller, H. J., Meyer, Helen U., and Carlson, E. A. 1955. Further information concerning the multi-locus nature of the dumpy series in *Drosophila*. (Abstract) *Rec. Genet. Soc. Amer.*, Vol. 24; and *Genetics*, 40: 585.

247. 1955. Genetic damage produced by radiation. *Science*, 121: 837-40.

248. 1955. How radiation changes the genetic constitution. *Internat. Conf. on Peaceful Uses of Atomic Energy;* article replicated by U. N., "A/Conf. B/P/234, U. S. A." Also published in *Bull. Atom. Sci.*, 1955, 11: 329-39; and in *Proc. of the Conf.*, 1956, 11: 387-99.

249. 1955. Comments on the genetic effects of radiation on human populations. *J. Hered.*, 46: 199-200.

250. 1955. Radiation and human mutation. *Scientific American*, 193: 58-68. (Paper read at 5th Annual Meeting of Nobel Prizewinners, Lindau, Germany, July 14, 1955.)

251. 1955. Correction of localization of crs and breaks of Y: bw$^+$. *D. I. S.*, 29: 146.

252. 1955. Improvement of stock "Maxy," for studying mutations at specific loci in the X of the male. *Ibid.*, pp. 146-47.

253. 1955. Male-sterility of transformed females despite provision of X: Y balance characteristic of males. *Ibid.*, p. 147.

254. 1955. Testing for third-chromosome mutations by means of criss-crossed lethals. *Ibid.*, pp. 147-49.

255. Muller, H. J., Herskowitz, I. H., and Oster, I. I. 1955. Effect of

narcosis on X-ray-induced mutations in sperm treated in inseminated females. *Ibid.*, p. 149.

256. 1956. On the relation between chromosome changes and gene mutations. *Brookhaven Symp. in Biol.* 8: 126-47.

257. 1956. The effects of radiation on the human constitution. *Proc. 1956 Military-Industrial Conf.;* under the title, "Race poisoning by radiation," in *Sat. Rev.*, June 9, 1956, pp. 9-11, 37-39; revised edition under the title "After effects of nuclear radiation," *J. Amer. Soc. Safety Engineers*, 1: 42-48.

258. 1956. In the cause of humanity. *The Humanist*, 16: 107-10.

259. Abrahamson, S., Herskowitz, I. H., and Muller, H. J. 1956. Identification of half-translocations produced by X-rays in detaching attached-X chromosomes of *Drosophila melanogaster*. *Genetics*, 41: 410-19.

260. Herskowitz, I. H., Muller, H. J., and Laughlin, J. S. 1956. The higher efficiency of ordinary X-rays than of 18 Mev electrons in inducing chromosome changes when applied to Drosophila spermatozoa. (Abstract) *Rec. Genet. Soc. Amer.*, Vol. 25; and *Genetics*, 41: 646-47.

261. Meyer, H. U., and Muller, H. J. 1956. The higher susceptibility of ring-shaped Y-chromosomes of Drosophila to loss both spontaneously and on irradiation of spermatozoa. (Abstract) *Rec. Genet. Soc. Amer.*, Vol. 25; and *Genetics*, 41: 653-54.

262. Muller, H. J. 1956. Man's place in living nature. I. U. Publications, separate, 15 pp.; *The Humanist*, 1957, 17: 3-13, 93-102; *Sci. Mon.*, 1957, 84: 245-57.

263. 1956. Interview, under editor's title, "Ways to reduce radiation hazards." *Scope Weekly* (CIBA), Vol. 1, No. 29, pp. 1, 13.

264. 1956. Genetic principles in human populations. *Amer. J. Psychiatry*, 113: 481-91; *Sci. Mon.*, 83: 277-86.

265. 1956. Another entire inversion formed by opening of a ring X. *D. I. S.*, 30: 140-41.

266. Muller, H. J., and Herskowitz, I. H. 1956. Reciprocal and half-translocations with a rod X chromosome produced by X-raying sperm and oocytes. *Ibid.*, pp. 141-42.

267. Morton, N. E., Drow, J. F., and Muller, H. J. 1956. An estimate of the mutational damage in man from data on consanguineous marriages. *Proc. Nat. Acad. Sci.*, 42: 855-63.

268. Muller, H. J. 1957. Further studies bearing on the load of mutations in man. *Proc. 1st Internat. Congr. Human Genet., Copenhagen, 1956; Acta Genet. et Stat. Med.*, 6: 157-68.

269. 1957. Damage from point mutations in relation to radiation dose and biological conditions. *Effect of Radiation on Human Heredity.* Geneva: World Health Organization, pp. 25-47.

270. Muller, H. J., and Oster, I. I. 1957. Principles of back mutation as observed in Drosophila and other organisms. *Proc. 5th Internat. Conf. of Radiobiol.*, Stockholm, 1956; *Advances in Radiobiology*, Edinburgh: Oliver and Boyd, pp. 407-15.

271. Muller, H. J. 1957. Potential hazards of radiation. *Excerpta Medica*, 11 (Section 14): 527-30.

272. 1957. Radioactive fallout and human progress. *Proc. Inter. Human-*

ist and Eth. Union, 2nd Congr., London, 1957, pp. 26-35 (also published as separate pamphlet, OudeGracht, Utrecht: I.H.E.U., Inc., 1958); *Canadian World Government News*, 1958, 2: 4-16 (under title "Radiation damage and the avoidance of war").

273. 1957. Pushing back the frontiers of biology. Broadcast in diverse languages, December 23, 1956, over the Voice of America as a component of their "Frontiers of Knowledge" series. Published under editor's title, "The immediate biological future," in *New Frontiers of Knowledge*, Washington, D. C,: Public Affairs Press, pp. 56-59; and in German translation under title "Grenzerweiterung der Biologie" in *Deutsche Universitätszeitung*, 12: 14-15; and in *Naturwissenschaftliche Rundschau*, 11: 208-10.

274. 1957. Possible advances of the next hundred years: a biologist's view. (Basis of address at Centenary of the Seagram Co., November 22, 1957, in New York.) Published in abridged form, as delivered, in *The Next Hundred Years, a Scientific Symposium*, New York: publication of Joseph E. Seagram & Sons, Inc., pp. 33-35; and (with errors) in the *New York Times*, December 8, 1957, Section 6, p. 13.

275. Herskowitz, I. H., Carlson, E. A., and Muller, H. J. 1957. Sex-chromosome loss following X-radiation of *D. melanogaster* sperm. *Rec. Genet. Soc. Amer.*, Vol. 26; and *Genetics*, 42: 376.

276. 1957. Science fiction as an escape. *The Humanist*, 17: 333-46.

277. 1957. Mutation studies of chromosome-3 simplified by "sifter-3" method. *D. I. S.*, 31: 139-40.

278. Muller, H. J., and Edmondson, Margaret. 1957. Transposition of entire 4-euchromatin into a fully functional Y. *Ibid.*, p. 140.

279. Muller, H. J. and Oster, I. I. 1957. Suppressor action effective with a sub-gene deficiency of a normally duplicated locus. *Ibid.*, pp. 141-43.

280. Muller, H. J. and Schalet, A. 1957. Further improvements in the "Maxy" stock for detection of specific-locus mutations. *Ibid.*, p. 144.

281. 1958. The radiation danger. *Colo. Quart.* 6: 229-54; reprinted in *Best Articles and Stories*, 2: 55-64.

282. 1958. Man's future birthright. University of New Hampshire separate, 24 pp.

283. 1958. Human values in relation to evolution. *Science*, 127: 625-29.

284. Bonsack, Walter K., and Muller, H. J. Human values (letters to the editor). *Ibid.*, pp. 1513-14.

285. 1958. The world view of moderns. University of Illinois 50th Anniversary Lecture Series, separate, 29 pp.

286. 1958. Evolution by mutation. *Bull. Amer. Math. Soc.*, 64: 137-60.

287. 1958. General survey of mutational effects of radiation. *Radiation Biology and Medicine*, W. D. Claus (ed.) (Director of Biology and Medicine, U. S. A. E. C.). Reading, Mass.: Addison-Wesley Publishing Co., Inc., Chap. 6, pp. 145-77.

288. 1958. Approximation to a gravity-free situation for the human organism achievable at moderate expense. Science, 128: 772.

289. 1958. Advances in radiation mutagenesis through studies on *Drosophila. Biol. Effects of Radiation (Proc. 2nd U. N. Inter. Conf. Peaceful Uses Atom. Energy*, Vol. XXII) Geneva: U. N., pp. 313-

21. Also published in *Progress in Nuclear Energy*. N. Y.: Pergamon Press, 1959, VI: 146-60.

290. 1958. The mutation theory reexamined. *Proc. X Int. Congr. Genet.*, 1: 306-17.

291. Meyer, Helen U., and Muller, H. J. 1958. Genetic effects of high doses of X-rays in oogonia. *D. I. S.*, 32: 137-38.

292. Meyer, Helen U., and Muller, H. J. 1958. Preliminary evidence of detrimental mutations originating at a comparatively high rate in untreated females. *Ibid.*, pp. 138-39.

293. 1958. An androgenetic homozygous male. *Ibid.*, p. 140.

294. 1958. Pseudo-crossing over near centromeres of the third chromosomes induced in late oocytes by X-rays. *Ibid.*, pp. 140-41.

295. Oster, I. I., Ehrlich, Elizabeth, and Muller, H. J. 1958. Further study of the mutants f^x and f^{+ih}. *Ibid.*, pp. 144-45.

296. 1958. How much is evolution accelerated by sexual reproduction? *Anat. Rec.*, 132: 480-81.

297. Herskowitz, I. H., Muller, H. J., and Laughlin, J. S. 1959. The mutability of 18 Mev electrons applied to Drosophila spermatozoa. *Rec. Genet. Soc. Amer.*, 28; and *Genetics*, 44: 321-27.

298. 1959. Science for humanity. *Bull. Atom. Sci.*, 15: 146-50, 176 (abridgement by E. Rabinowitch of article 285, The world view of moderns).

299. 1959. Darwin's achievement. *Int. Hum. and Eth. Union Inf. Bull.*, January, pp. 1-3.

300. 1959. In search of peace. *The Humanist*, 2: 69-70.

301. 1959. One hundred years without Darwinism are enough. *Sch. Sci. and Math.*, April, pp. 304-16; and *The Humanist*, 3: 139-49.

302. Meyer, Helen U., Ehrlich, Elizabeth, and Muller, H. J. 1959. Tolerance of gonial cells of *Drosophila melanogaster* for heavy X-ray doses divided into installments. *Rec. Genet. Soc. Amer.*, 28: and *Genetics*, 44: 527-28.

303. 1959. The guidance of human evolution. *Persp. Biol. Med.*, 3: 1-43. Summary in *The Centennial Papers, University of Chicago Darwin Cent. Cel.*, pp. 50-51. Excerpts in *Eugen. Quart.*, 6: 245-48.

304. 1959. Man's conquest of man (title in mimeographed copy only). *The Future of Man*. New York: Joseph E. Seagrams & Sons, Inc., pp. 33-36.

305. 1959. The prospects of genetic change. *Amer. Sci.* 47: 551-61.

306. Muller, H. J., and Meyer, Helen U. 1959. Further evidence of the relatively high rate of origination of "invisible" detrimental mutations. *Science*, 130: 1422.

307. Oster, I. I., Zimmering, S., and Muller, H. J. 1959. Evidence of the lower mutagenecity of chronic than intense radiation in *Drosophila* gonia. *Ibid.*, p. 1423.

308. Ostertag, W., and Muller, H. J. 1959. Genetic basis of somatic damage produced by radiation. *Ibid.*, pp. 1422-23.

309. 1959. A simplified breeding system for detecting sex-linked lethals in successive generations. *D. I. S.*, 33: 149.

310. 1959. An attached-X chromosome set-up of exceptionally high stability. *Ibid.*, pp. 149-50.

311. 1959. Antimorphic behavior of Cataract. *Ibid.*, p. 150.

312. 1960. The chromosomal basis of the mortality induced by X-rays in *Drosophila*. *Int. J. Rad. Biol.*, Spec. Suppl., pp. 321-25.

313. 1960. Evolution and genetics. *Problemi Attuali di Scienza e di Cultura*, Quad. No. 47. Rome: Accad. Naz. dei Lincei, pp. 15-37.

314. 1960. The meaning of freedom. *Bull. Atom. Sci.*, 16: 311-16.

315. 1960. Statement at Hearings before the Subcommitee on Reorganization and International Organization of the Committee on Government Operations of the U. S. Senate, 86th Congress, 1st session, in *The U. S. Government and the Future of International Medical Research; International Health Study, Pt. 1.* Washington, D. C.: U. S. Government Printing Office, pp. 126-34.

316. 1960. The integrational role of the evolutionary approach throughout education. *Educ. Theory*, 10: 274-79.

317. Zimmering, S., Oster, I. I., and Muller, H. J. 1960. The high effectiveness of fast neutrons in inducing minute deletions. *Science*, 131: 1322.

318. Muller, H. J., and Zimmering, S. 1960. A sex-linked lethal without evident effect in *Drosophila* males but partially dominant in females. *Genetics*, 45: 1001-2.

319. 1960. Do air pollutants act as mutagens? *Amer. Rev. Resp. Diseases*, 83 (1961): 571-72. Also included in mimeographed booklet *3rd Conf. on Res. in Emphysema*, 1960, pp. 55-56.

320. 1960. Letter to the editor. *The Humanist*, 20: 227-29, under editor's title "Modernized magic: a protest."

321. 1960. The permissible dose in the light of recent developments. *Trans. Internat. Comm. Radiol. Protect.* (Meeting with Experts on Somatic and Genetic Radiation Effects, held in Munich, 1959), pp. 38-43.

322. 1960. Genetic considerations. *The Great Issues of Conscience in Modern Medicine*, Hanover, New Hampshire: Dartmouth Medical School, pp. 16-18.

323. 1961. Ideals to live by. *The Humanist*, 21: 105-7. Review of *Science Ponders Religion*, Harlow Shapley (ed.). New York: Appleton-Century-Crofts, Inc., 1960.

324. 1961. Review of P. B. Medawar's *The Future of Man*, in *Perspectives in Biology and Medicine*, 4: 377-80.

325. Muller, H. J., Carlson, E., and Schalet, A. 1961. Mutation by alteration of the already existing gene. *Genetics*, 46: 213-26.

326. Muller, H. J., and Falk, R. 1961. Are induced mutations in *Drosophila* overdominant? I. Experimental design. *Ibid.*, pp. 727-57.

327. Meyer, Helen U., and Muller, H. J. 1961. Similarity of X-ray induced mutation rate in gonia of Drosophila females and males. *Rec. Genet. Soc. Amer.*, 30: 92-93; and *Genetics*, 46: 882-83.

328. 1961. The human future, in *The Humanist Frame*, Julian Huxley (ed.) New York: Harper & Brothers, pp. 401-14.

329. 1961. Life forms to be expected elsewhere than on earth. *The Amer. Biol. Teacher*, 23: 331-46.

330. 1961. Human evolution by voluntary choice of germ plasm. *Science*, 134: 643-49; reprinted in part in *Current*, January, 1962.

331. 1961. Germinal choice, a new dimension in genetic therapy. *Exerpta Medica* (Amsterdam) (Int. Congr. Series, No. 32, 2nd Int. Conf. of Human Genet., Rome, July, 1961), Abstract No. 294, p. E 135.

332. 1961. Survival. *AIBS Bull.*, 40: 15-24.
333. 1961. Letter to the editor. *Time*, 78: 12.
334. 1961. Letter to the-editor. *Science*, 134: 1916, 1917-18.
335. Zimmering, S., and Muller, H. J. 1961. Studies on the action of the dominant female-lethal *F1* and of a less extreme allele, *F1ˢ*. *D. I. S.*, 35: 103-4.
336. 1961. Genetic nucleic acid: the key material in the origin of life. *Persp. Biol. Med.*, 5: 1-23.